Spiralizer

Mouth-Watering and Nutritious Low Carb + Paleo + Gluten-Free Spiralizer Recipes for Health, Vitality and Weight Loss

By Kira Novac (ISBN: 978-1-80095-037-5)

http://www.amazon.com/author/kira-novac

All information in this book has been carefully researched and checked for factual accuracy. However, the author and publishers make no warranty, expressed or implied, that the information contained herein is appropriate for every individual, situation or purpose, and assume no responsibility for errors or omission. The reader assumes the risk and full responsibility for all actions, and the author will not be held liable for any loss or damage, whether consequential, incidental, and special or otherwise, that may result from the information presented in this publication.

A physician has not written the information in this book. Before making any serious dietary changes, I advise you to consult with your physician first.

Table of contents

Introduction-Revolutionize Your Health

Zoodler or spiralizer is another name known for the Spiral Vegetable Slicer. This amazing kitchen instrument lets you peel/ shred numerous and different vegetables to spiral form and can help you revolutionize your health!

This ground-breaking device will slice your normal vegetable into noodle-like shapes. Rather than cutting classic carrot sticks, boring cucumber half-circles, or dull zucchini slices to put on the top of your gloomy looking salads, with this contraption, you will be dining on huge streamers of vegetable pleasure.

Whether you are already a big fan of vegetables, trying a healthier diet, or just want to try something new, your chance to transform your unhealthy meals into healthy, delicious, more colorful, and appealing dishes is definitely available to you.

The vegetable slicer tool is simple to use. Just wash and peel your vegetables. At medium speed, start spinning the handle. The vegetable will then start spiraling down into noodle form.

The Spiral Vegetable Slicer may also come with three different plastic vegetable slicer blades, and each blade produces different vegetable cuts.

The spiral vegetable slicer tool can transform nearly any kind of vegetable into an outstanding noodle shape. As a result, the preparation of your vegetables becomes shorter and easier.

Health benefits of eating spiralized vegetables.

Eating spiralized food can help prevent heart attacks and heart diseases. Food rich in high sodium (Standard American Diet is full of processed foods...so SAD!) increases your blood pressure, so it's good to replace them with vegetables, which will make your body healthy and fit. Eating more nutrient-dense vegetables, rich in minerals and vitamins, while eliminating processed food (full of sugar, processed carbs, calories and chemicals), at the same time, helps in weight loss.

Spiralized food also helps in detoxing your body. Most spiralized vegetables, such as Zucchini, have plenty of water and help you stay hydrated and healthy. Most vegetables are full of fiber, and it's easier to digest them when you eat them in spiralized and slightly cooked form.

Veggies help stimulate your metabolism. You feel more energized! With a faster metabolism, your body performs efficiently to release the energy needed to get going. Metabolism improves absorption of nutrients, blood circulation, and digestion.

Spiralized vegetables are good for everyone! They can be of most help to those who have autoimmune diseases. It is because they are gluten free, natural, rich in nutrients, and Paleo diet friendly.

Vegetable slicers are very useful for those people who love cooking or want to cook in a healthier and more decorative style with convenience. Throughout the years, the number of vegetable slicers available on the market has continued to grow. It's mostly due to fact that there are more and more people who see the importance of having them in the kitchen and more and more people who want to eat a healthy diet.

Cooking can take a lot of time, and if you're a fan of vegetables, having a vegetable slicer may change your good kitchen experience into a great kitchen experience. Cutting vegetables can be a time consuming job, and you should have an appliance that will help make the preparation process a whole lot easier for you.

Regardless of which recipe you choose, do not be afraid to be creative and add or take away things, according to taste. Take what you like and reject the rest.

Free Complimentary Recipe eBook

Thank you so much for taking an interest in my work!

As a thank you, I would love to offer you a free complimentary recipe eBook to help you achieve vibrant health. It will teach you how to prepare amazingly tasty and healthy gluten-free treats so that you never feel deprived or bored again!

As a special bonus, you will be able to receive all my future books (kindle format) for free or only $0.99.

Download your free recipe eBook here:

http://bit.ly/gluten-free-desserts-book

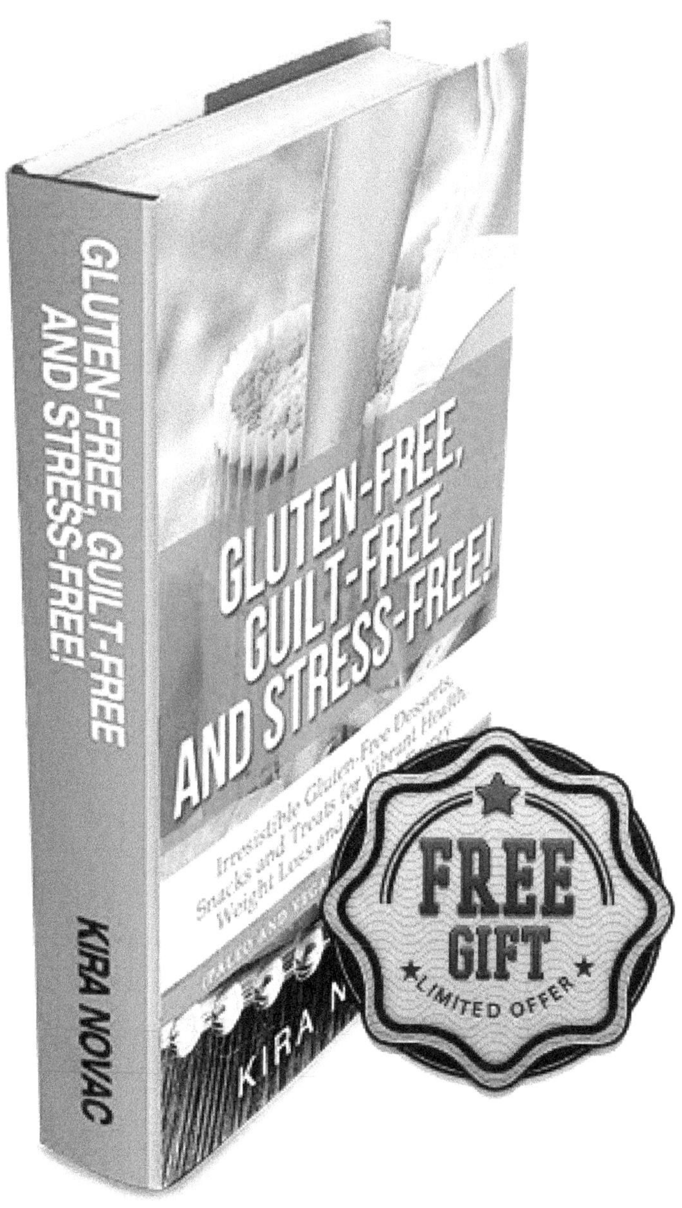
GLUTEN-FREE, GUILT-FREE
AND STRESS-FREE!
KIRA NOVAC
GLUTEN-FREE,
GUILT-FREE
AND STRESS-FREE!
FREE
GIFT
LIMITED OFFER

Paleo Chicken Recipes

Bacon-Wrapped Chicken Medallions

Servings: 2-3

Ingredients:

- 1 ½ lbs. boneless skinless chicken breast
- 8 to 10 slices raw bacon
- 3 spiralized carrots
- ½ teaspoon Chili powder
- ½ teaspoon paprika
- 1 spiralized cucumber (to garnish)
- 1 spiralized zucchini
- Pepper and Himalayan salt

Preparation:

1. Preheat your grill to high heat then reduce to medium-high.
2. Cut the chicken breasts into two or three large chunks. Spice your chicken with pepper and salt. Add the spiralized

ingredients (zucchini and carrots) and then dust with chili powder and paprika.

3. Using bacon piece, wrap each medallion. Secure it in place with a skewer wooden. Place the skewers on a grill and then cook on each side for 3 to 5 minutes.
4. Serve with spiralized cucumber on side.
5. Enjoy!

Orange Grilled Chicken with Mango Salsa

Mango salsa is a unique topping for citrus-flavored chicken. It is lightly sweet with a hint of freshness from the cucumber and salsa. Perfectly delicious!

Servings: 4

Ingredients:

- 4 boneless skinless chicken breast
- 1 tablespoon olive oil
- 2 tablespoons of fresh orange juice
- 1 small tomato, sliced in super thin slices
- Pepper and salt to taste
- 1 cucumber, spiralized
- ¼ cup fresh chopped cilantro
- 1 ripe mango, pitted and spiralized

Procedure:

1. Heat your grill to high heat. Mix the olive oil and orange juice in a basin. Add pepper and salt to the chicken for flavor. Brush with the marinade.
2. Place the chicken breasts on the grill. Now cook for about 10 minutes. Turn the chicken and brush again with marinade.
3. Cook the chicken for another 8 to 10 minutes or until it is fully cooked. Combine the remaining ingredients in a vessel and then serve over the hot chicken.
4. Enjoy!

Gingery Chicken and Veggies

Servings: 2

Ingredients:

- Two cloves of garlic, minced
- ¼ cup olive/coconut oil mixture
- 1 cup cooked chicken breast meat, diced and skinless
- 1 teaspoon Powdered ginger,
- Medium cucumber, spiralized
- ½ Red onion, sliced
- 2 carrots, spiralized
- ½ cup celery, chopped
- 1 cup chicken broth
- Half bell pepper, sliced
- Himalayan salt to taste

Procedure:

1. In heavy skillet, heat oil mixture and panfry onion and garlic.

2. Add the remaining ingredients (except cucumbers) and simmer until the vegetables are tender. Add some Himalayan salt to taste.
3. Serve with spiralized cucumbers for more nutrition.
4. Enjoy!

Roasted Cranberry Chicken

If you are tired of bland baked chicken, this roasted cranberry chicken is just what you need. It's full of flavor and cooked to perfection.

Servings: 2-3

Ingredients:

- 2 lbs. bone-in chicken legs
- 1 cup fresh cranberries
- ½ cup unsweetened cranberry juice
- 1 tablespoon evaporated cane juice
- 2 zucchini, spiralized
- Salt and pepper to taste
- 1 cucumber, spiralized (to garnish)
- ½ cup cilantro (to garnish)

Preparation:

1. Preheat your oven and grease an oven-proof skillet. Season the chicken with salt and pepper to taste.
2. Prepare your skillet over high-medium heat. Add your garlic and zucchini. Cook for one minute then add the chicken.
3. Cook your chicken until lightly browned on each side. Transfer the chicken to the oven and roast for about 20 minutes until the legs are cooked through.
4. Combine the cranberries, cranberry juice, and evaporated cane juice in a small saucepan. Boil until thickened.
5. Serve the chicken with raw, spiralized cucumber and cilantro on side.

Kenny's Barbecued Spicy Chicken

Servings: 2-3

Ingredients:

- 1 teaspoon fresh orange juice
- 2 teaspoons fresh lemon juice,
- 1 teaspoon fresh tarragon, finely chopped
- 2 scallions, finely chopped
- 1 teaspoon fresh sage, finely chopped,
- 1 teaspoon fresh thyme, finely chopped
- 1 teaspoon fennel seeds, toasted and crushed
- Four skinless, boneless chicken breast halves
- Black pepper to taste, freshly ground
- 2 cucumbers, spiralized
- 4 carrots, spiralized
- Olive oil

Procedure:

1. Combine all ingredients, except chicken and spiralized veggies, in large bowl.
2. Mix well to yield marinade.
3. Place chicken in the bowl, thoroughly coat, and marinate for one to two hours.

For grilling:

1. Fire up barbecue and grill chicken on medium heat, turning regularly while basting with marinade until the breasts are cooked.
2. Cook under the broiler, turning constantly while basting with marinade until done.
3. In the meantime, spiralize cucumbers and carrots.
4. Season with olive oil and Himalayan salt, and serve with the grilled chicken. Enjoy!

Roasted Chicken with Vegetables

If you have to feed a crowd, this roasted chicken with vegetables is perfect. Feel free to add whatever vegetables you like to make this recipe truly your own.

Servings: 2-3

Ingredients:

- One (4 to 5 lbs.) whole, raw chicken
- 2 tablespoon coconut oil
- 1 tablespoon dried rosemary
- Himalayan salt and black pepper, to taste
- 1 tablespoon dried oregano
- 2 cups baby carrots
- 2 medium sweet potatoes, spiralized
- 1 large yellow onion, chopped
- Zucchini, spiralized

Preparation:

1. Preheat your oven. Remove the giblet bag from the chicken's cavity and set it aside. Rinse your chicken, using cool water, and then pat it dry with towel papers.
2. Rub thc coconut oil into the skin of the chicken then season with rosemary, oregano, salt and pepper. Spread the rest of vegetables in the bottom of a roasting pan then place the chicken on top.
3. Place the roasting pan in oven and reduce the oven temperature to 400°F. Roast the chicken for 1 hour and 15 minutes then check the internal temperature with a meat thermometer.
4. If the temperature reads less than 165°F, return the chicken to the oven for five to ten minutes or wait until it's cooked through. Remove the chicken to a cutting board and let rest for about 15 minutes before carving.
5. Serve the chicken plus heated vegetables. Enjoy!

Breaded Chicken Tenders

Servings: 2-3

Ingredients:

- Onion salt
- 1 cup Almond flour
- 1 egg
- Garlic salt
- White meat chicken tender breast strips, all boneless
- 2 carrots, spiralized
- 2 apples, spiralized
- 1/2 cup alfalfa sprouts
- Himalayan salt
- Juice of 1 lemon
- Olive oil

Procedure:

1. Pour a cup of almond flour into zip lock bag. Add onion powder, seasonings, and garlic.

2. Dip all chicken white meat tender strips into beaten egg, then lightly coat in seasoning mixture/ flour.
3. Broil on high heat for ten minutes. Then broil and flip for another five to eight minutes. When the coating starts to turn brown on both sides, then they are ready.
4. Serve with spiralized apples and carrots. Sprinkle some olive oil, lemon juice, and Himalayan salt to taste.
5. Enjoy!

Chicken Tikka Masala

This dish smells great and tastes even better!

Servings: 2-3

Ingredients:

- 2 tablespoons coconut oil or ghee
- 1 small yellow onion, diced
- 4 garlic cloves, diced
- 2 pounds chicken thighs, skin removed
- 1 ½ cups coconut milk
- Fresh ginger, spiralized
- 1 ½ cups tomato, super thin slices
- 1 small yellow onion, diced
- 1 tablespoon garam masala
- 2 teaspoons cumin
- 4 carrots, spiralized
- Sea salt plus freshly powdered black pepper to taste
- 1 ½ teaspoons coriander
- 2 apples, spiralized
- 1 teaspoon turmeric

Procedure:

1. Turn slow cooker to high setting.
2. Add ghee or coconut oil.
3. Add garlic, carrots, apple, ginger and onions and let cook for 5-6 minutes.
4. Add all remaining ingredients to slow cooker. Cook covered until ready to be taken.
5. Serve over Cauliflower-Rice.
6. Enjoy!

Chicken Mole

This chicken dish has a rich chocolate sauce.

Servings: 2-3

Ingredients:

- 2 tablespoons ghee
- 4 cloves garlic, minced
- 1 medium yellow onion, diced
- 2 carrots, spiralized
- 2 pounds chicken pieces, skin removed
- 1/2 cup radish, spiralized
- 1 teaspoon cumin
- 1 can whole tomatoes, in super thin slices (use a spiralizer)
- 1 chipotle pepper, minced
- 3 tablespoons chili powder
- 1 ½ teaspoons cinnamon
- 3 tablespoons tahini or almond butter
- 2 tablespoons cocoa powder, unsweetened
- Sea salt and freshly ground pepper, to taste
- Fresh cilantro, chopped for garnish

Procedure:

1. Turn slow cooker on high. Add ghee. Heat for 5-6 minutes after adding ghee, onion and garlic. Add all remaining ingredients and chicken to slow cooker and then stir.
2. Turn heat to low. Cook while covered until the chicken is tender. Adjust seasoning and serve, topped with fresh cilantro.
3. Enjoy!

Paleo Chicken Soup

This chicken soup is wonderful for helping fight colds and flu.

Servings: 2-3

Ingredients:

- 6 stalks celery, chopped
- 1 tablespoon coconut oil or ghee
- 4 carrots, spiralized
- 1 Medium onion, chopped
- 2 pounds chicken pieces, skin removed
- 2 garlic cloves, minced
- 2 zucchini, spiralized
- 2 beets, spiralized
- 2 teaspoons thyme
- Chicken broth or 2 quarts water
- 1 teaspoon oregano
- 1 teaspoon rosemary
- Sea salt and freshly ground black pepper

Procedure:

1. Turn slow cooker on high setting. Add coconut oil or butter. Add garlic and onion and heat for 5-6 minutes. Add in remaining ingredients.
2. Boil on high temperaturc for five to six hours or on low setting for 8-10 hours. Remove chicken pieces from slow cooker. Eliminate meat bones, shred and return to pot.
3. Stir, adjust seasoning to taste, and serve.

Crockpot Chicken Curry

This chicken recipe is spicy and delicious.

Servings: 3-4

Ingredients:

- 2 pounds chicken parts, skinless, quartered
- 3/4 cup coconut milk
- 1 cup chicken broth
- 2 tablespoon tomato paste
- 3 garlic cloves, minced
- 4 carrots, spiralized
- 1 tablespoon ground ginger
- 6 tablespoon curry powder
- 2 zucchini, spiralized
- 2 bell peppers, chopped
- 1 yellow onion, thinly sliced
- Salt and pepper, to taste
- 1 dash red pepper flakes

Procedure:

1. Combine all ingredients (except for the chicken) in crock pot. Mix well to blend. Add the chicken; ensure that all pieces are totally submerged in the liquid.
2. Cover and cook on low setting for about 7 hours or on high setting for about 5 hours.
3. Serve.

Ginger-Orange Chicken Crockpot

Servings: 2-3

Ingredients:

- 2 pounds whole chickens, cut into parts
- 1/2 inch ginger, peeled and diced
- 2 carrots, spiralized
- 1 teaspoon sea salt
- 2 apples, spiralized
- 2 pearls, spiralized
- 1 garlic clove, peeled and smashed
- 2 large oranges, one juiced and one sliced
- 1 tomato, sliced
- 2 cucumbers, spiralized
- 1 chili pepper

Procedure:

1. In a slow cooker, place all the ingredients plus chicken; cover then cook for about 3 hours on high heat.

2. Afterwards, remove the chicken onto a chopping board; chili pepper can also be removed if desired. Using an immersion blender, puree everything left in the pot.
3. Slice chicken into desired cuts, plate, glaze with sauce and serve.

Mediterranean Savory Chicken Stew

Servings: 2-4

Ingredients:

- 2 pounds chicken breasts, boneless, skinless, halved
- 2 tablespoon ghee
- 1 zucchini, spiralized
- 1 large yellow onion, diced
- 4 cloves garlic, chopped
- 1/2 teaspoon coriander, grounded
- 2 radish, spiralized
- 1 teaspoon salt
- 1 28-oz. can crushed tomatoes
- 1/4 cup dried currants
- 1 bay leaf
- 1 teaspoon of cumin
- 1/4 teaspoon cinnamon
- A few inch ginger, spiralized
- Pinch of red pepper flakes
- 1/4 cup honey
- 3 tablespoons fresh parsley, chopped

Procedure:

1. Turn slow cooker to high setting. Add ghee and let melt. After adding onion and garlic, cook for five minutes.
2. Add in all the ingredients except for parsley. Cook on low heat for 3-4 hours or until the chicken is tender.
3. Serve topped with fresh parsley.

Teriyaki Wings

These chicken wings have a thick and tasty sauce...

Servings: 2-3

Ingredients:

- 1/2 cup coconut amigos
- 1/4 cup honey
- 1/2 cup orange juice
- ½ pineapple juice
- 4 tablespoons rice vinegar
- 2 teaspoon arrowroot flour
- 2 tablespoon fresh ginger, grated
- 4 cloves garlic, minced
- 2 tablespoon sesame oil
- 2 carrots, spiralized
- 2 teaspoon red pepper flakes
- 2 cucumber, spiralized
- 4 pounds chicken wings

Procedure:

1. Turn slow cooker to high heat. Mix all ingredients, except the chicken in a large bowl.
2. Place chicken in slow cooker. Pour marinade over chicken. Mix until chicken is thoroughly coated.
3. Cover and cook on high setting for 4 to 5 hours or low setting for 7-8 hours. You can cook until the chicken is ready to be eaten.
4. Optional: For a thicker sauce, remove wings from slow cooker and finish under broiler for 3-4 minutes.
5. Enjoy!

Chicken Fajita Soup

This soup is rich and flavorful and loaded with healthy veggies.

Servings: 2

Ingredients:

- 4 cloves garlic, minced
- 1 medium yellow onion, diced
- 1 bell pepper (red or green), diced
- 1 poblano pepper, diced
- 3 boneless, skinless chicken breasts (about 1 ½ pounds), cut into 2-inch pieces
- 2 zucchini, spiralized
- 4 cups chicken stock
- 1 can tomatoes (20 ounces), in thin slices
- 1 can tomato sauce (14.5 ounces)
- 1 can green chilies (4 ounces)
- 1 tablespoon chili powder
- 1 teaspoon cayenne pepper
- 1 teaspoon paprika
- 1 teaspoon oregano

- 1 bay leaf

For topping:

- Juice of 1-2 limes
- 1 avocado, cubed
- ¼ cup fresh cilantro, chopped

Procedure:

1. Turn slow cooker to low setting.
2. Add all ingredients to slow cooker, except toppings. Cook for 5-6 hours or until chicken is cooked through (internal temperature of 160 degrees F). Adjust seasonings as desired. Before serving, remove bay leaf and add lime juice.
3. Serve topped with avocado and cilantro.
4. Enjoy!

Roasted Chicken

This chicken is so easy. It just might replace your store-bought rotisserie chicken.

Servings: 4

Ingredients:

- 1 whole chicken (3-4 pounds)
- 1 tablespoon olive oil
- 1 pound baby carrots
- 4 cloves garlic, minced
- 1 teaspoon rosemary
- 2 apples, sliced
- 1 medium onion, chopped
- 1 teaspoon thyme
- Sea salt and freshly ground black pepper, to taste

Garnish:

- 2 cucumbers, spiralized

- 2 beets, sliced or spiralized
- 2 parsnips, spiralized
- Juice of ½ lemon
- Olive Oil
- Himalayan salt

Procedure:

1. Spread baby carrots and chopped onion on bottom of slow cooker.
2. Wash your chicken with cold water and then pat it dry. Brush the chicken's skin with olive oil. Put minced garlic inside chicken. Place the chicken in slow cooker, and then season it with rosemary, thyme, salt, and pepper.
3. Add the remaining ingredients and turn slow cooker to low setting and cook for 8 to 10 hours or until juices run clear and chicken is cooked through (internal temperature reaches 160 degrees F).
4. Garnish with spiralized veggies. sprinkle some olive oil and Himalayan salt, as well as some fresh lemon juice. enjoy!

Moroccan Chicken Tagine

An interesting blend of sweetness and spiciness your taste buds are sure to love.

Servings: 4-6

Ingredients:

- 6 boneless, skinless chicken breasts (could substitute thighs), cut into bite size pieces
- 1 eggplant, cubed
- 1 large yellow onion, sliced thin
- Olive oil, 2 tablespoons
- 4 large carrots, spiralized
- ½ cup dried apricots, chopped
- ½ cup dried cranberries, chopped
- 2 1/2 cups chicken broth
- 2 cucumbers, spiralized
- 3 tablespoons tomato paste
- Juice of ½ lemon
- 3 garlic cloves, minced
- 2 teaspoons cumin

- 1 teaspoon cinnamon
- 1 tablespoon freshly grated ginger
- 1 teaspoon freshly ground black pepper

Procedure:

1. Place eggplant cubes in colander. Sprinkle liberally with Himalayan salt. Let sit for 10-15 minutes. Rinse using cold water, pat dry with paper towels.
2. Heat your olive oil in large skillet. Add chicken and egg-plant and cook until the chicken is browned on all sides. Remove from heat.
3. Place chicken and eggplant into bottom of slow cooker. Add carrots, cucumbers, apricots, and cranberries.
4. Mix chicken broth, tomato paste, lemon juice plus spices in a large vessel. Pour over vegetables and the chicken
5. Cook on low setting for 7-8 hours or high setting for 4-5 hours or until chicken is cooked through and vegetables are tender.
6. Enjoy!

Chicken And Shrimp Gumbo

This Cajun-inspired dish is easy and very flavorful.

Servings: 2-3

Ingredients:

- 2 pounds skinless, boneless chicken breasts or thighs, cut into bite-size pieces
- 2 cans stewed tomatoes (14.5 ounces each)
- 2 cups chicken broth
- 1 large yellow onion, chopped
- 1 bell pepper, chopped
- 2 carrots, spiralized
- 3 stalks celery, chopped
- 4 cloves garlic, minced
- 2 zucchini, spiralized
- 1 teaspoon paprika
- 1 teaspoon ground fresh black pepper
- 1 teaspoon ground red pepper
- ½ teaspoon garlic powder
- 1-pound medium shrimp, unthawed

- ½ teaspoon onion powder
- ½ teaspoon cayenne pepper

Procedure:

1. Add all ingredients, except shrimp, to slow cooker. Stir them gently to combine.
2. Cover and cook on low setting for 6 hours. Add shrimp and cook until the shrimp is opaque.
3. Serve over Cauliflower-rice.

Cilantro Lime Chicken

Very easy and delicious Mexican-style chicken.

Servings: 2-4

Ingredients:

- 3 pounds boneless, skinless chicken breasts
- 6-ounce jar of salsa
- Juice of 1 lime
- 3 cloves garlic,
- 1 4-ounce can green chilies
- 1 ½ teaspoons cumin
- 1 cup radish, spiralized
- 1 teaspoon oregano
- 1 teaspoon chili powder
- 4 large carrots, spiralized
- 2 large parsnip, spiralized
- 1 teaspoon cayenne pepper
- ¼ cup fresh cilantro, chopped

Procedure:

1. Add all ingredients in slow cooker, except chicken. Mix with spoon until combined.
2. Add chicken and stir to coat with sauce. Cook on high for 4 hours or on low setting for 6 to 8 hours.
3. Shred chicken and serve over shredded cabbage.
4. Enjoy!

Paleo Fish Recipes

Lemon Coconut Haddock

There is nothing bland or boring about this fish. It is full of the flavors of lemon and coconut.

Prep Time: 30 minutes

Ingredients:

- 4 (4 to 6 oz.) haddock fillets
- 2 tablespoon fresh lemon zest
- ¼ cup shredded unsweetened coconut
- 2 tablespoon coconut flour
- Salt and pepper to taste
- Lemon wedges to garnish
- Garnish:
- 2 apples, sliced
- 2 carrots, spiralized
- 1 beet, spiralized
- ½ cup soy sprouts
- Himalayan salt

- Olive oil

Preparation:

1. Preheat your oven. Rinse the fish in cool water and pat dry with paper towel. For flavor, season with pepper and salt.
2. Combine the coconut, coconut flour and lemon zest in a small bowl. Arrange the haddock fillets on a roasting pan and sprinkle with the coconut flour mixture and then bake for 12 to 15 minutes, until the flesh of the fish is thoroughly cooked.
3. Serve hot with lemon wedges and spiralized veggies.
4. Sprinkle some olive oil and Himalayan salt to taste.

Baked White Fish and Mediterranean Salad

Fish and the Paleo diet go hand in hand—it's good for you. Any mild, white fish, such as cod or tilapia, works well here, but feel free to use what you have.

Servings: 2-4

Ingredients:

- 2 (6 to 8 ounce) white fish fillets
- Juice from 1 lemon
- 1 cucumber, spiralized
- ½ cup black olives
- 1 tomato, seeded and spiralized
- 2 radishes, spiralized
- 1 red onion, sliced
- Olive oil and red wine vinegar, to taste
- Freshly ground black pepper

Procedure:

1. Lightly spray baking sheet, using cooking spray after preheating your oven to 350 degrees F.
2. Place fish on baking sheet and then sprinkle with juice lemon. Bake for 10 to 12 minutes until fish flakes easily with a fork.
3. Combine cucumber, radish, olives, tomato, and onion in a large bowl. Drizzle vinegar and olive oil and season with pepper.
4. To serve, place the baked fillets on top of salad.
5. Enjoy, it's full of health!

Pan-Fried Trout with Kale

You'll find trout in most good fish markets these days, although if you can catch it yourself, it's so much better! Trout is a fairly lean fish. Nitrate-free bacon adds fat and flavor to this dish and pairs nicely with the kale.

Servings: 2

Ingredients:

- 2 strips of uncured, nitrate-free bacon
- 2 trout fillets
- Juice and zest from 1 lemon
- 2 cups kale, chopped
- Freshly ground black pepper
- ½ teaspoon dill

Garnish:

- 4 pineapple slices, chopped
- 1 cup radish, sliced or spiralized
- 2 cucumbers, spiralized

Procedure:

1. Cook the bacon over medium temperature in a large skillet. Transfer it to a plate and crumble it.
2. Sauté the trout in the bacon drippings until golden brown, firm, and opaque, about 7 to 10 minutes.
3. Transfer the fish to a plate and keep warm. Sauté the kale in the same pan for 4 to 6 minutes, until limp. Flavor using the black pepper (freshly ground) and dill. Don't overcook, as this will cause it to become tough and bitter.
4. Place the kale on two plates and serve the fish over it. Garnish with pineapple and spiralized veggies and sprinkle some lemon juice over it.
5. Enjoy!

Grilled Salmon with Grilled Veggies

Salmon is a meaty fish that performs beautifully on the grill. Just make sure you spray the grill first with a non-stick spray. And don't try to turn the fish until it's done. Salmon is cooked when it's firm to the touch and opaque. Don't overcook it.

Servings: 2

Ingredients:

- 4 salmon fillets
- ½ cup red bell pepper, chopped
- Freshly ground black pepper, to taste
- Juice and zest from 1 lemon
- ½ cup red sliced onion
- 1 cup zucchini, cut in rounds
- ½ cup carrots, spiralized

Procedure:

1. Preheat the grill. Place the salmon fillets on the grill and dust them with pepper, lemon juice, and zest. Cook for 5 to 8 minutes, turning halfway through. Transfer to a plate.
2. Spray the remaining ingredients after placing them on the grill.
3. Cook until tender or about fifteen minutes, while stirring frequently, so the onion doesn't burn.
4. Wait 5 minutes then serve.

Cod with Sautéed Mushrooms

Fresh cod fillets have a slightly firm texture and a mild, sweet flavor that pairs perfectly with sautéed mushrooms. Serve this delicious dish with steamed vegetables for a quick weeknight meal.

Servings: 4

Ingredients:

- 4 cod fillets
- 2 tablespoons olive or coconut oil
- ½ cup mushrooms, chopped
- 3 tablespoons full-fat coconut milk
- Freshly ground black pepper, to taste
- ¼ teaspoon dill
- 1 tablespoon lemon juice
- 1 tablespoon dried or fresh parsley

Garnish:

- 1 parsnip, spiralized

- 1 cup radish, sliced or spiralized
- ½ cup soy sprouts

Procedure:

1. Heat your oven to over 350 degrees F. With non-stick cooking spray, spray your cooking saucepan. Place put your fish in cooking saucepan. Bake your fish until white and firm.
2. After heating your cooking oil, add the mushrooms then cook until tender. Add the coconut milk and heat to warm. Season with freshly ground black pepper and dill.
3. To serve, place a fillet on each plate and drizzle the mushrooms and milk over the fish. Top with parsley plus juice lemon. Add spiralized veggies.
4. Enjoy!

Roasted Lemon Pepper Salmon Fillets

Salmon is one of the healthiest foods you can eat, as well as being pretty easy and fast to cook. It's high in protein and omega-3 fatty acids. You'll definitely find it on top of most Paleo's favorite lists. It's so delicious.

Servings: 2

Ingredients:

- 2 (6 to 8 ounce) salmon fillets
- 2 teaspoons lemon pepper seasoning
- 1 tablespoon olive oil
- 2 zucchini, spiralized
- 1 carrot, spiralized
- 4 cups tightly packed baby spinach
- 1 minced garlic clove

Procedure:

1. Preheat your oven. Coat salmon fillets on both sides with the lemon pepper seasoning.
2. Lightly spray a baking sheet with cooking spray and place fillets on top.
3. Roast salmon for about 15 minutes, flipping halfway through, or until fish flakes easily with a fork.
4. Add garlic and cook for thirty minutes. Add spinach, zucchini and carrots and cook until ready.
5. Divide spinach mixture evenly between two plates. Top with the salmon fillets and serve immediately.
6. Enjoy!

Fried Crab Cakes

Fried crab cakes are the perfect recipe for a special dinner at home. They are also easy enough to make if you want to feed an entire dinner party!

Servings: 2-3

Ingredients:

- 1 lbs. canned crab meat, drained well
- 1 large scallion, chopped fine
- 2 tablespoon red onion, minced
- 2 inch Ginger, spiralized or sliced
- 2 tablespoons paleo mayonnaise
- 1 teaspoon minced garlic
- 1 large egg
- 2 tablespoon blanched almond flour
- Salt and pepper to taste
- Coconut oil for cooking

Garnish:

- 1 avocado, sliced
- 2 cucumbers, spiralized
- 2 apples, spiralized

Procedure:

1. Crumble the crab by hand into a mixing bowl. Add the remaining ingredients, except the coconut oil. Mix well by hand then shape the mixture into patties.
2. Heat your oil over medium-high heat. Add the patties to the oil and cook on each side until browned. Drain on paper towels.
3. Serve with spiralized veggies and spiralized apples for more nutrition. Enjoy!

Grilled Lobster Tails

The summer is the perfect time to take advantage of fresh seafood, and nothing is more satisfying than these grilled lobster tails.

Servings: 2

Ingredients:

- 4 (6 to 8 oz.) lobster tails
- 2 tablespoons fresh chives, chopped
- 1 teaspoon garlic, minced
- ¼ cup coconut oil, melted
- 1 cup radish, spiralized
- 2 apples, spiralized
- Salt and pepper to taste

Procedure:

1. Preheat your grill on medium-high heat. Whisk remaining ingredients in a small bowl. Split the lobster tails using a pair of heavy duty kitchen shears.

2. Slide a metal skewer through each halved lobster tail to keep it from curling. Brush the coconut oil mixture on the lobsters and grill them for about 5 minutes until the shells turn bright red.
3. Flip the tails and brush with the coconut oil mixture again. Cook until the meat is cooked through, around four minutes. Serve hot.

Cajun Grilled Salmon Steaks

If you don't think you are a fan of fish, wait until you try this recipe to truly make up your mind. Tender and juicy, flavored with Cajun spices, it is truly delicious!

Servings: 4

Ingredients:

- 4 salmon steaks, about 1 inch thick
- 1 to 2 tablespoon olive oil
- ½ teaspoon ground coriander
- ½ teaspoon ground cumin
- ½ teaspoon chili powder
- ¼ teaspoon cayenne pepper
- ¼ teaspoon fresh ground pepper
- Lime wedges to serve

Garnish:

- 2 beets, spiralized

- 2 zucchini, spiralized and stir-fried in coconut oil until tender
- ¼ cup cilantro

Procedure:

1. Preheat the grill on medium-high heat. Brush both sides of the salmon steaks with olive oil.
2. Combine the spices in a small bowl then rub them on both sides of the salmon steaks. Lay the steaks on the grill and cook for about 3 to 4 minutes on each side.
3. In the meantime, you can stir-fry the spiralized zucchini in some coconut oil (use low or medium heat).
4. Serve hot with a lime wedge. Add spiralized veggies.
5. Enjoy!

Basil Lime Shrimp

Flavored with fresh basil and lime, this shrimp is refreshing and satisfying!

Ingredients:

- 2 lbs. raw shrimp, peeled and deveined
- Juice from 1 lime
- 1 cup fresh basil leaves, chopped
- Salt and pepper to taste

Garnish:

- 1 zucchini, spiralized and stir-fried in coconut oil
- 4 carrots, spiralized and stir-friend in coconut oil until tender

Preparation:

1. Rinse the shrimp with cool water and pat dry with paper towel.
2. Transfer the shrimp to a large plastic freezer bag and add the remaining ingredients.
3. Toss well to coat then wait 20 minutes.
4. Preheat a cast-iron grill pan, and then spray using cooking oil. Arrange the shrimp in a single layer on the grill.
5. Cook the shrimp for 2 to 3 minutes on each side or until cooked through.
6. Serve hot with spiralized veggies.
7. Enjoy!

Paleo Vegan & Vegetarian Recipes

Stuffed Baked Tomatoes

Stuffed with vegetables and fresh herbs, these stuffed baked tomatoes are equally suited for dinner or an appetizer.

Servings: 2

Ingredients:

- 6 medium ripe tomatoes
- 1 small zucchini, spiralized
- 1 tablespoon garlic, minced
- 1 yellow onion, diced
- 2 tablespoon fresh basil, chopped
- 1 tablespoon dried rosemary
- Salt and pepper to taste
- Olive oil as needed

Preparation:

1. Preheat oven to 375°F. Carefully slice top of every tomato. Turn the tomatoes upside down onto paper towel to drain.
2. Place the insides of the tomatoes in mixing vessel and then stir in zucchini, onion, basil, rosemary and garlic. Mix well. Season with pepper and salt.
3. Place the tomatoes in a baking dish and spoon the filling into them. Place the tops on the tomatoes, if desired.
4. Drizzle with olive oil and then cook until tender, 25 to 30 minutes. Yummy!

Spicy Vegetarian Curry

This spicy vegetarian curry is the perfect meal if you are not in the mood to cook. Simply chop a few vegetables, add the seasoning, and let it simmer.

Servings: 2-3

Ingredients:

- 1 lb. sweet potato, chopped and cooked
- 1 cup carrot, spiralized
- 1 cup celery, chopped
- 2 cups cauliflower florets, chopped
- 1 medium red pepper, chopped
- 1 medium green pepper, chopped
- 1 tablespoon coconut oil
- 1 tablespoon minced garlic
- 1 cup organic vegetable broth
- 1 (14 oz.) can coconut milk
- 2 zucchini, spiralized
- 2 tablespoon curry powder
- Salt and pepper to taste

Preparation:

1. Heat the coconut oil in a heavy skillet over medium heat. Cook for a minute after adding garlic. Stir in carrot, cucumber, plus sweet potatoes. Cook for 5 minutes.
2. Add the remaining vegetables. Also mix in vegetable broth, curry powder and coconut milk.
3. Season with salt and pepper to taste. Simmer for 30 minutes. Serve hot.
4. Enjoy!

Fried Zucchini and Dill Fritters

Flavored with fresh herbs and fried until crisp, these fried zucchini fritters very delicious.

Servings: 2

Ingredients:

- 2 large zucchini, spiralized
- 1 tablespoon coconut flour
- 1 large egg
- 2 tablespoon fresh dill, chopped
- 2 medium cucumber, spiralized
- 2 tablespoon red onion, minced
- 2 carrots, spiralized
- Salt and pepper to taste
- Coconut oil for cooking

Preparation:

1. Spread the spiralized zucchini in a colander and sprinkle with sea salt. Let the zucchini sit for 30 minutes then squeeze as much moisture out of it as possible.
2. Place the zucchini in a mixing bowl with the remaining ingredients. Stir the mixture until well combined. Liberally grease a heavy skillet with cooking oil and heat over medium heat.
3. Drop the zucchini mixture into the skillet, using an ice cream scoop. Leave about 1 ½ inches between each fritter, cooking them in two batches if needed.
4. Fry the fritters for 2 to 3 minutes per side until lightly browned. Drain the fritters on paper towel before serving.
5. Enjoy!

Grilled Pineapple and Sweet Potatoes

When you're craving potatoes, try sweet potatoes instead. They're high in carotene and fiber and lower in sugar and starch than white potatoes. They pair beautifully with pineapple on the grill for a sweet and smoky dish.

Servings: 2

Ingredients:

- 1 pineapple, cored and cut in cubes
- 2 tablespoons olive or coconut oil
- 2 large sweet potatoes, peeled and cut in cubes
- 1 tablespoon honey
- 1 teaspoon cinnamon
- Freshly ground black pepper, to taste

Garnish:

- 2 carrots, spiralized
- 2 apples, spiralized

Procedure:

1. Preheat the grill. Place the sweet potatoes on a microwave-safe dish. Cover them and microwave for 8 minutes. Sweet potatoes take a long time to cook, but microwaving them first accelerates the process.
2. Spray the grill basket with cooking spray. Place the sweet potatoes in the grill basket and grill them for 8 to 10 minutes, stirring frequently, until tender. Add the pineapple and grill for an additional 3 to 5 minutes.
3. Mix the oil, honey, and cinnamon in a bowl and pour over the pineapple and sweet potatoes. Stir to combine, cook for one more minute, and then remove from the heat.
4. Serve with raw, spiralized apples and carrots.
5. Enjoy!

Winter Veggie Stew

This hearty stew is vegan, but it's also very filling. Many people are surprised to find that a lot of vegan dishes fit the Paleo plan. Leafy greens, such as the kale and spinach in this dish, are loaded with fiber and protein, as well as vitamins and minerals that will keep your body going all day long.

Servings: 2

Ingredients:

- 1 small onion, minced
- 4 cups packed baby spinach
- 2 cloves garlic, minced
- 2 carrots, spiralized
- 6 cups of vegetable broth
- 2 tablespoons olive oil
- 1 cup mushrooms, spiralized
- 1 stalk celery, chopped
- 1 tablespoon Italian seasoning
- Freshly ground black pepper
- 1 large bunch Tuscan kale, chopped

- 1 (15-ounce) can of tomatoes, spiralized

Procedure:

1. Heat the oil in Dutch oven and over medium heat. Add the onions, garlic, carrots, mushrooms, plus celery. Cook for 10 minutes until veggies are soft.
2. Add the Italian seasonings, spinach, and kale and stir until everything is combined. Season with freshly ground black pepper.
3. Add the tomatoes with juices and vegetable broth. Bring to boil. Reduce heat and simmer until carrots are soft. Serve immediately.

Baked Southwestern Sweet Potato

Sweet potatoes are a great alternative to white potatoes on the Paleo diet, as they are loaded with fiber, vitamins, and minerals and have significantly less starch. They are perfectly fine and even healthy when eaten once in a while. It's a very easy and flavorful dish indeed.

Ingredients:

- 1 medium sweet potato
- 1 teaspoon cumin
- Freshly ground black pepper, to taste
- 2 tablespoons prepared tomato salsa
- 1 teaspoon chili powder

Garnish:

- 2 zucchini, spiralized and stir-fried in coconut oil
- Fresh cilantro, chopped

Procedure:

1. Preheat oven to 400 degrees F. Put sweet potato directly on the rack in oven.
2. Bake for 30 minutes and then remove from the oven. Prick all over with a fork. Allow to cool for 5 minutes.
3. Cut open the top and remove the skin's flesh. Put flesh in a bowl and mash with chili powder and cumin. Season with freshly ground black pepper.
4. Top with the salsa and cilantro. Serve with spiralized zucchini for more nutrition. Enjoy!

Peanut and Sweet Potato Stew

Adapted for the Paleo diet, it's a really flavorful and healthy dish.

Servings: 2

Ingredients:

- 1 medium onion, chopped
- 2 tablespoons olive oil
- 2 fresh jalapeños, seeded and minced
- ¼ teaspoon ground coriander
- 2 teaspoons ground cumin
- ¼ teaspoon ground cinnamon
- ⅛ teaspoon crushed red pepper
- 4 inches fresh ginger, spiralized
- 1 pound fresh green beans, trimmed
- 2 cloves garlic, minced
- 2 cups vegetable broth
- Freshly ground black pepper, to taste
- ¼ cup natural peanut butter
- 2 large sweet potatoes, peeled and cubed
- 1 (28-ounce) can diced tomatoes

- 5 carrots, spiralized

Procedure:

1. Heat the oil in a large Dutch oven or soup pot. Add the onions, jalapeño peppers, ginger, garlic, and spices. Cook for five minutes. Season with freshly ground black pepper. Add the sweet potatoes and cook for 5 minutes or more.
2. Add the green beans, tomatoes, plus vegetable broth and boil. Reduce heat and cook for 20 minutes. Heat until sweet potatoes are tender and can be pierced with a fork.
3. Stir in the peanut butter and spiralized carrots and simmer until heated through. serve immediately.

Stuffed Zucchini Boats

These stuffed zucchini boats are baked to the perfect level of tenderness, full of fresh vegetables, and garnished with green onion.

Servings: 3-4

Ingredients:

- 3 large zucchini
- 1 yellow bell pepper, chopped
- 1 small ripe tomato, sliced
- 1 red bell pepper, chopped
- 2 cucumbers, spiralized
- ¼ cup fresh chives, chopped
- Olive oil as needed
- Salt and pepper to taste

Preparation:

1. Heat your oven to 350°F.

2. Using a spoon or small knife, scoop out the middle of each zucchini half, leaving a ¼-inch border on all sides. Chop the zucchini flesh and place it in a bowl with the peppers, cucumber, and tomato.
3. Brush the zucchini boats with olive oil and sprinkle with salt and pepper. Lay on sheet baking. Bake for about 15 minutes until slightly tender.
4. Spoon the filling into the boats and bake them for an additional 20 minutes until the filling is hot. Sprinkle with chives to serve.
5. Enjoy!

Eggplant Parmesan

Fried eggplant slices served with tomato basil sauce makes a perfect Paleo dish! Yum!

Servings: 2

Ingredients:

- 1 large eggplant
- 1 teaspoon dried oregano
- ½ cup blanched almond flour
- 2 large eggs, beaten
- Salt and pepper
- 1 teaspoon dried basil
- Coconut oil for cooking
- 1 ½ cups organic tomato sauce

Garnish:

- 2 green apples, spiralized
- 2 beets, spiralized

Preparation:

1. Preheat oven to 400°F.
2. Slice the eggplant into ¼-inch thick slices and arrange on paper towels. Sprinkle liberally with sea salt. Wait 20 minutes. Pat dry the eggplant slices, and then dip in the egg.
3. Stir the almond flour and spices in a shallow dish. Dredge the eggplant slices in the flour mixture and put them aside.
4. Heat the coconut oil. Add the breaded eggplant slices and cook for 2 to 3 minutes on each side until browned. Transfer the eggplant to a baking dish and pour the tomato sauce over it. Cook until eggplant is tender.
5. Serve with spiralized apples and beets for more nutrition.

Salad Recipes

Rustic Chicken Salad

Very delicious!

Servings: 2

Ingredients:

- 2/3 cup Paleo Mayonnaise
- Two chicken breasts
- 1 teaspoon balsamic vinegar
- 2 garlic cloves, finely chopped
- 2 cucumbers, spiralized
- 1 teaspoon fresh pesto
- 1/ 3 cup basil, chopped
- 8 spring onions, chopped
- 2/3 cup roast eggplant, chopped
- 10 black olives, chopped and seeded
- Half diced avocado
- 2 carrots, spiralized
- 2 tomatoes, sliced

Procedure:

1. Boil chicken breasts in water until cooked, 15 to 20 minutes. Remove from the pan and allow it to cool.
2. In small bowl, combine paleo mayonnaise, garlic, pesto, vinegar, cucumber, carrots, basil and spring onions
3. Shred chicken into pieces when cooled and put in large salad bowl. Add tomatoes, eggplant, black olives and avocado.
4. Add mayonnaise dressing then combine well. Serve.
5. Enjoy!

Sweet Potato and Bacon Salad

Servings: 2

Ingredients:

- 1 onion, diced
- 4 cups sweet potato, peeled and diced
- Oil
- Sliced almonds
- 4, rashes bacon, diced (fat removed)

Garnish:

- 1 zucchini, spiralized and stir-fried in coconut oil
- ¼ cup cilantro

Procedure:

1. Steam diced sweet potato 5 to 6 minutes or until tender. Place in a medium-sized mixing bowl after removing from heat.
2. Meanwhile, place onion, oil and bacon in frying pan on medium heat then cook the bacon and onion until they turn brown.
3. Add onion and bacon and combine well. serve with sliced almonds, cilantro, and spiralized zucchini on top.

Yam and Kale Salad

Yam and kale are power foods, loaded with essential vitamins and other good stuff you need to achieve vibrant health. The flavor of this dish is deep and satisfying.

Servings: 2

Ingredients:

- 2 large yams, peeled and cut into 1-inch cubes
- Freshly ground black pepper, to taste
- 1 teaspoon thyme
- 1 medium onion, cut in half and sliced
- 3 tablespoons Olive oil. divided
- 3 cloves garlic, minced
- 2 tablespoons apple cider vinegar
- 1 pound kale, torn into pieces
- 2 zucchini, sliced with a spiralizer

Procedure:

1. Preheat oven to 400 degrees F.
2. Toss yams with two tablespoons of olive oil. Bake yams until tender and allow them to cool.
3. In a medium sauté pan, add the remaining tablespoon of olive oil. Add garlic plus onion and cook to a golden brown. Add the zucchini, kale, then cook until it wilts.
4. Combine the yams, kale, vinegar, and thyme together in a bowl. Season with freshly ground black pepper. Serve immediately.
5. Enjoy!

Easy Greek Salad

Avocado, sun-dried tomatoes, and artichoke, along with crunchy onion and bell peppers, create a satisfying salad loaded with flavor.

Servings: 2

Ingredients:

- 2 tablespoons balsamic rice vinegar
- 3 tablespoons olive oil
- 1 teaspoon Greek seasoning
- 1 ripe avocado
- 1 green bell pepper, sliced
- 1/4 medium red onion, sliced
- 1 cup black olives, pitted and cut in half
- 2 tomatoes, cut into bite-sized pieces
- 1/2 cucumber, halved and spiralized
- 1/8 cup sun-dried tomatoes packed in olive oil
- 1/8 cup artichoke hearts
- Freshly ground black pepper, to taste

Procedure:

1. Whisk the vinegar, olive oil, and Greek seasoning.
2. Combine the rest of the ingredients with the salad dressing. Season with freshly ground black pepper.
3. Let chill, covered, in the refrigerator for 30 minutes.
4. Serve chilled. Enjoy!

Arugula, Prosciutto, And Cantaloupe Salad

Prosciutto is the perfect match to melon, bringing out the salty, savory flavor of the ham and the sweetness of the cantaloupe. The arugula adds a nice spicy contrast, and the walnuts add a bit of crunch. This salad is best in the summer when you can get a fresh melon that is picked at the perfect time.

Servings: 4

Ingredients:

- 4 cups arugula, loosely packed
- 6 slices good quality prosciutto, cut into 1/2-inch strips
- 1/2 cantaloupe, seeds and rind removed, cut into 1/2-inch cubes
- 2 carrots, spiralized
- 1 cucumber, spiralized
- 1 cup walnuts, roughly chopped
- Freshly ground black pepper, to taste
- Olive oil, to taste

Procedure:

1. Divide the arugula, carrots, and cucumber among four plates.
2. Top the arugula with prosciutto, cantaloupe, and walnuts. Season with freshly ground black pepper.
3. Drizzle some olive oil over each salad.
4. Serve.

Crab and Mango Salad

Crab is a good source of protein and omega-3 fatty acids. The mango adds a nice sweet and sour component to the salad. One bite of this salad and you'll think you're on an island if you can eat it outside on a nice sunny day.

Servings: 2

Ingredients:

- 4 cups mixed baby greens
- 1/4 cup fresh cooked crabmeat, picked over for shells
- 1 mangos, peeled and spiralized
- 1 tablespoon fresh mint, roughly chopped
- 1/2 cucumber, peeled and spiralized
- Juice from 2 limes
- 2 teaspoons olive oil
- Freshly ground black pepper, to taste

Procedure:

1. Divide the mixed lettuce between two plates.
2. Toss the remaining ingredients in a vessel. Season with freshly ground black pepper.
3. Divide the crab salad between the two plates, heaping it at center of the lettuce.
4. Serve.
5. Enjoy!

Mushroom Salad

This salad can be prepared with any type of mushroom. Portobello mushrooms will add a good meaty side to the taste, and they will also absorb the marinade, making them extremely flavorful. Wild mushrooms are another variety that will add a pleasant, yet distinct taste to your salad. Any fresh green, such as arugula and baby spinach, which are two wonderful options may be used.

Servings: 2

Ingredients:

- 2 tablespoons plus 1/4 cup shallots, finely chopped and divided
- 3 tablespoons rice vinegar
- 11 tablespoons olive oil, divided
- 1 teaspoon fresh thyme
- 2 pounds mushrooms
- 4 carrots, spiralized
- Freshly ground black pepper, to taste
- 6 ounces fresh greens

Procedure:

1. Combine the 2 tablespoons shallots and vinegar in a small bowl. Beat the mixture. Put aside for 5 minutes to permit the shallots to absorb the vinegar. Once they have absorbed the vinegar, mix in 7 tablespoons of olive oil and set aside.
2. In a large skillet, add the remaining oil. Add the mushrooms and carrots and sprinkle with the thyme and some pepper. Depending on the type of mushrooms you use, the cooking time will vary. Add the 1/4 cup shallots to the mushrooms and continue cooking until the shallots are soft. Season with freshly ground black pepper.
3. Fill a large plate or bowl with the fresh greens. Place the mushrooms on top of the greens and top with the vinaigrette.
4. Serve.

Walnut and Beet Salad

Beets are a valuable root vegetable and are good source of dietary fiber and vitamin C. However, most people are not familiar enough with beets to use them regularly. This salad offers a quick and tasty way to incorporate beets into your diet.

Servings: 2

Ingredients:

- 2 tablespoons olive oil
- Freshly ground black pepper.
- 2 cucumbers, spiralized
- 4 medium red beets
- 2 apples, spiralized
- 2 tablespoons balsamic vinegar
- ⅓ cup walnuts, chopped

Procedure:

1. Preheat oven to 400 degrees F. Wrap each beet in foil and place on baking sheet. Roast in the oven for about an hour.
2. Remove beets from the oven and allow to cool. Once cool enough to handle, remove them from the foil. Remove the beets skin while still warm. Plastic gloves are suggested, so you do not stain your hands.
3. Mix the remaining ingredients with large, sliced chunks of beets in medium vessel. Season with freshly ground black pepper. Allow beets to saturate.
4. Serve and enjoy!

Hot Chicken and Zucchini Salad

This is a hot salad, featuring the unique combination of chicken and zucchini that is simple to prepare. Top with fresh almonds to complement the lemon and garlic mayonnaise.

Servings: 4-6

Ingredients:

- 4 zucchinis, sliced or spiralized,
- 1 tablespoon dried oregano
- 2 pounds chicken breasts, cut into cubes
- 3 tablespoons coconut oil
- Freshly ground black pepper, to taste
- 7 tablespoons olive-oil mayonnaise
- Juice from 2 lemons
- 1 large onion, chopped
- 2 cloves garlic, very finely minced
- 1 head romaine lettuce, washed and shredded
- Sliced almonds, optional

Procedure:

1. Add the chicken cubes and coconut oil in a large pan. Cook over medium-high heat until thoroughly cooked. Set aside.
2. Add the onion in the same pan and cook until soft, approximately 5 minutes. Add the zucchini and oregano. Season them with pepper. Cook until the zucchini is soft.
3. Mix the mayonnaise, lemon juice, and garlic into a small bowl. Add the cooked chicken, onion, and zucchini to the mayonnaise and stir well.
4. Add romaine lettuce, mix well, and serve in bowls. This hot salad is delicious topped with some almonds.

Enjoy!

Thai Ground Chicken Salad

Servings: 2

Ingredients:

- 2 teaspoons lime juice
- 2 teaspoons fresh ginger
- 1/2 teaspoon salt
- 1/2 teaspoon chili garlic sauce
- 1 teaspoon honey
- 1 ½ teaspoon extra-virgin olive oil,
- 1/2 cup carrots, spiralized
- 2 cups romaine lettuce leaves, shredded
- 1/4 pound extra-lean ground chicken
- ¼ cup red onion slivers
- 2 teaspoons dry-roasted cashews, chopped
- 1 teaspoon fresh cilantro leaves, chopped
- 2 teaspoons of fresh mint leaves, chopped

Procedure:

1. Combine the lime juice, ginger, chili, garlic sauce, honey and salt in a small bowl. Whisk, gradually adding oil, until blended.
2. Over medium-high heat, heat small nonstick frying pan until water spritz sputters on it.
3. Briefly remove the cooking pan from the heat with an oven mitt to mist lightly with spray olive oil. Add chicken to pan. Cook while breaking up meat into chunks with spatula, for 3 to 5 minutes, or until no longer pink. Remove from heat. Stir in one teaspoon of a reserved dressing.
4. Combine the lettuce, onion, carrot, mint, and cilantro in large serving bowl. Sprinkle with remaining dressing and toss. Sprinkle with the nuts and top with reserved chicken.
5. Serve and enjoy!

Chicken Apple Salad

Servings: 2

Ingredients:

- 6 oz. chicken
- Olive oil
- Half Granny smith apple, spiralized
- 6 cups cabbage, shredded
- 1/8 teaspoon cloves
- ½ teaspoon allspice,
- Pepper and sea salt to taste
- 4 carrots, spiralized
- 2 cucumbers, spiralized

Procedure:

1. Dice chicken. Heat olive oil in average skillet. Add the allspice, chicken and cloves. Cook, tossing often, until chicken is cooked through.

2. Shred the cabbage into a large salad bowl. Add the chicken and spiralized foods. Add pepper and salt for taste, then drizzle with olive oil.
3. Enjoy!

Carrot/Apple Salad

Servings: 1-2

Ingredients:

- 2 apples, spiralized
- juice of 1 lemon
- ¼ cup raisins
- 4 carrots, spiralized
- 1 teaspoon ginger
- 1 teaspoon stevia
- A few tablespoons of coconut milk

Procedure:

1. Mix all the ingredients in a big salad bowl.
2. Sprinkle some spices, stevia, coconut milk and lemon juice.
3. Enjoy!

Almond Chicken Salad

Servings: 2

Ingredients:

- 1 chicken breast meat, cooked and diced
- Flaxseed oil
- 2 cucumbers, spiralized
- ½ cup almonds, sliced
- 1 quarter red cabbage, chopped
- 1 butter leaf lettuce, shredded
- Freshly squeezed orange juice
- 2 apples, spiralized
- 1 romaine lettuce, chopped
- ¼ cup Medjool dates, chopped

Procedure:

1. Combine all ingredients, excluding liquids, in large serving bowl.

2. Then, toss with freshly squeezed orange juice and flaxseed oil
3. Serve.

Before you go, I'd like to remind you that there is a free, complimentary eBook waiting for you. Download it today to treat yourself to healthy, gluten-free desserts and snacks so that you never feel deprived again!

Download link

http://bit.ly/gluten-free-desserts-book

Conclusion

Thank you for reading my book, and thank you for committing to your health. My hope is that you have gained an understanding of how juicing can allow us to feel our best on a daily basis, lose weight naturally, and live disease-free.

The results you will see and feel including sustained energy, decreased mood swings and food sensitivities, increased fitness and so many others, will be the true motivation you need to commit and stay committed.

So... ***congratulations!*** You have taken an important step. Your body will surely thank you.

If you decide that daily juicing is the lifestyle for you, I hope you will try some of the recipes in this book as you keep experiencing its amazing mind and body benefits. Please let me know your favorites - the review section of this book is an excellent place to share your experience with other readers.

To post an honest review

One more thing... If you have received any value from this book, can you please rank it and post a short review? It only takes a few seconds really and it would really make my day. It's you I am writing for and your opinion is always much appreciated. In order to do so;

1. Log into your account
2. Search for my book on Amazon or check your orders/ or go to my author page at:

http://amazon.com/author/kira-novac

3. Click on a book you have read, then click on "reviews" and "create your review".

Please let me know your favorite motivational tip you learned from this book.

I would love to hear from you!

If you happen to have any questions or doubts about this book, please e-mail me at:

kira.novac@kiraglutenfreerecipes.com

I am here to help!

Recommended Reading

Book Link:

http://bit.ly/ai-box-set

Recommended Reading

Book Link:

http://bit.ly/juicing-diet-book

FOR MORE HEALTH BOOKS (KINDLE & PAPERBACK) BY KIRA NOVAC PLEASE VISIT:

www.kiraglutenfreerecipes.com/books

Thank you for taking an interest in my work,

Kira and Holistic Wellness Books

HOLISTIC WELLNESS & HEALTH BOOKS

If you are interested in health, wellness, spirituality and personal development, visit our page and be the first one to know about free and 0.99 eBooks:

www.HolisticWellnessBooks.com

Lightning Source UK Ltd.
Milton Keynes UK
UKHW050725280820
368971UK00008B/84

CU00690457

The Parish Clergy under the Later Stuarts

JOHN H. PRUETT

The Parish Clergy under the Later Stuarts

The Leicestershire Experience

UNIVERSITY OF ILLINOIS PRESS

Urbana Chicago London

Publication of this work was supported in part
by a grant from the Andrew W. Mellon Foundation.

Library of Congress Cataloging in Publication Data

Pruett, John H 1947–
The parish clergy under the later Stuarts.

Bibliography: p.
Includes index.
1. Clergy—England—Leicestershire. 2. Leicestershire, Eng.—History. I. Title.
BR763.L4P78 301.44′44 78-8174
ISBN 0-252-00662-3

For M. L. W.

Acknowledgments

I wish to thank the archival staffs of the Lincolnshire Archives Office, the Leicestershire Record Office, and Leicester Museum for allowing me the use of documents in their care and for generously offering advice that proved extremely helpful in my research. Thanks are due also to His Grace the Archbishop of Canterbury for permission to consult documents in the Lambeth Palace Library, and to the staffs of the Bodleian Library, Christ Church Library, Cambridge University Library, the Public Record Office, and the British Museum. D. M. Barratt, Christopher Hill, Kathleen Major, and Anne Whiteman all read my dissertation prospectus and offered valuable comments and criticisms; I am especially indebted to them for calling my attention to documents in the Bodleian Library and the Lambeth Palace Library that I might otherwise have overlooked. Many thanks, too, to W. F. Craven, who read the dissertation and offered sound advice. Lacey Baldwin Smith and Ann Lowry Weir read the revised manuscript and suggested a number of further revisions, some of which I have incorporated in this book; I am very grateful for their help. Finally, special thanks to Lawrence Stone of Princeton University, under whose direction most of this study was written. He not only supervised my research but even suggested the topic, and I am indebted to him for friendship and inspiration as well. All errors and misinterpretations are, of course, my own.

—J. H. P.

Contents

Introduction

> With the restoration of the king, a spirit of extravagant joy spread over the nation, that brought on with it the throwing off the very professions of virtue and piety; all ended in entertainments and drunkenness. . . .and they grow soon to find it a modish thing, that looks like wit and spirit, to laugh at religion and virtue.
>
> —Gilbert Burnet, *History of His Own Times*[1]

In every age there are men who believe that the times are out of joint, and that the old virtues are in retreat. But the Jeremiahs who lived under the later Stuarts were perhaps more accurate than most, for they lived in a period that was exceptionally strange and confusing. The Civil War and Interregnum had ended with many issues left unsettled, and the next half-century would see an awkward and often painful working out of acceptable relationships between King and Parliament, King and People, Anglican and Puritan. Many of the questions to which Englishmen sought answers under the later Stuarts were, either directly or indirectly, religious ones. Could the Church of England embrace more than one variety of Protestantism? If not, could it tolerate Dissent? What political and social roles might Dissenters be allowed to play? How long must a nation obey a monarch who seems to be subverting the very Church he has sworn to defend? Are monarchs who have been declared legitimate rulers by Parliament rightful rulers in the eyes of God? Spiritual questions like these produced political crises in late-Stuart England, yet many Englishmen agreed with Burnet that theirs was an age when interest in things spiritual was declining. So far as they spoke of the nation as a whole, they were probably correct. Religious enthusiasm had crested and broken during the Interregnum and, though by no means spent, had begun to flow backward. Many who lived in the ebb tide turned with relief to more pleasant pastimes and to the comforts of skepticism. Others, especially men of the cloth, lamented the decline of religious fervor and warned that the Church was in danger, whether from Dissenters on the left, Papists on the right, or freethinkers somewhere outside. Their cries of danger periodically revived some of the old spiritual passions, but as time wore on the odds were increasingly against them. It was their misfortune to be trapped in an awkward transitional period somewhere between the Age of Faith and the Age of Reason.

Many who regretted the erosion of piety called it a reaction against the excesses of the Interregnum; others blamed it on the licentiousness of Charles II's court or, more vaguely, on the spirit of the times. But some pointed to the clergy, accusing them of succumbing to the very secularism that it was their mission to combat. One of these critics was an Oxford don named John Eachard, who in 1670 published *The Grounds and Occasions of the Contempt of the Clergy and Religion*. Contempt for the clergy was so widespread, felt Eachard, that it could safely be taken for granted; he sought only to explain its causes, and to show how it hindered the work of the Church. The result was an unflattering portrait of the late-Stuart parish clergy—a portrait that subsequent writers have often accepted as at least partially accurate. According to Eachard, the clergy were held in contempt because of, quite simply, "the Ignorance of some, and the Poverty of others." Clerical ignorance was partly the fault of overly zealous schoolmasters, "ambitious of the glory of being counted able to send forth now and then to Oxford and Cambridge, from the little House by the Church-yard side, one of their ill-educated Disciples." Consequently "all kinds of Lads" flocked to the universities, "let their parts be never so low and pittiful, the instructions they have lain under never so mean and contemptible, and the Purses of their Friends never so short to maintain them there." If the gentry's sons received better training in the grammar schools, the ones who entered the universities with the Church in mind were generally "the weak, the lame, and usually the most ill-favoured"—younger sons too dim witted to be set up in trade or the law. Once at a university, both gentleman's son and plowman's boy were subjected to an outmoded curriculum, one that emphasized Latin and Greek at the expense of "useful" subjects like English oratory. Not surprisingly, the clergy's sermons often became pretentious, pedantic, and unintelligible to the laity.[2]

Contempt for the clergy also sprang from clerical poverty, which in turn resulted from the number of poorly endowed parish livings, and from the universities' overproduction of clerical candidates for the livings falling vacant. Eachard guessed that men in orders outnumbered parish livings by about two to one, and that clerical unemployment would continue to plague the Church until "we had some vent for our Learned ones beyond the Sea, and could transport so many Tunn of Divines yearly as we do other commodities with which the Nation is over-stocked." Poverty and unemployment were not merely degrading; they also prevented parsons from acquiring good libraries of religious literature, from dispensing charity in their parishes, and from sending their children into respectable occupations. Moreover, poverty tempted a parson to forsake "his own Study of a few Scurvy Books, and his own Habitation of Darkness" for more cheerful company in the local tavern, where he might fall victim to vice and iniquity. Poor parsons might also become dependent on their parishioners for charitable handouts, and with this dependence, said Eachard, came loss of self-respect and reluctance to criticize their parishioners' moral failings.[3]

Thus Eachard believed that contempt for the clergy was partly the product of forces beyond the clergy's control; much of the blame lay with irresponsible schoolmasters, an antiquated university curriculum, and poor parochial endowments. But Eachard also blamed the parsons themselves. Why, in the face of such meager rewards, did so many stubbornly take up clerical careers? Eachard doubted that the primary motive was an unselfish desire to serve the Church. Instead, some entered the clergy for pomp and vanity, thinking "the Pulpit the highest Seat in all the Parish," and assuming that as clergymen they would "take place of most, but Esquires and Right Worshipfuls." Others entered out of shameless exhibitionism, happily preaching overly learned sermons "out of simple phantastick Glory, and a great studiousness of being wonder'd at; as if getting into the Pulpit were a kind of Staging." And still others entered "for want of Employment in their Profession of Law, Physick, or the like; or having been unfortunate in their Trade, or having broken a Leg or an Arm, and so disabled from following their former Calling; or having had the Pleasure of spending their Estate, or being (perhaps deservedly) disappointed in their Inheritance." And so "if it be enquired by any one, how it comes to pass that we have so many in Holy Orders that understand so little, and that are able to do so little service in the

Church? If we would answer plainly and truly, we may say, because they are good for nothing else."[4]

Most of what Eachard wrote became the basis of Macaulay's description of the late-Stuart clergy. If Macaulay was less acerbic and more sympathetic, his ordinary parish clergy were still generally ill educated, poverty stricken, and socially contemptible.[5] Eachard had been attacked in his own day by critics who thought him malicious and irreligious,[6] and Macaulay soon inspired his own opponents, most notably Churchill Babington in the nineteenth century and P. H. Ditchfield in the early twentieth.[7] Both were willing to admit that poverty was a problem for many parsons, but the post-Restoration clergy they wrote about were generally well behaved, well educated, socially respectable, and adequately paid. They often sprang from the landed gentry and generally lived like gentlemen themselves, and they frequently penned poems and articles for literary and antiquarian journals. More recent historians have tried to strike a balance between these two extremes. According to Norman Sykes and A. Tindal Hart, Eachard's and Macaulay's unflattering portraits were more accurate than Babington's and Ditchfield's rosy ones, but we are reminded that this was a transitional era in which a "growing number" were "increasingly" better educated and socially more acceptable.[8]

The portraits painted by Whig, Tory, and compromise historians thus cover a wide spectrum, but they do have something in common: they are all hypotheses relying heavily on contemporary opinion and anecdote for support, mobilizing little of the concrete statistical evidence historians have come to expect and demand. What proportion of the late-Stuart clergy were in fact poorly educated? How many came from plebeian backgrounds? How widespread was the problem of poor parochial endowments? How well did the parish clergy satisfy their parisioners in the performance of their clerical duties? To what extent can they be blamed for the decline in religious fervor that most contemporaries agreed characterized the age?

Historians from Macaulay to Hart have tried to answer questions like these chiefly by citing individual case histories that may not be typical, and by quoting contemporary writers who may have been biased. As a result, they can sometimes be faulted for imprecision and overgeneralization. The only historical method really suited to answering many of these questions is the quantitative collective biography, an approach which permits generalizations to be grounded on firm statistical evidence. Several full-scale, statistically grounded studies of the early modern parish clergy have already been published, but they deal either with the pre-Restoration clergy or with the clergy of the eighteenth century.[9] Meanwhile, the few systematic social studies of the late-Stuart parish clergy that have been attempted are both limited in scope and potentially contradictory; one study of clerical probate inventories in Oxfordshire suggests a postwar decline in clerical wealth both absolutely and in comparison with the yeomanry, while a Warwickshire study of hearth tax returns suggests that parsons still significantly surpassed yeomen in housing standards.[10]

Clearly there is room for a statistically grounded social history of the late-Stuart clergy, but the methodology of collective biography creates a serious problem—it is necessary to select samples small enough to be manageable in a limited amount of research time, but not so small that they are atypical of the general population. One method of attack would be to select a sample of archdeaconries that, taken together, would represent the nation as a whole in terms of population density, economic structure, and social composition. But this would entail working with very large numbers of clergymen, and whatever the study might gain in typicality, it would inevitably lose in intensity and depth. Another approach would be to concentrate on a single county or archdeaconry with a clerical population small enough for intensive study, but one which would still offer some hope of representing the clerical population at large. After much thought and preliminary investigation, it was decided to adopt the latter strategy. Though this study draws on data from several parts of the country, it concentrates on the late-Stuart clergy of Leicestershire.

Leicestershire was probably a fairly average English county in the late-Stuart period. Located in the center of the English Midlands, it was more densely populated than the northern counties, but much less urbanized than the counties surrounding London. In the late seventeenth century the borough of Leicester had a population of just under 5,000. Some of its people were involved in cloth production, others in food marketing; but, as in most provincial towns of the period, the emphasis was on local services and handicrafts. A visitor in the 1680's described it as "an old stinking town, situated upon a dull river, inhabited for the most part by tradesmen."[11] The county's other towns included Loughborough, with just over 500 families in the early eighteenth century; Melton Mowbray and Ashby de la Zouch, with about 300 families each;

Market Harborough, with about 260; and Lutterworth, with about 200. They served as markets for the country's agricultural produce, for the rest of the county was overwhelmingly rural, and almost all of it was devoted to farming. The most fertile lands lay southeast of Leicester, a gently rolling area dotted with small villages and country churches. The visitor who thought Leicester a "stinking town" was charmed by this area, remarking that here he "fell into the land of spires, for making prospects round about me upon an indifferent hill for height. . .I told about four or five and twenty spires and towers. . .and yet the farthest of them did not seem to be much above five or six miles from me."[12] North of Leicester, soils were not as good, with northwestern soils being particularly hard to cultivate; farmers in these areas often relied on sheep and cattle grazing. But on the whole Leicestershire's lands were agriculturally productive, with only the small stony district of Charnwood Forest and one or two other areas given over to waste. Though only 10 percent of the county had been enclosed by 1607, enclosures were proceeding rapidly during the seventeenth century. The most active period of enclosure probably came between 1650 and 1700.[13]

Socially and politically the county was headed by a number of noble families: the Hastings family, Earls of Huntingdon; the Greys, Earls of Stamford; the Manners family, Earls of Rutland (Dukes of Rutland after 1703); the Noels, Viscounts Gainesborough; and the Sherards, Earls of Harborough. Before the Civil War the Hastings family had held almost unchallenged political hegemony in the county, but with the fall of their Royalist stronghold at Ashby de la Zouch in 1648, their power and prestige had gone into eclipse. They made a brief resurgence as high Tories during the reign of James II, but for all practical purposes the county's political leadership had passed to the other peers, who could normally expect to fill one of the county's seats in Parliament. The other seat was usually held by a representative of the county's greater gentry, families like the Fawnts, the Hartopps, the Ashbys, and the Palmers. But if the social outcome of Leicestershire's elections was generally predictable, the partisan outcome was not. The county elite had split during the Civil War, and in many cases the descendants of Civil War Parliamentarians and Royalists continued to fight it out in Anne's reign as Whigs and Tories. This division in the elite, the continuation of old issues and the rise of new ones, and the presence of a sizable class of independent yeoman voters made Leicestershire politics under the later Stuarts highly volatile.[14]

Ecclesiastically, Leicestershire coincided almost exactly with the Archdeaconry of Leicester, which in turn formed a small part of the Diocese of Lincoln. It was a difficult diocese to administer, sprawling as it did across 1,300 parishes in six different counties. Serving the diocese effectively would have taxed the abilities of any bishop, and Lincoln's bishops varied markedly in administrative competence. Thomas Barlow's episcopate (1675–91) was reportedly one of "learned inertia." Dubbed the "Bishop of Buckden who never saw Lincoln," he closeted himself in his episcopal residence at Buckden in Huntingdonshire, allegedly never entered Lincoln Cathedral after his consecration, and spent his time writing scholarly treatises which he seldom bothered to publish. But there was also William Wake (1705–16), a bishop who served the see as few had done before. A model administrator, he examined candidates for ordination with great care, met the heavy physical demands of diocesan tours, and maintained a voluminous correspondence with his archdeacons on diocesan affairs. Bishops Sanderson (1660–63), Laney (1663–67), Fuller (1667–75), Tenison (1692–95), and Gardiner (1695–1705) fell somewhere between these two extremes.[15]

As for Leicestershire itself, the county contained 205 parishes, of which 115 were endowed with rectories, 76 with vicarages, and 14 with perpetual curacies; the ratio of rectories to vicarages and curacies was almost identical to the ratio in England as a whole.[16] In addition, 31 parishes had chapels of ease—secondary churches serving secondary villages within a mother parish; there were 65 such chapelries in the county altogether, with a few parishes having as many as four or five apiece. Thus late-Stuart Leicestershire contained 270 clerical livings in all. On the other hand, there were seldom more than 200 Anglican clergymen holding county livings at any one time; the reason was pluralism—the practice of allowing a clergyman to hold two livings simultaneously. Over the years, of course, some parsons died or resigned, and others were appointed to take their places, adding to the number of parsons who served the people of Leicestershire during the late-Stuart period. About 980 clerics altogether are mentioned in episcopal registers, subscription books, and other records as having worked in the county between 1660 and 1714. They form a group large enough to offer a wide variety of individuals and types, but small enough to make intensive study possible. Overwhelmingly they were Cambridge alumni, but a sizable minority were Oxford men; they came from all parts of the country and from several different social classes, and they are probably a fairly representative cross-section of the

English parochial clergy of the period. They are the primary subjects of the study which follows.

The study opens with an account of the Restoration in Leicestershire, focusing on the problems faced by parish parsons in a time of ecclesiastical uncertainty and dislocation. Next comes a look at the general patterns of late-Stuart clerical careers, with special attention to the clergy's geographic origins, social backgrounds, university training, and search for permanent parish livings. From this we turn to the problem of clerical incomes—the sources from which they were drawn, the degree of variation in parochial endowments, and the change in clerical incomes over time. This is followed by an account of the parsons' day-to-day performance of their parochial duties. The parsons' houses are the subject of the next chapter; here something is glimpsed of the clergy's domestic lifestyle in the context of the village and county community. Then comes an account of the parish clergy's involvement in late-Stuart politics, followed by a concluding chapter which summarizes and pulls into focus what has come before.

NOTES

1. Burnet, *History*, I, 168; VI, 193.

2. Eachard, *Grounds and Occasions*, pp. 3-7, 15-17, 34-36, 47-81, 144-145.

3. *Ibid.*, pp. 102-137, 143-144.

4. *Ibid.*, pp. 48, 140-142, 147.

5. Macaulay, *England from the Accession of James II*, I, Ch. 3.

6. For example, "T.D.," *Hieragonisticon*, pp. 195-198.

7. Babington, *Mr. Macaulay's Character*; Ditchfield, "Errors of Lord Macaulay."

8. Sykes, *Church and State* and *From Sheldon to Secker*; Hart, *Country Parson*; *Country Priest*; and *Clergy and Society*. For similar treatments, see Mayo, "Social Status of the Clergy"; Savidge, *Queen Anne's Bounty*; and Best, *Temporal Pillars*.

9. Bowker, *Secular Clergy*; Barratt, "Parish Clergy Between the Reformation and 1660"; Hill, *Economic Problems of the Church*; Brooks, "Social Position of the Parson"; Hoskins, "Leicestershire Country Parson"; McClatchey, *Oxfordshire Clergy*; Warne, *Church and Society in Eighteenth Century Devon.*

10. Tyler, "Status of the Elizabethan Parochial Clergy"; Styles, "Social Structure of Kineton Hundred," p. 98.

11. Hoskins, *Provincial England*, p. 149; *H.M.C. Portland MSS*, II, 308.

12. Fletcher, ed., "Documents relating to Leicestershire," pp. 231, 301, 302, 305; *H.M.C. Portland MSS*, II, 307.

13. Hoskins, *Provincial England*, pp. 150, 162-166, 169; Fussell, "Four Centuries of Leicestershire Farming," p. 157; Beresford, "Glebe Terriers and

Open Field Leicestershire."

14. *Victoria History of Leicester*, II, 106–123.

15. Venables and Perry, *Lincoln*, pp. 304–313; Sykes, *William Wake*, I, 157, 166, 200, 204.

16. Lincolnshire Archives Office, Reg. XXXI–XXXVIII; *Specula* I and II; Stieg, "Parochial Churches in Bath and Wells," p. 212.

I

The Restoration in Leicestershire

Registers hitherto have been omitted by the Black Long Parliament and Cromwell's tyrannical usurpations; and now, blessed be God! restored under the peaceful reigne of our blessed Soveraigne Charles the Second, 1662.

—Thomas Pestell, in Packington parish register

Christmas, the sonne of old Christmas, was renewed the five and twentieth day of December, in the year of our Lord God 1660.

—Theophilus Burdett, in Burton Overy parish register[2]

Hell is broke loose; and the devil and his instruments are coming in to persecute the saints and the godly party.

—John Yaxley, from a sermon preached at Kibworth Beauchamp in 1660[3]

The return of the Stuarts and the restoration of Anglicanism meant different things to different Leicestershire parsons. For Thomas Pestell, evicted by the Puritans from Packington vicarage in the 1640's, the Restoration was a time of rejoicing and personal vindication. For Theophilus Burdett, a younger parson who had taken his degree in 1650, the Restoration brought a new living at Gumley, as well as the revival of old customs and rituals he could affectionately remember from his youth. For John Yaxley, the Puritan preacher at Kibworth Beauchamp, the Restoration meant expulsion from his pulpit, economic hardship, and the triumph of Anti-Christ. And, for the Church of England as a whole, the Restoration eventually meant repudiation of the ecclesiastical experiments of the past twenty years and the reconstruction of a national church nearly identical to the one of 1640. Reestablishment proceeded swiftly and was virtually complete by the end of 1662, but there were obstacles that had to be overcome along the way, and success ultimately came at the price of permanently alienating a substantial minority of parsons and their parishioners from the nation's religious mainstream. The purpose of this chapter is not so much to explain why the restoration of Anglicanism happened as it did (for this is a question that has already been thoroughly studied[4]), but to trace the impact of the Restoration on individual parsons at the local level, and to suggest some of the problems the parochial clergy faced in a time of ecclesiastical confusion and rapid change.

CIVIL WAR AND INTERREGNUM

The Civil War began in Leicestershire in March, 1642, as a contest between Royalists and Parliamentarians for control of the county militia. The county was divided in the fighting that followed, and so were the county's parsons. While some were staunch Royalists, others were strong Parliamentarians, and still others desperately wished to avoid committing themselves to either side. The nature of available evidence makes it extremely difficult to estimate the exact strength of Royalist, Parliamentarian, and neutralist sentiment among Leicestershire's clergy. Roughly two in five of the county's parish incumbents of 1642 were forced to resign by Puritan committees during the Civil War and Interregnum, but by no means all of them were dedicated Royalists and Anglicans.[5] Some were evicted less for active opposition to Parliament than for failure to lend Parliament sufficient positive support. The rector of Loughborough, for example, obligingly offered to observe the fasts of both King and Parliament, and the Royalist rector of Swepstone turned Parliamentarian in 1643, swearing that he had favored the Royalists only "before men could well recollect themselves and resolve what course to take"; but in the end both were expelled.[6] Others were removed on grounds of personal immorality, or for failing to perform their parochial duties, though charges like these were sometimes fabrications designed to smear religious and political undesirables. And roughly one in ten of the evicted were only "half-sufferers"—pluralists forced to give up one living but allowed to keep another. When allowances like these are made, perhaps a quarter of Leicestershire's parsons of 1642 were firm supporters of Church and King.

Life was difficult for the evicted clergy; the process of eviction itself sometimes involved physical cruelty, and during the war a few parsons suffered acutely indeed. One of them was Thomas Pestell, the Royalist vicar of Packington. During the war the Puritans plundered his parsonage several times, and in 1646 his father claimed there was "not a bed leaft. . .nor a bitt of Bread or cupp of Drinke or any earthly provision left for sustenance." Pestell finally fled to the Earl of Huntingdon's Royalist stronghold at Ashby de la Zouch. The Puritans quickly charged him with subversion and dereliction of duty, and ordered him evicted from his living. Pestell returned to Packington a few weeks later, hoping to resume his ministry, but his Puritan successor soon showed up with a troop of Puritan soldiers. Aiming their pistols at Pestell as he tried to hold a service, they took away his Anglican prayerbook and replaced it with a ballad. They then forced him to sit while his successor preached a sermon, one which examined the supposed sins of Thomas Pestell himself. According to Pestell's sister, he later rallied to Prince Charles at Worcester; captured shortly after the battle, he was about to be hanged when a woman in the crowd claimed he was a relative of hers, and thereby saved his life.[7] Pestell's brother, the rector of Cole Orton, was another wartime sufferer. Besides being evicted from his living, he was beaten by Puritan soldiers "with above 100 blows. . .on his back, arms, and shoulders till all was blacke as a shooe."[8] Fearing similar treatment, the Reverend Richard Benskin of Humberston fled to a Royalist garrison in Nottinghamshire; when the garrison was taken by a Parliamentary regiment, Benskin was killed in the crossfire. And then there was Edward Lawrence, the Royalist rector of Beeby. For refusing to take the Puritan Covenant, he was made to spend a damp night in the open air, bringing on the fever that killed him.[9]

A few Royalist parsons relinquished their livings only after a bitter fight. When the parson of Kibworth Beauchamp heard that a Puritan was coming to take over his pulpit, he defiantly fortified his parsonage, locked himself inside, and refused to budge. The Puritan County Committee was forced to send soldiers to break down part of the house, "not without bloodshed," before the intruder could be installed.[10] Samuel Cotton of North Kilworth, imprisoned by the Parliamentarians in 1645, was replaced by a Puritan parson the following year. In 1647, accompanied by some Royalist veterans, he stormed North Kilworth parsonage, allegedly kicked the usurper's pregnant wife, disarmed the parishioners who opposed him, and held the house and church by force until the County Committee again removed him.[11] The Royalist vicar of

Garthorp was just as stubborn. After spending a year in a Puritan prison, he returned to his parish and refused to recognize the new Puritan incumbent. Besides treating his parishioners to illegal Anglican services, he got hold of the church doorkey and locked his rival out. He was again removed, but for twenty years he kept a hat with seventeen cuts in it as a memento of his sufferings for Church and King. Presumably the cuts were made during a midnight raid by the Parliamentarians, who, after several unsuccessful attempts to capture him, "surprized him at last, being in bed; and with their swords and pistol-cocks cut and wounded him to that degree that his skull was broke and his life in great danger."[12]

About a third of Leicestershire's evicted clergy were allowed to return to their old livings or to find new ones during the 1650's. Though many of them were still Anglicans at heart, they had decided for the time being to adapt to Puritan rule. Meanwhile, the others shifted for themselves as best they could. Through their wives, they could claim a fifth of their former revenues in order to support their families; but these stipends were grossly inadequate, forcing many evicted parsons to rely on friends and relatives for charitable assistance. Some found work as chaplains in the homes of sympathetic country gentlemen, but this was declared illegal in 1655; and those who turned to schoolteaching were subject to arrest for Royalist subversion.[13] The permanently evicted who were still alive in 1660 would reclaim their livings eagerly, and they would not be inclined to treat their Puritan usurpers with kindness and affection.

While eviction records roughly suggest the extent of clerical Royalism, the number of parsons who were Parliamentary Puritans is almost impossible to determine. Of the parsons who kept their livings during the Puritan regime, by no means all were Puritan diehards; many were simply adaptable moderates. Records of Puritan Nonconformity at the Restoration give little help, either. Roughly a fifth of Leicestershire's clergy of 1662 refused to return to the Anglican Church, but this figure tells little about the extent of clerical support for the Puritans during the war. For one thing, almost half of the Nonconformists of 1662 were young men who had entered the clergy after the war was over; at the same time, some of the conforming parsons were former Puritans disillusioned by the excesses of the Civil War and Interregnum.[14] But it seems likely that parsons willing to commit themselves firmly to either side were in the minority. Certainly most Leicestershire parsons escaped both eviction by the Puritans and ejection by the Royalists at the Restoration; as highly adaptable moderates, they were primarily concerned with hanging onto their livings, protecting their families, and riding out the storm. There are few clues as to how they reacted to the events going on around them, for parsons who stayed out of trouble seldom attracted attention, and they left few records behind. Probably they inwardly cursed the hot-blooded partisans in both camps, kept their personal inclinations to themselves, and cautiously trimmed their sails to suit prevailing winds.

At any rate, by the late 1650's their ranks were being thinned by death and by voluntary resignations for better livings in other counties. Natural attrition of this sort, coupled with evictions, produced a great deal of turnover in Leicestershire's parishes: between 1642 and 1659, four out of five parish livings changed hands. The new faces of 1659 belonged to parsons whose previous careers varied enormously.[15] Six or seven were men of obscure backgrounds and apparently no university training, most of whom were probably Puritan radicals who would never have entered the ministry before the war; one of these was John Smith of Wanlip, a former London hatter. At the opposite extreme were ten or eleven former loyalists who had been permitted to resume their calling. They had promised to submit to Puritan rule, but most were probably crypto-Anglicans hoping for a Stuart restoration. Forty others were middle-aged parsons, ordained before the war, who had recently arrived from parishes in other counties. They included both committed Puritans and compromising moderates, none of whom had been evicted for loyalism; all of them had simply left poor livings in their old counties for better ones in Leicestershire. Finally, there were the young college alumni—parsons who had attended the universities since the mid-1640's. Arriving in Leicestershire in the 1650's, they had filled many of the vacancies created by evictions, deaths, and voluntary resignations; by 1659 they held over 40 percent of the county's parish livings. As college alumni, they had helped to make up losses in the number of Leicestershire parsons with university training. Loyalist evictions and an influx of untrained Puritan preachers during the war had in fact brought a drop in the number of Leicestershire parsons with university degrees, from 90 percent in 1642, to about 70 percent in 1651; but thanks to the younger generation, the level had returned to 80 percent by 1659. On the other hand, the abolition of episcopacy had taken its toll: of the incumbents of 1659, only 58 percent had been episcopally ordained.

How much dislocation would a Stuart restoration bring? That would of course depend on the nature of the Restoration church settlement, a settlement that would inevitably deal with a number of ticklish issues; and in 1659, few could accurately predict how those issues would be resolved. For one thing, there was the question of titles to clerical livings acquired during the Civil War and Interregnum. Would a Stuart government consider such titles valid? This was a question that Leicestershire's parsons pondered, for by 1659 only one Leicestershire parish in five was still being served by the incumbent of 1642. In 40 percent of the county's parishes, new incumbents presided because of normal clerical attrition; here the incumbents of 1642 had either died in office or resigned voluntarily. Their successors could not be considered usurpers, but in many cases they had picked up these livings in highly irregular ways–through congregational elections, or through Cromwell's manipulation of episcopal and royal patronage, or through pressure exerted in various forms on their ostensible lay patrons. What would happen to parsons with titles like these? And then there were the parsons who had benefited from the eviction of loyalists–in 1659 they held 40 percent of the county's parish livings, and they contemplated a Stuart restoration with a great deal of anxiety. In half of these parishes, evicted loyalists had since died, perhaps giving their successors a tenuous claim to the positions they had usurped; but in the other half, evicted loyalists were still alive and awaiting restitution. Would a Stuart government restore them and expel their usurpers?

More importantly, a Restoration settlement would involve crucial decisions about the Church itself. If the Anglican Church were reestablished, would it be the Church of 1642? Or would the Church be reformed and broadened, made more "comprehensive" than before, in order to accommodate moderate Puritans? If a Stuart government decided to reject reform, how would the parish clergy react? How many could accept a return to the Church of William Laud? Here there was a great deal of uncertainty. Although half of Leicestershire's incumbents of 1659 had been ordained as Anglicans before the war, some of these had long been Puritan sympathizers, and others had become Puritan converts during the Civil War and Interregnum. There was a special uncertainty about the younger generation, those parsons who had entered the clergy since the Civil War had ended, and who now held over 40 percent of the county's parish livings. Despite all the risks involved, one in eight had secretly received Anglican ordination from refugee bishops during the Interregnum;[16] these could be counted on to support an Anglican reestablishment. But many others, trained in colleges the Puritans had carefully purged, would strongly oppose a Laudian settlement and would try to carry some of their parishioners with them. At the opposite extreme were the surviving ejected loyalists, eager to achieve personal vindication, cool to reform, and anxious to reclaim their livings at the earliest opportunity. The situation on the eve of the Restoration was potentially explosive, and the political community needed to proceed cautiously.

RESTORATION AND REACTION

Charles and Clarendon did proceed cautiously. The Declaration of Breda, issued in April, 1660, vaguely promised religious toleration but left the final decision to Parliament. Charles thus neatly declined to commit himself on the nature of the church settlement, though the Court's choice of moderate Puritan preachers as royal chaplains during the following weeks caused a flurry of speculation: Did Charles favor reformation of the Church as a compromise solution? Meanwhile, a royal proclamation published on June 1 temporarily confirmed all parsons in their livings until "our Parliament shall take order therein, or an eviction be made by due course of law."[17]

Some Anglicans in Leicestershire and other counties were too impatient to imitate Charles's policy of caution and delay. At dawn on August 17, William Beridge, Richard Clark, and John Brian quietly entered Kibworth Beauchamp parsonage armed with a sword, two pistols, and a pitchfork. Brian kept watch at the doorway while Beridge and Clark proceeded upstairs. First they entered the maids' room and dragged them out of bed; then they entered Parson Yaxley's room, tore off his covers, threw the entire household out on the road, bolted the door, and stood guard inside. Though Yaxley left peacefully, his wife was furious to find herself wearing only her underclothes, and she decided on bold measures. After borrowing a waistcoat from her sister in town, she rounded up a band of old Parliamentary veterans. With them she returned to the parsonage and demanded possession, threw stones at its defenders, called them Cavalier dogs and rogues, and threatened to burn the place down. It ended unhappily—Clark fired at Mrs. Yaxley from the window, blinding her and disfiguring her face, and six days later a new incumbent was instituted by the Archbishop of Canterbury. The Royalist incumbent whose living Yaxley had usurped was dead by this point, but Yaxley had made many enemies. As an avid Puritan and Parliamentarian, he had converted Kibworth Beauchamp's baptismal font into a horse trough, called for Charles I's trial, rejoiced in its outcome, and preached against the Stuart restoration.[18]

If Yaxley's enemies had waited a little longer, they might have evicted him legally, for on September 13 Charles signed a bill clarifying the status of those incumbents whose livings had been irregularly obtained. Surviving ejected loyalists were to be restored and their usurpers expelled; parsons nominated to livings during the Interregnum by legitimate patrons, but refused admission by Puritan committees, were now to be installed. Incumbents not affected by these stipulations could keep their livings, provided that they had not, like Yaxley, petitioned for Charles I's trial, opposed his son's restoration, or denounced infant baptism. At the time nothing was said about conforming to the old Anglican liturgy. Thus Puritans who had not obtained their livings through the eviction or non-admission of surviving parsons could presumably continue in their livings, and for the time being use whatever liturgy they thought best, as long as they were neither opposed to infant baptism nor publicly hostile to the Stuarts.[19]

The act was therefore moderate, but it brought ejections in nearly one-fourth of Leicestershire's parishes. Under the terms of the act all but a few of the surviving loyalists quickly reclaimed their livings. One of the few who did not was Thomas Sturges; he may have failed to regain Higham rectory for moral reasons, but he apparently continued to live in the parish and was described as an "esquire" in the hearth tax rolls.[20] Loyalist restorations accounted for about thirty-one of these ejections, but in only eight of these cases did the ejected parsons later become Nonconformists.[21] The others would have been quite happy to stay on as Anglican ministers, but they now had to look for livings elsewhere. Jonathan Clay, for example, had taken a degree at Cambridge in 1649, had been appointed to Appleby in 1656 on the eviction of Abraham Mould, and would conform to the Anglican Church in 1662. But when Mould was restored in 1660, Clay was forced to move to the rectory of Heather, where his income was only half of what he had earned at Appleby.[22] There were similar difficulties at Belton. William Parkes, the original incumbent, had been evicted as a loyalist by October, 1646, when a Puritan committee installed John Watts in his place. Perhaps because Belton was worth only £40 a year, Watts left in 1653, and there was no full-time minister at Belton for the next two years. Finally the parishioners invited Nicholas Hill of Derbyshire to be their vicar. Though the Earl of Huntingdon, the legitimate patron, gave his approval, Hill had to travel to London to acquire the necessary titles. When the Restoration came, Hill was willing to become a conforming Anglican, but the act restoring evicted ministers gave him serious cause for alarm: William Parkes, the original loyalist incumbent, was still alive. Parkes offered to allow Hill to continue at Belton in return for certain financial considerations, which amounted to nearly £50 in 1660. Hill paid the money, but Parkes showed up at Belton anyway to reclaim his living; Hill was ousted, and Parkes stayed there until his death in 1662. The Dowager Countess of Huntingdon then reinstated Hill, but Hill himself died two years later.[23] Nonconformists were not the only parsons dislocated by the ejections of 1660.

There were also ejections in sixteen parishes where there were no evicted loyalists to be restored. In most of these cases the reasons for ejection are unclear.[24] Since all of the ejected parsons refused to conform in 1662, it seems likely that they were removed as religious and political extremists; they had presumably petitioned for Charles I's trial, opposed his son's restoration, or denounced infant baptism. In some cases the charges brought against them may have been false, and this was almost certainly true of the ejection at Witherley. The incumbent presented by the Crown in 1633 had died by 1660, but his widow and her friends busied themselves in pressing charges against his successor. In October, 1660, they persuaded two poor laborers and an innkeeper to swear that the Reverend John Chester had "been against infant baptism and the King." Though Chester vehemently denied both charges, and was ready to produce credible witnesses on his behalf, the county justices refused to allow him to question his accusers or to defend himself against their allegations. He was summarily ejected and ordered to turn his living over to the Reverend William Bucknall. When Chester's servants refused Bucknall admission to the parsonage, Bucknall broke down the door with a sledgehammer, threw some of Chester's goods into the street, and kept the rest.[25]

There were similar scenes in other parishes, for the series of ejections had begun to take on the character of a witch-hunt. Chester admitted that it was "not my case alone but the condition of divers able men, and I am informed that they will out everyone that were settled by the former powers." When the parson at Fenny Drayton offered to speak up for Chester, he was "threatened to be put out, though he was settled before the wars."[26] If the advocates of the Act for Settling Ministers had in fact aimed at moderation, they had erred by placing enforcement of the act in the hands of Cavalier justices of the peace—in their determination to make England safe for the Stuarts, the justices sometimes went beyond the bounds of legality or allowed other old Cavaliers to do so.[27] After all, Yaxley was expelled in August, 1660, on charges that would not be statutorily valid until September; Chester, in October, on charges that were probably false; and at Wanlip the justices replaced the Puritan incumbent with an Anglican parson who had not yet received a title to the living from his bishop.[28] Moreover, it is by no means certain that most of the evicted loyalists waited for Parliamentary permission before reclaiming their livings. Writing about the situation in England as a whole, Richard Baxter claimed that returning Royalists had already ejected "many hundred" parsons by mid-July, two months before Parliament told them they could do so.[29] Certainly there were premature ejections in Essex, where on July 22 the vicar of Earles Colne told his diary of "Ministers pittifully put out of their livings while others advanced." In December the hunt was still in progress; the vicar had heard that "lists are taken of the fanatique, and all honest men that are not as formal as others are so accounted."[30]

While evictions were being carried out by local justices, or by private parties if the justices looked the other way, church officials were resurrecting the old ecclesiastical courts. This took time, for action was impeded by delays and rapid turnover in high clerical appointments. Robert Sanderson was not consecrated to the see of Lincoln until October, 1660, and though the Archdeacon of Leicester had survived the Interregnum, he quickly resigned to become Dean of Ely and was replaced in July, 1661, by Robert Hitch. Hitch in turn resigned for a Yorkshire archdeaconry and was followed in August, 1662, by Clement Breton, the rector of Church Langton.[31] Moreover, the courts' coercive powers were restored only in late July, 1661, and until the passage of the Act of Uniformity twelve months later the courts were unable to enforce observance of the Anglican liturgy.[32] But a visitation of at least some Leicestershire parishes was apparently conducted as early as November, 1660, and correction courts were proceeding against individual Leicestershire parsons and parishioners in early July, 1661, at least three weeks before their coercive powers were legally restored.[33] Before the passage of the Act of Uniformity, the courts apparently dealt only with such matters as tithes and church rates in the case of the laity, and with personal morality and clandestine marriages in the case of the clergy. The rector of Markfield, for example, was tried in July, 1661, for public drunkenness, and again in March, 1662, for performing a clandestine marriage.[34]

But even in 1661 bishops and parishioners were trying to pressure Puritan incumbents into conforming to Anglican standards. One such parson was John Wright of Edmundthorp, a clergyman theoretically protected by the Act for Settling Ministers. As long as Wright was not opposed to infant baptism, he could for the time being use whatever liturgy he chose. Yet he received the following letter from the Bishop of Lincoln, written from London on March 21, 1661:

> I have received a Complaint against you under the hands of your Parishioners that you not onely neglect to reade divine service according to the Lawes of the Land. . .but that you have alsoe refused for Sundry years together to administer the Sacrament of the Lords supper. Whether you bee ordained a Minister or not I know not, but if you bee you are bound both in Conscience and by the Lawes to perform this duty Thrice att Least every yeare. . . .Wherefore I thought good hereby in a freindly mannor to admonish you of your duty and that you would take the matter into your Consideration, that if hereafter you receive any Damage or harme for the neglect thereoff, you may thanke yourselfe for it, when you had so faire a warning. . . .If you shall appeare to be of a Refractary and unpeaceable spiritt, you cannott reasonably expect any favour from
>
> Your loveing freind and Diocesan
> Rbt:Lincoln[35]

In 1661 bishops could only admonish Puritans still clinging to parish livings: John Wright was still at Edmundthorp in early August, 1662, and had yet to use the prayerbook, wear a surplice, or offer communion.[36] But with Charles II's assent in July, 1662, to the Act of Uniformity, such incumbents' days were numbered. By the terms of the act, only episcopal ordination would be recognized as valid; clergymen must declare their "unfeigned assent and consent" to everything in a slightly revised Anglican prayerbook, subscribe to all of the Thirty-nine Articles, and promise to conform faithfully to the Church of England. Incumbents who refused to comply by St. Bartholomew's Day (August 24, 1662) would be deprived of their livings, and any parson who refused to conform would be liable to three months' imprisonment if he tried to preach thereafter.[37] The passage of this act dashed all hopes of a compromise settlement, one that might have accommodated moderate Puritans; with only a few differences in minor details, it was the Church of William Laud that was to be reestablished.

At least in Leicestershire, the act did not produce a mad dash for ordination before August 24. Many of the men who became parsons during the Interregnum must have decided soon after the Restoration what sort of settlement they could accept, for the majority were episcopally ordained in 1660 and 1661. But there were still some signs of wavering, and a few last-minute decisions. One of the incumbents ejected as a Nonconformist on St. Bartholomew's Day had been episcopally ordained in November, 1661; at the time he had probably hoped for a compromise settlement, and perhaps he was still vacillating in early August.[38] And then there were a few conforming parsons who accepted ordination at the last possible moment: Robert Harrison of Witherley waited until August 22, a close call.[39] The vicar of St. Martin's in Leicester was another late conformer, for the churchwardens reported on August 5 that he had only recently begun to use the prayerbook and wear a surplice.[40] The curate at Aston Flamville was still wavering just three weeks before the August 24 deadline. The churchwardens sympathetically reported that they did not know if Mr. Perce was in orders, but he was a "discreet man and a good teacher"; formerly he had not used the prayerbook, but he now read some prayers taken from it, and the week before he had baptized a child according to its liturgy. He had never worn a surplice or offered communion, but, they carefully added, he had always visited the sick. Probably this was the Henry "Peirce" who had been ejected from Claybrook two years earlier, and apparently in the end he did conform.[41]

As St. Bartholomew's Day approached, Anglican officials had still other problems to contend with, for a visitation begun on August 5 revealed that many Leicestershire churches were physically unprepared for a revival of Anglican worship.[42] Some church buildings still showed signs of war damage, but this was apparently a minor problem restricted to a few isolated parishes; most of the thirty churches reported as needing structural repairs were probably victims of ordinary parochial neglect. Between August 5 and

August 14 the Bishop of Lincoln issued commissions to local carpenters, masons, and glaziers to inspect all churches in particular deaneries and to remedy any defects.[43] This may have done little good, however, for parochial neglect was a longstanding problem, one that would continue beyond the Restoration. Of more immediate concern was the shortage of surplices, revised prayerbooks, tables of church canons, and books of homilies: deficiencies in one or more of these things affected almost every church in Leicestershire. In the August visitations, churchwardens from some parishes reported that local women were already sewing surplices and would have them ready before August 24, and that they themselves would procure a book of canons "before they goe out of town." Revised prayerbooks were harder to come by. The new prayerbook had been synodically approved in December, 1661, but an official transcript could not be prepared for the King until February 24.[44] Apparently there were further delays in printing and circulation, for about forty Leicestershire churches reported that they had not been able to acquire copies by August 5. As late as August 19 thirteen Leicestershire parsons were complaining that they still had not received prayerbooks and could not read the new Anglican liturgy before August 24; this was probably not a Puritan delaying tactic, for all the parsons who complained were conformists.[45] As for the reaction of the laity to the coming day of reckoning, Leicestershire churchwardens in early August were generally striking a cheerful note. At St. Martin's in Leicester, most of the parishioners who had previously neglected to attend church were now coming and showing "more conformity than formerly." And from Aston Flamville the churchwardens wrote: "We have few except Mr. William Turvile that did stand up or did put off their hats until the last Sunday, and then they all [did] according to the Article."[46]

But as August 24 drew nearer, fear of resistance to the Act of Uniformity and rumors of Puritan plans for a general rising caused uneasiness at court.[47] When St. Bartholomew's Day passed without bloodshed, and with few signs of popular discontent, apprehension gave way first to surprise and then to relief. Though the nation's Nonconformist parsons numbered about 1,760 (perhaps one English parson in five), in most cases they left the Church peacefully. Comparisons with the number of parsons evicted during the Civil War and Interregnum are risky, but probably only about half as many parish clergymen were turned out by the Anglicans in 1660-62 as had been turned out by the Puritans earlier.[48] In Leicestershire the ratio of evicted Anglicans to ejected Puritans was roughly two to one; at least half of the Leicestershire ejections of Nonconformists had come before 1662.[49]

What did all of this mean for Leicestershire? First, although the ejected Nonconformists accounted for only about a fifth of Leicestershire's parish clergy, the removal of conforming Anglicans from livings where evicted loyalists were restored raised the number of parishes directly affected by ejections and restorations to roughly one in three. Other parishes were affected indirectly when conforming Anglicans resigned from poor livings to pick up better ones where ejections had created vacancies. When we throw in the livings that changed hands through death, about half of the county's parishes experienced clerical turnover between 1660 and the end of 1662.[50] The scramble for benefices left some of the poorer livings temporarily vacant; three weeks before St. Bartholomew's Day, seven parishes and four chapelries were already without parsons, and all of these cures were worth less than £50 a year. Conforming parsons were no doubt shopping around for better livings.[51]

But if the ejections created a shortage of available parsons, the shortage could not have been severe, and it did not last long. Throughout England, bishops were feverishly ordaining more than enough clerical candidates to make up for losses at the Restoration, and within a few years contemporaries were complaining that there was a surplus of men in orders.[52] In some cases bishops closed their eyes to educational attainments that were inferior or practically nonexistent,[53] but generally it was not necessary to do so. Most of the young men who had entered the clergy in the 1650's were university alumni, and the resurgence in college enrollments at the Restoration sent even more alumni into the clergy. By 1670 the proportion of Leicestershire parish incumbents with university degrees had risen as high as 95 percent.[54]

The major long-term problem created by the character of the Restoration settlement was the alienation of a significant minority of parsons and parishioners from the Established Church. With the exception of the ex-hatter and four or five other men whose past careers are obscure, Leicestershire's ejected Nonconformists fell into two roughly equal groups: older parsons who had been episcopally ordained before the war, about half of whom had arrived in Leicestershire during and after the war from posts in other counties; and younger men who had attended the universities after the war, only about half of whom had completed their degrees, and only a third of whom were Leicestershire natives. As compared with the Leicestershire clergy who conformed at the Restoration, the Nonconformists were slightly more likely to be recent arrivals from other counties, and younger men with inferior educational credentials. Most of them eventually became ministers to Dissenting congregations or found teaching jobs in Dissenting schools. Though some returned to the counties of their birth or headed for London, the majority remained in Leicestershire, at least for a time.[55]

A few of the ejected clergy stayed on good terms with the parsons who conformed. Henry Watts, an ejected Nonconformist who had been episcopally ordained in 1661, was held "in great esteem" by his Anglican successor at Swepstone, and the two kept up a friendly correspondence. Watts became the first regular Presbyterian minister at Hinckley; when he died in 1691, the Anglican rector of Barwell delivered the funeral sermon and praised Watts's "obliging temper and gentlemanly behaviour, his great friendliness. . .his great moderation and charity, which recommended him to all the gentlemen of the neighbourhood, who treated him with great respect."[56] Another popular Nonconformist was Samuel Shaw, the ejected rector of Long Whatton. Although a Dissenter, he was appointed master of Ashby de la Zouch's Anglican grammar school in 1668 and received a teaching license from Archbishop Sheldon in 1670. He was apparently liked by many of the Anglican clergy. When the vicar of Ashby de la Zouch died, he left Shaw £20 and a choice of "my best cloke" or "my best book," and he named Shaw one of the two executors of his will.[57] Shaw and Watts were exceptions, however. Most of the ejected Nonconformists faced Anglican hostility, and at least six who continued to preach were at some point imprisoned or heavily fined.

The hostility was of course mutual, and in a few cases it was the Dissenters who took the offensive. The churchwardens at Redmile testified in April, 1663, that, as the rector was pouring water into the baptismal font, three young men later charged with Dissent "fould it and threw it up and down the seats and washt themselves and others with it." In the same month three others were accused of entering Ashby Magna's church and defacing the font; likewise the curate at North Kilworth complained in 1663 that local Dissenters "doe often molest us and disturbe us in the church." In August, 1682, two Quakers entered Lutterworth church in the middle of a service, one crying that he "was sent from God to inform those people the way to truth." He then denounced the minister as a "hireling, a persecutor of the Children of Light." And in October, 1694, the churchwardens of Billesdon charged the local Dissenting schoolmaster with "suffering his Schollars to Lay their Excrement in the Church Yard and Church Porch."[58] But far more typically it was the Dissenters who were attacked, often at the instigation of Anglican parsons like Henry Noble of Frowlesworth. Hearing in November, 1682, that Dissenters were holding a service nearby, Noble "presently after morning sermon ordered the constable with some help to go and suppress them, which he did."[59]

On the other hand, some of the parsons who conformed in 1662 remained Puritans at heart; sometimes openly, sometimes covertly, they continued to observe old Puritan traditions within the Church of England. They crop up now and then in the records of the ecclesiastical courts, but how many of them there actually were cannot be known—covert Puritans would not be hauled into the courts for correction if influential parishioners could prevail on the churchwardens to keep silent. But even if the incidents recorded in the documents do not tell us the full extent of Dissent within the Church, they do give some interesting indications of the forms it took.

One of the accused was the Reverend Gilbert Woodward of Wanlip, charged in 1663 with taking his communion standing. In May he was ordered to conform, and the churchwardens reported in June that he "did receive the Sacrament himself kneeling on Whitsunday last."[60] Another was William Barton, vicar of St. Martin's in Leicester. Though Barton conformed in 1662, he had previously aroused suspicion by "declaring himself for a Congregational Church only," and in November, 1662, his contract as town lecturer stipulated that he preach only "upon catechistical heads according to his Majesty's injunction." In 1664 and 1668 he was hauled into the ecclesiastical courts for gross violations of Anglican rubrics and canons. His offenses included not using the Psalms as responsive readings, not reading the litany, ending his services with a sermon rather than with the prescribed liturgy, neglecting to baptize with the sign of the cross, baptizing in private homes in an irregular fashion, neglecting to read a certificate of excommunication against a local Dissenter, and allowing the Dissenter to attend his sermons. Barton was rescued by a letter from influential parishioners testifying that he was a conforming member of the Anglican Church, and he continued to serve St. Martin's until his death.[61]

Meanwhile John Yeo, the curate at Breedon, told his parishioners in 1672 that it was wrong to have godparents at baptism, and the vicar of Bitteswell was warned in the 1680's to wear his surplice, observe the liturgy specified in the prayerbook, and not to use "another catechism." Similarly, the vicar of Wymeswold was accused in 1670 of being "unconformable to the doctrine, rites, and ceremonies of the Church of England." He had refused to wear a surplice and had "spoken and preached publickly irreverently or scornfully" against it; even worse, he had offered communion to people from outside the parish and had willingly administered it to people who were "sitting, standing, lying, or leaning, and not kneeling."[62] In 1697 the Bishop of Lincoln was still complaining that many clergymen in his diocese were administering communion to parishioners who were kneeling by their seats in the nave, not at a communion table in the east end. He admonished them to observe the rubrics, adding that there was "great inconvenience in consecrating in so strait a place as an ally of the church, and delivering Bread and wine in narrow seats, over the heads, and treading upon the feet of those who kneel without disturbance."[63] Suspicions of irregularities continued even into the eighteenth century. In 1706 Bishop Wake noted in his diary that he had instituted Edward Jolley to the vicarage at Wigston Magna; Jolley was a "bold, popular man, yet I hope a sincere Conformist." Wake's misgivings were probably justified: Jolley had at one point been a Nonconformist preacher, and rumor had it that he was still "not a strict observor of the Rubrick." Though his patron was technically the Haberdasher Company of London, the initiative behind his appointment to Wigston had come through a vigorous letter of recommendation by the parishioners themselves, and Wigston Magna was a hotbed of Dissent.[64]

But cases like these practically dry up in the Leicestershire records after 1690, perhaps because a new generation of parsons had taken over. Some of the generation who conformed on St. Bartholomew's Day had been moderate reformers disappointed by the character of the settlement; in contrast, the younger generation had been trained in colleges the Restoration had made safe for Anglicanism, and the great majority had imbibed a militant hatred of Dissent. When the Oxford graduate of the 1680's who was serving Witherley in 1718 was asked if there were Dissenters in his parish, he replied, "I bless God wee have noe such abominable assembly nor ever have had since I came here twixt 30 and 40 years [ago] and I promise *in verbum sacerdotis* there never shalt [be] if I can possiblie prevent it."[65] His colleague at Horninghold, an Oxford graduate of the 1670's, was just as vitriolic. "One Presbyterian Synagogue of Satan is upheld [here]," he informed the bishop in 1715, "sometimes by some few poor Straglers whose Soul-Seducing and Soul-Damning Teacher is sometimes Pyot." His report was accompanied by two biblical verses showing that "synagogue" was justifiable nomenclature for a Nonconformist meeting house.[66]

If a desire for personal revenge against the Puritans had died off with the wartime Anglicans, its place had been taken by the younger generation's smugness and self-satisfaction. For preconfirmation catechizing, the parson at Horninghold used only the standard church catechism, "there being no need of any other to explain such a Plain and Sufficient System of Soul-Saving Christianity."[67] Humphrey Haines, another Leicestershire parson and a graduate of the 1690's, wholeheartedly agreed: Anglicanism, he told his parishioners, protected its flock "on the one hand from the wild freaks of Enthusiasm" to which the Dissenters were prone, and "on the other from the gross follies of superstition" so evident among the Papists. "You who have the happiness to be brought up in the Church of England," he advised his congregation, "thank God for that unspeakable mercy," for you are members of a "true and sure part of Christ's holy Catholic Church, and in her bosom you are inevitably safe."[68]

And so the Anglican restoration was accomplished. In the beginning there had been a period of confusion and uncertainty, as the government tried to work out a viable church settlement. While parsons with Puritan inclinations and irregular titles waited nervously for the outcome, evicted loyalists sometimes reclaimed their livings with illegal haste, and some county justices anticipated Parliamentary legislation by ejecting incumbents where there were no evicted loyalists to be restored. When the Laudians ultimately triumphed, some of the problems their victory entailed were quickly overcome: the expulsion of those parsons who could not accept the settlement, a temporary shortage of parsons to supply a few of the poorer livings, delays in acquiring the prayerbooks and other paraphernalia the settlement required. The long-term effects of the settlement were more serious. When the Laudians refused to accommodate more of the moderate reformers among the clergy and the laity, they let the rift in the fabric of the nation's religious life grow wider than necessary, exacerbating social and political problems that would trouble the country for years to come.

NOTES

1. Quoted in Nichols, *Leicester*, III, 930.

2. *Ibid.*, II, 534n.

3. Quoted in *Victoria History of Leicester*, I, 388n.

4. Bosher, *Restoration Settlement*; Whiteman, "Re-establishment"; Abernathy, *English Presbyterians and Stuart Restoration.*

5. The number of Leicestershire parsons who were at least temporarily evicted or who were refused admission by the Triers during the 1640's and 1650's was between 85 and 98. Information on these men, and on all of the Leicestershire clergy of 1640-62, comes from: Lincs. Arch. Off., Reg. XXXI-XXXIIb; L.C. V; Leics. Museum, 1D41/28/356-591; Foster, ed., "Admissions to Benefices and Compositions for First Fruits," pp. 144-176, 322-336; Venn and Venn, *Alumni Cantabrigiensis*; Foster, *Alumni Oxoniensis*; Matthews, *Walker Revised* and *Calamy Revised*; and Nichols, *Leicester.*

6. Matthews, *Walker Revised*, pp. 235, 236, 245.

7. *Ibid.*, pp. 241-242; Nichols, *Leicester*, III, 927-930; Buchan, *Poems of Pestell*, pp. xli-xlix.

8. *Ibid.*

9. Matthews, *Walker Revised*, pp. 231, 239.

10. *Ibid.*, p. 238.

11. *Ibid.*, pp. 233-234.

12. *Ibid.*, p. 243; Nichols, *Leicester*, II, 192.

13. Matthews, *Walker Revised*, p. xxvi.

14. Based on the sources listed in note 5. In *Calamy Revised*, Matthews presented 49 Leicestershire parsons for consideration. Of these, four (S. Blackerby, S. Muston, T. Doughty, W. Black) were named by Matthews as conforming Anglicans who either resigned voluntarily for other livings or were evicted because sequestered Anglicans were restored. This was probably the case with two others he accepted as after-conformists, both of whom left because sequestered incumbents were restored: B. Southwood became a Northamptonshire vicar (p. 453), while T. Jenkins became vicar of Theddingworth in October, 1662 (Lincs. Arch. Off., Reg. XXXIIb, p. 60). Since there was no surviving sequestered incumbent to be restored at Claybrook, Henry Peirce's ejection may have been for political or religious radicalism; he was probably an after-conformist. Cockain, the master of Castle Donington school, may not have been a parson, and Matthews apparently did not count him as one. Matthews also listed but apparently did not count three other parsons Calamy named as ejected but for whom there was no other evidence (J. Weston, Hudson, Cheshire). The number of Leicestershire parsons who refused to accept an Anglican settlement was therefore between 41 and 44.

15. Information on the incumbents of 1659 comes from the sources listed in note 5.

16. Based on the sources listed in note 5. Most of the Interregnum ordina-

tions are recorded in the *Liber Cleri* of 1662: Lincs. Arch. Off., L.C. V.

17. Bosher, *Restoration Settlement*, pp. 107, 150-151.

18. Nichols, *Leicester*, II, 650-652.

19. Bosher, *Restoration Settlement*, pp. 178-179.

20. Matthews, *Walker Revised*, p. 246.

21. The eight Nonconformists were S. Oldershaw, Jos. Lee, O. Bromskill, W. Grace, T. Hill, W. Smith, R. Drayton, and S. Doughty. See Matthews, *Calamy Revised*.

22. Matthews, *Walker Revised*, pp. 240-241; Lincs. Arch. Off., Reg. XXXIIb, p. 44.

23. Nichols, *Leicester*, III, 642; Lincs. Arch. Off., Reg. XXXIIb, p. 62.

24. T. Langdale, W. Hornaby , H. Peirce, G. Wright, M. Boheme, J. Shuttlewood, R. Adams, W. Sheffield, J. Yaxley, M. Clarke, J. Smith, S. Shaw, J. Chester, J. St. Nicholas, T. Lowry, M. Patchet. See Matthews, *Calamy Revised*.

25. Matthews, *Calamy Revised*, pp. 113-114; Nichols, *Leicester*, IV, 1010n.

26. Matthews, *Calamy Revised*, pp. 113-114.

27. Bosher, *Restoration Settlement*, p. 200.

28. Nichols, *Leicester*, III, 1097; Matthews, *Calamy Revised*, p. 283.

29. Bosher, *Restoration Settlement*, p. 165.

30. Josselin, *Diary*, pp. 135, 136.

31. Le Neve, *Fasti Ecclesiae Anglicanae*, II, 26, 62-63.

32. 13 Car. II, st. 1, c. 12.

33. Leics. Museum, 1D41/13/67,68.

34. *Ibid.*, 1D41/13/68, ff. 3, 17v.

35. Leics. Rec. Off., DE 565/4909, unnumbered item.

36. Leics. Museum, 1D41/13/70, f. 89.

37. Bosher, *Restoration Settlement*, p. 250.

38. Matthews, *Calamy Revised*, p. 514.

39. Lincs. Arch. Off., L.C. VI, f. 191v.

40. Leics. Museum, 1D41/13/70, f. 13v.

41. *Ibid.*, 1D41/13/70, ff. 33-35. The churchwardens said that Mr. Perce had been at Aston Flamville for two years and that he was the son-in-law of the Reverend John Pitts, the incumbent. Henry Peirce was ejected from Claybrook in 1660 (Matthews, *Calamy Revised*, p. 384) and could quite easily have been hired as a curate by his father-in-law at that point.

42. Leics. Museum, 1D41/13/70. This was also the case in Buckinghamshire and in the Dioceses of Exeter and Salisbury. See Brinkworth, ed., *Episcopal Visitation Book for Buckingham* and *Victoria History of Wiltshire*, III, 44.

43. Leics. Museum, 1D41/14/II/25,30,31,32b.

44. Bosher, *Restoration Settlement*, p. 249.

45. Leics. Museum, 1D41/14/II/23.

46. *Ibid.*, 1D41/13/70, ff. 13v., 33-35.

47. Bosher, *Restoration Settlement*, p. 259.

48. Matthews, *Calamy Revised*, p. xiii and *passim*; Matthews, *Walker Revised*, pp. xiii xv and *passim*. Matthews agreed with Walker that the number of deprived loyalists exceeded Calamy's 2,000 ejected Nonconformists "many times over," but gave his own figures for the parish clergy in terms of the number of parishes that underwent sequestration (2,425) rather than the number of loyalists sequestered. Some of these parishes were held by plural-

ists who lost only one living, while in other parishes two or more loyalists were deprived at different times. The problem is complicated by the deprivation of bishops, cathedral dignitaries, minor canons, and university fellows, many (but not all) of whom held parish livings as well, and some of whom were pluralists who lost only one living. See *Walker Revised*, pp. xiii–xv.

49. The number of Leicestershire parsons who refused to accept an Anglican settlement was between 41 and 44. The number of parsons who were at least temporarily evicted by the Puritans or who were refused admission by the Triers was between 85 and 98. See notes 5 and 14.

50. Based on the sources listed in note 5.

51. Leics. Museum, 1D41/13/70, ff. 5v.–7, 8, 27v., 59, 69v., 81.

52. Eachard, *Grounds and Occasions*, p. 143.

53. Whiteman, "Re-establishment," pp. 115–116.

54. Based on the sources listed in note 5. And see below, pp. 42–43.

55. Based on Matthews, *Calamy Revised*, and on the sources listed in note 5.

56. Nichols, *Leicester*, III, 1040; Matthews, *Calamy Revised*, p. 514.

57. Matthews, *Calamy Revised*, p. 435; Venn and Venn, *Alumni Cantabrigiensis*, Pt. 1, IV, 53; Public Record Office, P.C.C. Wills, 1674, f. 60: Alexander Jones.

58. Leics. Museum, 1D41/13/68, f. 44; 1D41/13/67, f. 11v.; 1D41/14/III/82; 1D41/13/82, f. 82v.; Nichols, *Leicester*, IV, 264.

59. Nichols, *Leicester*, IV, 184.

60. Leics. Museum, 1D41/14/III/57; 5D33/462, f. 3.

61. Venn and Venn, *Alumni Cantabrigiensis*, Pt. 1, I, 101; Leics. Museum, 1D41/13/77, ff. 12, 15; 1D41/4/XXXII/62-63; Billson, *Leicester Memoirs*, pp. 59-60.

62. Leics. Museum, 1D41/4/XLVI/58; 1D41/4/XXXIII/78-84; 1D41/4/XXXII/65–66.

63. Quoted from Venables and Perry, *Lincoln*, p. 320.

64. Lambeth Palace Library, MS 1770, f. 28v.; Christ Church Library, Wake MSS, CCXXXIV, ff. 70, 71; Fletcher, "Documents relating to Leicestershire," p. 357.

65. St. Paul's Library, MS 17-D-20 (on microfilm at Leicester Museum), n.f.: Witherley.

66. Wake MSS, CCLXXVII, n.f.: Blaston.

67. *Ibid.*

68. Leics. Museum, 1D41/51/43,53: rough drafts of sermons by Humphrey Haines.

II

Parsons in Search of Benefices: Clerical Career Patterns in Late-Stuart Leicestershire

A NOTE ON METHODOLOGY

From what geographic and social backgrounds were the late-Stuart parish clergy recruited? How much formal training did they have? Who were the patrons who named the county's parish incumbents? How did clergymen go about establishing contacts with them? How many parsons remained mere curates all their lives, and why? These are some of the questions this chapter will try to answer, primarily by examining the men who formed two kinds of statistical samples. The first consists of all men who were Leicestershire clergymen at particular times, and these have in turn been divided into parish incumbents and stipendiary curates. Strictly speaking, incumbents were either rectors or vicars, men who held livings at least theoretically endowed with some or all of their parishes' tithes. But there were a few parish livings, the perpetual curacies, that were endowed with only annual monetary stipends; the curates who served these livings had tenure once they had been licensed by their bishops, and they were the sole parsons responsible for providing church services in their parishes. There were only fourteen Leicestershire parishes endowed with perpetual curacies in the period covered by the samples, and most were held in plurality by men who were rectors or vicars in neighboring parishes. The curates who held these livings have therefore been included in the lists of parish incumbents, while curates who served only chapelries within parishes, or who were hired by incumbents as assistants or as full substitutes, have been treated separately.

The second sort of sample consists of men who were ordained to the priesthood within a particular time span and who at any subsequent date turned up in Leicestershire as rectors, vicars, or curates of any description. The great majority of clerical candidates were ordained in their twenties, and as a result the parsons in these samples, unlike the parish incumbents at particular times, were members of the same generation. The samples chosen on this basis are the ordinands of 1660–69 and the ordinands of 1705–14, the first and last decades of the period under study. The former sample contains a slightly more diverse age group than the latter, for about a third of its members were university students of the late 1640's and 1650's who could not be episcopally ordained until the Restoration. But generally speaking both groups of ordinands are composed of young men in search of benefices, while the parish incumbents were men of widely divergent ages who had already established themselves in the profession.

The names of the parsons included in these samples have been taken from episcopal registers and surveys, presentation deeds, induction mandates, subscription books, and *Libri Cleri* drawn up for visitations.[1] Many of these documents record dates and places of ordination and university credentials as well, and this information has been supplemented by data drawn from published college and university registers.[2] The same registers are the chief source of data on the parsons' geographic and social origins; when possible, this information has been expanded with the help of genealogical sources both published and unpublished.[3] Naturally there are gaps in the data available; but for most of the sample parsons there is complete information about place of birth, father's social status, colleges attended and degrees taken, date and place of ordination, parishes served, names of patrons, and date of death. Through this information we can reconstruct the general patterns of clerical careers in late-Stuart Leicestershire, and illustrate those patterns with case histories of parsons who were typical of the mainstream.

GEOGRAPHIC AND SOCIAL ORIGINS

Late-Stuart Englishmen lived in a time when local loyalties were still intense, a time when men's affections focused on their counties and parishes, and on the ideal of the local community. For many Englishmen, the phrase "my country" could still mean "my county." "County," in its idealized version, in turn meant a collection of small, self-contained parishes, each one a tightly knit community of individuals living together in harmony—growing up, marrying, and dying in the company of lifelong friends and neighbors. In practice, seventeenth-century communities were being disrupted by geographic mobility, social upheaval, and political division; the ideal of community continued to assert itself, however, perhaps in reaction against the very forces of change by which it seemed threatened.

In 1675 a Cheshire rector named Zachary Cawdrey charged that one of these disrupting forces was the current system of ecclesiastical patronage. In olden days, Cawdrey wrote, the church patron was usually the greatest landowner in the parish, a pillar of the local congregation, a gentleman personally involved in the spiritual life of the village. He chose the local parson as carefully as he chose his own wife, and the man he picked was someone with whom the parishioners could feel at home. But now the right to pick the parish parson had fallen into the hands of strangers to the community—"how ordinarily is the next advowson (yea sometimes the perpetual) bought by a rich Shooe-maker, Rope-maker, or Ale-draper, who hath a son to preferre, and yet who hath not one foot of Land in the Parish, to which he hath bought the Presentation, nor lives within many miles of it?" Worse still, the patron was not required to choose a parson who was already a member of the local community. Instead, he was "permitted to wander in his choice, from one end of the Land to the other," forcing the parishioners to accept a parson with whom they were not familiar and with whom they might not get along.[4]

And so, ideally, the late-Stuart parson was a local man, a native of the county if not of the parish itself; his patron was a local gentleman, resident in the parish and personally familiar with its wants and needs. If the situation in Leicestershire was typical, Cawdrey had good reason to complain that contemporary reality violated the ideal. In the late seventeenth century, about a third of the men who held Leicestershire's advowsons lived outside the county, and only a third of Leicestershire's parishes had resident patrons.[5] Patrons who lived outside Leicestershire usually picked parsons from outside the county, and even patrons who lived in Leicestershire often ventured far afield in their selections. In the century that followed the Civil War, less than half of Leicestershire's parish clergy were Leicestershire natives. A quarter came from counties that adjoined Leicestershire, and between a quarter and a third came from other, more distant counties, a few from

Geographic Origins of Leicestershire's Clergy

(Figures in parentheses represent the men whose origins are known.)

	Parish Incumbents			*Ordinands*	
	1670 (N = 180)	1714 (N = 175)	1750 (N = 159)	1660-69 (N = 171)	1705-14 (N = 116)
Leicestershire	31% (43%)	41% (45%)	37% (38.5%)	25% (34%)	38% (39%)
Adjoining counties	26% (36%)	25% (28%)	24% (25%)	21% (29%)	25% (26%)
Other counties	15% (21%)	25% (27%)	35% (36.5%)	27.5% (37%)	34% (35%)
Unknown	28%	9%	4%	26.5%	3%

places as far off as Scotland and Wales.[6] Late-Stuart parsons as a group must have been among the most geographically mobile men of their day.

They were equally varied in terms of social origins: some were the sons of landed aristocrats, while others were the offspring of the laboring poor. How many parsons were recruited from any one social class can be estimated only very roughly, for available sources are either irritatingly vague or distressingly incomplete. The most useful sources are published college and university registers, and even these are not as informative as one might wish. Oxford officials made some effort to record the social status of each student's father, but prosperous merchants and poor husbandmen were usually lumped together as simply "plebeians." Cambridge officials were even more careless, often neglecting to record social status altogether; consequently, the modern editors of the Cambridge registers turned to published genealogical sources for supplemental information, but these sources were inevitably biased against parsons born into obscure, plebeian families. For the purposes of this study, information from published college and university registers has been expanded with data drawn from other genealogical sources, but most of these suffer from a similar bias. Despite a thorough search, the percentage of parsons whose social origins remain obscure still runs as high as 41 percent for the incumbents of 1670. (The results are given in the table on social origins.[7])

Although one might be tempted to ignore the parsons of unknown origins, instead looking only at those whose origins have been documented, to do this would be to assume that the parsons

Social Origins of Leicestershire's Parsons

(Figures in parentheses represent the men whose origins are known.)

	Parish Incumbents			*Ordinands*	
	1670 (N = 180)	1714 (N = 175)	1750 (N = 159)	1660–69 (N = 171)	1705–14 (N = 116)
Esquires and above	4% (7.5%)	6% (7%)	7.5% (9%)	4% (6%)	3% (5%)
Gentry	9% (15%)	16% (21%)	17% (21%)	8% (14%)	19.5% (26%)
Clergy	24% (40%)	24% (31%)	30% (37%)	23% (38%)	31% (43%)
Physicians, lawyers, schoolmasters	--	2% (2%)	4% (5%)	--	2.5% (3%)
Plebeians	22% (37.5%)	30% (39%)	22.5% (28%)	26% (42%)	16.5% (23%)
Unknown	41%	22%	19%	39%	27.5%

of unknown origins were a random sample of all parsons—an assumption that would almost certainly be false. Because of the socially biased nature of the sources, the great majority of the parsons whose fathers were clergymen or gentlemen have probably been identified, and a majority of those whose origins remain unknown were probably plebeians. If one makes this allowance for the biased nature of the sources, then roughly 15 to 25 percent of the late-Stuart clergy were the sons of the landed upper classes, 25 to 35 percent were offspring of the professional classes, and the rest came from plebeian families. Almost all of the plebeians whose precise backgrounds are known came from the middling and lower-middling ranks of society; their fathers were yeomen, merchants, tradesmen, and skilled craftsmen. The sons of poor laborers crop up occasionally, but they were clearly exceptions, for economic reasons not difficult to guess. An Oxford student of the late seventeenth century who worked for part of his keep estimated that his university education cost him over £30 a year, quite apart from what he spent on books, clothes, and linen;[8] this sum was generally beyond the means of the really humble. If a small minority of the clergy came from the bottommost ranks of English society, a larger minority came from the top, and the great majority came from somewhere in between.

Almost all of the parsons who sprang from professional families were the sons of other clergymen. The Church was after all a natural choice for a parson's son, and a feeling of professional pride encouraged clerical fathers to prod their sons toward the pulpit. Leicestershire parsons often bequeathed their libraries to their sons, suggesting a desire for continuity and perpetuation of the family calling. The Reverend John Boylston of Market Bosworth, for example, bequeathed his library to his sons Joseph and Septimus in 1678, with the stipulation that they "use and not sell it" for at least seven years; both were children at the time, and both eventually entered the Church.[9] Some wealthy parsons even purchased rights of presentation to parish livings for sons who were still minors. One was Joseph Chambers of Croft, who paid £400 for Croft's advowson in 1689, when his son Samuel was only five years old. In his will of 1695, Chambers left the advowson to young Samuel, along with a library that Samuel was directed to bequeath to his own son, should he ever have one. Just as Joseph Chambers had hoped, Samuel became rector of Croft in 1708; and soon after Samuel died, he was followed as rector by his own son James.[10] All told, 31 percent of the parish incumbents of 1670 sent sons into the clergy, along with 27 percent of the parish incumbents of 1714.[11] Though it was usually the eldest son who was tapped, parsons with above-average incomes sometimes contributed two sons to the Church, occasionally even three.

On the other hand, there was a limit to the number of sons the parish clergy could groom for the priesthood. Clerical dynasties were in fact quite uncommon—only about 9 percent of the incumbents of 1670, and only about 5 percent of the incumbents of 1714, were parsons' sons who sent their own sons into the clergy. The reasons for discontinuity in the clergy's ranks varied. A few parsons never married, while some who did marry had no sons who survived to adulthood. Others had sons who were temperamentally unsuitable for clerical careers, or who obstinately refused to abide by their fathers' wishes. The Reverend John Eliot of Church Langton apparently tried and failed to persuade his son to enter the Church, and his will speaks caustically of his son's perversity in neglecting his education.[12] Humphrey Michel of Horninghold was equally disappointed by his son John: "J.M. was drunk and running about like a drunken sot," he confided to his diary in 1707, "though he promised his mother upon her death bed he would not lead such a drunken course of life any more; and when I asked him where he had been, he answered, like Gehazi to his master, he had been nowhere."[13] Whether or not a parson was able to provide a son for the Church also depended on the parson's income. The poorer parsons found college fees burdensome, and perhaps their own financial disappointment discouraged them from pushing clerical careers on their sons. Of the parish incumbents of 1714 who earned less than £60 a year, only 12 percent are known to have had clerical sons, compared with 43 percent of those earning £160 a year or more.

The evidence is too scanty to allow a definitive statement about what happened to parsons' sons who did not enter the Church. Of the parish incumbents of 1714, about 5 percent amassed sufficient capital to set their sons up as landed gentlemen, but they generally did so by marrying well themselves. Only nine are known to have sired physicians, lawyers, or schoolmasters, and six of these were incumbents with above-average incomes. Judging from the father-son clergy ratios already mentioned, a majority of the wealthier parsons with adult offspring were probably sending at least one son into the Church, while most of the others were probably channeled into the other professions, or apprenticed, or set up in trade. For the eldest sons of parsons in the middle-income ranks, the Church was quite likely the single most common career choice, but the majority must have entered various other occupations—occasionally the other professions, but much more commonly crafts and trades. Finally, the vast majority of the parsons at the bottom end of the scale must have watched their children sink into the plebeian classes; the only son mentioned in the will of Edward Fisher of Thrussington (who earned about £30 a year) was an apprentice, and the eldest son of John Swan of Diseworth (about £40 a year) was a common laborer.[14] John Eachard in fact complained about "the poor and contemptible Employment that many Children of the Clergy are forced upon, by reason of the meanness of their Fathers Revenue." Similarly, Swift wrote that the daughters of the poor vicar of less than £60 a year "shall go into service, or be sent 'prentice to the sempstress of the next town; and his sons are put to honest trades."[15]

As a result, the late-Stuart parish clergy was not an inbred profession. A substantial minority of parsons came from clerical families, and a substantial minority sent their own sons into the Church. But because of the number of sons who chose other occupations, the inability or unwillingness of poor incumbents to groom sons for the Church, and failures in the male line, the clergy in this period was never remotely capable of replacing itself genetically. Men moved into the clergy from a variety of backgrounds, and most of their offspring moved back out again.

In view of the data's deficiencies, one hesitates to draw firm conclusions about changes in social recruitment over time. But it does appear that the gentry's representation in the clergy virtually doubled under the later Stuarts; that there was a modest increase in recruitment from the professional classes; and that the sons of the gentle and the professional classes were together displacing the sons of plebeians. There are valid reasons for thinking that this was in fact the case. In the late seventeenth century, gentlemen's sons were finding clerical careers socially more acceptable than in Elizabeth's reign, ideologically safer than under the early Stuarts. At the same time, rising taxes and stagnating rents were forcing many gentle families to concentrate the great bulk of their estates on eldest sons, leaving the Church as a respectable alternative for younger sons who in better days might have inherited landed estates of their own.[16] If the gentry's representation did not increase substantially after 1714, it was probably because more lucrative and increasingly respectable alternatives were opening up in medicine, law, and trade. What did not change during these years was the predominance of the lower ranks of the gentle classes over those at the top. Ordinary gentlemen's sons consistently outnumbered the sons of esquires by two to one, and the only baronet's son in the samples was the rector of Market Bosworth, Leicestershire's richest parish living.

Meanwhile, plebeians' sons were finding clerical careers increasingly unattractive. Plebeians had constituted the great majority of the parish clergy on the eve of the Reformation, but with the Reformation came clerical marriages and, shortly thereafter, clerical sons—new competitors for parish livings. Other problems arose to plague plebeians in the 1620's, when the universities began turning out a surplus of clerical candidates for the livings annually falling vacant.[17] In the fierce scramble that followed, plebeians were shortchanged by a patronage system biased in favor of clerics with superior social connections. As we shall see, plebeians had a hard time finding permanent livings, and those who did find livings were generally relegated to the poorest available. After the Civil War, still other difficulties cropped up to discourage them. One was the postwar decline in local free schools, the major academic breeding grounds for plebeians bound for the Church.[18] Another was the economic plight of small to middling freeholders caught between rising taxes and sluggish farm prices.[19] Such conditions made it harder for yeomen's sons to finance a university education; the same conditions also encouraged more younger sons of hard-pressed gentlemen to enter the clergy, thereby reducing the number of livings available to plebeians. Another possible factor was the postwar decline in religious enthusiasm. Gentlemen's sons might continue to enter the Church for the sake of respectability, parsons' sons out of professional loyalty, and both could expect a fair return for their labors. But plebeians' sons, with less chance of material success, probably needed a strong sense of mission—and, after the religious exhaustion of the Civil War, fewer may have felt a real sense of calling. Then, too, they may have been discouraged by the expulsion of Dissent from the Church, for they came from the middling ranks of lay society where Dissenting sentiments were most common.

Whatever the reason, plebeians' sons, who formed a majority of the parish clergy well into the seventeenth century, were slowly being displaced. They were hardly weeded out altogether, for they still constituted perhaps a third of the county's parish incumbents of 1750. But they were definitely a minority among the young men being ordained to the priesthood during the last years of Anne's reign, and it may in fact have been the late-Stuart period that saw the final shift within the clergy in favor of recruits from the gentle and professional classes. Whenever the shift occurred, it would in the long run enhance the social prestige of the clergy as a whole, giving it a tone that was both more professional and more genteel.

LEARNING AND LETTERS

"In this year about the end of April," wrote Abraham de la Pryme in 1690, "I began to set forward for Cambridge, to be admitted there an accademian."[20] Though de la Pryme eventually became a clergyman in Yorkshire, his account of student life at Cambridge in the 1690's would have sounded familiar to the parsons of Leicestershire; most of them were Cambridge graduates like him, and many of them were alumni of de la Pryme's own college, St. John's. At the age of seventeen or eighteen they had left their families and old familiar friends to test themselves in a strange new environment. Apprehensive about their future and more than a bit homesick upon arrival, they were first subjected to a brief examination of their knowledge of Greek and Latin. De la Pryme found, to his relief, that the ordeal was not as trying as he had feared: "First, I was examined by my tutor, then by the senior dean, then by the junior dean, and then by the master, who all made me but construe a verse or two a-piece in the Greek

Testament, except the master, who ask'd me both in that and in Plautus and Horace too. Then I went to the registerer to be registered member of the College, and so the whole work was done." Before long the students fell in with the day-to-day routines of college life. "We go to lecturs every other day, in logics," de la Pryme wrote, "and what we hear one day we give an account of the next; besides we go. . .every night and hear the sophs and junior sophs dispute, and then some is called out to conster a chapt[er] in the New Testament; which after it is ended, then we go to prayers, and then to our respective chambers."[21]

But many university students, and especially those bound for the priesthood, were required to do more than attend to their studies. As servitors and sizars, they helped pay their way through college by waiting on students from families wealthier than their own. "We are seven of us," an early Georgian servitor wrote his parents from his college at Oxford, "and we wait upon the Batchelors, Gentlemen Commoners, and Commoners at meals. We carry in their Commons out of the Kitchen into the Hall, and their bread and beer out of the Buttery; I call up one Gentleman Commoner, which is ten shillings when he's in town, and three Commoners, which are five shillings on the same conditions."[22] Clerical candidates whose fathers were gentlemen or wealthy clergymen normally escaped such service, but they were the exceptions. Roughly two-thirds of Leicestershire's late-Stuart parsons had been servitors or sizars in their college days, including most of those whose fathers were lower-to-middling parish clergymen, and virtually all of those whose fathers were plebeians. John Eachard regretted the practice, thinking "Bed-making, Chamber-sweeping, and Water-fetching" rather undignified callings for future clerics.[23] So did Thomas Brockbank, a clerical candidate at Oxford who took his degree sooner than he wanted rather than "stay any longer under that slavery."[24] But regardless of what they thought of it, most late-Stuart parsons waited table in their college days. Many of them could not have financed their education any other way.

Their undergraduate studies included ancient and modern philosophy, literature, astronomy, geometry, and rhetoric—the course of learning most late-Stuart academicians considered necessary for a broad humanist education. But some, including John Eachard, felt that this was poor preparation for a clerical career, that there ought to be more emphasis on English oratory and Protestant theology.[25] They definitely had a point, for the undergraduate curriculum was decidedly more secular than religious. The master's curriculum, however, included theological studies, and most clerical candidates in the late seventeenth century did stay on for master's degrees. They also dabbled in scholarly fields not always covered in the regular curriculum: "In this my fresh-man's year," de la Pryme recorded, "by my own propper studdy, labour and industry, I got the knowledge of all herbs, trees, and simples, without any body's instruction or help, except that of herbals: so that I could know any herb at first sight. I studdied a great many things more likewise, which I hope God will bless for my good and his honour and glory, if I can ever promote anything thereoff."[26]

Sometimes there were pleasant diversions as well: "Yesternight we had good sport!" de la Pryme wrote. "There came a great singer of Israel into the college. . .The lads got him into the kitchin, and there they were as joyfull of him as if he was a mountebank, and they made him sing all their supper time. . . .And after that they carried him in tryumph, as it was, into the hall, and set him on his feet on the high round table there, and made him sing to them for an hower together, and then what became of him I do not know." After three years of university life, de la Pryme could write that "This year. . .I began to look more about me than before, and to take better notice of things, as having got more knowledge and experience than I had before."[27] Like most undergraduates entering their final round of studies, he had discovered within himself a degree of sophistication he had not previously noticed.

And then at last came graduation. De la Pryme again provides a detailed account:

> 1694. January. This month it was that we sat for our degree of batchelors of arts. We sat three days in the colledge and were examin'd by two fellows thereof in rhetorick, logicks, ethicks, physicks, and astronomy; then we were sent to the publick schools, there to be examined again three more days by any one that would. Then when the day came of our being cap'd by the Vice-Chancellor, wee were all call'd up in our soph's gowns and our new square caps and lamb-skin hoods on. There we were presented, four by four, by our father to the Vice-Chancellor, saying out a sort of formal presentation speech to him. Then we had the oaths of the dutys we are to observe in the university read to us, as also that relating to the Articles of the Church of England, and another of allegiance, which we all swore to. Then we every one register'd our own names in the university book, and after that, one by one, we kneel'd down before the Vice-Chancellor's knees, and he took hold of both of our hands with his, saying to this effect, 'Admitto te,'

> &c. . . .About six days after this. . .we go all of us to the schools, there to answer to our questions, which our father always tells us what we shall answer before we come there, for fear of his puting us to a stand. . . .But we all of us answer'd without any hesitation; we were just thirty-three of us, and then having made us an excellent speech, he (I mean our father) walk'd home before us in triumph, so that now wee are become compleat battchellors, praised be God![28]

It had not always been like this. In 1576 only 15 percent of Leicestershire's clergymen were university graduates, and by 1585 the figure was still only 31 percent. But by the death of Elizabeth a majority of Leicestershire's clergymen were degree-holders, and on the eve of the Civil War the figure had risen to 90 percent. The most common degree had in fact become the Master of Arts, and the M.A. remained an almost standard degree among parish incumbents for at least another century.[29] Unlike the B.A., it involved extensive theological training, and after 1604 it was required of all parsons who wished to hold two livings in plurality. Then, too, it helped clerical candidates pass the time between taking their B.A.'s at the age of twenty-one or twenty-two and reaching the age the canons required for priestly ordination, twenty-four. It also gave parsons an advantage over mere B.A.'s in the clerical job market, and it was believed to confer upon them the status of gentlemen as well: "I have no pedigree, nor coat of arms, nor ever had; nor do I presume to any," the rector of Cole Orton wrote in 1683. "I am a Master of Arts; and that makes me a gentleman, and that a worshipful one: and I care not to go higher."[30] Consequently, students who could afford to stay on for a master's degree generally did so, and those who could not were often the sons of plebeians: men of known plebeian origins accounted for 30 percent of the parish incumbents of 1714 as a whole, but for at least 46 percent of those who held only bachelor's degrees. The number of Leicestershire parsons with the more advanced divinity degrees varied between 3 and 11 percent, and a few clergymen held degrees in medicine and law.

The dramatic improvement in the clergy's academic credentials between the Reformation and the Civil War was by no means limited to Leicestershire. In the Diocese of Worcester, the number of parsons with university degrees rose from 14 percent in 1560 to 84 percent in 1640; in the Diocese of Oxford, the figures rose during the same years from 38 to 96 percent.[31] A number of factors combined to produce this striking upsurge in the number of university-trained clergymen. One was a sharp rise in the academic

Leicestershire Degree-Holders

	Leicester Archdeaconry		Parish Incumbents			
	1585 (N = 228)	1603 (N = 188)	1642 (N = 189)	1670 (N = 180)	1714 (N = 175)	1750 (N = 159)
B.D., D.D.	3%	11%	10%	5%	3%	8%
LL.B., LL.D.	1%	0	1%	0	2%	8%
M.A.	12%	29%	62%	66.5%	65%	52%
B.A.	15%	18%	17%	23%	26%	26%
M.D.	0	0	0	.5%	1%	1%
No degree	69%	42%	10%	5%	3%	5%

	Ordinands	
	1660–69 (N = 171)	1705–14 (N = 116)
B.D., D.D.	7%	8%
LL.B., LL.D.	.5%	4%
M.A.	55%	50%
B.A.	28%	35%
M.D.	.5%	0
No degree	9%	3%

standards expected of the sixteenth-century clergy by an increasingly literate laity, and especially by Puritans convinced that godly learning was the surest antidote for popish poisons. Another factor was the growing availability, before the war, of higher education to the sons of plebeians. This was in turn the product of charitable bequests to colleges and the local schools they drew upon, the rising living standards of rural freeholders and the urban middle classes, the ability of the poor to work their way through college by waiting on a growing number of gentlemen's sons, and, at least before the 1620's, a ready demand for university-trained incumbents.[32] When higher education became less available to plebeians after the war, the result was not a decline in the number of clerical degree-holders but a drop in the number of plebeian parsons. Their heightened difficulties in financing a college education after 1660 help account for their declining representation among the parish clergy as a whole.

Throughout this period the usual choice of a university for Leicestershire natives was Cambridge. Of the incumbents of 1670 who had been born in Leicestershire, at least 65 percent were

Cambridge alumni; in 1714 the figure was 71 percent, and in 1750 it was 73 percent. They differed widely in their selection of particular colleges, but their most common choices were Emmanuel (12 out of 51 in 1714), St. John's (10), and Clare (10). Those who went to Oxford concentrated on Lincoln College (8 out of 19), with Magdalen Hall (4) a runner-up. There was an equally strong preference for Cambridge among the parsons born in counties that adjoined Leicestershire, while Oxford graduates were often recruits from the south or the extreme north, or their sons.

The feeling that the clergy must be at least as well educated as the laity continued under the later Stuarts. "When the People are become so much better informed," Bishop Wake wrote in 1707, "the Clergy should, in proportion, be advanced in their Understanding of Divine Things," for the "accidental Effects of this Knowledge, in the increase of Errors, nay, even of Heresie and Prophaneness. . .rend it absolutely requisite for a Clergy-Man to be well provided to defend his Faith."[33] Wake could be fairly well satisfied with his clergy's academic credentials, for the high standards of university training established for the clergy in the century before the Civil War continued to prevail for at least a century thereafter.

And yet some still doubted that the clergy's training was adequate. When Eachard cited the "ignorance of some" as a cause of contempt for the clergy as a whole, he spoke not of non-graduates but of degree-holders, alumni who had mastered an impractical, outmoded curriculum. The parsons' colleges, Eachard believed, had emphasized rote learning rather than understanding, Latin and Greek rather than English oratory; instead of producing good pastors and preachers, the universities were turning out hordes of hopeless pedants.[34] At the same time, bishops complained that much of what the parish clergy learned at school left them soon after graduation. In 1675 the Bishop of Bath and Wells reported his shock at the number of poorly educated parsons in his diocese, many of them university graduates. One could not even "construe a sentence of the plainest Latin imaginable; yet he hath been priest six years and was ordained by the late bishop of Bristol."[35] Fifty years later, Bishop Reynolds of Lincoln was appalled at the ignorance of a deacon who was applying for priestly orders:

> I find that in these ten years since his being made deacon, he hath forgot most of his Greek and Latin. He can just read a verse or two in the Greek Testament, and turn an article out of Latin into English, but he

Universities Attended

	Parish Incumbents			*Ordinands*	
	1670 (N = 180)	1714 (N = 175)	1750 (N = 159)	1660–69 (N = 171)	1705–14 (N = 116)
Cambridge	65.5%	63%	59%	61.5%	73%
Oxford	20%	30%	32%	21%	23%
Both	1%	4%	4%	3.5%	3%
Other	.5%	.5%	1%	.5%	0
A degree-holder, university unknown	9%	2%	2%	7.5%	0
No record of university attendance	4%	.5%	2%	6%	1%

seems to do it memoriter rather than upon any strength he hath in the Latin language or in the rules of syntax. But what is still worse, he is utterly ignorant of everything that relates to the doctrines of the Articles and of every branch of divinity.[36]

But the situation could hardly have been as serious as they implied. If the examples of clerical ignorance that the bishops cited carried shock value, it must have been because they were extreme cases. Certainly the reason Bishop Wake gave for not requiring parish incumbents to take out preaching licenses, still technically mandatory, was that he had a "better Opinion, both of your Learning and Discretion, than to suppose that any among you, who has been admitted to a Cure of Souls, should not be fit to preach to the People to whom it has pleased God to call him."[37] And even if Eachard was right that some parsons were pedants rather than sound preachers, ordinary laymen registered few complaints. Leicestershire churchwardens almost never cited late-Stuart parsons for preaching poor sermons, and there were no complaints at all about the quality of their learning.[38] Though late-Stuart parsons were expected to be university graduates, the state of their learning seems to have worried university dons like Eachard more than it did local parishioners.

Moreover, there is evidence that many of the clergy continued their studies after ordination. Probate inventories show that almost all late-Stuart Leicestershire parsons had libraries of some sort, a few of which were valued at over £100; an average clerical library was worth about £10, and Immanuel Bourne's, valued at £5, ran to 120 volumes.[39] Probate inventories do not list specific titles, but most parsons' libraries probably consisted chiefly of sermons, theological treatises, and philosophical works, with a sprinkling of histories, geographies, and medical textbooks. Certainly Bishop Wake assumed that religious works would provide the core of a clerical library, and he offered his clergy advice about what sort of books they should buy. "I do not think it necessary," he said, "for you to burden your selves with a numerous Variety of Books in all Parts of Controversial as well as Casuistical Divinity; One or Two of the last and best in every Kind may suffice."[40] The diaries of the parsons of Blaston and Muston show that they were also reading such works as *Eikon Basilike*, Ben Gurion's *History of the Jews*, and Schultetus' *Armamentarium Chirurgicum*.[41] Country parsons also subscribed to political newsletters: "Stayed home all day," wrote a Yorkshire parson in 1692, "reading an Account of Publique Affairs, in a piece called 'The present state of Europe,' which cometh out monthly." The parson of Blaston in Leicestershire was subscribing to Rockingham's newsletter in 1711, and in 1707 he was sharing a subscription to the *Monthly Mercury* with a local gentleman.[42]

Bishop Wake suggested that the clergy share their books with their parishioners and the poorer members of their profession, and hold book-study groups to

> discourse over such Matters, as both the present Condition of the Church, and the Iniquity of the Times, make it requisite for a Clergy-Man to be acquainted withal. This would not only keep up a useful Neighbourhood among you, but would greatly contribute to the Increase of Learning in the Church; and enable you the better to answer the Ends of your Ministry, both in feeding the Flock of Christ, and in securing it against such as would otherwise be more likely to scatter and divide it.[43]

He had in fact "with great Satisfaction heard that some of this Diocese. . .keep up Stated Meetings among Themselves for this very End." One such group may have been the religious society founded by William Fenwick, the rector of Hallaton. About twelve members of the clergy in Fenwick's neighborhood were taking turns meeting at each other's houses in 1700, apparently as a local chapter of the S.P.C.K. Besides distributing sermons and religious tracts to their parishioners, they were taking up collections for missionaries in the plantations.[44]

A surprising number of provincial parsons even sought national recognition through religious and scholarly publications: 10 percent of Leicestershire's incumbents of 1670 are known to have published something, along with 8 percent of the incumbents of 1714.[45] Overwhelmingly their works were religiously oriented, consisting primarily of sermons, devotional tracts, and, in the case of William Barton of St. Martin's Church in Leicester, several collections of popular hymns. Some had secular interests as well. Samuel Carte of Eastwell and St. Martin's was a noted amateur archaeologist and antiquarian, a colleague of Browne Willis, and the author of a history of Leicester. Edward Wells of Cotesbach, a former fellow of Christ Church, published arithmetic, astronomy, and geometry textbooks, along with an edition of Xenophon and a collection of maps of Palestine. Thomas Pestell of Lutterworth and Richard Duke of Blaby were both poets; Anthony Blackwell, rector of Elmesthrop and master of Market Bosworth school, wrote two guidelines on literary style, citing classical and New Testament writers as examples of good taste. Andrew Glenn, rector of Hathern, was an amateur botanist; he toured Sweden and Italy collecting specimens, and his will mentions an herbarium containing 700 indigenous and 200 exotic plants.[46]

Parsons like these sometimes felt intellectually stifled in the provinces and complained about their difficulties in pursuing their studies. "My searches into antiquity are very imperfect," Samuel Carte wrote his son from Leicester, "for want of proper books in this place." In 1715 he was again complaining, this time to Browne Willis, that "your books have not reached this place," there "being few that are lovers of antiquities."[47] After spending several years in a university environment, any parson might feel intellectually cramped in the country parish he had been called upon to serve. "I got to Cambridge," a North Country parson wrote in 1694 during a reunion with old college friends, and "blessed God for my being got out of the country, for when I was there they wearyed me almost of my life by saying that all learning was foolish further than that that would make the pot boyl. So little praise and thanks had I for studdying so much at Cambridge."[48] According to Joseph Addison, the contemporary essayist, even the local gentry cared little for scholarly accomplishments. Sir Roger, Addison's archetypal country gentleman, was "afraid of being insulted with Latin and Greek at his own Table," and so he asked a friend to find him a "Clergyman rather of plain Sense than much Learning, of a good Aspect, a clear Voice, a sociable Temper, and, if possible, a Man that understood a little of Back-Gammon." Luckily, just such a parson turned up, a pleasant man who became Sir Roger's domestic chaplain, parish priest, and affable companion. If he was also a good scholar, Sir Roger was happy to report that "he does not shew it."[49]

Some parsons were content to settle into a life of intellectual sterility in the countryside, but others felt deprived and did their best to escape. One of these was Henry Knewstubb of Muston, whose interests included music, archaeology, numismatics, and medicine. In the summer of 1669 he attended three concerts in his native Grantham; the next March he inspected some Roman ruins near Stoke and took home some of the bricks. He also collected ancient coins and, as a part-time physician, read classical medical textbooks. (Whenever Knewstubb killed a patient, quipped a friend, he was able to collect both a physician's fee and a parson's mortuary.) Knewstubb tried hard to win institution to Grantham vicarage, hoping to gain easier access to its concerts, and to return to an atmosphere somewhat more stimulating than rural Muston's. Unfortunately, his hopes were never realized.[50] Was he a typical country parson? It is impossible to know for sure; if some country parsons published scholarly treatises, and almost all owned substantial libraries, how diligently the average parson read his books and continued his studies is really a matter of conjecture. But the clergy's scholarly abilities were probably not of overwhelming concern to their parishioners. As a Yorkshire parson of 1695 put it, they really "mind not your degrees, nor your long continuance at the University; a man that never saw any College, or an undergraduate, if he can but talk at a great rate and get interest, will be preferr'd before a Master of Arts."[51] And so if Eachard was correct that the ignorance of some parsons led to contempt for all, he was probably speaking from the sophisticated vantage points of Oxford, Cambridge, and London, not on behalf of the great majority of parishioners who lived in country villages.

ORDINATION

After graduation, the next stage in a clerical candidate's career was to find a bishop who would ordain him. When it came to ordaining the parsons of Leicestershire, the Bishop of Lincoln was surprisingly underrepresented: over half of the county's parsons were ordained by the bishops of other dioceses. There were two reasons for this. First, unordained candidates for Leicestershire's livings sometimes turned to other bishops when the Bishop of Lincoln was ill or out of reach. Second, many parsons arrived in Leicester-

Episcopal Ordination of Leicestershire's Clergy

	Parish Incumbents			*Ordinands*	
	1670 (N = 180)	1714 (N = 175)	1750 (N = 159)	1660-69 (N = 171)	1705-14 (N = 116)
Lincoln	25.5%	48%	50%	38%	37%
Peterborough	20%	15%	3%	6%	22%
Lichfield and Coventry	8%	6%	3%	11%	3.5%
Oxford	8%	3%	3%	6%	3%
Other	33%	17%	24%	26%	19%
Unknown	5.5%	11%	17%	13%	15.5%

shire after serving livings in other dioceses, where they had been ordained by the bishops in charge. Quite often they came from parishes in the neighboring Diocese of Peterborough, but others came from dioceses as distant as Exeter, Chester, and Carlisle.

Theoretically, late-Stuart ordinations were strictly regulated by the Canons of 1604 and by a series of subsequent royal injunctions and circular letters. Candidates for orders, for example, were supposed to be ordained only on the four Sundays following Ember weeks, and only in their bishop's parish church or cathedral. Candidates for the diaconate had to be at least twenty-three years old, priests twenty-four, and it was recommended that candidates spend a full year as deacons before being ordained to the priesthood; it was expressly forbidden that they be ordained to both orders on the same day. They were also to offer evidence of immediate preferment to a rectory, vicarage, curacy, or cathedral prebend; or be university fellows, conducts, or chaplains; or be M.A.'s who had lived at the university at their own expense for at least five years. Furthermore, candidates were required to provide letters testimonial from college officials or parish ministers certifying their soundness in doctrine, learning, and personal morality, and bishops were expected to examine candidates (or have their subordinates do so) to insure their fitness for holy orders.[52] Such requirements were designed both to maintain acceptable standards among the clergy and to limit their numbers, but the extent to which they were observed varied with the particular requirement and with the integrity of the individual bishop.

Judging from Leicestershire's ordinands, the age requirements were enforced fairly strictly. Naturally there were exceptions: Samuel Holbrook, vicar of Ashby de la Zouch, could not have been more than twenty-two when he was ordained priest by the Bishop of Chester in 1711, and even Wake of Lincoln, one of the most scrupulous late-Stuart bishops, ordained German Pegg of Leicester to the priesthood at the age of twenty-two or twenty-three.[53] But in the great majority of cases the age requirements were obeyed. Most clerical candidates took their bachelor's degrees at the age of twenty-one or twenty-two and then waited until they were twenty-three before being ordained as deacons, an inconvenient hiatus that encouraged many to stay on for M.A.'s. The recommendation that deacons wait at least a year before being ordained to the priesthood was also generally followed. The exceptions came mostly at the Restoration, when the scramble to ordain a sufficient number of conforming Anglicans resulted in many instances of parsons being ordained to both orders within a matter of days. By the end of the century this was quite uncommon, and diaconates had lengthened in most cases to at least a year. The average interval between orders was in fact almost three years, and diaconates of five or six years were not unusual. A few deacons without prospects of becoming parish incumbents postponed the effort and expense of priestly ordination for even longer periods of time. Isaac Taylor, teacher and curate of Barleston chapelry in Market Bosworth, spent over twenty years as a deacon before Wake prodded him into priestly orders in 1710,[54] but his case was highly exceptional. The great majority of parsons received both orders in their middle or late twenties, even if they were curates without immediate prospects of higher preferment.

The requirements regarding the time and place of ordination were largely ignored, principally because bishops had to attend Parliament in London and were absent from their dioceses for much of the year. Of the forty-two ordinations that Wake held as Bishop of Lincoln, only two were in Lincoln Cathedral; the others were held in London, in Stamford, and at Wake's episcopal residence at Buckden.[55] On the other hand, Wake was scrupulously careful about examining candidates for orders, reading their letters testimonial, and checking the validity of their titles to vacant livings. He almost always turned down candidates who seemed unqualified or who needed further study, as the following passage in his diary illustrates:

> With Mr. Archdeacon Huntingdon I examined three for priest's and four for deacon's orders; and approved them. Two I put off for this

> ordination; one I refused for want of a sufficient knowledge in divinity. The next evening I spoke with the gentleman and directed him what method to pursue in his studies, promising him that if I saw his improvement answer my expectations the next ordination, I would then admit him to priest's orders.[56]

Archbishop Sharp of York also enjoyed a reputation for care and discrimination. One of the parsons he ordained was Abraham de la Pryme, who described in his diary the examination to which he was subjected:

> As soon as the time of the Ordination came on I went to York, and from thence to Bishopsthorpe, to get into priest's orders. Having been examined by the Bishop's two chaplains, who made me conster in the Greek Testament and in Cicero's Epistles, and having asked me a great many questions, how I proved the being of the Trinity against the Socinians, and such like, I then went to the Bishop, who likewise asked me a great many questions relating to divinity.[57]

But other bishops were notoriously lax. Wake examined and rejected one candidate for the priesthood as deficient in learning, and recorded his amazement that the Bishop of Peterborough had ordained him deacon the previous September: "God forgive his lordship for it," reads the entry in his diary. On another occasion when Wake turned away an unqualified candidate, the young man quickly headed for Peterborough and told the bishop there of his "poor and discouraging circumstances, the present advantageous offers that are made him, and the pressing solicitations of his relations and other neighbours." Once again, the Bishop of Peterborough cheerfully obliged.[58]

Such abuses brought loud complaints from the Crown and the more conscientious members of the episcopal bench. Contemporaries also agreed that many bishops were remiss in examining letters testimonial and titles to vacant livings. All too frequently, testimonials were written by college officials and parish parsons with but a passing acquaintance of the candidates in question; titles to vacant livings were often nothing but parsons' promises to hire candidates as curates when they really had no such intention. A series of royal injunctions and circular letters demanded that these abuses be halted,[59] seriously frightening some clerical candidates. "How to get a title, I am allmost at a loss," Thomas Brockbank wrote in 1695, shortly after one of the injunctions was issued, "for now none but real ones will be taken."[60] But some bishops continued to be easy-going: the Bishop of Derry's chaplain "putt us in fear by telling [us that] the bishop would insist upon formal titles," a clerical candidate wrote in 1718; "but his lordship made no scruple at mine, and after some conference accepted Mr. Hall's credentials."[61] Unless a bishop were as exacting as Wake, it was probably not very difficult for a degree-holder of the right age to win ordination. If Wake's reputation frightened him off, there were always other bishops who were much more lenient.

CAREER PROSPECTS AND THE VICTIMS OF SURPLUS

What were the chances that an ordinand would eventually find a parish living? That depended on two things, both of which varied over time: the number of young men entering the Church, and the extent to which plural holdings reduced the number of livings available. Between 1560 and 1620, an ordinand's prospects were comparatively good. The violent religious fluctuations of 1533–59 had frightened many young men out of entering the clergy, thereby reducing the competition for church livings. At the same time, Elizabethan church reformers managed to reduce the extent of pluralism, thereby increasing the number of clerical openings. The result was a shortage of ordained clergymen, one that continued in some parts of the country into the early seventeenth century. As late as 1586, there were only 270 rectors, vicars, and curates in the Archdeaconry of Oxford, while in 1526 there had been 371.[62] Young men entering the Church during these years consequently had little trouble finding parish livings, and prospects were especially bright for ordinands with university degrees.

After 1620, openings became harder to find. For one thing, the early Stuarts permitted a growth in plural holdings, which reduced the demand for full-time parish incumbents. In Leicestershire, for example, the number of parish livings held in plurality rose from 13 percent in 1603 to 23 percent in 1642.[63] During the same period, college enrollments were climbing to unparalleled heights, creating an annual surplus of clerical candidates for a shrinking number of clerical openings. By the 1620's, the number of clerical candidates annually leaving the universities exceeded the number of livings annually falling vacant by something like 25 percent. Most of the surplus candidates eventually found jobs of some sort. Many became teachers, lecturers, and domestic chaplains, while others became parish curates, often assisting rectors and vicars who held livings in plurality. But these were generally second-rate, poorly paying jobs, and many of the young men who held them despaired of finding permanent parish livings of their own.[64]

Career prospects improved during the Civil War, at least for parsons amenable to Puritan rule. College enrollments fell off, reducing the competition for church livings; the eviction of loyalists created new vacancies; and the Long Parliament cracked down on pluralism, greatly increasing the number of parish livings available. After the Restoration, career prospects again dimmed. While the ejection of Puritan Nonconformists created vacancies, many of these were quickly snapped up by returning loyalists. College enrollments generally remained below prewar levels, but pluralism returned with the Stuarts and continued to spread. About 32 percent of Leicestershire's parish livings were being held in plurality in 1670, a figure which rose to almost 40 percent by 1714, and then to 49 percent by 1750. Not surprisingly, contemporaries agreed that career opportunities for young men entering the clergy were generally bad. In the 1670's John Eachard thought the nation "perfectly overstock'd with Professors of Divinity, there being scarce Employment for half of those who undertake that Office."[65] "I am sometimes very much troubled," Addison wrote in 1711, "when I reflect upon the three great Professions of Divinity, Law, and Physick; how they are each of them overburdened with Practitioners, and filled with multitudes of Ingenious Gentlemen that starve one another. . . .How many men are Country Curates, that might have made themselves Aldermen of London by a right Improvement of a Smaller sum of Mony than what is usually laid out upon a learned Education?"[66] And in the 1730's Swift still thought that "as matters have been for some time, and may probably remain, the fewer ordinations the better."[67]

Exactly how serious was this problem? Figures for Leicestershire's ordinands of 1660-69 and 1705-14 provide some answers, but they do not tell the whole story. For one thing, they omit young graduates who despaired of finding livings and who decided not to seek ordination. Nor do the figures include men who, in applying for ordination, were rejected for want of genuine titles; however, in view of frequent complaints that many men were sneaking into orders with false titles, those turned away for want of genuine titles were probably not very numerous. The figures do indicate what job prospects were like for young men who entered the Church—how many were able to find permanent livings as rectors, vicars, and perpetual curates, and how many others were forced to remain stipendiary curates, teachers, and domestic chaplains. Apparently, the surplus of men in orders over parish livings was not as severe as contemporaries thought. Fully 91 percent of the ordinands of the 1660's are known to have become tenured parish incumbents, either in Leicestershire or in other counties, along with 84 percent of the ordinands of 1705–14. Only 10 or 15 percent were condemned to spending the rest of their lives as stipendiary curates, teachers, and chaplains; moreover, a few of these died soon after ordination, before they really had a chance to look around, and others may have found permanent livings without leaving a record of their having done so.[68]

But the job market for young parsons admittedly remained tight, and it seems to have grown tighter for the ordinands of 1705–14. At the same time, it took longer for young parsons in the early eighteenth century to find permanent livings than it had for their predecessors in the 1660's. The median time period between taking a bachelor's degree and finding a permanent post increased from six years for the ordinands of 1660–69, to eight years for the ordinands of 1705–14. Then, too, many of those who did find permanent livings were stuck with poorly endowed ones of less than £50 a year. And so a shortage of livings continued to worry young parsons under the later Stuarts, and competition for the better livings continued to be hectic. In fact, some parsons turned to sniffing out parish livings that had not yet fallen vacant. In 1702 a young cleric wrote the Bishop of Chester that the parson of Cartmel's illness had "grown to that height as to make people despair of his recovery. I hope your Lordship will not be offended with this Information, and I wo'd hope for your Lordship's pardon If I intimate a desire not of his Death, but to succeed him if he die."[69] Similarly, in 1699 a friend wrote Sir John Verney, a patron of several livings, on behalf of his nephew "if our Doctor King should dye." But "there is little hope of that," Verney's friend continued, "for he is a lusty strong man, & more likely to bury all Chelsey before he goes." Therefore "I hope you will remember him when Mr. Butterfield dyes, for he is most likely to go first."[70]

Throughout the late-Stuart period, job prospects were disproportionately bad for two (largely overlapping) groups of candidates: those of plebeian origins, and those who held only B.A.'s. Among the ordinands of the 1660's, there is evidence of preferment to a rectory, vicarage, or perpetual curacy for only 89 percent of those of plebeian or unknown origins, against 92.5 percent for the sons of professionals and 95 percent for the sons of gentlemen. Among the ordinands of 1705-14, the figures are 78 percent for parsons of plebeian or unknown origins, 82 percent for professionals' sons, and 96 percent for the sons of gentlemen. At the same time, 95 percent of the ordinands of the 1660's who had M.A.'s found livings, against 85 percent of those with B.A.'s; for the ordinands of 1705-14, the figures are 91 percent for the M.A.'s, 71 percent for the B.A.'s.

All of this was reflected in the social and educational backgrounds of the stipendiary curates serving Leicestershire's parishes in 1671 and 1700.[71] Some of the men listed as curates in the *Libri Cleri* of those years were in fact incumbents of parishes in Leicestershire and adjoining counties who were picking up additional income. A few others were listed as curates in chapelries within the parishes they actually served as incumbents; still others were parsons serving parishes endowed with perpetual curacies (usually in conjunction with other benefices), and these have already been treated as incumbents with the rectors and vicars. If we subtract these men, we are left at each date with thirty-one parsons who were hired as stipendiary curates by parish incumbents, and who had no other known sources of professional income except schoolteaching. In terms of geographic origins they were roughly similar to the parish incumbents of 1670 and 1714, but at each date they were drawn disproportionately from plebeian and unknown backgrounds, and they were much less likely than the general run of ordinands to have master's degrees. They were also much less likely to find permanent benefices—there is no record of preferment to a permanent parish living for 52 percent of the curates of 1671, or for 39 percent of the curates of 1700.[72] Stipendiary curates were clearly atypical of the mainstream of Leicestershire's parsons. There were two reasons for this. First, plebeians and parsons with only B.A.'s were more likely to form a backlog of men who remained curates all their lives, inflating the representation of plebeians and mere B.A.'s among the curates as a whole. Second, gentlemen's sons, the sons of the wealthier clergy, and parsons who stayed on for M.A.'s were more likely to have livings waiting for them when they took their degrees, and consequently were more likely to avoid apprenticeship as curates altogether.

Parsons who did begin as curates were generally hired by pluralists unable to serve two livings simultaneously, or by incumbents of livings with one or more chapelries besides the main parish church, or by incumbents too ill or elderly to discharge

Stipendiary Curates in Leicestershire Parishes

(Figures in parentheses represent the men whose origins are known.)

	1671 (N = 31)	1700 (N = 31)
	Geographic Origins	
Leicestershire	26% (40%)	42% (46%)
Adjoining counties	26% (40%)	22.5% (25%)
Other counties	13% (20%)	26% (29%)
Unknown	35%	10%
	Social Origins	
Gentry and above	10% (17%)	10% (14%)
Professionals	16% (28%)	22% (34%)
Plebeians	32% (55%)	35.5% (52%)
Unknown	42%	32%
	Degree-Holders	
B.D., D.D.	3%	3%
LL.B., LL.D.	0	0
M.A.	16%	29%
B.A.	65%	59%
No record of degree	16%	9%

their duties properly. It was relatively uncommon for a curate to be the son of the parish's incumbent; only two of the thirty-one curates in the *Liber Cleri* of 1700 fell into this category. Two or three others were hired by brothers or uncles, but most were hired by men who were not their relatives, usually on the strength of recommendations from friends, bishops, college heads, or other university officials. Their stipends varied enormously, primarily with their employers' generosity and the values of the livings they served, and to a lesser extent with the number of church services they were required to perform. In 1671 a curate hired by the vicar of Melton Mowbray (a living worth about £60 a year) received only £5 for serving Welby chapel, while the curate at Sibsdon (£160 a year) received £40. The highest stipend on record for a late-Stuart Leicestershire curate was the £100 paid to John Cave for serving Nailstone; the incumbent was his father, however, and his father's own income was well over £200 a year. Most stipendiary curates received only £20 or £30 a year, though some also received room and board in the parsonage, and others supplemented their incomes by teaching school.[73] In view of the duties they had to perform and the discrepancy between their stipends and the incomes of their employers, many might well consider themselves severely underpaid. In 1714 the curate hired by the rector of Barwell, a living worth well over £200 a year, was paid only £25 annually. His duties included offering two Sunday services with sermons, as well as prayers on Wednesdays and Fridays, to a congregation of six hundred. Bitterly resenting this, he left for South Carolina as a missionary in 1723.[74]

Curates were clearly an underprivileged class among the late-Stuart clergy. Drawn disproportionately from the plebeian classes, they might find themselves stuck in the curate stage forever, carrying out most of the duties of their employers and receiving scant financial rewards for their services. As for why the plebeians were most likely to remain underpaid curates, we need to look more closely at the ways in which parsons went about becoming parish incumbents.

PARSONS IN SEARCH OF BENEFICES

Between the newly ordained parsons and the benefices they hoped to serve stood the men who owned the county's advowsons, the right to present parsons to the bishop for institution to particular livings.[75] Advowsons were considered freehold property, and as such they could be bought, sold, traded, mortgaged, bequeathed, or freely given away. If a patron wished, he could also sell or give away the right to present upon the next vacancy only, after which the advowson returned to the regular patron, or to his heirs or assigns. A patron's right to pick an incumbent was nearly absolute, for although advowsons were subject to certain legal restrictions, these had little importance in practice. A patron, for example, could not present himself, even if he were a parson; nor could he indulge in outright simony—accepting money for presenting a particular candidate. But nothing prevented a patron from selling the advowson, or even a right of next presentation, to someone with a friend or relative to present; so long as the new patron accepted no money himself, the presentation would be accepted as valid. And parsons who bought advowsons could in practice appoint themselves by taking advantage of a convenient legal fiction: they simply turned their advowsons over to trusted friends, who as legal patrons then presented them to their bishop.

Bishops could technically veto nominees who seemed unfit (except in the case of a few livings, which were called donatives), but late-Stuart bishops of Lincoln seldom exercised this option. Once a patron's choice was made, episcopal institution followed almost automatically.

In certain special cases, the right to present passed temporarily to the bishop, the archbishop, or the Crown. The Crown, for example, gained a right of next presentation when patrons were convicted of simony (a rare occurrence), and when vacancies were occasionally created by the promotion of incumbents to the episcopal bench. When a patron allowed a living to stand vacant for more than six months, the power to present passed temporarily to the bishop of the diocese; if the bishop was similarly negligent, the power to present passed in another six months to the archbishop of the province; if the archbishop did not fill the living within six months, the power to present then passed to the Crown. This seldom happened in practice, however. Leicestershire patrons almost always moved quickly when vacancies occurred, often making their presentations within days after a death or resignation. Excluding the years 1660–62, when there were a number of Crown presentations confirming parsons with insecure titles in their livings, cases of royal and episcopal intervention were comparatively uncommon, affecting only one Leicestershire parish in five in the late-Stuart period, and only one-tenth of the incumbents who served Leicestershire parishes during that time.

Leicestershire's single most important patron was the Crown, with about thirty advowsons, but these formed only 16 percent of all the advowsons in Leicestershire. The Duke of Rutland came second, with fourteen or fifteen advowsons, and was followed by the Earl of Huntingdon, who held six. Below this level, ownership was much more widely distributed: in 1714 four individuals held three or four advowsons apiece, seventeen held two each, and the rest held only one. Patrons with only one or two advowsons controlled about two-thirds of the county's parish livings in the late-Stuart period, and they accounted for about 90 percent of the county's patrons. The majority lived in Leicestershire, but less than half in the parishes whose incumbents they named. Because of the number of advowsons held by the Crown, corporate bodies, and patrons with more than one advowson, only a third of the county's parishes had resident patrons.

Overwhelmingly Leicestershire's patrons belonged to the topmost strata of society, and the great majority of them were laymen. In 1714 peers controlled one Leicestershire living in five, knights and baronets one in ten, esquires one in four, and mere gentlemen about one in twenty. A few parish clergymen had purchased advowsons for themselves or their sons; they controlled one county living in ten. Seven colleges and universities had acquired advowsons to nine livings in the county; Emmanuel College, Cambridge, controlled two of the county's richest livings, Loughborough and Thurcaston, both of which were worth about £200 a year in the early eighteenth century. Members of the Haberdasher Company of London chose the vicars of Diseworth and Wigston Magna, and they alternated with Christ's Hospital in London in choosing the vicar of Bitteswell. Relatively few advowsons were held by bishops and religious chapters. The only parson regularly chosen by the Bishop of Lincoln was the vicar of Evington; the Dean and Chapter of Lincoln Cathedral presented only to Gumley; and the prebendary of St. Margaret in Lincoln Cathedral chose the vicar of St. Margaret's parish in Leicester. The parsons of Belgrave, Ibstock, and Orton on the Hill were picked by the Bishops of Lichfield and Coventry, Rochester, and Oxford, respectively, and the vicar of Hinckley was chosen by the Dean and Chapter of Westminster.

These patrons were sometimes willing to sell grants of next presentation, but not so frequently as one might think simply by counting grants recorded in presentation deeds and episcopal registers. In some of these cases, patrons were making grants to trusted friends who would then present the patrons' sons or brothers—a convenient way of avoiding the appearance of nepotism. In other cases, the grants were legal fictions in which advowson-owning parsons made temporary grants to trusted friends in order to have themselves presented. If cases like these are excluded, genuine grants of next presentation affected only one Leicestershire parish in five between 1660 and 1714, and they involved only one-tenth of the presentations made during those years.[76] But there was a brisk market for perpetual advowsons—the right to present in perpetuity. Between 1603 and 1640, roughly 35 percent of the county's perpetual advowsons passed to families with different surnames; 20 percent more changed hands between 1640 and 1670, and another 25 to 30 percent between 1670 and 1714.[77] Despite the changes in ownership, each social class's share of the county's advowsons remained fairly stable over time. The major exception lay in the class of mere gentlemen, whose share fell from 20 percent in 1603 to 4 percent in 1714,

Distribution of Advowsons among Different Social Groups

	(N = 205)			
	1603	1640	1670	1714
Crown	14%	15%	15%	16%
Peers	18%	20%	23%	22%
Knights and baronets	16%	13%	14%	11%
Esquires	12%	23%	21%	25%
Gentlemen	20%	6%	7%	4%
Parish clergymen	3%	5%	6%	10%
Merchants	1%	1%	0	0
Yeomen	2%	0	0	0
Bishops, colleges, and corporate bodies	5%	9%	9%	10%
Unknown	9%	8%	5%	2%

with most of the drop coming before the Civil War. But here the figures can be deceiving. Some patrons who styled themselves "esquires" in 1642 had inherited advowsons from grandfathers who had called themselves "gentlemen" in 1603, and the "esquires" of 1714 undoubtedly included some wealthy merchants and lawyers who might not have used that title under the early Stuarts. Thus the apparent decline in the number of advowsons held by mere gentlemen reflects not so much a substantial shift toward the topmost ranks of society as the upper strata's continued hold on the ownership of advowsons, and the inability of those further down to crack their monopoly.

Given this upper-class control of ecclesiastical patronage, how did young parsons go about winning livings? The most direct method, though not the most common, was simply to buy one's way in by purchasing an advowson or a grant of next presentation. Contemporaries normally expected a grant of next presentation to cost about as much as the living would be worth to its incumbent in an average year, and perpetual advowsons would usually go for two or three times that amount. But prices varied with the expected longevity of the current incumbent, and this could complicate negotiations considerably. If the incumbent was young and healthy, the advowson's value might be fairly low, while a sudden illness or rumors of a resignation could cause the price to skyrocket. A presentation to Fenny Drayton, a Leicestershire rectory worth £88 a year, was sold for £120 in 1693; in 1694 the Earl of

Rutland turned down an offer of £300 for a grant of next presentation to Redmile, a living worth £120 a year, whose rector was leaving for Aylestone. The perpetual advowson of Frowlesworth, a living worth £90 a year, went for £250 in 1700, and the perpetual advowson of South Sheepy (worth £100 a year) cost about £360 in 1695.[78] Most contemporaries saw nothing wrong with the traffic in livings, provided that it was conducted with some discretion. In 1701, for example, a North Country parson received the following letter from a friend:

> Lady Otway has often spoke to me to enquire for a Purchaser that would buy the perpetual Advowson of Windermere; she sayes she has a good Title, & that will be easily seen, I believe she is very honest, and would not put a cheat upon any person: She proposes to sell the perpetuall Advowson for £200, or would sell the Next Presentation for one yeares Value. . . .She sayes it is worth £80 per annum at least. If You please to enquire into the true Value, and will give one yeares Value for the next Presentation, it may be purchased in your Fathers name, or any other Friend or Relation that You can trust, who may present You upon the Avoidance. . .and that is both lawfull and just.[79]

But when sales degenerated into unseemly auctions, contemporaries blushed. In 1714 a London merchant named Garret placed the advowson of Humberston vicarage in the hands of an Exchange broker named Hawkins, directing him to get as much as he could for a grant of next presentation. On November 1 the Archdeacon of Leicester reported to Bishop Wake that

> Mr. Ward, by the bye, ask't him whether he had got a Customer for his Living, to which he replyed that he was treating with 3 persons, and that the best Bidder should have it. A Lawyer told me that he had actually bought it, but his Friend was squeamish. Mr. Dodsworth, a Merchant (and Neighbour to Mr. Garret) made close application to him in the behalf of Mr. Marsden, but he wrote me word it was not to be come at honestly, for Hawkins was sent to tell him that he would have £50 (which he calls one years revenue) who ever had it. The man talks of it in publick, as if it were no sin, and who ever is the Clerk presented to your Lordship, he must be a wretched one, and 'tis very fit he should know what all the Countrey will think of him: for there is the greatest presumption of the Living being simonically obtained that I ever yet heard of.[80]

The archdeacon's disgust suggests that such flagrant auctioneering was infrequent. It probably was, for, as has been noted, grants of next presentation affected only 10 percent of Leicestershire's parish incumbents in the late-Stuart period. Nor did all of these grants involve an exchange of cash. The patron of Theddingworth, for example, freely gave a presentation to a friend in trust for "a very honest clergyman's widow. . .left miserably poor with five or six children"; and in 1692 the friend apparently arranged to have the widow's son presented to the living.[81] Available evidence in fact suggests that in late-Stuart Leicestershire only one incumbent in six owed his appointment to the purchase of an advowson, whether temporary or perpetual.[82] If the traffic was no more brisk than that, part of the reason was that clergymen from plebeian families could seldom afford the prices demanded. At the same time, clergymen from gentle and professional families often found it unnecessary to buy their way in, for in many cases they were already assured of getting livings through kinship connections with the county's patrons.

Patrons saw nothing amiss in appointing their relatives to vacant livings, especially when their relatives were clearly qualified in other respects. Bishop Sanderson of Lincoln, for example, felt that his appointment of one Parson Howle to a vacant living in 1661 was entirely justified by "his abilityes, former sufferings, present necessities, and neare relation to mee."[83] Nor did contemporaries object when parsons born without the right connections managed to acquire them through marriage, for advantageous marriages were an acceptable means of getting ahead in life. Thus John Thomlinson's interests in the unmarried daughter of Glenfield's patron were not abnormally calculating, even when he wrote that the "lady's living is about 3 miles from Leicester, 300l. per annum, and she has 1,200l., and other sisters may die." Nor need he have felt guilty when he married the girl and got the living.[84] Patrons quite naturally appointed their relatives, even recently acquired sons-in-law, for loyalty to one's family was considered a mark of virtue. Sir Edward Smith, the patron of Husband's Bosworth, quite naturally appointed his relation Thomas Smith to the living in 1694, and upon Thomas's resignation in 1700 he appointed Thomas's brother Roger. Quite naturally, too, the Dixies of Market Bosworth appointed John Dixie to their living in 1685, and Beaumont Dixie in 1729. In 1688 Sir Thomas Hazlerigg of Nosely even reached up into Newcastle to locate a distant cousin for his living at South Hallaton.[85] Patrons with relatives too young to be appointed sometimes presented temporary incumbents, in order to keep their livings warm until their relatives came of age. Often this was accomplished by a resignation bond in which the interim incumbent, as a condition of getting the living, promised to resign when his patron asked him to. On other occasions, financial arrangements were involved. Elizabeth Vincent, the patroness of South Sheepy in 1705, paid the incumbent £1,000 to resign within three years in order to clear the way for her son William, then a student at Cambridge. When William decided to stay on for a law degree, the contract had to be renegotiated, but he finally succeeded to the living in 1712.[86]

The benefits of kinship connections were most evident when advowsons were owned by the incumbents themselves. The result was sometimes a clerical dynasty, the clerical succession at Appleby providing an outstanding example. Appleby's advowson was purchased in James I's reign by a prosperous yeoman named William Mould, who in 1610 presented his son Thomas to the living. Thomas served the parish until his death in 1642, and was succeeded by his son Abraham; Abraham's patrons were ostensibly Samuel Hodgkinson and John Prior, clerks, but they were actually patrons only through a grant of next presentation, made to them by Thomas Mould before his death, on the understanding that Abraham would be the beneficiary. Abraham was evicted by the Puritans in 1656, but he was restored in 1660 and continued to serve Appleby until he died in 1684. In his will he bequeathed his son Isaac "my whole parsonage and all my books," and Isaac succeeded him in 1685 under the patronage of Samuel Sanders, Esq., by virtue of another deceptive grant of next presentation. At Isaac's death in 1721 the advowson passed to his brother Thomas, and Thomas thereupon presented Jacob Mould, apparently his son and Isaac's nephew. When Jacob died in 1731, his son Thomas was still a minor; moreover, the advowson, under the terms of Isaac Mould's will, had by this time passed to another brother, who decided to present George Gell, probably not a relation. By the time the next vacancy occurred, in 1743, the advowson had passed to some cousins named Dawson. Thomas Mould had by now taken a bachelor's degree and could have resumed the family succession, but the Dawsons instead presented John Vaughan, who was in turn followed by Francis Gibbs in 1758. Perhaps Thomas Mould was offered Appleby and declined it; at any rate, he remained in the parish as English master in the grammar school until his death in 1792. But if the succession of Moulds had been broken, it had been a long one: father, son, grandson, and great-nephew had presided at Appleby from 1610 to 1737, with the exception of a four-year interruption during the Interregnum.[87] Similarly, the Burnabys began serving Asfordby in

1666 and presided there, with a few interruptions, into the twentieth century. Other Leicestershire dynasties included the Masons of Ashby Magna (1586-1684), the Beridges of Barrow (ca. 1617-95), and the Burdetts of Burton Overy (1582-1710).[88]

The influence of family connections extended beyond cases of outright nepotism. Parsons' sons, for example, often entered the Church knowing that they would be provided for by their fathers' patrons. The succession at Buckminster, a Leicestershire living in the gift of the Duke of Devonshire, provides a good illustration. When the Reverend Samuel Dixon died in 1695, after a half-century of service in the parish, the Duke made Dixon's son John his successor. John's son Edward had just entered Cambridge when John died in 1718, forcing the Duke to place John Burman in the living for the time being. However, Burman obligingly resigned in 1720 when Edward was ordained, and Edward Dixon served the parish until his death in 1763. Three Owsleys served Glooston under the Earls of Cardigan between 1660 and 1744; the Earls of Gainesborough had two Daniel Naylors in their pulpit at Pickwell (1688-90, 1706-12); John Turner followed James Turner under the patronage of Lord Rockingham at Garthorp; two Ithiel Smarts held the Earl of Huntingdon's living at Ashby de la Zouch (1652-61, 1676-91); and in 1713 John Vaughan was presented by the Earl of Huntingdon to Belton, the parish his father had served in the 1670's.[89]

How frequently were ecclesiastical appointments actually influenced by kinship connections like these? There is evidence of outright nepotism, involving either perpetual advowsons or grants of next presentation, for only 8 percent of the parish incumbents of 1670, and for only 18 percent of the incumbents of 1714.[90] These include cases in which patrons presented parsons with the same surnames, cases in which patrons presented parsons with different surnames who are known to have been relatives, and cases in which parsons themselves owned advowsons and had themselves presented by friends or relatives. These figures are undoubtedly too low. In view of the impossibility of tracing all the family connections within an intensely inbred county society, there are certainly some relatives with different surnames who have been overlooked. But perhaps the figures should not be too much higher, for while the great majority of the county's patrons belonged to the governing classes, probably half of the county's late-Stuart parish incumbents came from plebeian backgrounds. If there were undocumented kinship connections between well-heeled patrons and some of the humbler parsons, they were probably distant and quite infrequent.

But the importance of family connections was by no means restricted to cases of outright nepotism. As has been noted, some patrons appointed their clerical clients' sons; if we add these appointments to the ones made by outright nepotists, family influence was instrumental for at least 22 percent of the incumbents of 1714. There were certainly other cases in which families who did not own advowsons brought informal influence to bear on families who did, as well as cases in which family connections influenced appointments to livings controlled by bishops, colleges, other corporate bodies, and the Crown. And even if family connections still influenced only a minority of Leicestershire appointments, they were quite important to parsons with above-average social connections. Of the parish incumbents of 1714 who were gentlemen's sons, at least 42 percent had gained their livings through nepotism. Of those who were sons of professional men, at least 29 percent had been appointed by relatives or indirectly by themselves; if we include the sons of parsons who held livings under the same patrons, this figure rises to 44 percent.

If perhaps half of the parsons of gentle and professional backgrounds were thus assured of getting livings, plebeians' sons and the sons of the poorer clergy found the going more difficult. Born without the right social connections or enough money to purchase advowsons, they had to rely on a variety of other methods to get ahead. But their prospects were far from hopeless. College officials, bishops, peers, and some of the greater gentry were busily operating a clerical placement service, one that was national in scope, with major recruiting offices at Cambridge, Oxford, and London. Working along complex and extensive communication lines, they were constantly scooping up unemployed parsons from one part of the country and depositing them safely in livings in another. Often there were unemployed friends and relatives they were obliged to take care of first. The results were sometimes unfortunate: "The clark of Sedgefield is lately dead," the Dean of Durham wrote in 1685,

> and I am not yet resolved how to dispose of the place. . . .Poor Sisterton is, I know, a weak brain man, and doth still, I fear, often faile in point of drink; but I conceive the poor man as harmlesse and innocent a drunkard (if hee deserves the name) as any in England: and if I do bestow it on Sisterton, it shall be for the sake of my godson, his son Denys, to bee supplied by him till the young man bee of age.[91]

But members of the placement service never had enough friends and relatives to fill up all the livings at their disposal, and they were not averse to helping out parsons whose only assets were piety and dedication. For the poor but deserving clergyman, the essential task was to make members of the service aware of his presence.

One tactic was to do extremely well in school. Richard Hill of Worcestershire entered Emmanuel College, Cambridge, in 1675; he worked hard, waited on tables, won a fellowship, and stayed on to become a bachelor of divinity. Continuing to serve the college as a fellow, he also worked as a curate in two parishes ten miles away, returning to Cambridge each Sunday night. It was an arduous schedule, but Hill protested that he was "never tired; never in those days wearied with the holy service of that most holy day." He so impressed his friends at Emmanuel that in 1701 he was unanimously elected by the master, fellows, and scholars to the college's Leicestershire rectory of Thurcaston. He arrived there six weeks later and, with an income of £200 a year, became one of the county's wealthiest parsons.[92] There were others who benefited in the same way. Christ's, Emmanuel, St. John's, and Peterhouse consistently appointed distinguished alumni to their five Leicestershire livings, all of which were handsomely endowed. Almost all of their appointees held divinity degrees and had served their colleges as fellows for at least ten years before their appointments. In 1714 one of them was the Master of Christ's—his parish living was simply a sinecure, which he served by hiring a curate—but the others had retired from teaching and were resident in their parishes.[93] Advanced scholarship was not as necessary for poor-to-middling college livings. The Chancellor and Scholars of Oxford habitually appointed Oxford alumni to their living at Syston, worth only £50 a year, but the parish's four incumbents of 1671–1718 held only master's degrees, and they were appointed soon after graduation.[94] When it came to the poorest college livings, those worth less than £50 a year, college heads were much more careless. Most of the incumbents who served Wymeswold, Great Bowden, and Market Harborough under the later Stuarts were not even alumni of the colleges that appointed them.[95] Nevertheless, university patronage was important for some alumni, and appointees to college livings in Leicestershire arrived from places as distant as Cornwall, Lancashire, and Cork.

Parsons who failed to attract sufficient attention at college sometimes headed for London. The capital was the great nexus of the national patronage circuit, for the bishops and peers who were the system's major operators spent much of their time there attending Parliament; ambitious parsons in search of livings naturally flooded into the city to meet them. One who arrived in Leicestershire along this route was Abel Ligonier, a French Protestant refugee who fled to England in the 1680's. He quickly established contact with the Bishop of London, who introduced him to the Countess of Northampton, who in turn reported by letter to the Countess of Rutland that the Frenchman was a "very ingenious person in his conversation." It so happened that the Countess of Rutland was seeking a tutor for her sons, and she quickly hired Ligonier as tutor and family chaplain. Five years later her husband appointed him vicar of Croxton Keyrial.[96]

Jonathan Swift told of a poor farmer's son at Oxford who "by the most extreme parsimony, saved thirty-four pounds out of a very beggarly fellowship" and "went up to London, where his sister was waitingwoman to a lady, and so good a solicitor, that by her means he was admitted to read prayers in the family twice a day." He managed to "get the good word of the whole family" and, eventually, a country living in the family's gift.[97] Stories like these sent still more parsons scurrying to the capital. "You see the London ministers gett all the preferments," a Norfolk clergyman wrote a friend in 1691, "and therefore, if possible, fix your brother there."[98] In the late-Stuart period enough were arriving to provoke a royal injunction against the "many Clergy men that flock up to London uncall'd," only to "loyter here about the Citty." Some were bringing "great scandall to their profession by haunting Coffee-houses and other public places. . .carrying away preferments from those whose modesty & sence of duty keeps them upon the places where their business lyes."[99]

Those who stayed in the country often sought their livings through the post, and in many cases it was their bishops they petitioned. But bishops had a number of close associates they had to satisfy first, as a letter from William Wake, by this time Archbishop of Canterbury, makes abundantly clear:

> I have a pretty many benefices in my gift, but not many desirable; neither the value nor the situation of the most part of them being such as to encourage any considerable person to reside upon them. Such as they are, I distribute them as fast as they become vacant to my friends and domestics. For the lesser sort, I have a large list of expectants whom I endeavour in their order to provide for. For the better, my chaplains have had the most of them.[100]

Similarly, the Bishop of London's wife reported that "his lordship had so many upon him for livings, that he knew not what to do—his chaplain had gott nothing yet, etc.";[101] and in 1661 Bishop Sanderson of Lincoln complained to the dean that he was completely swamped with petitions from parsons who were "for the most part to mee Strangers."[102] But episcopal patronage was never limited to livings in the gift of the bishops themselves. As their petitioners knew full well, bishops exercised influence over the disposition of livings in the gift of other men. Thus in April, 1714, Wake of Lincoln received a letter from the Reverend Richard Marsden thanking him for his "most pressing Interest with the Lord Chancellor for me, and. . .since your Lordship has assured me you will as soon as it is decent put the new Arch-Bishop again in mind of his promis: I have not the least apprehension but [that I shall] be successful in obtaining a Benifice that may be a Comfortable Subsistence for my family."[103] Bishops also exercised influence over the vast number of livings in the gift of peers and the greater gentry. In 1695 the Earl of Rutland, who had lately acquired Abel Ligonier indirectly through the Bishop of London, wrote the Bishop of Lincoln: "my Son's Governor having imparted to me your Lordship's respects in reference to the Disposal of the Rectory of Knipton, I do with thanks to your Lordship accept the overture, and have upon Mr. Hawkins's Resignation given my presentation to Mr. Griffin."[104]

Bishops who put parsons in touch with peers could hardly have provided a more worthwhile service. Peers usually held advowsons to several livings of varying incomes, enabling worthy clients to advance up their patrons' ladders of preferment as livings fell vacant through deaths and resignations. Thus under the Earl of Rutland's patronage Abel Ligonier advanced from Croxton Keyrial to Redmile to Bottesford; the first was worth only £40 a year, the last about £300. Under the same patron, Lewis Griffin hopped from Knipton to Whitwell, and then took over Bottesford when Ligonier died; Gustavus Hawes skipped from Croxton Keyrial to Redmile to Aylestone; and Derham Huddleston went from Barkstone to Branston to Woolsthorp in Lincolnshire. Ashby de la Zouch, worth less than £50 a year, was a jumping-off point for several clients of the Earl of Huntingdon. In 1671 Alexander Jones moved from there to Puddletown, Dorset, a move duplicated by Henry Hooton in 1693; Ithiel Smart left Ashby for Packington in 1690; and Cadwalader Vaughan traded in the Earl's living at Belton for Osgathrop in 1679.[105] Peers were also adept at getting their clients livings in the gift of the Crown. The Earl of Stamford, for example, acquired Edward Stokes as a domestic chaplain in the 1690's and presented him to livings at Ratby and Willoughby Waterless. In 1711 the Crown presented Stokes to Blaby, and he held it in plurality with Willoughby until his death in 1724. Similarly, Edward Vernon's presentation to the Crown's living at Muston in 1706 followed his acquisition of the Earl of Rutland's living at Redmile in 1698, and Theophilus Brooks had been presented to Belton and Markfield by the Earl of Huntingdon in 1690 before picking up the Crown's living at Norton by Twycross in 1699.[106]

Parsons unable to break into this national patronage circuit sometimes wandered several years from parish to parish, taking temporary jobs as curates, then pushing onward in hopes that permanent livings would eventually turn up somewhere. "Drive as much as may be all wandering and unemployed Clergy out of your Dioceses," late-Stuart bishops were told by the Crown,[107] but curates continued to wander. They were hoping to find local gentlemen with livings at their disposal and no relatives clamoring for presentation. Happily, their patience was often rewarded. Hopkin Thomas of Wales left Oxford in 1690 to become curate to his uncle at Earl Shilton; three years later the Pochins, one of Leicestershire's gentle families, presented him to Barkby vicarage. Edmund Carter of Hertfordshire, an Emmanuel graduate, arrived in Loughborough in 1698 as curate to a fellow alumnus, and two years later the Lowe family presented him to Goadby Marwood.[108] Such cases were fairly common. Many patrons quite altruistically appointed parsons on the basis of experience and merit, and sometimes they even followed the advice of ordinary parishioners who liked a parson who had passed through their village. A clergyman moving to Shawell in 1698 told the bishop that he would be succeeded at his former living by one Mr. Purchas, noting that the patron "freely gave his consent. . .being verry willing to gratifie the parish in their request."[109] Similarly, in 1706 the parishioners of Wigston Magna petitioned the parish's patron on behalf of Mr. Jolley, "a stranger in these parts, of whom they seem to be very fond"; the patron obligingly presented Jolley to Wigston Magna later that year.[110] Local initiative also helped determine Crown appointments to livings in Leicester. Certainly this was the case at St. Martin's in 1696 and 1697, and it seems to have been a general trend in the town as a whole. William Coltman, for example, had been hired as a curate by the lay sequestrators of St.

Leonard's before being named vicar of All Saints' by the Crown in 1664; William Thomas had been a local schoolmaster for four years before being called to All Saints' in 1683; and William Fox was presented to St. Mary's by the Crown in 1689, six years after he had been hired there and at St. Nicholas' as a curate. If the Crown allowed a measure of local autonomy in the town, it was undoubtedly because its town livings were all poorly endowed, and their incumbents dependent on voluntary parochial contributions.[111]

Although the parsons who benefited most from the system of ecclesiastical patronage were those born with the right connections, talented parsons of humble origins were sometimes able to do very well. The career of William Gilbert, son of a Leicester tanner, provides an example. Gilbert took his bachelor's degree at Cambridge in 1680 and was licensed to teach in Market Bosworth, a parish whose patron and resident gentleman was Sir Beaumont Dixie. In 1685 Gilbert was serving as curate at the Dixies' other living at Cadeby. The next year he was curate at Market Bosworth to Dixie's son John, and finally in 1688 the Dixies named him rector of Cadeby, worth about £60 a year. Five years later the incumbent of the neighboring parish of Newbold Verdun died. That living was worth about £50 a year, and it was probably through the Dixies' influence that Gilbert was presented by the Duke of Norfolk in 1694. He held both livings until his death in 1719, with a combined income of about £110 a year.[112]

How exceptional was Gilbert's career? A table on p. 72 gives some indication of the relationship between social origins and clerical incomes for Leicestershire's parish incumbents of 1714. The income distribution was constructed from a survey of parish livings made in the first decade of the eighteenth century, and it takes into account income from plural holdings, prebends, schoolteaching, and extra stipends earned by incumbents who served as curates to incumbents in other parishes.[113] The four income brackets divide the incumbents as a whole into four roughly equal groups, and the figures show the proportion of parsons from a given social background to be found in each income bracket.

Not surprisingly, gentlemen's sons were generally in the top half of the income distribution in 1714, plebeians' sons in the bottom half, and professionals' sons in the middle. By the time the incumbents of 1714 died, a few more had become pluralists and others had exchanged poorly endowed livings for ones with better returns. As a result, several had moved into higher income brackets, but the general pattern was still the same: gentlemen's sons were even more concentrated at the top, professionals' sons still firmly in the middle, and plebeians' sons still generally at the bottom. There was some social mobility, with about 40 percent of the plebeians' sons eventually earning above-average incomes—but this is offset by the fact that plebeians' sons had a harder time finding parish livings in the first place, with the number who never became tenured incumbents running as high as a fifth for the ordinands of 1705–14. Able clergymen of plebeian origins who developed the right connections could prosper in the late-Stuart Church, but they had a harder time finding permanent livings than the sons of gentlemen and professionals, and their economic prospects were on the whole much dimmer. Given the market conditions of the late seventeenth century, a plebeian's son was quite likely to find a parish living eventually, but the odds were strongly against his becoming a member of the clerical elite.

Did late-Stuart parsons resent a patronage system that favored the wealthy and the well connected? Swift tended to doubt it; the vicar who earned only £40 per year was "usually the son of some ordinary tradesman or middling farmer," and despite his poverty he was "happy, by being born to no higher expectation."[114] In a deferential and highly stratified society, few men could legitimately aspire to rise much above the stations into which they were born; hence many parsons who spent their entire lives serving the poorer cures may have been relatively content with their lot in life. Certainly this was true of John Bold, for fifty years the poorly paid curate of Stoney Stanton. Born in Leicester in 1679, Bold took his bachelor's degree at Cambridge and began serving Stoney Stanton in 1702. He was by all accounts an exemplary curate, holding services twice a week, catechizing regularly, and faithfully visiting the sick. He attracted attention by publishing several sermons in a polished, Addisonian style—sermons which brought him a number of invitations to rich parish livings. But he chose to stay at Stoney Stanton, earning a curate's salary that never rose above £30. He boarded with a local farmer's family and lived frugally, his breakfast consisting of water gruel, his supper of milk pottage. Each year he gave a third of his salary to charitable causes, and when he died in 1751, he left £20 to found a lectureship for the people of his parish.[115] If Bold was one of the poorest clergymen in the county, his piety and humility made him one of the most beloved.

Some parsons, however, grew dissatisfied with serving God in lowly places. The Reverend Humphrey Michel, for example, hoped to rise into the upper ranks of his profession, and relegation to the

Parish Incumbents of 1714: Distribution of Income

	All Incumbents (N = 175)	*Gentry and above* (N = 38)	*Professionals* (N = 45)	*Plebeians* (N = 53)	*Unknowns* (N = 39)
A. *In 1714*					
£0–59	24%	18.5%	16%	30%	31%
60–99	31%	16%	40%	38%	26%
100–159	24%	26%	31%	17%	23%
160+	21%	39.5%	13%	15%	20%
B. *At the time of their deaths:*					
£0–59	17%	13%	2%	26%	26%
60–99	29%	16%	36%	34%	26%
100–159	26%	21%	42%	17%	25%
160+	28%	50%	20%	23%	23%

lower ranks made him sour and embittered. Born in Birmingham about 1650, Michel was the son of a butcher. He took his bachelor's degree at Oxford in 1670 but could not afford to stay on for a master's. Arriving in Leicestershire as curate to a fellow alumnus, he was appointed within a few years to Blaston rectory and Horninghold vicarage, both of which were poorly endowed. With an income of only £40 per year, Michel longed for better livings and a chance to pursue his calling in more rewarding ways. Unfortunately, he was stuck with Blaston and Horninghold until the day he died.[116] His feelings of frustration were scarcely alleviated when he compared himself with his three clerical neighbors, the parsons of North Hallaton, South Hallaton, and Medbourne, for each possessed all the advantages of birth, wealth, and education that Michel sorely lacked. The rector of South Hallaton was William Fenwick, M.A., son of a Newcastle physician; he had been appointed to his living by his cousin, Sir Thomas Hazlerigg of Nosely, and he received an annual income of about £90. The Reverend George Stavely, rector of Medbourne, was the son of Thomas Stavely of Belgrave, Esq. After taking his master's degree at Cambridge, he had been appointed to Medbourne on a grant of next presentation, and his income was about £180 a year. And then there was Theophilus Burdett, M.A., the rector of North Hallaton. The Burdetts had been Leicestershire clergymen since the 1580's; Theophilus's father had been rector of Gumley, his uncle Henry was rector of Burton Overy, and his great-grandfather had been the Earl of Kent. In addition to the £90 he earned annually at North Hallaton, he held Nether Broughton in plurality to complete his revenues of £175.[117]

Michel had long envied these three their easy prosperity, and in 1700 his frustrations finally exploded. When Fenwick, Burdett, and Stavely sided with a local gentleman whom Michel was suing for nonpayment of tithes, Michel furiously attacked them, accusing them of betraying their profession and maliciously assaulting one of their less fortunate colleagues. They were "velvet cushioned doctors," he stormed, "pompous, periwig'd powdered priests," members of a "foppish fraternity." Michel was particularly bothered by their wigs, expensive symbols of a lifestyle he could not afford and could only scorn with false humility. Fenwick's wig was especially galling, for it was the longest and fullest of the three; Michel felt obliged to warn him that "by such modern, Popish, and Pagan Pride, Pomp, and Vanity. . .you'l at Last Provoke. . .natural Envy and Antipathy, if not to the downfall, yet to the Detriment of our Dearest Church." Lest this happen, Michel prayed that Fenwick would make such a "due distinction between your Proud Person and humble function, that our Priesthood may not so bitterly suffer for the sake of your Periwig-Pates, as Troy did for Helena." Then came the ultimate jab: St. Paul "hath excluded all effeminate Persons (parsons not excepted) from the Kingdom of God."[118]

In the feud that followed, Burdett sneered at Michel's humble origins, and Michel immediately lashed back:

> But what ailes Garagantua to be so mad that a butcher's son become a parson, when [your own] wife sold Butter, cheese and eggs at Harborough cross? Where's the hurt, where's the shame? For were not the antient sacrificers in a manner so many slaughterers? Is not Garagantua's next proud self-conceited, vainglorious neighbour but little better than the son of a collier? Is there not now a right-reverend prelate the son of a taylour? A learned priest hard by the son of a Baker? . . .And another the son of a card-maker? Were not Cardinal Wolsey and Lord Chief Justice Scrogs both the sons of a Butcher?[119]

In the end Michel fell back on reverse snobbery, telling Burdett that the "honest butchers" and the "honest hogherds" were far "more honourable than any such priestly prigs," and that eventually Burdett's preaching would be "peack'd and Indicated as pitiful pedantry." Where, after all, would Burdett be without "Nuncle Harry's" Burton Overy? Certainly not in the two rich livings that were "but middling maintenances for his voracious Paunch and Sparrow mouth." Probably he would have been relegated to the poor chapelry of Burton Lazars, a cure "more proper for such unprofitable animals."[120]

Deferential habits and assumptions may have blunted the edge of class antagonism within the clergy's ranks, but they did not obliterate it altogether. Some parsons clearly sensed the injustice of a patronage system that favored the rich and the well born, and a few protested vehemently, and impotently, against it.

TENURE AND TENACITY

The ideal parson was one whose roots in his parish were deep and widespread. He settled into a benefice early in his career, faithfully served it the rest of his life, and baptized in his declining years the children of the parishioners whom he had christened when he first arrived. This was one ideal that in fact tended to coincide with reality. Though many parsons wandered about in search of livings during the early stages of their careers, most found parish livings by the time they were thirty and stayed there until they died. The major exception involved the few parsons who served the poorest benefices, those worth less than £50 a year; most of these kept their eyes open for livings where financial rewards were greater, and almost half eventually resigned and moved on. But most parsons held livings worth more than £50 a year, and these men settled in for the rest of their days. Only one in five ever resigned to accept a living elsewhere.[121]

Settling down was possible because parsons instituted by their bishop automatically gained tenure. They could be deprived if proved in some way unfit for their posts, but, aside from the ejections at the Restoration, deprivations were exceedingly rare in late-Stuart Leicestershire. Six incumbents and two curates were removed between 1688 and 1716 as Non-Jurors and Jacobites; the vicar of Croxton Keyrial was deprived in 1701 for having officiated for forty years on forged orders; and a vicar of St. Martin's was deprived in 1712 for gross neglect of his parish duties. In all other cases of neglect, and of immorality as well, ecclesiastical courts relied instead on timely warnings or temporary suspensions of up to three years. Suspended parsons were put on punitively small stipends, but at the end of their terms of suspension they regained full rights to their benefices' endowed revenues. Even suspensions were relatively uncommon; they were used almost entirely against a handful of chronic offenders, most of whom had repeatedly performed clandestine marriages.[122]

If tenure made long service in the same parish possible, the clerical job market made it almost unavoidable. With men in orders outnumbering parish livings, the average parson might feel lucky to find any sort of benefice at all. Furthermore, with rich livings generally reserved for parsons with superior social connections, a middling living of £70 or £80 a year was all the average parson could reasonably aspire to. Even if he had wanted to move onward and upward, his chances of doing so were limited. But many parsons were quite happy to settle down, for they lived in a time when men still believed in the ideal of a settled community. After spending several years as students and wandering curates, most were ready to find a parish that would eventually become a home. Even a cynical Oxford don like Humphrey Prideux came to feel the need for a more settled way of life—in the 1680's, he resigned from his academic post and accepted a parish living in Norfolk. In a letter to a close friend he explained his reasons for the move:

> I begin now to be desirous of quiet. . .quiet is, in my judgment, infinitely preferable to the trouble and vexation which usually attend greater preferments. . . .My thoughts are much averse from aspireing to high places. I see nothing but trouble and vexation in them, and therefore, to tell you the whole of my heart, there is nothing which I doe soe desire in this world as to be fixed in a station once for all, where I may have as little trouble as possible besides that which is the duty of my profession, and from whence I may noe more remove till I dy.[123]

Many of Leicestershire's parsons felt the same way. One of them was Henry Grove, formerly of Shropshire, appointed to the Leicestershire rectory of Witherley in 1689. He settled into the parish community, married the daughter of one of his predecessors, and acquired the living's advowson for his son Gregory. In 1718 he could write his bishop, with a great deal of pride and some exaggeration, that "I do personallie reside and live in the Parsonage House, and have done constantly twixt 30 and 40 years, I bless God." He continued to serve the parish until his death in 1745, and just as he had wished, his son succeeded him in his ministry.[124] Another example is that of Richard Hill, a Cambridge fellow for twenty years before his presentation to Thurcaston in 1701. He was over forty when he arrived in Leicestershire, but for the rest of his life he was, as he put it, "constantly resident, a constant preacher, and a constant housekeeper." His affection for

Thurcaston grew as the years passed, and just before his death in 1733 he endowed a charity school for the poor children of his parish. In doing this he admitted that he was moved by many things—by his gratitude to God for his many blessings, by his desire to train up poor children in Christian piety, but, perhaps most of all, by his wish that "the founder of this most holy Bible school, though dead and buried in his grave, [might] still continue to live, to speak, to teach, and to preach to this his beloved parish, even till he rises again. Amen."[125] If many parsons arrived in their parishes as strangers to their parishioners, they soon settled down and began to establish roots that spread deeply and widely, helping to bind together the local communities they had been called upon to serve.

NOTES

1. Lincs. Arch. Off., Reg. XXXI-XXXVIII; Sub. I, IIa-VIb; L.C. V-XVII; P.D. (typescripts); *Specula* I and II; L.T. and D.; Lic/Sch/1; Leics. Museum, 1D41/28/356-1260 (file card index); 1D41/34 (typescript).

2. Venn and Venn, *Alumni Cantabrigiensis,* Pts. 1 and 2; Foster, *Alumni Oxoniensis,* Pts. 1 and 2; Burtchaell and Sadleir, *Alumni Dubliniensis;* Wood, *Athenae Oxoniensis*; Peile, *Christ's College*; Venn, *Gonville and Caius College.*

3. Burke, *History of the Commoners* and *Dictionary of the Landed Gentry*; *Dictionary of National Biography*; Longden, *Northamptonshire and Rutland Clergy*; Nichols, *History and Antiquities of Leicester*; Fletcher, *Leicestershire Pedigrees*; Maddison, ed., *Lincolnshire Pedigrees*; Clay, ed., *Familiae Minorum Gentium*; Hartopp, *Wills Relating to Leicester*; *Freemen of Leicester*; and *Leicestershire Marriage Licenses*; and wills and administrations proved in the Archdeaconry of Leicester (available at Leicestershire Record Office).

4. Cawdrey, *Patronage*, pp. 1, 28, 40-44.

5. Information on Leicestershire's ecclesiastical patrons comes from bishops' registers, *Libri Cleri*, presentation deeds, induction mandates, parochial surveys, and histories of Leicestershire and its parishes: Lincs. Arch. Off., Reg. XXXI-XXXVIII; L.C. V-XVIII; P.D. 1600-1720 (typescripts); *Specula* I and II; Leics. Museum, 1D41/28/356-1260 (file card index); Lambeth Palace Library, Cod. Misc. 960-965; Nichols, *Leicester*; *Victoria History of Leicester*; Foster, ed., *State of the Church*.

6. Based on the sources listed in notes 1, 2, and 3.

7. *Ibid*.

8. Brockbank, *Diary and Letter Book*, p. vii.

9. Public Record Office, Prerogative Court of Canterbury Wills, 1678, f. 138; Leics. Rec. Off., PR/I/100/125; PR/I/115/50; and PR/--, *passim*.

10. P.R.O., P.C.C. Wills, 1695, f. 46; Venn and Venn, *Alumni Cantabrigiensis*, Pt. 1, I, 318-319; Nichols, *Leicester*, IV, 583.

11. This and subsequent information on the clergy's sons comes from the sources listed in notes 1, 2, and 3.

12. Leics. Rec. Off., PR/1734, unnumbered: John Elliot.

13. Michel, "Diary," p. 188.
14. Leics. Rec. Off., PR/1692/2; PR/1740, unnumbered: John Swan.
15. Eachard, *Grounds and Occasions*, p. 127; Swift, *Prose Works*, III, 252.
16. Stone, "Social Mobility," pp. 19-20, 27, 37-38, 53.
17. Curtis, "Alienated Intellectuals," pp. 30-34.
18. Stone, "Social Mobility," pp. 46-47.
19. *Ibid.*, pp. 27-28.
20. de la Pryme, *Diary*, p. 19.
21. *Ibid.*, pp. 19-20.
22. Quoted from Sykes, *Church and State*, pp. 192-193.
23. Eachard, *Grounds and Occasions*, p. 20.
24. Brockbank, *Diary and Letter Book*, p. 42.
25. Eachard, *Grounds and Occasions*, pp. 5-7, 34-36.
26. de la Pryme, *Diary*, p. 20.
27. *Ibid.*, pp. 27, 31.
28. *Ibid.*, p. 32.
29. Information for 1576, 1585, and 1603 comes from Foster, *State of the Church*. Information for other years comes from the sources listed in notes 1 and 2.
30. Nichols, *Leicester*, III, 739.
31. Barratt, "Parish Clergy Between the Reformation and 1660," pp. 86-87.
32. Stone, "Educational Revolution," pp. 67-68, 71-72.
33. Wake, *Bishop of Lincoln's Charge*, pp. 9-10.
34. Eachard, *Grounds and Occasions*, pp. 5-7, 47-60.
35. Bodleian Library, Tanner MS 42, f. 167.
36. Christ Church Library, Wake MSS, CCCV, f. 459; Bishop Reynolds to William Wake, August 12, 1724. Quoted from Sykes, *Church and State*, p. 202.
37. Wake, *Bishop of Lincoln's Charge*, pp. 19-20.
38. Leics. Museum, 1D41/21, unnumbered boxes; 1D41/13/67-83; 1D41/11/68,73-77; 1D41/4/XXVIII-LVI; 1D41/14/II-IV.
39. Leics. Rec. Off., PR/I/73/182, and *passim*.
40. Wake, *Bishop of Lincoln's Charge*, p. 10.
41. Michel, "Diary," pp. 191, 194; Nichols, *Leicester*, II, 290.
42. Meeke, *Diary*, p. 56; Michel, "Diary," pp. 188, 195.
43. Wake, *Bishop of Lincoln's Charge*, p. 11.
44. Allen and McClure, *Society for Promoting Christian Knowledge*, pp. 86-87.
45. Based on the *British Museum General Catalogue of Printed Books* and *Supplements*; and on Wing, *Short-Title Catalogue of Books Printed. . . 1641-1700*.
46. *Ibid.*, and Nichols, *Leicester*, I, 596; III, 846; IV, 55, 574n.; Buchan, *Poems of Pestell*.
47. Quoted from Greaves, "Eighteenth-Century High Churchman," pp. 272-274.
48. de la Pryme, *Diary*, p. 45.
49. Addison, *Spectator*, II, 90-91.
50. Nichols, *Leicester*, II, 289-290.
51. Brockbank, *Diary and Letter Book*, p. 80.

52. Phillimore, *Ecclesiastical Law*, I, 113-123.
53. Lincs. Arch. Off., *Speculum* II, p. 285; Reg. XXXVI, pp. 159, 198; Foster, *Alumni Oxoniensis*, Pt. 1, II, 727; III, 1136.
54. Lincs. Arch. Off., L.C. XII, f. 135; L.C. XIV, p. 209; Reg. XXXVI, p. 139.
55. Sykes, *Church and State*, p. 97.
56. Lambeth Palace Library, MS 1770, December 20, 1705. Quoted from Sykes, *William Wake*, I, 160.
57. de la Pryme, *Diary*, p. 187.
58. These quotations are taken from Sykes, *Church and State*, p. 113; and Sykes, *William Wake*, I, 160.
59. Bodleian Library, Tanner MS 80, f. 114; Cawdrey, *Patronage*, p. 40; Sykes, *Church and State*, pp. 96-115; Venables and Perry, *Lincoln*, pp. 310-314, 322-323.
60. Brockbank, *Diary and Letter Book*, p. 81.
61. Thomlinson, "Diary," p. 167.
62. Barratt, "Parish Clergy Between the Reformation and 1660," pp. 8-9.
63. The figures for 1603 are based on Foster, *State of the Church*, p. 459. The figures for subsequent dates are based on the sources listed in notes 1 and 2. Parsons who held livings outside the archdeaconry are usually noted in the *Libri Cleri* and the *Specula*. Presentation deeds at Lincolnshire Archives Office have been checked for those who held livings in plurality within Lincoln Diocese, and most of the inter-diocesan pluralists are recorded in the *Index to the Act Books*.
64. Curtis, "Alienated Intellectuals," pp. 30-34.
65. Eachard, *Grounds and Occasions*, p. 143.
66. Addison, *Spectator*, I, 78, 80.
67. Swift, *Prose Works*, III, 262.
68. Based on the sources listed in notes 1 and 2. There is certainly no record of preferment for any of them in the Diocese of Lincoln; nor do they appear in Longden's *Northamptonshire and Rutland Clergy*. Venn's and Foster's editions of the Cambridge and Oxford registers are not always complete in this respect, so some may have found livings in other dioceses.
69. Brockbank, *Diary and Letter Book*, p. 235.
70. Verney, ed., *Letters*, I, 365.
71. Lincs. Arch. Off., L.C. VI, ff. 181-224v.; L.C. XV, ff. 211-232.
72. Based on the sources listed in notes 1, 2, and 3.
73. Lincs. Arch. Off., L.C. VI, ff. 192, 220; L.T. and D., September 19, 1688, for John Cave; *Speculum* I, *passim*; Foster, *Alumni Oxoniensis*, Pt. 1, I, 251-252.
74. Wake MSS, CCXXXVII, n.f.: Richard Ludlam to William Wake, October 2, 1714; Venn and Venn, *Alumni Cantabrigiensis*, Pt. 1, III, 115.
75. Information on Leicestershire's patrons comes from the sources listed in note 5.
76. *Ibid.*
77. *Ibid.*
78. Wake MSS, CCXXXVI, n.f.: Fenny Drayton advowson; *H.M.C. Rutland MSS*, II, 155; Nichols, *Leicester*, I, 616-617; IV, 186; Leics. Rec. Off., DE 40/20/25.
79. Brockbank, *Diary and Letter Book*, p. 204.

80. Wake MSS, CCXXXVII, n.f.: John Rogers to William Wake, September 1, 1714.

81. Lincs. Arch. Off., Ben/6/2; P.D. 1679/19; P.D. 1692/44; P.D. 1692/21.

82. Based on the sources listed in note 5.

83. Lincs. Arch. Off., Muniments of the Dean and Chapter, Dvii/3/B/19.

84. Thomlinson, "Diary," p. 167.

85. Lincs. Arch. Off., Reg. XXXIV, f. 87; Reg. XXXVIII, p. 204; P.D. 1694/27; P.D. 1700/26; Venn and Venn, *Alumni Cantabrigiensis*, Pt. 1, II, 131, 132; IV, 109; Foster, *Alumni Oxoniensis*, Pt. 1, IV, 1383; Nichols, *Leicester*, IV, 184; Hill, *Parish of Langton*, p. 218.

86. Leics. Rec. Off., DE 40/20/6; Lincs. Arch. Off., P.D. 1712/38; Cawdrey, *Patronage*, pp. 25-26.

87. Lincs. Arch. Off., P.D. 1642/68,69; P.D. 1684/58; Reg. XXXVII, p. 127; Reg. XXXVIII, pp. 255, 440, 561; P.R.O., P.C.C. Wills, 1684, f. 60 (Abraham Mould); Venn and Venn, *Alumni Cantabrigiensis*, Pt. 1, III, 222-223; Nichols, *Leicester*, IV, 432-433, 437.

88. Lincs. Arch. Off., Reg. XXXV, f. 18v.; Reg. XXXVIII, pp. 6, 84, 134; P.D. 1623/61; P.D. 1640/32,33; *Speculum* II, pp. 285, 293; Leics. Rec. Off., DE 108/2860/32; Nichols, *Leicester*, III, 17n., 78-79, 553; *Victoria History of Leicester*, V, 74; Venn and Venn, *Alumni Cantabrigiensis*, Pt. 1, I, 139, 256, 259-260; III, 157; Pt. 2, I, 455-457; Foster, *Alumni Oxoniensis*, Pt. 1, I, 211; III, 984.

89. Lincs. Arch. Off., Reg. XXXI, p. 5; Reg. XXXIIb, p. 1; Reg. XXXIII, ff. 98v., 141; Reg. XXXIV, ff. 11, 102v.; Reg. XXXV, ff. 25, 45; Reg. XXXVI, pp. 22, 190; Reg. XXXVII, pp. 50, 111; Reg. XXXVIII, pp. 220, 419; P.D. 1718/3; Venn and Venn, *Alumni Cantabrigiensis*, Pt. 1, II, 46-47; IV, 92.

90. Based on the sources listed in notes 1, 2, 3, and 5.

91. Granville, "Remains," p. 195.

92. Nichols, *Leicester*, III, 1074-76; Leics. Museum, 1D41/2/712.

93. At Kegworth: M. Honywood, J. Covel; at Loughborough: N. Hall, G. Bright, J. Alleyne; at Thurcaston: E. Wright, R. Alfounder, R. Hill; at Medbourne: T. Dwyer; at Stathern: W. Norwich, J. Clarke, R. Cooke, A. Perne. See Venn and Venn, *Alumni Cantabrigiensis*; and Lincs. Arch. Off., *Speculum* I, *passim*.

94. D. Parry, R. Langmead, T. Davies, W. Hesketh. See Foster, *Alumni Oxoniensis*; and Lincs. Arch. Off., *Speculum* I, *passim*.

95. J. Berry, J. Guy, R. Wilshiere, J. Bland, R. Atkins, J. Boddington, W. Pettifer, T. Heyrick, J. Wootton. See Venn and Venn, *Alumni Cantabrigiensis*; Foster, *Alumni Oxoniensis*; and Lincs. Arch. Off., *Speculum* I, *passim*.

96. *H.M.C. Rutland MSS*, II, 115-117; Lincs. Arch. Off., Reg. XXXV, ff. 6v., 20v.

97. Swift, *Prose Works*, III, 296.

98. Prideaux, *Letters*, p. 148.

99. Bodleian Library, Tanner MS 80, ff. 116-117.

100. Quoted from Sykes, *William Wake*, I, 239.

101. Thomlinson, "Diary," p. 167.

102. Lincs. Arch. Off., Dean and Chapter, Dvii/3/B/19.

103. Wake MSS, CCXXXVII, n.f.: Richard Marsden to William Wake, April 19, 1714.

104. Lincs. Arch. Off., L.T. and D., 1695/11: Earl of Rutland to the Bishop of Lincoln, August 29, 1695.

105. Other examples are D. Naylor, S. Rogers, and C. Tanner (with the Noels as patrons); and J. Major, T. Sawbridge, and W. North (with the Manners family as patrons). Lincs. Arch. Off., Reg. XXXV, ff. 6v., 20v., 46v.; Venn and Venn, *Alumni Cantabrigiensis*, Pt. 1, I, 286; II, 333, 423, 484; III, 128, 234, 266, 480; IV, 23, 92, 199; Foster, *Alumni Oxoniensis*, Pt. 1, II, 611, 742; IV, 1534.

106. Lincs. Arch. Off., Reg. XXXIV, f. 115; Reg. XXXV, ff. 17, 48, 60; Reg. XXXVI, pp. 16, 144, 158; P.D. 1690/79; Venn and Venn, *Alumni Cantabrigiensis*, Pt. 1, IV, 166, 299.

107. Bodleian Library, Tanner MS 80, f. 116.

108. Lincs. Arch. Off., Reg. XXXIV, f. 104v.; Reg. XXXV, ff. 17, 54v.; Reg. XXXVI, p. 149; L.C. XIII, f. 136; Leics. Rec. Off., PR/1696/62; Venn and Venn, *Alumni Cantabrigiensis*, Pt. 1, IV, 9; Foster, *Alumni Oxoniensis*, Pt. 1, IV, 1471; Whitley, *Parish of Sapcote*, pp. 68–71.

109. Lincs. Arch. Off., L.T. and D., 1698/6; Edward Sherrier to the Bishop of Lincoln, August 15, 1698.

110. Wake MSS, CCXXXIV, f. 70; Lincs. Arch. Off., P.D. 1706/48.

111. Lincs. Arch. Off., L.C. VI, f. 224; L.C. IX, ff. 154v., 155; Reg. XXXIII, f. 27; Reg. XXXIV, f. 107; Nichols, *Leicester*, I, 593.

112. Venn and Venn, *Alumni Cantabrigiensis*, Pt. 1, II, 215; Hartopp, *Freemen of Leicester*, p. 165; Lincs. Arch. Off., L.C. X, f. 96v.; Reg. XXXIV, ff. 86v., 94v., 106v.; Reg. XXXV, f. 19; *Speculum* I, *passim*.

113. For a fuller explanation of the derivation of this income distribution, see below, pp. 95, 110*n*2.

114. Swift, *Prose Works*, III, 267.

115. Nichols, *Leicester*, IV, 975.

116. Foster, *Alumni Oxoniensis*, Pt. 1, III, 1008; Venn and Venn, *Alumni Cantabrigiensis*, Pt. 1, III, 181; Leics. Museum, 1D41/13/78, f. 79v.; 1D41/4/XLVIII/75; Lincs. Arch. Off., L.C. VI, f. 200; L.C. VIII, f. 96; Reg. XXXIV, f. 19; Ben/8/6,7.

117. Venn and Venn, *Alumni Cantabrigiensis*, Pt. 1, I, 256; II, 131, 132; IV, 152; Hill, *Parish of Langton*, p. 218; Lincs. Arch. Off., *Speculum* I: Hallaton, Medbourne, Nether Broughton.

118. Leics. Museum, 1D41/4/XLVIII/74–77.

119. *Ibid.*, 1D41/4/XLVIII/75.

120. *Ibid.*, 1D41/4/XLVIII/75.

121. Based on the sources listed in notes 1 and 2. The livings' values are derived from Wake's *Speculum*. See below, p. 110*n*2.

122. Overton, *Non-Jurors*, pp. 471ff.; Nichols, *Leicester*, II, 150n., 162; IV, 933–934; Lincs. Arch. Off., Reg. XXXV, f. 77v.; Reg. XXXVI, p. 188; Leics. Museum, 1D41/13/67–83.

123. Prideaux, *Letters*, p. 145.

124. St. Paul's Library, MS 17-D-20, n.f.: Witherley; Leics. Rec. Off., DG 22/1/5; Nichols, *Leicester*, IV, 1016.

125. Nichols, *Leicester*, III, 1057, 1074–76.

III

The Wealth of the Parish Clergy

Man is not simply an economic animal, and parsons are not merely men; although their bodies are firmly planted in this world, their thoughts are often directed toward another. Nevertheless, we can learn a great deal about the parish clergy by examining the economic aspects of their calling, and in the process we can discover a good deal about their day-to-day relationships with their parishioners. Fortunately for the purposes of this study, Englishmen in the Tudor-Stuart period churned out massive collections of documents dealing with clerical incomes. The most useful of these are ecclesiastical terriers—lists of assets with which parish livings were endowed and from which parish incumbents drew their revenues. Terriers were largely a response to the laity's gradual nibbling away at ecclesiastical property, whether in the form of land or customary tithes; by filing records of what incumbents were due, churchmen hoped to check the laity's appetite and prevent further losses. Many terriers survive from the sixteenth century, but they become more numerous and far more detailed under the later Stuarts. In the first decade of the eighteenth century an especially informative series was compiled and preserved for nearly every parish in the Diocese of Lincoln.[1] The same decade also brought a survey of parish livings for the Commissioners of Queen Anne's Bounty, whose task was to discover the extent of clerical poverty and to raise the value of all livings worth less than £50 per year. This was in fact the most thoroughgoing attempt to document clerical incomes since the *Valor Ecclesiasticus* of the 1530's, and it was supplemented in the Diocese of Lincoln by a survey which Bishop Wake compiled for his own information.[2] These documents, and others like them, provide much valuable information on the level of clerical incomes, the sources from which they were drawn, and the extent to which clerical incomes changed over time.

THE SOURCES OF CLERICAL INCOMES

A typical late-Stuart parish living was endowed with several sorts of income, and the incumbent automatically gained title to them once he had been formally instituted and installed. These sources of income normally included tithes (theoretically a tenth of his parishioners' annual incomes); a tract of land called a glebe; a parsonage house; fees for marriages, burials, and other special services; mandatory fixed offerings paid each year, usually at Easter, by individuals living in the parish; and legally prescribed death duties, or mortuaries, on his parishioners' estates. What all of these added up to varied enormously from parish to parish—the values of Leicestershire's parish livings began at £6 or £7 a year at Kirby Bellairs, and soared to over £400 at Market Bosworth. About a third fell below £50 per year, designated by the act establishing Queen Anne's Bounty as the clerical poverty line of 1704. Middling benefices worth £50 to £100 a year formed another third. Then came the juiciest plums of the parochial preferment tree, the top third with revenues of £100 or more per year, the objects of clerical envy or aspiration.[3] When we examine the sources of late-Stuart clerical incomes, the reasons for this wide variation in the values of parish livings become clearer.

Tithes

The sources of production from which tithes were drawn had always been overwhelmingly agrarian, and in late-Stuart Leicestershire they were almost exclusively so. Shopkeepers and craftsmen customarily owed only fixed yearly offerings of a few pence apiece, while day laborers and the producers of new manufactured goods had been completely exempted from tithes since the 1540's.[4] A few Leicestershire parsons still collected tithes from grain mills, but in most cases mill tithes had long been converted into small fixed-money payments, and these represented only a tiny proportion of tithe income.[5] The great bulk of a parson's tithes thus came from his parishioners' farm produce, and tithe income in turn accounted for most of the annual value of his living. Somerby, for example, had a glebe of about thirty-five acres, but tithe income still accounted for about 80 percent of the vicar's revenues in 1707.[6] Though the glebe attached to Cossington rectory was considerably larger (about sixty acres), tithes still formed well over 80 percent of the rector's income in the early 1660's.[7] Even though a contemporary clergyman disparaged tithes as too susceptible to lawsuits, arguing that "the most comfortable and sweetest part of the Ministers revenue" lay in his house and glebe,[8] most parsons had only to glance at their account sheets to know that he was wrong.

How much a parson realized from his tithes depended on a variety of factors, including the size of his parish, the fertility of its soil, and year-to-year variations in harvest levels and livestock diseases. In 1690 the parson of Great Dalby thought his tithes were worth £16 "one year with another," but that "if a rott of sheep comes, it cannot be worth above £5."[9] Perhaps sheep rot had set in that year at Melton Mowbray, for although wool tithes usually brought in £20, the vicar feared that "this yeare it will not bee worth halfe so many."[10] The annual accounts kept by a late-Stuart rector in Nottinghamshire show what fluctuations like these could mean for a country parson over a period of a quarter-century: between 1676 and 1701 his revenues averaged about £185 a year, but they ranged from a low of £109 in 1688 to a high of £246 in 1698.[11] When contemporary parsons reported the value of their livings, they were therefore submitting rough estimates based on their experience during the past several years.

The level of tithe income also depended on what sort of agrarian tithes a parson was permitted to collect, for agrarian tithes came in two varieties, and not all parsons could collect both. The great tithes consisted of corn, hay, wood, and other products that grew directly out of the ground, while the small tithes consisted chiefly of animal produce and fruit, including lambs, pigs, wool, apples, and honey. In parishes endowed with vicarages, the great tithes had usually been taken over by monasteries for their own uses during the Middle Ages and had normally passed into lay hands during the Reformation, leaving vicars only the small tithes; meanwhile, rectors continued to collect tithes both small and great. This distinction between rectors and vicars was not consistently followed, however. Over a third of Leicestershire's vicars got part or all of the hay tithes, and many got some corn as well, if it was grown in the small closes adjoining houses within the village. This extra income was a godsend for some of the poorer vicars—in 1707, hay tithes accounted for over a third of the vicar of Belton's

Annual Values of Leicestershire Parish Livings, 1706-7

	All livings	*Rectories*	*Vicarages*	*Perpetual curacies*
Unknown	4	3	1	0
£0-9	5	0	3	2
10-19	6	0	4	2
20-29	15	1	11	3
30-39	14	0	12	2
40-49	27	5	20	2
50-59	12	9	3	0
60-69	18	10	8	0
70-79	15	8	5	2
80-89	19	15	3	1
90-99	5	4	1	0
100-109	20	18	2	0
110-119	3	3	0	0
120-129	14	12	2	0
130-139	1	1	0	0
140-149	3	3	0	0
150-159	1	1	0	0
160-169	4	4	0	0
170-179	1	1	0	0
180-189	5	4	1	0
190-199	1	1	0	0
200+	12	12	0	0

income of £48 a year.[12] In other parishes, variations from the norm were even more marked. The incumbent of Barrow was a vicar, but he got all of the great tithes of grain in the village fields and only half of the small tithes.[13] In contrast, the rector of South Croxton got only half of the tithes from the upper end of the parish, while in the lower end he held half of the small tithes, half of the hay tithes, and a third of the tithes of grain.[14] But most vicars collected only the small tithes, and these were usually much less valuable than the great tithes. At Saxby the great tithes were worth about £30 in 1707, the small tithes less than £5; at Narborough the great tithes were valued at over £60 in 1690, the small tithes at about £20.[15] Largely as a result of this variation, rectories were normally worth two or three times as much as vicarages. The poorest livings of all were the perpetual curacies, where monasteries and laymen had taken over all of the tithes and usually all of the glebe. The curate was generally left with only a small fixed stipend, one which fell in real value as prices increased.

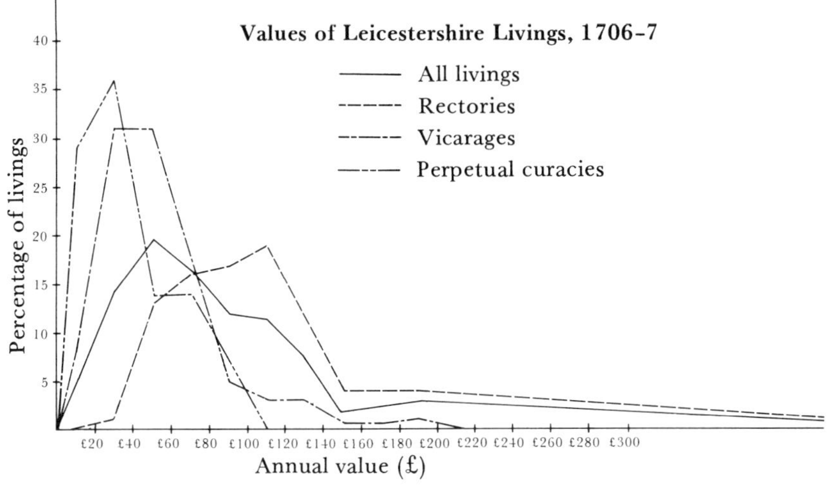

Tithe income also varied with the extent to which tithes could be taken in kind. In many parishes, tithes had at some point been converted into fixed money payments, which were called moduses; a modus might apply to the tithes of particular lands within a parish, or to the tithes of particular farm products throughout an entire parish. In either case, inflation gradually eroded the real value of the modus, which of course reduced the parson's real income. At Sproxton, for example, milk tithes had been commuted in the late Middle Ages to two pence for each milking cow, and the parson's returns amounted to only a few shillings in 1707; at Bringhurst, where milk tithes could still be collected in kind, the returns were almost £30.[16] How much damage a modus did depended on when it had been contracted. Those contracted before the great inflationary spiral of the sixteenth and early seventeenth centuries were the most harmful, but even relatively recent moduses gave late-Stuart parsons cause for complaint. The rector of Shangton, for example, agreed in 1634 to accept £12 a year for the tithes of a farm worth £120 a year. By 1664 the farm had risen in value to £200 a year, and though the rector sued to have his tithes raised accordingly, the payment was apparently still £12 in 1707.[17]

Though late-Stuart parsons well understood the havoc that moduses could wreak, some were still busily contracting fresh ones, a few even agreeing to convert all their tithes into fixed payments when their parishes were enclosed.[18] By Anne's reign, the tithes of highly perishable items like milk and eggs had been commuted in almost every parish, and moduses on foals were also fairly common. Pieces of land were covered by moduses in one Leicestershire parish out of three, and tithes had been completely converted into fixed cash payments in one parish out of four. But these figures should not obscure the rest of the picture—the pieces of land subject to moduses were often quite small, and some moduses had been contracted when the worst of the Great Inflation was over. Moreover, Leicestershire parsons had the right to take at least some tithes in kind in three parishes out of four, and the last tithes to be commuted were almost always the ones of greatest value: corn, hay, lambs, and wool.[19] The great majority of late-Stuart clerical incomes were in fact still firmly tied to agricultural production rather than to fixed money payments, and as long as farm prices were good, most parsons could face inflation without too much dread.

Actually, it is surprising that moduses had spread no further than this, for they could be quite attractive to the clergy in the short run. By agreeing to a modus, a parson could avoid the effort and bother of collecting tithes in kind, as well as the expense of storing them until they could be disposed of. In addition, he could protect himself against poor harvests and livestock epidemics; he could avoid costly tithe disputes with his parishioners, who sometimes underreported their crop yields and the size of their sheep flocks; and he knew that his bishop would be inclined to accept whatever moduses he contracted.[20] Yet in Anne's reign moduses were still the exception rather than the rule. Perhaps late-Stuart parsons still remembered the Great Inflation of the sixteenth and early seventeenth centuries and feared that it would reoccur in their own lifetimes. Or perhaps their self-restraint sprang from professional loyalty to the parsons who would succeed them in their livings.

Another factor may have been the existence of alternatives to moduses, alternatives by which a parson could take cash for tithes without permanently damaging the real value of his living. A parson could, for example, lease his tithes to a tenant; the tenant thus assumed the bothersome task of collecting and storing the tithes, while the parson received a convenient cash rent. Naturally, the rent was always somewhat less than the full value of the tithes, for tithe tenants in effect charged a commission for their labors. Nevertheless, cash rents were so convenient that some parsons still found leasing preferable to taking tithes in kind. Tithe leases had caused problems during the Great Inflation, when some parsons foolishly signed long-term tithe leases of ninety-nine years or more. As inflation gradually eroded the real value of their rents, they and their successors were threatened with economic ruin, at least until their leases expired and could be renegotiated. During the reigns of Elizabeth and Charles I, Parliament acted to contain this problem by forbidding parsons to sign leases that would bind their successors;[21] by the late seventeenth century, virtually all of the most damaging leases had lapsed. Late-Stuart parsons in Leicestershire seem to have learned from their predecessors' mistakes, and most in fact dispensed with tithe leases altogether. Only a few of the tithe suits handled by Leicestershire's church courts during the late-Stuart period were initiated by laymen holding tithe leases; over 90 percent of the litigants were the parsons themselves.[22]

A more popular alternative was the temporary tithe composition—an agreement by the parson to accept cash in lieu of tithes for the time being, with the understanding that a permanent modus was not being contracted, and that the parson or his successor could resume taking tithes in kind if he wished. Thus in 1708 the vicar of Tugby reported that he was accepting 13s.8d. per yardland in lieu of his small tithes, but that the next incumbent would have the right to take his tithes in kind. Shackerston's vicar preferred cash payments for individual items: 5s. for a tithe calf, ls. for a tithe pig, 2s.2d. for a tithe lamb; but he had the right to take these tithes in kind if he wished.[23] The only danger involved in agreements like these was that, if renewed too often, they might slowly grow into hallowed customs difficult to break. Apparently this had happened at Cadeby, where the parson complained in 1708 that his rectorial tithes had "by long custom, as is supposed, grown into Rates."[24] Stoney Stanton's terrier of 1697 stated that small tithes were due in kind but were being compounded "at present" for 5s. per yardland; seventy years later, when the parish was enclosed, the parishioners considered this payment an "ancient modus."[25] Parsons often recognized this threat and acted accordingly. Edward Wilson of Nailstone accepted cash payments for tithes in part of his parish, but in 1708 he wrote, "I have taken Tythe in kind to prevent their pleading Custom against the Rector."[26]

Accepting temporarily contracted money payments brought most of the ease and convenience of moduses and, if parsons were careful, none of the long-term disadvantages. How widespread this practice was is uncertain. Barns and stables in many livings were more extensive than the size of their respective glebes necessitated, so presumably they were being used to store tithes taken in kind.[27] Probably most incumbents took some of their tithes in kind when they had the right to do so; the important point is that most kept their options open, protecting themselves and their successors against future inflation.

When it actually came to taking tithes in kind, the custom of the parish dictated the exact procedures to be followed. With wheat and other arable crops there were few problems, for such tithes could easily be taken at harvest time according to the tenth shock or the tenth bushel. Things became considerably more complicated when tithes were taken on livestock, for a parishioner's lambs, fleeces, and pigs were seldom exactly divisible by ten. The most common practice was for the parson to accept a half-penny for each fleece (or lamb, or pig) when a parishioner had fewer than seven. This was an ancient custom, and in terms of late-Stuart price levels it shortchanged the incumbent. However, if the parishioner had seven, eight, or nine fleeces, it was the parishioner who was shortchanged, since most incumbents could then take an entire fleece and pay the parishioner a half-penny for each fleece short of ten.[28]

Local custom also decreed the procedure the parson had to follow in choosing the particular tithe item. At Great Dalby the parishioner removed one fleece in ten, and the parson then chose the one he judged second best. At South Kilworth the parishioner removed two fleeces, and the parson chose the third best, "having the liberty to turn the fleeces with a stick for his better knowledge." At Tilton the parson had to stand aside and let the tithe fleece be chosen by a five-year-old boy, and his tithe lamb was the last of ten to run out of the pen.[29] Local custom even dictated how long parishioners had to let tithe animals selected by the parson continue to suckle, and parishioners were careful that favors extended to one incumbent did not become established customs owed to his successors. In 1683 the parishioners of Castle Donington allowed the vicar's tithe lambs to suckle after May Day, but forced him to admit in writing that this "was not a thing of Right Dewe to mee, but a neybourly courtesye which I doo and uppon the like occasion shall with thankfullnesse acknowledge."[30]

Livestock tithing was further complicated by the fact that livestock, unlike arable crops, were not firmly rooted to the soil; during the course of a year, they might be moved, bought, or sold across parish lines. Was a parson entitled to collect full tithes on livestock that grazed in his parish during only a part of the year? Since laymen had long felt that this would be unfair, livestock entering or leaving a parish during the year were customarily subject to small money payments representing a partial tithe. These had long been fixed at something like a penny a head—a ridiculously low rate, in terms of late-Stuart price levels—and the vicar of Sproxton thought this had become "a very unreasonable custom."[31] Livestock owners in neighboring parishes could in fact take advantage of this loophole by selling their livestock to each other; then arguing that their livestock had entered the parish during the year, they could claim to owe only a partial tithe, forcing parsons to resort to tithe suits to protect their revenues. Half the village sometimes showed up for these affairs, with each villager professing intimate knowledge of his neighbors' flocks and herds, but often disagreeing with his neighbors on essential details.[32]

Suits like these could be lengthy and expensive. "Hee who goes to law, when hee can possibly avoid it," counseled a Sussex parson in 1664, "is an absolute foole, and one that loveth to be fleeced. I ever got by losing, and lost by striving to get."[33] And so a parson who felt cheated in his tithes often saved legal action as a last resort and tried other remedies first, including an appeal to the offender's conscience. Humphrey Michel of Blaston even tried public humiliation, denouncing local tithe evaders in the course of his sermons. When one of them died unrepentant in 1701, Michel turned on the man's widow, sending her a most disturbing letter. He had received only £4 from her family for tithes, he said, but that "being not a Groat in the Pound-rent to the minister of God's word and Sacraments is but an old Sacrilegious Payment." She could hardly expect to "escape the Torment of hell, much less enjoy the Glories of Heaven" by paying so little, and "Eternal wo be to you, if in this your fleeting state of Repentance you make me not a full and Speedy Recompence for your detention of my Tythes."[34] If tactics like these failed, a parson might convince the offender to call in a neutral third party as arbitrator. Thus in 1695 the parson of Sibsdon agreed with a local farmer to summon a neighboring clergyman as an impartial judge in their tithe dispute, each posting a bond of £100 to abide by his decision. The clergyman decided that the farmer owed the parson of Sibsdon £4, and the tithe was promptly paid.[35]

Many tithe disputes still ended up in the courts. Between 1660 and 1710, Leicestershire's church courts handled over three hundred such cases; they involved one Leicestershire incumbent in four, with some parsons entering more than one suit during their careers. Sometimes the suits were trivial, like the vicar of Wistow's suit in 1711 for Easter dues and a churching fee (1s.½d. altogether), or the vicar of St. Margaret's suit in 1688 for a fixed annual payment of 2s.6d.[36] Such cases were unfortunate. They often arose from purely personal vendettas; they antagonized the people of the parish who were called in as witnesses; and they consumed time and legal costs ludicrously out of proportion to the sums involved. But other cases were much more significant: attempts to break moduses (or to prevent temporary agreements from becoming moduses) were frequently the issue. Suits involving moduses on land occurred at Allexton, Stockerston, and Theddingworth; on milk at Queniborough and Asfordby; on hay at Bitteswell; and on calves at Ab Kettleby.[37] These suits, together with the trivial ones, suggest that many late-Stuart parsons not only were defending every penny of their incomes to the hilt, but were taking the offensive against unfair tithe commutation as well.

Moduses were seldom broken if parishioners could prove ancient custom. Until the late seventeenth century, when terriers began to list established tithing customs with regularity, parsons were at a disadvantage if they were new to a parish and if their predecessors had left insufficient records of their rights. In situations like these, parsons were sometimes confronted with "ancient" customs that the parishioners had recently invented. Isaac Hoyland thought this had happened when he came to Deisworth in 1666, for he "had not the benefit of anything that was Mr. Twitty's to inform me of the antient manner of paying small tithes in my parish; so that I fear I may. . .have wronged the vicarage in some particulars, and could not help it."[38] John Horberry was also suspicious when he became rector of Gumley in 1699. The churchwardens drew up a terrier listing several tithing customs unfavorable to the incumbent, and Horberry signed the document—with the proviso that he assented only until he could investigate further.[39] Some parsons even discovered that relevant documents had been mysteriously spirited away; thus in 1712 a Leicestershire rector complained to Bishop Wake that a parishioner "detains from my sight an Antient Book, setting forth many Rights belonging to the Church of Misterton."[40]

Even when a parson managed to win his suit in the church courts, that might not be the end of the matter. Church courts had no means of coercion at their disposal except excommunication, and that threat was no longer as frightening as it had been earlier, especially when the offenders were Dissenters. Consequently, tithe suits that began in the church courts often ended up in the secular courts, where recalcitrant parishioners could be threatened with prison sentences. Some parsons in fact decided to head straight for the secular courts and to avoid the spiritual courts altogether. As the rector of Clayworth explained in 1683, "all I could do at them, was to excommunicate them, which was only their not going to Church &c. So I beginning to think that to proceed with them in the spiritual court would be of small effect, I was perswaded to put in a bill against them in the Exchequer."[41] So many tithe suits were shifting into the secular courts in the late seventeenth century that a contemporary complained that "the power of the spiritual Court. . .at this day signifieth very little, if any thing; the temporal Courts haveing engrossed all matters of that nature into their own hands." He thought that most parsons eventually obtained justice there, but "the methods which they are forced to pursue. . .are become so tedious, troublesome, vexatious, dilatory, and chargeable, that the remedie is worse than the disease."[42]

Tithes were obviously unpopular with many parishioners, and simple villagers were adept in the methods of lightening their annual tribute. They coyly offered incumbents moduses that were easy to collect but advantageous to the laity in the long run; they invented ancient customs; they encouraged parsons to let temporary agreements slip into old unbreakable traditions; they occasionally indulged in a bit of sheep-smuggling. Parishioners in fact schemed much like twentieth-century income-tax evaders, with tithe-gathering parsons cast in the role of an unpopular Treasury Department. John Eachard thought that the parson who succeeded in getting full value for his tithes would be counted "a Caterpillar, a Muck-worm, a very Earthly-minded man, and too much sighted in this lower World, which was made, as many of the laity think, altogether for themselves."[43] Even so, most parsons were willing to risk unpopularity in getting their just due. Since tithes accounted for the great bulk of their revenues, it was a risk they felt they had to take.

Glebes

Most livings were endowed with land as well as tithes, but there was a great deal of interparish variation in the amount of land that incumbents had at their disposal. One Leicestershire parson in five had only a small house lot, while the rector of Market Bosworth farmed a widely flung glebe of about 280 acres. Poor livings (those worth less than £50 a year) averaged about twelve acres each, middling livings (£50-£99) about forty acres, and rich livings (£100 or more) a little over eighty.[44] The average parson's glebe was thus roughly comparable to the average yeoman's farm, which in Leicestershire in the same period averaged about thirty or forty acres.[45]

Some parsons leased their glebes to tenants. Glebe leases were not systematically filed with church officials, however, and the extent of leasing can be estimated only indirectly. The fact that most livings came equipped with barns and stables cannot be used as evidence that parsons were themselves engaged in farming; outbuildings were also used to store tithes taken in kind, and in any event might be leased to tenants along with the glebe. Perhaps the best estimate of the extent of leasing comes from inventories taken of the parsons' personal property at their deaths. Inventory entries like "corn in the barn" or "peas in the garrett" or "three sheep in the field" do not necessarily indicate that the parson was engaged in farming, for entries like these may refer to tithes that had been taken in kind. But when inventories specify corn still standing in the field, or livestock herds of twenty or more, or farming tools worth more than £5, it is probably safe to assume that the parson was farming at least part of his glebe. Similarly, when inventories of goods left by parsons with glebes mention none of these things, this is fairly good evidence of leasing. Of forty-eight inventories taken between 1670 and 1685 of the estates of Leicestershire parsons who had glebes, there is strong evidence of farming in 79 percent; for the period 1695-1710, the figure drops to 61 percent. Apparently most late-Stuart parsons in Leicestershire did farm their own glebes, though the inclination to lease may have been increasing by the turn of the century. At the same time, the inventories show a shift among parsons from arable farming to livestock husbandry, paralleling a shift taking place among Leicestershire farmers generally: 27 percent of the parsons were predominantly graziers in 1670-85, against 42 percent in 1695-1710.[46]

That so many parsons were directly engaged in farming is hardly surprising. Clerical farming was in fact a tradition of several centuries' standing, and—at least in Leicestershire—most parsons were still of rural background in the late-Stuart period, and quite familiar with farming techniques. Moreover, tenants were often careless in their farming practices, and careless tenants sometimes ruined glebes in a few years by poor husbandry. In the 1690's the rector of Markfield was complaining that the previous incumbent had leased the glebe to tenants who "soon plowd that out of heart, and at the said Mr. Pestell's death they were so barrend and unfruitful that the Tenant, tho he paid rent for the field land, refused to plow som parts of the Arable Land."[47] Parsons probably trusted themselves more than tenants to get the best long-term returns from the soil. By farming their own glebes, most could in fact be self-sufficient in food, or even raise a surplus for sale. Their parsonages almost always contained butteries, malting rooms, bakehouses, and storage chambers for corn and peas; here the fruits of their husbandry were kept until needed, and the business of baking and brewing and churning went on as in most other English farmhouses. As for whether they farmed their glebes with their own hands, there is little direct evidence for Leicestershire. Many of the poorer clerics with small glebes undoubtedly worked their own land, though some contemporaries felt that this was demeaning.[48] But middling-to-wealthy parsons with sizable glebes often employed farm hands, some of whom lived in small chambers or garret rooms in the parsonage house, or in makeshift chambers over the barn.[49]

Parsonages

In late-Stuart Leicestershire, nine parish livings in ten were endowed with parsonage houses, ranging in size and comfort from four-room cottages to twenty-room mansions.[50] Parsonages will be dealt with more fully in a subsequent chapter, but it is worth noting here that they sometimes became positive sources of income, rather than just residual assets. Parsons holding two livings often found themselves with a parsonage they did not need; while some turned the extra house over to a resident curate, many preferred leasing to lay tenants and pocketing the rent. Unfortunately, there are no systematic records of such practices, but available evidence tentatively suggests that one Leicestershire parsonage in ten was being leased to lay tenants in 1712.[51] Unfortunately, this source of income was less available to poor pluralists than to wealthy ones. The poorest livings were the ones most likely to lack parsonages, and poor pluralists often had to live in the one parsonage available to them. Moreover, when poor livings did have parsonages, they were usually small cottages with a very low rental value. In 1707 Hopkin Thomas, a parson with two poor livings, was residing in his parsonage at Barkby and letting his other parsonage at Hungerton for £4 a year. This rent included a barn, a small close, and the churchyard, and in any event represented only 6 percent of his income from the two livings.[52] Because parsonages attached to middling and wealthy livings were much larger and more valuable, wealthy pluralists got considerably more by leasing their extra parsonages, even if the returns still represented only a small fraction of their incomes.

Offerings, fees, and mortuaries

The rest of a parson's endowed income came from fixed annual offerings, from fees for marriages, burials, and other official duties, and from mortuaries due from the estates of his parishioners at their deaths. Fixed offerings had been collected in medieval times at four religious festivals each year; in seventeenth-century Leicestershire they were generally collected only at Easter, though at Slawston they were still due at the feasts of the Annunication and St. Michael. Most commonly they amounted to only two pence per communicant, but in some parishes custom differentiated among adult householders, apprentices, wage laborers, and communicating children living with their parents. In other parishes Easter offerings were paid by houses, sometimes in addition to payments by individual communicants: Loughborough houses with two doors paid four pence, while houses with only one door paid two pence. Easter offerings formed only a tiny part of a parson's income, seldom more than three or four pounds, and often much less than that. A few parsons thought the returns were not worth the effort involved in collecting them, and either leased their offerings or allowed them to lapse. At Rotherby they had gone uncollected "so long that no particular dues can be ascertained."[53]

Fees for the performance of religious offices seldom amounted to much, either. Most parsons charged four to six pence for the churching of women, but baptisms were generally free. Burials were only six to eight pence, though more might be charged if the body was buried inside the church. Marriages brought in substantially more, commonly 2s.6d. for marriages by banns, 5s. for marriages by license. Terriers also listed mortuary fees, graduated according to the size of the estate; they ranged from nothing at all for the poorer estates to 10s. for estates of over £40. They were still being collected in some parishes, but in many if not most parishes they had either lapsed or were slowly dying out. Even in parishes where they were regularly collected, the returns seldom amounted to much: "In Thirty four years I have received two mortuaries, and no more have been due," the rector of Galby reported in 1707, "the Inhabitants capable to pay are so few."[54]

THE DISTRIBUTION OF CLERICAL INCOME, AND THE PROBLEM OF CLERICAL POVERTY

Clerical incomes depended on a number of things: the values of parish livings, the extent of plural holdings, the values of the particular livings that were combined, and the amount of extra income incumbents earned by teaching school or by working as part-time curates for the incumbents of other parishes. Incumbents who were pluralists, teachers, and part-time curates were recorded in episcopal registers, subscription books, *Libri Cleri*, and archepiscopal dispensation records.[55] In addition, Bishop Wake's surveys of 1706–7 recorded the values of parish livings, curates' stipends, and teachers' salaries. By combining all these sources, one can arrive at a fairly good estimate of the distribution of income among the incumbents of 1714. A much more approximate picture results from using these values to estimate an income distribution for the incumbents of 1670; most livings were probably worth somewhat less in 1670 than during the reign of Anne, but probably not so much less as to distort the picture entirely. The values of extra-parochial preferments like college fellowships and cathedral prebends are not as well documented for this period. Only a few Leicestershire parsons held such preferments, however, and most of these parsons already received incomes of over £200 a year from their parish livings. As a result, one can be fairly certain about the distribution of income among the clergy who earned less than £200 a year, albeit less certain about how far above that figure some clerical incomes rose. The results are given in the table on income distribution.

Clerical incomes were vastly unequal, a result of great inequality both in the values of livings and in the financial benefits of pluralism. Pluralists formed about a quarter of Leicestershire's late-Stuart parish incumbents. About half of them combined two livings worth more than £50 apiece, lifting them into the top half of the clerical income distribution, and in some cases into the top 20 percent. Another quarter of the pluralists combined a living worth more than £50 a year with one worth less than that, placing them all in the middle and upper-middle range of £60 to £140 a year.

Income Distribution for Parish Incumbents, 1670 and 1714

	1670 (N = 180)	1714 (N = 175)
£ 0–19	3%	1%
20–39	9%	7%
40–59	17%	16%
60–79	16%	17%
80–99	11%	14%
100–119	13%	10%
120–139	5%	8%
140–159	4%	6%
160–179	3%	4%
180–199	5%	5%
200+	14%	12%

Roughly another quarter held two livings worth less than £50 each, and some of these pluralists remained quite poor. Foxton and Lubenham, for example, were held jointly in both 1670 and 1714, and their common incumbent's income at each date was less than £40 a year. But economic inequality was slightly offset by a tendency for poor incumbents to pick up extra earnings by serving as curates to incumbents in neighboring parishes. Five were doing so in 1670, as were fifteen in 1714. A few others supplemented their incomes by teaching. Such part-time work, together with the frequency with which poor livings were held in plurality, meant that clerical poverty was less widespread than one might assume simply by looking at the number of poorly endowed livings. While about a third of Leicestershire's parish livings were valued at less than £50 a year in Bishop Wake's survey, incumbents receiving less than £50 a year formed less than 20 percent of the incumbents as a whole.

There was little change in the distribution of clerical income in the late-Stuart period, and, despite the gross inequality, there were no absolute breaks in the clergy's income spectrum. About a fifth of Leicestershire's parish incumbents received incomes that ran from £160 a year to at least £400; below them came another quarter with between £100 and £160; below them another quarter with between £60 and £100; and finally there was the clerical proletariat, the 20 or 30 percent with less than £60 a year. The majority of these poor clerics were vicars, parsons who collected only the small tithes of their parishes; a few were perpetual curates tied to fixed stipends eroded by inflation; and others were incum-

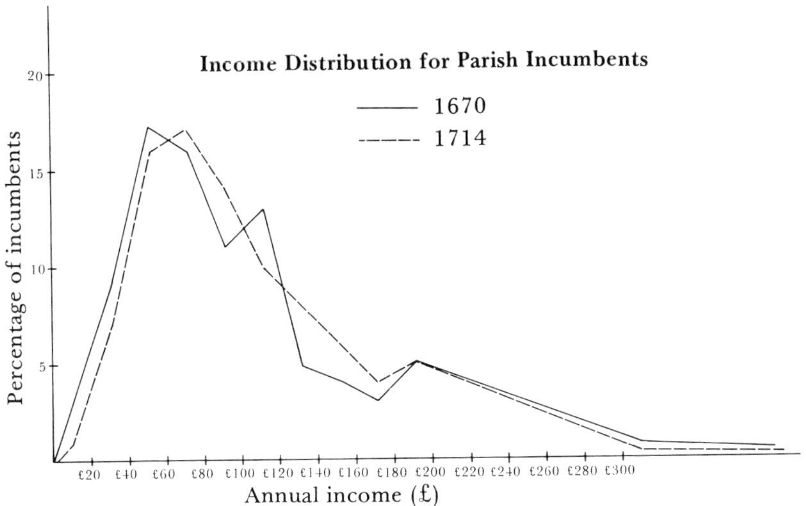

bents of livings where foolish predecessors had contracted moduses before or during the Great Inflation. If we add to them the clerics who were merely stipendiary curates, roughly a third of Leicestershire's late-Stuart parsons were living on incomes of less than £60 a year.

It was this bottom group that worried many late-Stuart Englishmen, for they knew that clerical poverty could have serious consequences, both for the clergy and for the cause of religion in general. White Kennett, the Archdeacon of Huntingdon, felt that poor economic prospects discouraged many able and learned men from entering the Church, forcing bishops to ordain men with inferior qualifications.[56] Bishop Wake regretted the fact that poverty inevitably led to pluralism and nonresidence, depriving parishioners of the daily spiritual counsel of clergymen constantly resident in their parishes.[57] John Eachard feared that poor parsons who depended on their parishioners for charitable gifts were less likely to criticize their flock's moral transgressions; only an economically independent clergy, he felt, could guide parishioners in the paths of righteousness.[58] Addison agreed that poverty undermined the clergy's moral authority—in fact, he felt that "the ordinary People are very hardly brought to regard any Truth, how important soever it may be, that is preached to them, when they know there are several Men of five hundred a Year who do not believe it."[59] This was a sad commentary on the values of the age, but churchmen as different as Burnet, Kennett, Atterbury, and Stillingfleet tended to agree with it. All of them insisted that the English Church could succeed in its mission only if its clergy were learned, able, resident, and respectable; all felt that clerical poverty bred parsons who were ignorant, incompetent, nonresident, and socially contemptible.[60] Hence they saw far more at stake than simply the clergy's economic status, for they believed that the Church's economic condition influenced its ability to encourage true religion and virtue.

The result was a series of attempts to remedy the situation. In a declaration of August, 1660, Charles II encouraged bishops, deans, and cathedral prebendaries to contribute to the endowments of the poorer parish livings, a call he renewed by royal injunction in 1667. During the same reign, an act was passed for uniting poorly endowed parishes in cities and corporate towns, and for encouraging gifts of endowments to livings worth less than £100 a year.[61] Eachard's *Grounds and Occasions of the Contempt of the Clergy and Religion* appeared in the 1670's. Despite its cynicism, it was an honest attempt to examine the causes and consequences of clerical poverty, and it effectively demonstrated the urgency of the problem. In 1704, Parliament finally responded by passing the act to establish Queen Anne's Bounty. The act dealt with two ecclesiastical taxes (first fruits and tenths) which the Crown had been collecting from the clergy since the reign of Henry VIII. Both taxes were based on the values of parish livings as estimated in the 1530's, tenths being roughly equal to 10 percent of the living's annual value, and first fruits amounting to almost the entire annual value; an incumbent paid first fruits only upon induction to the living, while tenths were due each year. In the late seventeenth century most of the proceeds were spent on pensions for court favorites, but the Bounty Act called for using this revenue to attack the problem of clerical poverty. Under the terms of the act, first fruits and tenths were no longer due from livings worth less than £50 a year. These livings would in fact be selected by lottery to receive permanent augmentations in their endowments, and the endowment funds would in turn be derived from the first fruits and tenths still being collected from the wealthier livings. The nation's livings had to be surveyed in order to determine which ones qualified for the Bounty; this took time, and the first actual augmentations were not made until 1714. The act thus initiated a redistribution of clerical income, admittedly on a limited scale. The funds made available were in fact so limited, and clerical poverty so widespread, that the act was only a partial solution to the economic problems of the Church.[62]

Still, a partial solution was better than nothing, and Queen Anne, by consenting to the act, won the undying gratitude of many of the parish clergy. Certainly this was the case in Leicestershire, where one parish living in three stood to benefit, and where clerical poverty did cause serious problems. Wigston Magna's incumbent in 1712 thought his income of £30 a year insufficient to support his children or to "bear me out in a part any ways becoming the Grandeur of my function."[63] Incumbents of poor benefices sometimes found themselves nearly bankrupt during their first year in a new parish, what with induction fees, moving costs, and other expenses. John Hagger wrote Bishop Wake in 1706 that his appointment to Whitwick had cost him £30 in fees and repairs to the parsonage; this was the entire yearly value of his living, and he had a family to support.[64] Before the passage of the Bounty Act, such incumbents had often fallen behind in their ecclesiastical taxes–in 1682 no tenths had been paid at Theddingworth for two years, at Whitwick for eleven years, at Hose for twelve years, and at Queniborough for a quarter-century.[65] Probate inventories show that poor incumbents often lived like ordinary peasants,[66] and court records suggest that many were tempted to augment their incomes illegally by performing clandestine marriages.[67] Few managed to set enough aside during their lifetimes to support their widows and children in any degree of comfort. In 1666 Anne Lawrence, the widow of the vicar of Shepshead, petitioned to be included among the clergy widows benefiting from the charity of the late Bishop of Rochester. Her husband's income of about £30 a year had been scant reward for his loyalty to the King during the Civil War, and his death in 1665 had left her and her children without a place to live or means of support.[68]

Poverty was especially serious in the urban parishes of Leicester, where practically all tithes had been converted into fixed money payments before or during the Great Inflation. St. Martin's parish had no glebe except the churchyard and a small garden adjoining the parsonage. In 1706 the incumbent reported that no tithes had been paid for over sixty years and that the living was worth only about £20 a year, of which the Crown received £5 as an annual pension.[69] The incumbent of St. Mary's, a living worth about £12 a year, reported in 1708 that "the very Church-yard is impropriated and so likewise are all the Tythes and Easter offerings."[70] Tithes had long been commuted at St. Nicholas's, its terriers of

1700 and 1708 merely listing minuscule quarterly money payments due to the incumbent from each house, and the small fees charged for churchings, marriages, and burials.[71] Valued at only £6 a year, the living was held in plurality with St. Mary's during most of the late-Stuart period. Their common incumbent in the 1660's was the Reverend Josiah Bond, who supplemented his income from the two livings by teaching school, while his wife earned a small yearly salary by washing the church's linen.[72]

Still, the extent of clerical poverty and the seriousness of its consequences should not obscure the rest of the picture. As already indicated, clerical incomes covered a wide range in the late-Stuart period. Middling parsons received incomes which Gregory King thought comparable to those of middling freeholders,[73] and for every parish where an incumbent struggled to feed and clothe his family, there was another where the parson's standard of living was among the highest in the village.[74] The ranks of the clergy in fact covered much the same economic spectrum as lay society, and, in terms of annual income, most parsons fitted into the middle or upper-middle ranks of English society as a whole.

THE MOVEMENT OF CLERICAL INCOME, 1535–1714

So far clerical incomes have been treated rather statically. In terms of the sources from which clerical incomes were drawn, continuity with previous centuries was indeed more striking than change. However, the level of clerical incomes changed significantly over the years, and the trend was generally upward. During the century and a half that followed the Reformation, agricultural production grew tremendously, both through physical expansion of cultivated acreage and through increased productivity per acre. By 1714 English farms were able to feed a substantially larger population than had existed in the sixteenth century, and without the periodic years of dearth that had lasted into the 1620's.[75] For incumbents with glebes and tithes in kind, expanding agrarian production meant rising incomes. In 1714 parsons were getting more from their glebes and were collecting tithes on greater agrarian yields than had their predecessors in the 1530's.

Even more significant was the role played by differential inflation. Between the Reformation and the death of Anne, prices almost quadrupled, but land values and agricultural prices rose even more rapidly than prices as a whole, bringing profits in the long run to incumbents with glebes and tithes in kind. The rise, however, was quite uneven. Grain prices and land values rose faster than the prices of lambs and wool, so that rectors with large glebes and tithes on grain profited more than vicars with smaller glebes and tithes drawn mostly from animal produce. Moreover, wool prices were actually falling behind prices in general in the first half of the seventeenth century, suggesting that many vicars suffered declining revenues in terms of real income.[76] The result was that clerical incomes tended to become increasingly unequal. In 1535 Wymondham and Tilton started off fairly evenly at about £12 a year. By 1603 Wymondham, a rectory with great and small tithes and a glebe of about sixty acres, had risen to £60 a year; Tilton, a vicarage with only small tithes and no glebe, had risen only to £40. By 1707 Wymondham was worth £90 a year, Tilton £60.[77]

After 1603, however, the rise in the general price level began to slacken, and after about 1650 the Great Inflation came to a halt. When this happened, the chief impetus behind the rise in many clerical incomes before 1650 was removed. As a result, the late seventeenth century has often been seen as a period of stagnation or decline in the economic condition of the clergy.[78] Nevertheless, there is evidence that after 1650 many clerical incomes continued to rise. For one thing, the second half of the seventeenth century saw important voluntary contributions to poorly endowed benefices. In 1688 Tobias Rustatt, a wealthy courtier and son of a late rector of Skeffington, donated the impropriated rectory of Breedon to a commission of trustees; after his death in 1693 they used the proceeds to augment poor livings at Breedon, Whitwick, Sileby, Withcote, Slawston, and probably St. Mary's in Leicester. Similarly, in 1659 Sir Verney Noel turned over his part of the impropriated rectory of Fleckney to the parish's incumbent, more than doubling the income of a landless curate who had previously received only £20 a year. Lord Elgin augmented the salary of the curate of Owston in 1662, and the prebendary of St. Margaret's raised his vicar's salary in 1673; Lord Carrington improved South Croxton's endowment by £16 a year in 1675, while the Bishop of Lichfield and Coventry increased the stipend of Belgrave's curate.[79] These and similar augmentations in a few other Leicestershire parishes were usually quite small; since they were aimed at the poorer livings, however, they did help offset some of the growth in economic inequality which inflation had fostered.

Then, too, much of the increase in agricultural productivity associated with the Tudor-Stuart period came after 1650, through the spread of improved techniques of arable farming and livestock husbandry.[80] Even though farm prices were sluggish, late-Stuart incumbents may well have profited from expanding agrarian output. In addition, the decades after 1650 were probably the crucial ones for the conversion of arable land to pasture in Leicestershire and other Midland counties, a process in which the parsons themselves were involved.[81] For vicars this could bring tremendous profits. Land devoted primarily to arable crops paid few tithes to vicars, the bulk of whose tithes came from animal produce; but when farmers changed over to pasture, vicars suddenly found tithable lambs and wool-bearing sheep grazing in their parishes, and their incomes rose accordingly. Nor would this necessarily hurt rectors, since rectors received tithes on animal produce, too. Admittedly, tithes on livestock were more susceptible to costly tithe disputes, but unless conversion to pasture brought a real decline in a parish's gross income, most rectors probably did about as well as before conversion, and perhaps even a little better.

Finally, clerical incomes benefited from postwar enclosures. While eighteenth-century enclosures usually brought the conversion of tithes into extra glebe land, seventeenth-century enclosures varied in the tithe arrangements that resulted. Sometimes they did bring conversion into land, as at Fenny Drayton in 1656, Great Peatling in 1658–59, and Little Peatling in 1665; partial conversion into land occurred at Galby, Laughton, Leire, and Theddingworth.[82] In other late-Stuart enclosures, incumbents held onto tithes in kind, though they might accept temporary money payments open to future revision; this happened at Barwell, Garthorp, and probably Peckleton.[83] But late-Stuart parsons confronted with wholesale enclosures more often made the mistake of converting their tithes into fixed money payments; this was the procedure at Catthorp in 1656, Shawell in 1664 and 1669, Cossington in 1666, Claybrook in 1681 and 1694, Witherley in 1699–1700, and in a few chapelries within other parishes.[84] After 1750, a new round of inflation seriously eroded the values of these livings. In the short run, however, no immediate harm resulted, since late-Stuart price levels were relatively stable. In fact, enclosures probably benefited almost all of the late-Stuart parsons whose parishes were involved. Glebes rose in value when scattered strips were exchanged for compact closes, and parishioners anticipating greater returns were often willing to set fixed stipends above what ministers had received when tithes were taken in kind. When tithes did remain in kind, incumbents might realize even greater returns from increased productivity. The enclosure at Cossington in 1666 provides one example. In April, 1667, a commission of neighboring ministers reported the effects of enclosure on the rector's income. Their findings were highly favorable:

	Before enclosure	*After enclosure*
The glebe	£ 14-00-00	£ 25-00-00
Three closes	10-00-00	10-00-00
Tithes in kind	118-13-04	2-10-00
Fixed tithe payments	0	127-16-00
Total	£142-13-04	£165-06-00
Improvement	£ 22-12-08[85]	

The vicar of Theddingworth also profited when his parish was enclosed between 1707 and 1714. Sir Richard Newdigate, who owned most of the land in the parish, agreed to convert his tithes into land worth over £25 a year, the other freeholders agreeing to a modus of about £5 more. This made tithe income from the enclosed land about £30 in all; in contrast, before the enclosure, tithes on unenclosed land had brought in only £15 a year. The vicar's glebe of twenty acres doubled in value, too. As a result of all these, enclosure raised the vicar's annual income by over £20.[86] Similarly, the enclosure of Snareston chapelry in 1680 raised the rector of Swepstone's annual income by £13, and the rector of Catthorp's revenues rose from about £50 to about £70 after the enclosure of 1656.[87]

Incumbents understandably registered few complaints. The rector of Rotherby apparently had to be removed in the 1660's before his parish could be enclosed, and the rectors of North and South Hallaton complained that they had suffered in the enclosure of Blaston in the early 1650's. The vicar of Galby claimed he had been shortchanged when his parish was partially enclosed, but in 1707 he admitted that "Ten pounds and above have within four or five years been laid to our Church yearly forever. . .and this freely to silence complaints for the future."[88] This is about the only hostile testimony from late-Stuart parsons in Leicestershire regarding contemporary enclosures. Whether through fear of lawsuits or because of heightened concern for clerical incomes, late-Stuart parishioners were usually careful to placate the parson when his parish was enclosed—in fact, when local freeholders signed articles of agreement to enclose their parish, the parson's name was usually second or third in the list. Perhaps one Leicestershire parish in eight underwent total enclosure between 1650 and 1714, and a few chapelries within other parishes were enclosed as well. Less extensive and largely unrecorded enclosures were proceeding in still other parishes, probably bringing greater returns for their incumbents, too.[89]

And so there are a number of reasons for thinking that clerical incomes rose during the late-Stuart period, and that a number of factors contributed to the rise. But how much did these and other factors affect clerical incomes during the Tudor-Stuart period as a whole? Surviving surveys of parish livings provide a rough indication. For almost all of the livings in England and Wales, there is the *Valor Ecclesiasticus* of the 1530's, thought by Habakkuk to be fairly accurate and reliable.[90] For Leicestershire, Lincolnshire, and Essex, there are Puritan surveys compiled during the first decade of the seventeenth century; for several counties there are the Commonwealth surveys of 1650–51; for the Diocese of Worcester, a survey of 1664; and for Leicestershire, Buckinghamshire, Huntingdonshire, and Hertfordshire, the values in Bishop Wake's survey of 1706–7.[91] These surveys must be treated with some caution. Since livings varied in value from year to year due to harvest fluctuations and livestock diseases, the values in the surveys are really approximations and must be regarded as such. Then, too, the surveys are not always strictly comparable: in particular, the 1535 survey did not include the value of parsonage houses, while the other surveys did. Even though the surveys provide a less-than-perfect picture of the change in clerical incomes over time, the trends they show are still so striking that they are worth noting. The mean values of rectories and vicarages at various times are given in the table, and the percentage changes in each case have been adjusted for changes in the general price level according to the Phelps Brown-Hopkins price index.[92]

What do all of these figures suggest? Christopher Hill used them (except those from Leicestershire, Buckinghamshire, and Huntingdonshire) to argue that the clergy's real income did not increase between the Reformation and the Civil War. His argument rested on two assumptions: first, that a great deal of the real increment in the values of rectories actually went to laymen holding tithe leases, rather than to the parsons themselves; and second, that the surveys of 1650–51 provided an overly optimistic picture of the change in the values of livings since the survey of 1535.[93]

In regard to leasing, Hill's argument can be faulted in several respects. First, he cites figures from the Diocese of Worcester as an indication of frequent leasing, with a third of the diocese's parsons leasing all or part of their revenues in 1585.[94] It does not neces-

County	Rectories: Date	Number	Mean value	Price index	Percentage change	Vicarages: Date	Number	Mean value	Price index	Percentage change
Leicestershire	1535	105	£ 15-19-05	155		1535	67	£ 8-14-00	155	
	1603		67-13-00	475	+39%	1603		25-16-00	475	-3%
	1707		110-00-00	591	+31%	1707		48-00-00	591	+50%
Bucks., Herts., Hunts.	1535	165	15-17-00	155		1535	100	10-15-00	155	
	1650		103-00-00	667	+51%	1650		36-00-00	667	-22%
	1707		123-10-00	591	+35%	1707		51-10-00	591	+61%
Essex	1535	154	14-09-06	155		1535	88	13-00-10	155	
	1609		64-17-10	475	+47%	1609		43-10-11	475	+9%
	1650		83-19-07	667	-8%	1650		50-11-09	667	-17%
Lincolnshire	1535	50	13-00-07	155		1535	42	8-05-11	155	
	1604		30-04-01	475	-24%	1604		13-12-04	475	-46%
Wiltshire	1535	32	13-02-08	155		1535	26	13-09-11	155	
	1650		86-00-00	667	+52%	1650		51-00-00	667	-12%
Nottinghamshire	1535	10	7-18-09	155		1535	10	6-07-11	155	
	1650		47-10-00	667	+39%	1650		20-00-08	667	-27%
Suffolk	1535	17	13-01-02	155		1535	15	9-16-00	155	
	1650		51-18-10	667	-7%	1650		36-09-04	667	-14%
Worcestershire	1535	83	13-18-04	155		1535	48	12-06-10½	155	
	1650		64-03-04	667	+7%	1650		42-02-08	667	-21%
Diocese of Worcester	1535	110	12-04-04	155		1535	80	10-14-11	155	
	1664		79-16-09	646	+57%	1664		36-03-03	646	-19%

sarily follow, however, that all or even most of these leases were contracted for extremely long periods of time, or in other unfavorable ways; it is quite possible that many parsons were fully aware of the dangers of long leases in a period of great inflation, and that they were careful to keep their leases short (although some, as shown in the few examples Hill cites, obviously did not). Second, most of these leases must have come up for renewal in the early seventeenth century, bringing sudden windfalls to incumbents whose revenues had been frozen, and discouraging them from repeating the mistakes of their predecessors. They were already being discouraged from doing so by Parliamentary legislation: certainly 13 Eliz., c. 20, and 3 Car. I, c. 5, forbade parsons to contract leases that would bind their successors. In any case, one-third of Worcestershire's parsons is not a very large proportion, especially if some were leasing only part of their revenues. Of course, Hill is right to insist that some of the gains in the values of livings were temporarily lost through leasing. However, it seems unlikely that most were, even in the period between the Reformation and the Civil War, and it is highly unlikely that this was a problem after the Restoration, when price levels generally flattened out.

In regard to the surveys of 1650–51, Hill felt that the values they gave were too high, partly because they included the values of parsonage houses (the 1535 survey did not), and partly because the values of Worcestershire vicarages seemed higher in 1650–51 than he expected.[95] But there are grounds for thinking that the values in the 1650–51 surveys are really too low. In the first place, if the values they give are either accurate or too high, then the real values of Essex rectories must have been declining in the first half of the seventeenth century; and if Leicestershire rectories increased between 1650 and 1707 at anything like the rate of rectories in nearby Buckinghamshire, Huntingdonshire, and Hertfordshire, then the values of Leicestershire rectories must have stagnated under the early Stuarts, too. This seems unlikely for both Essex and Leicestershire, because land values and corn prices in the early seventeenth century were still rising faster than prices in general. In addition, if the 1650–51 values are either high or accurate, then rectory values in Buckinghamshire, Huntingdonshire, and Hertfordshire must have increased by at least 35 percent in real terms between the Civil War and the death of Anne. Even with some rectors reaping profits from increased productivity and enclosures, this seems a bit much for a period of sluggish farm prices. Finally, though the samples for Worcestershire and the Diocese of Worcester do not completely coincide, rectories in this area must have risen faster in value during the fourteen years after 1650 than they had between the Reformation and the Civil War; this, too, seems rather strange.

The only explanation for these anomalies is that the surveys of 1650-51, at least for rectories and probably for vicarages as well, do not really represent the change in real values that had occurred since the 1530's. The surveys of 1650-51, it must be remembered, were made at a time of severe ecclesiastical dislocation. Many unpopular parsons must have been faced with heightened resistance to tithe payments, and parsons fearing ejection by Puritan committees may not have invested much time and energy on farming their glebes. Consequently, the values of livings in 1650 were probably somewhat below the level of 1642, perhaps by as much as 10 or 20 percent, and the increase made in the values of rectories between the Reformation and the Civil War must have been even greater than the figures suggest. At the same time, vicarages may have been keeping pace with inflation, rather than falling drastically behind.

If one accepts all these arguments, the overall picture is as follows. During and after the Reformation, clerical incomes benefited from differential inflation and rising agricultural productivity. By 1707 both rectors and vicars were substantially better off, in real terms, than their predecessors of 1535. The real values of Leicestershire rectories had in fact risen by something like 81 percent, and those of vicarages by 45 percent; in Buckinghamshire, Hertfordshire, and Huntingdonshire, the respective figures were 105 and 26 percent. Furthermore, this rise was probably reflected for most parsons in improved living standards; by 1666 a third of the parsonage houses in Leicestershire fell in the top 10 percent of all houses in the county in terms of hearths subject to tax, and only a quarter fell in the bottom 80 percent.[96] By 1666 most rectors and vicars had therefore attained much higher living standards than the great majority of their parishioners, most of whom, as copyholders and landless laborers, had been unequipped to weather the inflationary storm. On the other hand, the rise was highly uneven. Before 1640, rectors with grain tithes and large glebes profited far more than vicars; in fact, most vicars in 1640 were probably getting no more, or even somewhat less, than their pre-Reformation predecessors, and they now had the additional burden of wives and children to support.

Clerical incomes probably received a setback during and immediately after the Civil War, but there was a rapid recovery with the return of religious and political stability. Though farm prices were now sluggish, many post-Restoration incumbents continued to profit from increased productivity, enclosures, and voluntary augmentations. In the case of vicarages, most of the gain in real income must in fact have come during the late-Stuart period, with the rapid conversion of arable land to pasture. Probably for the first time, vicars' incomes were rising faster than those earned by rectors.

But what about perpetual curates? By all accounts, the Great Inflation should have impoverished parsons tied to fixed stipends. It probably did in the sixteenth century, but their real incomes rose by 94 percent in Leicestershire between 1603 and 1707, and by 58 percent in Buckinghamshire, Hertfordshire, and Huntingdonshire between 1650 and the death of Anne.[97] Apparently patrons and other interested parties were becoming concerned with the economic plight of perpetual curates, and with the threat this seemed to pose to the Church's mission. Their augmentations, though not obliterating the vast inequality in clerical incomes, did mean rising living standards for many curates during the course of the seventeenth century.

And so there are good reasons for thinking that most clerical incomes rose substantially between 1535 and 1714. All of this, however, refers to gross incomes; net incomes after taxes may have been another matter. In view of the scarcity of clerical account books for this period, changes in net incomes are extremely difficult to estimate. Still, there are indications that tax levels for parsons rose significantly during the late seventeenth century, and that this erased some of the increase in the gross values of clerical livings. Parish parsons had never been lightly taxed. Under the Tudors and early Stuarts, parsons had paid clerical subsidies, first fruits, and tenths, as well as occasional forced loans and benevolences, making them one of the most heavily taxed groups in the nation.[98] Under the later Stuarts, taxing methods changed somewhat; clerical subsidies were allowed to lapse, and the poorer clergy were completely discharged from first fruits and tenths. But tax levels still rose substantially after 1690, as the nation struggled to meet the costs of William's and Anne's wars against France. Window taxes fell on parsonages; clergymen in the 1690's were required to pay poll taxes at the same rate as country gentlemen, even though their incomes were generally lower; parsons paid heavy excise taxes along with everyone else; and an unprecedentedly heavy land tax fell on tithes as well as glebes.[99] By the first decade of the eighteenth century, the rector of Kimcote was paying a full 20 percent of his income in taxes, with the land tax taking by far the biggest single portion.[100]

This undoubtedly helps explain a sharp decline in the values of the personal estates of Leicestershire's parish clergy between 1670 and 1710. Probate inventories of parsons' estates in the Archdeaconry of Leicester show a drop in median values from £134.10s. in 1670-85 to £81.9s.2d in 1695-1710–a fall of roughly 40 percent.[101] Perhaps these figures should be viewed with caution. For one thing, the samples they are based on are fairly small–sixty inventories for 1670-85, forty-six for 1695-1710; inventories in fact survive for only 45 percent of those parsons known to have died between 1670 and 1685, and for only 33 percent of those who died between 1695 and 1710. Then, too, the latter sample is slightly biased toward parsons in poor livings, as well as toward the sons of plebeians–and hence toward parsons with less outside income from inheritances and dowries.[102] Finally, the decline came not in the values of household goods and furnishings, which remained at a constant level, but in the values of leases, promissory notes, crops, and livestock owned by the parsons at their deaths. If parsons in the latter period were more inclined to rent their glebes to tenants, and to invest the proceeds in assets that would not show up in probate inventories (i.e., freehold land), the apparent decline might be explained away. Still, the drop seems too sharp to be ignored completely. In fact, it suggests that heavy wartime taxes were making serious inroads on clerical incomes–not enough to erase the gains made since the 1530's, but probably enough to offset most of the gains made since the 1650's. Certainly wartime taxes were creating difficulties for late-Stuart yeomen and country gentlemen–a fact which helps explain the Tories' widespread appeal in the rural parts of Britain, where the land tax was felt most severely.[103] In view of this, economic frustration may have been as crucial as religious motives in explaining the vehement hatred many country parsons felt for the Whigs and their political policies.

But one must also take a long-term view, recognizing that the century and a half that followed the Reformation was for most parsons a time of quite substantial economic gains. Like the middling freeholders they most resembled in income and economic resources, few suffered unduly in the Great Inflation; most eventually profited and rode the inflationary tide to new levels of prosperity, finding themselves substantially better off than their predecessors of 1535. In terms of gross incomes, most were probably better off than their predecessors of 1650, though heavy taxation may have made the closing years of the Stuart dynasty a time of economic difficulty and retrenchment.

NOTES

1. The ones for Leicestershire parishes are mainly in Lincs. Arch. Off., Terriers, vol. 23, and in boxes of terriers numbered 13, 17, and 18. About a thousand other terriers, including at least two or three for almost every parish in the county, are in Lincs. Arch. Off., Terriers, vol. 8 (chiefly terriers of the 1620's and 1630's), and in Leics. Museum, 1D41/2/1-777 (primarily terriers of the late seventeenth and early eighteenth centuries).

2. These surveys are recorded in Bishop Wake's *Speculum* (Lincs. Arch. Off.), published as Fletcher, ed., "Documents relating to Leicestershire." For most benefices the *Speculum* gives both the values submitted for Queen Anne's Bounty and the values Bishop Wake collected in 1706 and 1707 for his own information (for a rough draft of the *Speculum* based on these returns, see Christ Church Library, Wake MSS, *Notitia Episcopatus Lincoln*, I-III). When a living was worth more than £50 or £80 a year, the returns for Queen Anne's Bounty seldom provided a specific figure. Therefore, for purposes of uniformity, Wake's returns, which were specific for almost all livings, have been used to compile this table, along with a few values from glebe terriers and Bounty returns when Wake's returns are incomplete or highly suspect.

3. *Ibid*.

4. Hill, *Economic Problems of the Church*, pp. 86-91.

5. Two mills in Melton Mowbray brought in 2s.6d. in 1690 (Leics. Rec. Off., DG 36/107); two in Burton Overy together paid 10s. in 1707 (Lincs. Arch. Off., Terr., vol. 23, pp. 158-159).

6. Lincs. Arch. Off., Ben/8/61; Leics. Museum, 1D41/2/633.

7. Leics. Museum, 1D41/2/159; Leics. Rec. Off., DG 676/6.

8. Cawdrey, *Patronage*, p. 27.

9. Leics. Museum, 1D41/2/194.

10. Leics. Rec. Off., DG 36/107.

11. Gill and Guilford, eds., *Rector's Book*, pp. 82, 124, and *passim*.

12. Lincs. Arch. Off., Ben/8/58.

13. Leics. Museum, 1D41/2/50.

14. Lincs. Arch. Off., Ben/8/61.

15. *Ibid*.; Leics. Museum, 1D41/2/474.

16. Lincs. Arch. Off., Ter., vol. 23, pp. 837-838; Ben/8/61; Ter., Box 17/12.

17. Leics. Museum, 1D41/4/XXX/3-23; Lincs. Arch. Off., Ter., vol. 23, pp. 780-781.

18. For example, Leics. Museum, 1D41/2/143,160,592; Leics. Rec. Off., DE 322/1/3/1; Nichols, *Leicester*, IV, 112-113.

19. Based on the sources listed in note 1.

20. Parishioners and incumbents often reported major enclosures involving tithe commutations to their bishops, but I have found no evidence of bishops refusing to consent to Leicestershire tithe communtations between 1660 and 1714.

21. 13 Eliz., c. 20 and 3 Car. I, c. 5. See Hill, *Economic Problems of the Church*, pp. 114-117.

22. Leics. Museum, 1D41/11/68,73-77.

23. Lincs. Arch. Off., Ter., vol. 23, pp. 830-831, 967; Leics. Museum, 1D41/2/247.

24. Lincs. Arch. Off., Ter., vol. 23, p. 240.

25. Leics. Museum, 1D41/2/669; Nichols, *Leicester*, IV, 964.

26. Lincs. Arch. Off., Ter., vol. 23, pp. 684-685.

27. Houghton parsonage, for example, had seven bays of barns and other outhouses in 1707, but no glebe (*ibid.*, 412-413). Long Whatton's glebe was less than five acres, but the rector had ten bays of outhouses in 1674, including two barns, a stable, and a cowhouse (Leics. Museum, 1D41/2/745).

28. For example, see Bitteswell: Leics. Rec. Off., DE 759/15. This was also the case in much of Warwickshire: See Barratt, *Terriers of Warwickshire*, pp. xxxvii-xxxviii.

29. Lincs. Arch. Off., Ter., vol. 23, pp. 253-258, 976-977; Leics. Rec. Off., DE 66/2904/1.

30. Quoted in Townsend, "Castle Donington."

31. Lincs. Arch. Off., Ter., vol. 23, p. 836.

32. For example, Leics. Museum, 1D41/4/XXXI/91-100; 1D41/4/XXXII/43-44, 168-171; 1D41/4/XXXIII/35-45; 1D41/4/L/123-127; 1D41/4/LIII/69-70.

33. Moore, "Journal and Account Book," p. 90.

34. Leics. Museum, 1D41/4/XLVIII/74.

35. *Ibid.*, 1D41/4/XLVIII/1-8.

36. *Ibid.*, 1D41/4/LIII/154; 1D41/4/XLVI/50-56.

37. *Ibid.*, 1D41/4/XXXVIII/134-135, 140; 1D41/4/XXXV/169-174; 1D41/4/XXXI/91-100; 1D41/4/XXXV/23-26; 1D41/4/XXXIII/35-45; 1D41/4/XXXI/31-39; 1D41/4/LIII/71-89.

38. Nichols, *Leicester*, III, 748.

39. Lincs. Arch. Off., Ter., vol. 23, pp. 373-375.

40. Christ Church Library, Wake MSS, CCLXXVIII, n.f.: Misterton.

41. Gill and Guilford, *Rector's Book*, pp. 60-61.

42. Bodleian Library, Tanner MS 80, ff. 122-123v.

43. Eachard, *Grounds and Occasions*, p. 117.

44. Lincs. Arch. Off., Ter., vol. 23; Ter., boxes 13, 17, 18; Leics. Museum, 1D41/2/1-777.

45. Hoskins, *Provincial England*, pp. 158-162. Using probate inventories for the years 1669-72, Hoskins found that the typical yeoman farmer had 20-30 acres of sown arable land, and that an average yeoman farmer had about 20% of his land under grass. Apparently this means that a typical Leicestershire yeoman farmer had 25-38 acres of land in all.

46. Probate records in Leics. Rec. Off.; PR/I/--.

47. Leics. Museum, 1D41/4/XLVI/151-152.

48. Eachard, *Grounds and Occasions*, pp. 114-115.

49. For example, at Aylestone, Carlton Curlieu, Kirkby Mallory, Medbourne, Sapcote, Seagrave, and Willoughby Waterless: Leics. Rec. Off., PR/I/: 70/7, 78/178, 83/39, 83/154, 83/242, 85/145, 101/80.

50. Lincs. Arch. Off., Ter., vol. 23; Ter., boxes 13, 17, 18; Leics. Museum, 1D41/2/1-777.

51. Wake MSS, CCLXXVII-CCLXXVIII. This is explicitly stated for

eleven parsonages. In another twenty-two parishes with parsonages, the incumbent was nonresident and had no resident curate, so most of these parsonages were probably leased, too.

52. Lincs. Arch. Off., Ben/8/61; Fletcher, "Documents relating to Leicestershire," pp. 235, 288.

53. Lincs. Arch. Off., Ter., vol. 23, pp. 345, 639-641, 746, 808-809, 902-910, and *passim*; Ben/8/61; Ter., Box 13/30; Leics. Museum, 1D41/2/707.

54. Lincs. Arch. Off., Ter., vol. 23, pp. 345, 349, and *passim*.

55. See above, p. 76*n*1.

56. Kennett, *Impropriations*, pp. 161-164.

57. Wake, *Bishop of Lincoln's Charge*, pp. 28-29.

58. Eachard, *Grounds and Occasions*, pp. 136-137.

59. Addison, *Spectator*, II, 111; Eachard, *Grounds and Occasions*, pp. 129-130.

60. Savidge, *Queen Anne's Bounty*, pp. 5-9.

61. Kennett, *Impropriations*, pp. 253-272, 324-346.

62. Savidge, *Queen Anne's Bounty*, pp. 26-27, 60-61.

63. Wake MSS, CCLXXVIII, n.f.: Wigston Magna.

64. *Ibid.*, CCXXXVI, n.f.: John Hagger to William Wake, February 22, 1705/6.

65. Lincs. Arch. Off., Ben/8/7.

66. See below, pp. 140-141.

67. For example, Leics. Museum, 1D41/13/68, ff. 8, 25; 1D41/13/76, ff. 124, 219v.; 1D41/13/78, ff. 35, 39, 105v., 131.

68. *Calendar of State Papers, Domestic: Charles II*, VI, 313; Fletcher, "Documents relating to Leicestershire," p. 334.

69. Lincs. Arch. Off., Ter., vol. 23, p. 608; Lambeth Palace Library, *Notitia Parochialis*, Cod. Misc. 962, number 678.

70. Lincs. Arch. Off., Ter., vol. 23, pp. 616-617; Fletcher, "Documents relating to Leicestershire," p. 298.

71. Lincs. Arch. Off., Ter., vol. 23, pp. 620-622; Leics. Museum, 1D41/2/402.

72. Lincs. Arch. Off., L.C. V, f. 215; L.C. VI, f. 221; Leics. Museum, 1D41/34/1 (typescript copy); 1D41/40/4; Bellairs, "Accounts of the Churchwardens of St. Mary's."

73. Savidge, *Queen Anne's Bounty*, p. 9.

74. See below, pp. 143-145.

75. Thirsk, ed., *Agrarian History*, IV, 199, 206.

76. *Ibid.*, IV, 607-608, 695, 627, 632, 820-821, 844-845.

77. Leics. Museum, 1D41/2/720,775; Lincs. Arch. Off., Ter., vol. 23, pp. 974-982; Fletcher, "Documents relating to Leicestershire," pp. 351, 360; Nichols, *Leicester*, I, xcvi.

78. Hart, *Country Priest*, pp. 118-119.; Tyler, "Elizabethan Parochial Clergy," pp. 93-94; G. V. Bennett, "Conflict in the Church," in Holmes, ed., *Britain after the Glorious Revolution*, p. 164.

79. Lincs. Arch. Off., Ben/3/4; Ter., vol. 23, pp. 105, 137-139, 173, 179, 305-313, 910; Leics. Museum, 1D41/2/398,623; Nichols, *Leicester*, III, 688-689, 692; *Victoria History of Leicester*, V, 88, 274.

80. Thirsk, ed., *Agrarian History*, IV, 199, 206.

81. Hoskins, *Provincial England*, pp. 162-166, 169; Beresford, "Glebe Terriers," pp. 79, 81, 100.

82. Lincs. Arch. Off., Ter., vol. 23, pp. 348-349, 600-604; Leics. Museum, 1D41/2/241-247; 35' 29/411,412; Leics. Rec. Off., EN/198/1,2; EN/251/1; EN/321/1; Leics. Museum, 1D41/2/207.

83. Lincs. Arch. Off., Ter., vol. 23, pp. 353-357; Leics. Museum, 1D41/2/516; 1D41/2/669b.

84. Lincs. Arch. Off., Ter., vol. 23, pp. 805-806; Leics. Museum, 1D41/2/143,592; 18D67/980; Leics. Rec. Off., DE 66/4301/1; DE 66/2504; DE 322/1/3/1; DG 676/6.

85. Leics. Rec. Off., DG 676/6.

86. Wake MSS, CCXXXVI, n.f.: John Rogers to William Wake, June 2, 1707.

87. Nichols, *Leicester*, IV, 94; Fletcher, "Documents relating to Leicestershire," p. 254; Lincs. Arch. Off., Ben/2/62/2,3.

88. Nichols, *Leicester*, III, 399n; Leics. Museum, 1D41/2/278,243-244; Lincs. Arch. Off., Ter., vol. 23, pp. 348-349.

89. Beresford, "Glebe Terriers," pp. 79, 81, 100; Hoskins, *Provincial England*, pp. 162-166, 169.

90. Habakkuk, "Monastic Property."

91. For Leicestershire, Buckinghamshire, Hertfordshire, and Huntingdonshire, the values for 1707 are taken from Wake's *Speculum* (see note 2), and the 1535 values from the *Speculum* and from Ecton, *Thesaurus*. The Leicestershire survey of ca. 1603 is from Bodleian MS Carte 77, ff. 112-118v. Nichols thought these were the Commonwealth returns and quoted extensively from them, but internal evidence shows they belong to the first decade of the seventeenth century: see Moore, "Livings in the Reign of James I." The Commonwealth returns for Buckinghamshire, Huntingdonshire, and Hertfordshire are from Lambeth Palace Library, CommXIIa/3/1-119 and CommXIIa/10/210-374. The values for Essex, Lincolnshire, Wiltshire, Nottinghamshire, Suffolk, Worcestershire, and the Diocese of Worcester are from Hill, *Economic Problems of the Church*, p. 111.

92. Phelps Brown and Hopkins, "Prices of Consumables." For each survey a mean price index for the appropriate ten-year period is used; i.e., with the assumption that between 1530 and 1609 the price index rose from 155 to 475, meaning an increase of 206%. The other assumed increases are: 1600-1709, 24%; 1600-1655, 40%; 1646-1709, -11%; 1530-1709, 281%; 1530-1655, 330%; 1530-1669, 317%; 1646-69, -3%.

93. Hill, *Economic Problems of the Church*, pp. 110-112, 114-117.

94. *Ibid.*, p. 114.

95. *Ibid.*, pp. 110-112.

96. See below, pp. 144-147.

97. Based on nine perpetual curacies in Leicestershire, and on twenty-nine in Buckinghamshire, Hertfordshire, and Huntingdonshire. For sources and adjustments for changes in the price index, see notes 91 and 92.

98. Hill, *Economic Problems of the Church*, pp. 188-195.

99. Bodleian Library, Tanner MS 80, f. 121; 4 Wm. and Mary, c. 1; 7 Anne, c. 1.

100. Leics. Museum, 1D41/4/LV/21-35.

101. Leics. Rec. Off., PR/I/--.

102. Despite the fact that the drop for the clergy as a whole may not have been as substantial as the inventory figures imply, there almost certainly was a drop. It continues to show up within the samples, even when parsons are sorted into groups based on annual incomes, and into groups based on the social status of their fathers.

103. Holmes, *Politics in the Age of Anne*, pp. 159–162.

IV

The Parsons in Their Parishes

PRAYERS AND SERMONS

When William Wake began his first visitation as Bishop of Lincoln in 1706, he issued a declaration to his clergy listing the standards that he expected them to meet. They were to hold services every day if they could get a congregation; at the very least they should offer prayers on Sundays, Wednesdays, Fridays, holy days, and holy day eves. They were to preach both on Sunday mornings and on Sunday afternoons, teach children the church catechism throughout the year, offer communion at least three times annually, reside in their parishes, visit the sick, dispense charity, admonish local sinners, reprove parishioners who neglected to attend church, bind up village quarrels, and live with all men "in a general State not only of Peace, but if it be possible, of Love and Friendship."[1] Most parsons were probably quite willing to rise to the challenge, but they found themselves confronted with a number of obstacles, including both an apathetic laity and poor parochial endowments.

"I should esteem it a mighty happiness had I the opportunity of reading our service publickly every day," Parson Oakeley of Lutterworth wrote Wake in 1711, "but it is my hard fate to be seated where I can rarely obtain the small number of two or three to make up a congregation upon the festivals, much less. . .on other daies."[2] His complaint was a common one in late-Stuart Leicestershire: in parish after parish, parsons confessed their inability to get their parishioners to come to church as often as they should. In Oakeley's parish and undoubtedly in many others, the trouble lay less with Dissenters than with nonreligious absenters, people who "either through lazyness, prophaneness, or both, worship God no way." Complaints of lay apathy toward weekday services occur too frequently to be dismissed entirely as lame excuses offered by lazy incumbents. The vicar of Ashby de la Zouch held a Wednesday lectureship and faithfully called his parishioners to attend it, but in 1713 it was "not at all frequented," and his archdeacon was negotiating to have it transferred to Sunday afternoons.[3] The parson of Blaston tried to hold daily common prayer services in his parish church, but in 1700 he wrote that "Persecution cousened me of my Key, Then stole the Bell-Rope, then the Bell clapper, and then (to Top up the Sacrilegious climax) the very Bell itself, thus forcing us to a discontinuance of the daily sacrifice."[4] In 1718 the rector of South Kilworth wrote that he had never been "so happy yet as to gain a congregation for service on the weekdays, unless on some solemn festival." The parson of Church Langton wrote in the same year that he had offered weekday services "whilst any one in the parish would come to joyn with the minister," but the parishioners refused to come except on Sundays. And though the parson of Witherley held special services on holy days, the only parishioners who showed up were the members of the parson's own family.[5] The result was that weekday services were held far less frequently than Bishop Wake would have liked. In 1718, fewer than 10 percent of Leicestershire's parishes had prayer services every day; only 20 percent had regular services on Wednesdays, Fridays, and holy days; another 20 percent had weekday services on holy days only; and almost half dispensed with weekday services altogether.[6]

Parishioners were also remiss when it came to catechizing. The rector of Hoby claimed in 1673 that he had repeatedly tried and failed to get his parishioners to send their children, and that he could not "bring them to church on his back." The parson of Congestone charged in 1674 that when he gave "notice the last Sunday of his intent to Catechize, they shutt the Church door and would not suffer him to come in, but went many of them to a Conventicle held in Mr. Palmer's house at Temple Hall, the pretended patron of Congeston."[7] The rector of Lutterworth wrote in 1711 that he believed the "vile profaneness and growing schism of the present age is greatly owing to the want of catechizing; but how to oblige Parents to submit their children to it is what I want to be informed; I have endeavoured it to the utmost, but could never yet obtain the tenth part of such as were capable."[8] Complaints of poor attendance at catechizings were made by parsons in about a quarter of Leicestershire's parishes in 1718. Lay apathy was most serious in Leicester's urban parishes, but it was common even in the countryside.[9] The rector of South Hallaton had often reproached negligent parents, but without results; at Market Bosworth the children in the charity school came regularly, but not many others came at all; at Walton on the Wolds the children came only "by fitts and starts"; and at Church Langton no children had shown up for catechizing during the past two years. Attendance was also sporadic at Packington, as the Reverend Michael Hutchinson discovered when he arrived in the parish in 1706. He immediately began a series of catechistical lectures, and the "Parishioners seemed so fond of it that they not onely sent their children and servants to be instructed, but resorted in as great numbers themselves as they did to the morning sermon." Unfortunately, "this good humour spent itself by degrees," attendance fell off, and Hutchinson "thought it advisable to let it drop for awhile."[10]

Bishop Wake fully understood all this, but still believed that the clergy should redouble their efforts:

> It is with a very sensible concern that I hear so many complaints of the gross ignorance of the common people in the things of God, and of the too general neglect of catechising, which seems to have been the chief occasion of it. I do not charge my brethren of the clergy as the only faulty persons in this matter. I am too sensible that there is a very great remissness in parents and masters, who do not sufficiently encourage or constrain their children and youth to come to catechising. But I am fully convinced that it is still in the power of the clergy to do a great deal more good than is yet done in this way, if they will but diligently apply their thoughts and endeavours to effect it.[11]

Sadly, those who responded to Wake's challenge with imagination and zest were often disappointed with the results. "I prevailed upon the young people to come to my house," the parson of South Kilworth reported in 1718, "under the notion of teaching them to sing." After a few jolly songs, he slipped in a little doctrinal lecture, but the children soon caught on to his strategy, lost their enthusiasm for singing lessons, and stopped coming.[12]

Although lay apathy toward catechizing and weekday services worried parsons throughout the late-Stuart period, their worries markedly increased after 1689. Before that date people who neglected to attend church or who refused to send their children to catechizings could be reported by local churchwardens to the ecclesiastical courts, and the courts could excommunicate obstinate, chronic offenders. The courts' coercive powers had not been completely effective; excommunication had simply ceased to terrify many laymen, and some parishioners lived for years as excommunicants without showing signs of suffering from it. After

1689, official toleration for Dissenters made ecclesiastical discipline even less effective than before, and many parishioners were able to avoid church services of any sort. "The Act of Toleration hath almost undone us," a Norfolk parson complained in 1692; "in a short time it will turn halfe the nation into downe right atheisme." He went on to explain why toleration was such a serious threat:

> I doe not find it in my archdeaconry. . .that conventicles have gained anything at all thereby, but reather that they have lost. . . .More lay hold of it to separate from all manner of worship to perfect irreligion than goe to them; and although the Act allows noe such liberty, the people will understand it soe, and, say what the judges can at the assizes, or the justices of peace at their sessions, or we at our visitations, noe churchwarden or constable will present any for not goeing to church, though they goe noe where else but to the alehouse.[13]

Leicestershire parsons felt the same way. "Catechism is in great measure omitted," the parson at Knighton wrote in 1718, "but I dare not use severe methods, lest they should absent wholly from Church."[14] Before 1689, parsons might try to coerce negligent parishioners by having them turned in to the church courts, and then hope for the best. After 1689, they were afraid even to report them.

Lay apathy also showed up in the physical condition of church buildings and church fabric. Although churchwardens were required to notify ecclesiastical officials at visitations about any defects, and to see that they were speedily remedied, there were loud complaints from the clergy that the full extent of negligence went unreported. In 1666, the rector of Saddington wrote that his parish's churchwardens were unlikely to see to "the repairs of those sad ruines which the negligence or timorousness of late officers hath caused." Previous churchwardens had been guilty of "dancing after the pipes of some Grandees in the Paresh and according to their dictates presenting a perjured Omnia bene at the Visitation." There were serious consequences: "If you knew the State of the Steeple, Church, and Church-yard, and (generally) people too, you'would conclude that tame officers are altogether unsuitable for the cure of many sad distempers."[15] Similarly, the rector of Seagrave wrote Wake in 1715 that the churchwardens

> drive on from one year to another and suffer things to run into disorder and have very little regard (I may say none at all) to a great many particulars mentioned in the Book of Articles. If the outward Case of

the Church will but stand, they readily give an Omnia Bene in other things, for no other reason but because they will not spend the parish-money upon such things as they think needless or useless.[16]

Meanwhile, the parson of Appleby was complaining that his church was badly out of repair and that the churchyard walls were ready to fall; services had in fact been interrupted one Sunday, when swine broke through the crumbling walls and entered the church itself. The parish's flagon was nothing but a "base quart pott," and a shortage of seats forced the children to sit in the chancel, where "they are want to bee very disorderly by reason of the remoteness of the place."[17]

Going over the heads of the churchwardens to report defects to the archdeacon or the bishop made a parson highly unpopular with his parishioners, who then had to pay for repairs. Despite this, some parsons were quite willing to shoulder the responsibility. The curate of Oadby, for example, turned the churchwardens in for not raising a parish levy to provide a silver cup, a silver patten, a communion carpet, a hearsecloth, and a table of kinship degrees within which marriage was forbidden. This was in 1686; the churchwardens had been reporting "Omnia bene" since 1662.[18] Consequently, ecclesiastical officials sometimes decided to ignore churchwardens' presentments altogether, and to ask the parsons themselves about the condition of churches and church fabric. In 1692, commissions of parish clergymen were appointed for each deanery in Leicestershire, with authority to inspect churches personally and to report any defects to their archdeacon. By this method, it was hoped, the clergy could stand up in a body against lay neglect and avoid the personal risk of reporting defects in their parishes individually. Churchwardens in the 1690's were handing in presentments that read "Omnia bene" about 90 percent of the time; according to the clergy's returns of 1692, however, churches and chapels failed to meet required standards in three Leicestershire parishes out of four.[19]

The churchwardens at Pickwell had consistently claimed nothing amiss in their parish, except for a few absenters and obstinate excommunicants. But in 1692, the clergy found the church out of repair and the roof leaking; the communion table needed replacing, the font needed repairing, and the church needed a new flagon and communion cloth; the communion rails and the belfry door were out of repair; and the church lacked a book of homilies, a book of canons, and a table of kinship degrees. At forty-seven churches the churchyard walls needed repairing, and at Desford the clergy found the churchyard walls broken down and "two swine rooting up the graves." Nave walls were structurally unsound in fourteen churches, and the church at Market Harborough was so decayed that "the Curate hath nothing to defend him from the weather while he performs the office of burial." Laymen had let chancels fall into disrepair in twenty churches, and a chancel wall at Eaton was on the verge of collapse. Thirty-seven churches lacked a book of canons or a book of homilies or a table of kinship degrees (sometimes all three); thirty-five were deficient in communion cups, pattens, and communion carpets; Dunton Bassett's communion cup was kept at a local alehouse. Bibles and prayerbooks were either falling apart or of the wrong edition in twenty-six churches. Floors needed repairing in thirty-eight churches, and roofs needed repairing in fifteen others; at Prestwold the roof was about to cave in, and leakage was so serious at Buckminster that the chancel walls were "most abominably polluted with a green filth." Defects in belfries and spires were reported in sixteen churches; Shearsby's steeple was about to fall, and the steeple at Packington had been totally ruined for forty years. All things considered, it probably did little good to have the clergy report on the true state of churches and church fabric. Similar clerical commissions had been appointed before this, and the clergy's returns of 1692 show that there had been little improvement since the clergy last reported in 1674.[20] Laymen continued to be aroused by religious issues and religious crises between the Restoration and the death of Anne, but their concern was not always reflected in the physical upkeep of their churches.

Another obstacle in the Church's path was the number of poorly endowed livings, for poor parochial endowments often led to pluralism, nonresidence, and fewer church services than Bishop Wake would have liked. Roughly a third of Leicestershire's parishes were held in plurality in the late-Stuart period, and roughly a quarter of the county's parsons were pluralists.[21] Some pluralists were shockingly greedy and lazy: about a quarter of Leicestershire's pluralists combined livings worth more than £50 apiece and hired curates at paltry salaries to serve their second parishes for them. The Reverend Samuel Hartopp of Little Dalby and Cold Overton, for example, provided his curate at Cold Overton with a parsonage and only £20 a year in 1712, while his own income from both livings was well over £200. Most pluralists held relatively poor livings, however, and those who were unable to afford curates for their second parishes usually tried to serve both of their livings simultaneously. A few of the poorer clergy also tried to augment their incomes by teaching school, even though sometimes their teaching duties took them away from the parishes they were supposed to serve as rectors and vicars. "Mr. Salter has taken an House here," the Archdeacon of Leicester wrote Bishop Wake from Carlton Curlieu, "and has taken many Gentlemens sons to boarding, so that I doubt he will hardly keep his word with your Lordship for his residence at Peatling."[22] Other poor incumbents augmented their incomes by working as part-time curates to better-paid incumbents in other parishes; five were doing so in 1670, and eighteen in 1712. One of them was Edmund Carter of Goadby: "I wish you could persuade [the rector of Eastwell] to keep some other Curate who has not a Church of his own to look after," Wake wrote the Archdeacon, for "this is not Canonical: Nor does Mr. Carter need it."[23] Carter's income at Goadby was in fact over £100 a year, but most of the other part-time curates had livings worth less than half that amount.

Since the poorer livings were more likely to be staffed by pluralists unable to hire resident curates, or by incumbents working as schoolteachers or as part-time curates in other parishes, nonresidence was most common where livings were least adequately endowed. In 1712 one out of three Leicestershire livings worth less than £50 a year had no resident parson. Even middling livings worth between £50 and £100 a year went without resident parsons in one case in five, while almost all of the wealthier livings did have resident clergymen of some description.[24] The result was that the poorer livings usually were the ones that had fewer church services than Bishop Wake recommended.[25] Although almost all of the livings worth £100 a year or more had two Sunday services in 1718, parishioners were being summoned only once in half of the poorer livings; many of the incumbents of these poorly endowed livings held morning services in one parish and afternoon services in the parishes which they held in plurality or served as curates.[26] The difference between wealthy and poor livings in regard to weekday services was almost as marked.[27]

When it came to communion services, Wake asked only that communion be offered frequently enough for parishioners to receive the sacrament three times a year. Monthly communion was quite uncommon in this period except in London and the larger provincial cities and towns, where, during the reigns of William and Anne, it was becoming increasingly fashionable. In Leicestershire in 1718, communion was offered monthly only in Leicester's

How Leicestershire Parishes Were Being Served, 1712

(N = 201)

	All livings	*Wealthy livings*	*Middling livings*	*Poor livings*
By a resident parson				
The incumbent	71%	80%	72.5%	61%
A curate	8.5%	14%	6%	6%
Total	79.5%	94%	78.5%	67%
By a nonresident parson				
The incumbent	15.5%	0	14.5%	31%
A curate	5%	6%	7%	2%
Total	20.5%	6%	21.5%	33%

urban parishes, in the bustling market towns of Loughborough and Melton Mowbray, and in five or six country parishes where parsons were unusually zealous. A few other parsons offered communion between five and ten times annually, but in most parishes the custom was only three or four communions a year.[28] Infrequent communions were partly a legacy of the Protestant Reformation, but they also reflected the laity's reluctance to provide money for communion wine. "In the afternoon," a Yorkshire parson of the 1690's wrote in his diary, "I gave notice that I intended to administer the Sacrament the next Sunday. Some think it will put the town to much charge, and were against it. Lord make us better Christians, and teach us our duty: but alas, we love this world better than heaven, and our bodies better than our souls. The Lord forgive us, and form our hearts anew." When the parson died, he left his parish "nine pounds to be placed in good hands," with the interest "to be paid yearly to buy wine for communion."[29]

What about sermons? Wake asked his clergy to choose "the most plain and practical Subjects," and to treat them in a "plain, familiar Manner, and with as much Warmth and Devotion as you are able."[30] Nevertheless, contemporaries charged that many late-Stuart sermons were far from being plain, practical, and familiar. "For there be a sort of Divines," Eachard wrote, "who if they but happen of an unlucky hard word all the week, they think themselves not careful of their Flock, if they lay it not up till Sunday and bestow it amongst them in their next Preachment." Far too many parsons, he continued, used tortuous analogies and obscure Greek phrases, or tried to "bring in twenty Poets and Philosophers (if they can catch them) into an hours talk." The result was often "high tossing and swaggering Preaching; either mountingly Eloquent, or profoundly Learned."[31] Fifty years later Jonathan Swift was saying much the same thing, especially about the clergy's "frequent use of obscure terms, which by the women are called hard words, and by the better sort of vulgar, fine language." Swift found this sort of pretension "among the clergy of all distinctions, but especially the younger practitioners," and admitted that he could not "easily call to mind any clergyman of my own acquaintance who is wholly exempt from this error." On the other hand, certain changes had taken place by Swift's day. He had, for example, "lived to see Greek and Latin almost entirely driven out of the pulpit, for which I am heartily glad." He also felt that the clergy had "almost given over perplexing themselves and their hearers with abstruse points of Predestination, Election, and the like"; instead, they were preaching simple ethical precepts that could be applied in daily life.[32]

The late-Stuart period was in fact a time of transition in popular sermon styles. Early Caroline preachers like Donne, Andrewes, and Laud had perfected the two-hour baroque sermon, replete with elaborate metaphors, precious similes, and classical citations. Intellectually impressive, the baroque sermon style appeared just as university degrees were becoming standard for ordinary parish incumbents; it was in fact the perfect vehicle for displaying the clergy's newly acquired erudition. After the Civil War there was a growing demand for sermons that were simpler, more straightforward, and more direct. Preachers were urged by critics like Eachard not to flaunt their learning, but to speak to the ordinary parishioner in a way that he could easily understand. The change in taste came for a variety of reasons, including the example of some of the Puritan preachers of the Interregnum, the Cambridge Platonists' emphasis on clarity and simplicity, the need to keep parishioners from running off to Dissenting chapels, and perhaps even the clergy's realization that by this time it was no longer necessary to prove that they were university graduates. At any rate, sermons became shorter and plainer as the century wore on; masters of the new, straightforward style, Tillotson in particular, sold widely in the countryside and were increasingly imitated.[33] In fact, they were sometimes plagiarized: in 1711 Joseph Addison wrote about a country gentleman who had given his parson

Frequency of Sunday Services in Leicestershire Parishes, 1718

	(N = 166)			
	All livings	*Wealthy livings*	*Middling livings*	*Poor livings*
One	21%	5%	18%	43%
Two	75%	92%	79%	51%
One in parish church, one in chapelry	4%	3%	3%	6%

Frequency of Weekday Services in Leicestershire Parishes, 1718

	(N = 166)			
	All livings	*Wealthy livings*	*Middling livings*	*Poor livings*
Every day	8%	10%	5%	10%
Wednesdays, Fridays, and holy days	21%	30%	25%	8%
Holy days only	20%	22%	21%	14%
Wednesdays and Fridays in Lent	3%	2%	3%	3%
None	48%	36%	46%	65%

"copies of all the good Sermons which have been printed in English, and only begged of him that every Sunday he would pronounce one of them in the Pulpit." The parson happily obliged, preaching Tillotson one Sunday and Calamy the next. Addison saw nothing wrong with this practice: "I could heartily wish that more of our Country-Clergy would follow this Example; and instead of wasting their Spirits in laborious Compositions of their own, would endeavour after a handsome Elocution, and all those other Talents that are proper to enforce what has been penned by greater Masters. This would not only be more easy to themselves, but more edifying to the People."[34]

When it came to delivery, Swift thought that too many parsons were addicted to reading their sermons: "You will observe some clergymen with their heads held down from beginning to end, within an inch of the cushion, to read what is hardly legible; which, besides the untoward manner, hinders them from making the best advantage of their voice: others again have a trick of popping up and down every moment from their paper to the audience, like an idle school-boy on a repetition day."[35] Late-Stuart parishioners preferred that parsons at least appear to deliver their sermons extemporaneously, and Swift offered a piece of valuable advice to parsons who feared that extemporaneous addresses were beyond them:

> I knew a clergyman of some distinction, who appeared to deliver his sermon without looking into his notes, which when I complimented him upon, he assured me he could not repeat six lines; but his method was to write the whole sermon in a large plain hand, with all the forms of margin, paragraph, marked page, and the like; then on Sunday morning he took care to run it over five or six times, which he could do in an hour; and when he delivered it, by pretending to turn his face from one side to the other, he would (in his own expression) pick up the lines, and cheat his parishioners by making them believe he had it all by heart.[36]

Whether most late-Stuart parsons followed Swift's advice, there is no way of knowing. In their visitation presentments Leicestershire churchwardens never commented on the quality of their parsons' sermon delivery, though there were a few complaints about parsons who mumbled their prayers. The vicar of St. Martin's, for example, was chided in 1677 for not reading his prayers "audibly and distinctly," and in 1683 the vicar of Lockington was said to "mumble [the prayers] over and read them in such a mumbling and low tone of speech and irreverent Manner, that few or none of the parishioners then assembled to heare divine Service wuld or culd understand what [he] read."[37] Nor do available records tell us much about Leicestershire sermons from the standpoint of style and content. The few sermons that have been published may not have been typical of the general mainstream, and churchwardens commented only on sermons that seemed heretical. The vicar of Lockington was accused of sacrilege in 1669 when he compared his late patron's sufferings during a lengthy illness with Christ's sufferings on the cross, and in 1713 a Leicestershire parson who read dangerous books shocked his parishioners by preaching that "Our Saviour's sufferings were exemplary only and not vicarious."[38] Parishioners also made occasional complaints about parsons who omitted sermons altogether, or who preached only once on Sunday. In 1676, for example, a gentleman of Saddington pronounced the rector of Gumley "a dume Dogg, as well as the rest of the ministers aboute you, who doe not preach twice every Sunday or Lords day as our [rector] doth."[39] As for the quality of the clergy's sermons, Leicestershire churchwardens voiced no complaints. Their silence is in fact suggestive: parsons who preached frequently enough and who aroused no suspicions of heresy were probably satisfying their parishioners. It may be that ordinary parishioners were less exacting about the style and content of their parsons' sermons than critics like Swift and Eachard supposed.

LOCAL EDUCATION

In the early sixteenth century, the country parson was often both preacher and teacher. He trained many of the village boys who went to the universities before the Reformation, for quite often he was his parish's only source of scholarly learning. After the Reformation, however, the Church lost much of the control it had exercised over local education; the drastic increase in the number of local schools during the century that followed also greatly expanded the number of teaching jobs open to laymen.[40] By the late-Stuart period, the great majority of the people licensed to teach school in Leicestershire were in fact members of the laity.[41] Even so, the clergy's involvement in local education remained important: one Leicestershire parish in four had some sort of school in 1718, and one school in three was being taught by a man in orders. Most teaching parsons were poorly paid curates whose academic jobs brought them from £5 to £40 a year in extra income; only eight teaching parsons were full parish incumbents, and overwhelmingly they were the incumbents of the county's poorer livings.[42] Those parsons who taught school did so largely out of economic necessity.

Some parsons were involved in local education in other ways. In 1718 the rector of Little Ashby was paying for three or four children who attended the local dame school, where a woman of the parish taught them the rudiments of reading, writing, and arithmetic. In the same year, the rector of Aylestone was financing the education of ten poor children in his parish, and other parish incumbents were contributing to the support of charity schools and dame schools at Blaby, Narborough, Shawell, Congestone, Ibstock, and Kirkby Mallory.[43] Some parsons also left small sums for schools and scholarships in their wills. In 1683 John Summerville, rector of Barkstone and master of the grammar school at

Loughborough, founded scholarships to Jesus College, Cambridge, for boys who had attended his school and who planned to take a master's degree. The rector of Bottesford founded a charity school for the children of his parish in 1711, and schools were founded or rebuilt at Barrow, Stathern, and Hallaton by parish incumbents in the 1720's and 1730's.[44]

Meanwhile, Richard Hill, rector of the rich living of Thurcaston, was moved by the "infinite, eternal, and mysterious charity of God" toward him to build a charity school and a master's house on his glebe in 1715. His gift was perpetuated in his will, and the statutes he drew up for the school illustrate the parish clergy's ideas about what sort of education was suitable for the children of the poor. Though the children were to learn reading, writing, and arithmetic, the emphasis was on "the adorning of their heaven-born souls with good morality," and on "true, orthodox, and steady Christianity." Not surprisingly, the school was carefully placed under clerical control. Its trustees were to be the parsons of Thurcaston, Loughborough, and Rothley; the rector of Thurcaston was to choose the master, who must be "sober, grave, learned, orthodox," and the master would double as the parish clerk. He would lead the children in prayers twice daily, teach them the services of morning and evening prayer, and instruct them in the catechism. Three times a week he would accompany them to church, the children all carrying their Bibles and walking "two and two abreast, according to their seniority"; he would also make sure that they pronounced a solemn "Amen" at the end of each prayer. By combining "good morality, useful learning, and sound, devout, well-formed, orthodox Christianity," the school would teach the children of the parish to "spend the Lord's day well, and to live like good Christians all the days of their life."[45]

Hill's emphasis on simple piety and "useful" learning typified prevailing thought on the education of the poor during the decades after the Restoration. The period saw a retreat from what Lawrence Stone has called the "educational revolution" of 1560–1640, and, despite the charity-school movement of William's and Anne's reigns, most schools were being hurt by social and intellectual conservatism and by declining enrollments.[46] But if only a minority of parish parsons were actively teaching school or, like Hill, founding charity schools of their own, the clergy as a whole were more concerned with perpetuating godly learning than were most groups in this period. In terms of their incomes, they probably contributed more heavily than most toward this end.

THE PARISHIONERS RATE THEIR PARSONS

When parsons were negligent or immoral, they could be reported by local churchwardens to their archdeacon or their bishop, and parsons presented for such offenses could then be tried and disciplined in the ecclesiastical courts. Churchwardens' presentments and ecclesiastical court records do not provide a completely accurate picture of how well the clergy were performing their duties, for these documents tell us both too much and too little. On one hand, unpopular parsons were sometimes accused of offenses they never committed; on the other, popular parsons who occasionally shirked their duties might go entirely unreported. The records are still very useful, for they do suggest the extent to which parsons were living up to their parishioners' expectations, and how well they were getting along with their parishioners on a day-to-day, personal basis. What do the records show? Between 1662 and 1714, charges of one sort or another were brought against 213 Leicestershire parsons.[47] Their offenses fell into three categories: moral lapses, failure to keep parsonages and church chancels in repair, and offenses in the performance of specifically clerical duties, like preaching and catechizing; furthermore, some of these 213 parsons were presented for offenses in more than one category. This is a fairly large figure, even in comparison with the total of 950 parsons who officiated in Leicester Archdeaconry between those two dates, for it indicates that roughly one Leicestershire parson in five became a subject of complaint.

But the record is not really as bad as it looks. For one thing, about half of these 213 men were presented solely for letting parsonages and chancels fall into decay.[48] Parishioners were rightly concerned about this offense, because future incumbents would be wary of taking on parishes where they might have to spend large sums of money for repairs immediately upon induction. Besides, if an incumbent sued his predecessor for dilapidations, half the parish might be called in as witnesses, costing them time and inconvenience. Chancel dilapidations were a minor problem, accounting for only 15 percent of dilapidation presentments in general, and most such defects were quickly remedied. Failure to keep parsonages and outbuildings in repair was the major grievance, with about a third of the county's parsonages being reported out of repair at some point during the period. On the other hand, since relatively few parsons were cited for dilapidations more than once or twice, the great majority apparently repaired any defects as soon as they were reported.

Moral lapses, the offenses that could arouse the most vehement anti-clericalism, were quite uncommon. One of the few scandalous Leicestershire clerics was Thomas Parsons of Swinford, presented in 1689 for public drunkenness, swearing, and fornication with one Jane Allen. He repented and was absolved of his sins, but the following year he was again presented, this time for "being several times overtaken in Drinke for 3 Months last past." On this occasion he was suspended, but his pledge to reform, and the intercession of neighboring parsons, brought about his reinstatement in 1691. Nine years later he was again accused of tippling and swearing, offenses he apparently repeated in 1703. This led to another suspension, more repentance, and yet another reinstatement. In 1709 it was noted again that Parsons had been swearing, frequenting alehouses, and drinking to excess, but he was never deprived of his living. In 1712 he was still resident in his parish, and he was performing his clerical duties to the general satisfaction of his parishioners.[49]

Leicestershire's most spectacular clerical sinner was undoubtedly Edward Vernon, the rector of Redmile. In September, 1707, he was observed by several persons at Waltham fair to be "more than ordinarily free and familiar" with Elizabeth George, a serving woman. When they left the fair together, they were followed by suspicious neighbors to a field and discovered "in a very undecent and suspitious posture. . .she lying upon her back with her clothes up and [he] with [his] breeches down, upon her, comitting the abominable Sin of adultery or Incontinency with her." Several witnesses later admitted that a heavy rain made it hard to see just what Vernon was doing–and even Vernon himself was not sure, for, as he later confessed, drunkenness had clouded his memory of what had happened that fateful night. But he and Elizabeth George were hardly strangers: he had often been seen to "kiss, hugg, and embrace" her at the public house in Melton Mowbray where she worked. Witnesses in fact testified that he had crept up the public house stairs one night "in the dark in hopes to find the said Elizabeth in bed wherein he thought she lay." Unfortunately, he had entered the wrong bedroom, and had begun to be "very free with the person in bed, who proveing to be a man and awaked out of his sleep by his the said Edward's actions towards him, ask'd who was there and what they would have or to what purpose, upon which the said Edward Vernon, perceiving his mistake, made out of the chamber as fast as he could."

When Vernon begged Bishop Wake to extricate him from his adultery trial, Wake refused to help him. The Bishop indignantly noted that when Vernon came to see him he "rambled after his usual manner and was full of complaints against others, but knew nothing amiss in Himselfe." For his part, Archdeacon Rogers thought Vernon a man "of so much learning and so little discretion that I never met with the like." He was appalled that Vernon seemed to "have no remorse, and when he came to see me at night, he smelt so strongly of drink that his breath was noisome." Vernon had other influential clerical friends who eventually won him a pardon, but he never won the forgiveness of his patron, the Duke of Rutland. Their relations were hardly improved when Vernon's son shot one of the Duke's deer near Belvoir Castle. When the Duke demanded Vernon's dog in return, Vernon insolently retorted that his son would keep the dog to "pisse upon the Duke of Rutland's grave," and that the "surly old fellow of Belvoir Castle" was but a "pittifull Shitten Turd of a Duke." The Duke wrote Wake beseeching him to get Vernon out of Leicestershire, for he could not rest "easy or quiet in my own House with so troublesome a Person in my Neighbourhood." Vernon was temporarily suspended as morally unsound, but in 1712 he was back serving his parish, and he was still there in 1718. As for the son who shot the Duke's deer, he eventually became an eminent London clergyman, an antiquarian, and a Fellow of the Royal Society.[50]

There were other parsons who strayed from the paths of virtue. One of them, a rector of Witherley, remained in "Drunken Fitts" for ten days at a time; another, a vicar of Lockington, offered to teach his parishioners "a way to make a woman miscarry with child though within a month of her delivery." Then there was a rector of Wymondham who, for some odd reason, rode in a race in Nottingham "against a woman in a high Crowned hat."[51] Swift felt that such parsons exposed their entire profession to charges of vice and hypocrisy, for "whoever happens to see a scoundrel in a gown, reeling home at midnight. . .is apt to entertain an ill idea of the whole order, and at the same time to be extremely comforted in his own vices."[52] Still, only twenty Leicestershire parsons were reported for moral offenses between 1662 and 1714, just 2 percent of the parsons who served Leicestershire's parishes during that time. The vast majority of the local clergy apparently heeded Bishop Wake's advice to "Preach by your Lives, as well as by your Doctrine, to be a constant Sermon to your Flock."[53]

When it came to specifically clerical duties, churchwardens had more to complain about. Between 1662 and 1714, a total of 113 parsons were presented for clerical offenses, ranging from preaching too seldom to refusing to wear their surplices. Some of them were presented simultaneously for moral offenses and dilapidations as well. A fairly substantial number of these offenders were parsons who conducted clandestine marriages—illegal unions between couples who had neither issued banns nor obtained valid marriage licenses. The parties involved were often marrying without their parents' consent or in order to conceal a premarital pregnancy. They were usually willing to pay substantial sums to parsons willing to unite them. Overwhelmingly the clergy who obliged them were poorly paid curates and the incumbents of poorly endowed livings, parsons to whom this source of income was a constant temptation. In the 1660's, a curate of Enderby who had been accused of performing a clandestine marriage in fact cited as his defense his meager stipend of £8 a year.[54] Ecclesiastical officials could easily understand, and they often let first offenders escape with a warning. But about half of the parsons reported for clandestine marriages were chronic offenders, and many of these were temporarily suspended for periods ranging from a few months to two or three years. This led to further economic hardship, since suspended parsons were paid punitively small stipends from the proceeds of their livings. The vicar of Wigston Magna, for example, received only £13 a year while on suspension for clandestine marriages in the 1680's. In 1685 he petitioned for an increase in his stipend, claiming that he was unable to clothe himself.[55]

Complaints about parsons who neglected to offer frequent and regular church services were more common, and most of the parsons complained about were nonresident pluralists. In April, 1669, Charles Asfordby was the incumbent of both Foston in Leicestershire and Mablethorpe in Lincolnshire; the churchwardens at Foston complained that he had been nonresident for two years, and that during that time he had held no weekday services, had offered Sunday services only in the morning, and had not offered communion at all. In May, 1679, the churchwardens of Walton on the Wolds cited their rector, who was also the vicar of Barrow, for letting his parsonage fall into disrepair, preaching less than once a month, not celebrating communion, and not catechizing for four or five years. And in 1683 the patron of Lockington accused the vicar, a pluralist, of frequently neglecting Sunday services and omitting services on holy days altogether. He had also neglected to bury several parishioners, and if their families had not gone several

Clerical Offenses Committed by 113 Leicestershire Parsons, 1662-1714

	Percentage of offending parsons	*Percentage of all parsons*
Neglect of services		
General neglect	28%	3%
Omitting weekday services only	6%	<1%
Omitting catechizing only	9%	1%
Nonresidence (no complaint about neglect of services specifically made)	4%	<1%
Clandestine marriages	21%	2.5%
Unlicensed curates	7%	<1%
Others	13%	1.5%
Combinations of the above	12%	1%

miles to find another parson, the "Corps must have layd above ground and stunk and have bin put into the ground without Christian buryall."[56]

Offenses like these were serious, and a few parsons were accused of neglect several times during their careers. But reports of clerical negligence should be viewed in a wider perspective. For one thing, most offenders needed only one warning to prod them into better performance, and the majority were not reported again for neglect of services. Moreover, such complaints were aimed at only a small minority of the clergy; only about 7% of Leicestershire's parsons were cited for neglecting church services during the late-Stuart period. Then, too, about two-thirds of the citations for neglecting services were made before 1688: parsons working under William and Anne had an extremely good record in satisfying their parishioners in this matter. It may be that churchwardens became markedly less meticulous about reporting clerical neglect after 1688, but it seems equally likely that the parsons themselves, under the watchful eyes of diligent bishops like Gardiner and Wake, and increasingly aware of the need to guard against Dissent, were becoming more conscientious about their duties.

CONCLUSIONS

Judging from the evidence available for Leicestershire, the late-Stuart period was not a golden age in the history of the Church of England. About a third of Leicestershire's parishes were held in plurality, and one parish in five lacked a resident parson. A quarter of the county's parishes had only one Sunday service in 1718, while almost half omitted services on weekdays. Apathetic laymen let their churches and church fabric fall into disrepair; catechizings were often poorly attended; and the coming of official toleration enabled the nonreligious to avoid church services altogether. Nevertheless, it would be difficult to prove that the clergy were grievously neglectful of their calling, or that they bore a heavy responsibility for the problems of the Church. Some of them were nonresident pluralists, but pluralism was often a regrettable necessity when livings were inadequately endowed. Very few parsons became rich through pluralism, and those who did were usually careful to provide their second parishes with constantly resident curates. A few parsons betrayed their profession by committing serious moral offenses, but, at least in Leicestershire, scandalous parsons were a very small minority. While many parsons held fewer church services than their bishops would have liked, most held as many as their parishioners would attend, and relatively few clerics were ever charged with shirking their parochial duties. The great majority of the clergy apparently managed to live up to their parishioners' expectations. If they failed to conform completely to Wake's ideal of the perfect parson, they probably served their parishes as best they could in circumstances that were often trying.

NOTES

1. Wake, *Bishop of Lincoln's Charge*, pp. 30–32.
2. Wake MSS, CCXXXIV, f. 280.
3. *Ibid.*, CCXXXVI, n.f.: John Rogers to William Wake, April 18, 1713.
4. Leics. Museum, 1D41/4/XLVIII/76.
5. St. Paul's Library, MS 17-D-20, n.f.: South Kilworth, Church Langton, Witherley. (On microfilm at Leicester Museum.)
6. *Ibid.* See also the table on p. 124.
7. Leics. Museum, 1D41/13/79, f. 68; 1D41/13/78, f. 155v.; 1D41/13/81, f. 14.
8. Wake MSS, CCXXXIV, f. 280.
9. St. Paul's Library, MS 17-D-20.
10. *Ibid.*
11. Quoted in Sykes, *William Wake*, I, 182.
12. St. Paul's Library, MS 17-D-20, n.f.: South Kilworth.
13. Prideaux, *Letters*, p. 154.
14. St. Paul's Library, MS 17-D-20, n.f.: Knighton.
15. Leics. Museum, 1D41/14/IV/39.
16. Wake MSS, CCLXXVIII, n.f.: Seagrave.

17. Leics. Museum, 1D41/4/XXXI/66.

18. *Ibid.*, 1D41/13/82, loose paper at f. 34; 1D41/21, unnumbered boxes.

19. *Ibid.*, 1D41/18/15-20; 1D41/4/XLVII/37-42.

20. *Ibid.*, 1D41/18/13-14.

21. Information on pluralism comes from the sources cited in note 1 of the second chapter.

22. Wake MSS, CCXXXVI, n.f.: John Rogers to William Wake, April 18, 1713.

23. *Ibid.*, CCXXXV, f. 45.

24. *Ibid.*, CCLXXVII-CCLXXVIII.

25. St. Paul's Library, MS 17-D-20.

26. *Ibid.*

27. *Ibid.*

28. *Ibid.*

29. Meeke, *Diary*, p. 24.

30. Wake, *Bishop of Lincoln's Charge*, p. 21.

31. Eachard, *Grounds and Occasions*, pp. 47-50.

32. Swift, *Prose Works*, III, 201, 211, 217.

33. Hart, *John Sharp*, pp. 65-67.

34. Addison, *Spectator*, II, 91-92.

35. Swift, *Prose Works*, III, 207-208.

36. *Ibid.*

37. Leics. Museum, 1D41/13/80, f. 101v.; 1D41/4/XLI/6-11.

38. *Ibid.*, 1D41/4/XXXII/7-8; Wake MSS, CCXXXIV, f. 348.

39. *Ibid.*, 1D41/4/XXXVI/15.

40. Stone, "Educational Revolution," pp. 69-75.

41. Lincs. Arch. Off., Sub. IIa-III, V-VIb; Lic/Sch/1; L.C. V-VI, VIII-XVII; *Speculum* I; Leics. Museum, 1D41/34/1-3 (typescript); 1D41/35/1-58.

42. St. Paul's Library, MS 17-D-20; Lincs. Arch. Off., *Speculum* I.

43. *Ibid.*

44. *Ibid.*, and Nichols, *Leicester*, II, 92, 360, 547; III, 896; Hill, *Parish of Langton*, p. 278.

45. Nichols, *Leicester*, III, 1074-76; Leics. Museum, 1D41/2/712.

46. Stone, "Educational Revolution," pp. 69-75.

47. Based on all the surviving churchwardens' presentments for 1662-1714 (1D41/21, unnumbered boxes), the archdeaconry's late-Stuart correction court and instance court act books (1D41/13/67-83, 1D41/11/68, 73-77), loose court papers relating to court proceedings (1D41/4/XXVIII-LVI), and visitation papers (1D41/14/II-IV), all in Leicester Museum. Churchwardens' presentments do not survive for every visitation, but almost all gaps can be filled by using the court act books listed above, while the loose court papers give detailed accounts of some of the cases tried in the ecclesiastical courts.

48. Only those parsons who were rectors were responsible for keeping church chancels in repair. In parishes endowed with vicarages or perpetual curacies, chancel maintenance was the responsibility of the person or persons who owned the great tithes—men who in the late-Stuart period were generally members of the laity.

49. Leics. Museum, 1D41/13/82, ff. 58v., 63v., 70v., 91v., 102, 103; 1D41/4/XLVIII/108-109; 1D41/13/83, f. 17; Wake MSS, CCLXXVIII, n.f.: Swinford.

50. Leics. Museum, 1D41/4/L/105-107; 1D41/4/LIII/35-38; Wake MSS,

CCXXXIV, ff. 27-28, 30, 62, 128, 144, 197, 238; CCLXXVII, n.f.: a letter between the returns from Bottesford and Bowden, written to Wake by Edward Lane, November 26, 1709; Lambeth Palace Library, MS 1770, ff. 9, 28v., 65, 80, 89, 95v.; Venn and Venn, *Alumni Cantabrigiensis*, Pt. 1, IV, 299.

51. Leics. Museum, 1D41/4/XLI/6-11; 1D41/4/XLVII/64-65; 1D41/4/XLVIII/48.

52. Swift, *Prose Works*, III, 38.

53. Wake, *Bishop of Lincoln's Charge*, p. 21.

54. Leics. Museum, 1D41/13/68, f. 25.

55. *Ibid.*, 1D41/4/XLI/110-113.

56. *Ibid.*, 1D41/13/76, f. 171; 1D41/4/XLI/6-11; 1D41/13/80, f. 137v.

V

The Parsons at Home

Only a few of the houses that stood in late-Stuart Leicestershire still stand today, usually with subsequent additions and alterations that obscure their original appearance.[1] Thanks to a rich collection of documents, however, historians can learn a great deal about the houses of the late-Stuart clergy—and a great deal, too, about the clergymen themselves. Among the most useful of these documents are ecclesiastical terriers, those important bits of paper and parchment which recorded the Church's parochial possessions. Before the 1670's Leicestershire terriers seldom described parsonages in detail, usually only noted their size, and often failed to mention them at all. Toward the end of the century, descriptions became more elaborate. Between 1706 and 1709 a series of terriers covering most Leicestershire parishes not only provided lists of rooms, but also told with what materials parsonages were built, roofed, and floored. Through late-Stuart hearth tax returns, one can examine parsonages in the context of the village and county community. Bishops' faculties record alterations in size and structure, and churchwardens' presentments record physical upkeep and nonresidence. Finally, there are clerical probate inventories—itemized catalogs of the personal property that parsons owned when they died. Detailed inventories became less common toward the end of the seventeenth century and almost disappeared altogether after 1720; but when they survive, they conduct us through the rooms of houses that have long since vanished, meticulously listing the furnishings these houses once contained. Through inventories, we know that a certain passage led to the kitchen, that another passage led to the study. We see the clock on the mantel, the poker by the hearth. We open the cupboards and look at the pots. Indeed, the convergence of all these sources of information in the late-Stuart period is practically unparalleled in scope and detail. Documents relating to parsonages before the Civil War are not nearly as complete, and the fading out of inventories after 1720 creates a gap that cannot be bridged until the early nineteenth century. By that time, many of these old houses had been drastically altered or entirely swept away.

PARSONS WITHOUT PARSONAGES, AND PARSONAGES WITHOUT PARSONS

About one parish in ten lacked a parsonage, a disadvantage sometimes causing considerable hardship. Belgrave, for example, had a large and commodious brick parsonage attached to the rectory, but the rectory was impropriated and leased to a layman throughout this period, giving William Floyer much discomfort when he arrived in Belgrave to be its curate. "When I first came into this Country," he wrote his bishop in 1715, "I was so put to it for an house that I was forc'd to live in a Papist family; it occasioning some reflections I left, and with much troubled was favoured, as the people think, with a Lodging where the water this last flood gush'd up from under the Boards, which is so damp it spoils all my Books and Cloaths." Floyer felt obliged to ask permission to spend the winter with a neighboring vicar.[2] Cole Orton also lacked a parsonage, the old one having been burned during the Civil War when soldiers raided its Royalist incumbent; the building was not replaced until 1721.[3] Things were as bad at Fleckney. There the Reverend William Buckley had antagonized Edward Smart, a yeoman and one of the lay impropriators, by calling his marriage to his dead wife's sister incestuous. In 1671 Smart stripped the house of its floors, stairs, and doors. He then turned animals into it, and by 1676 the house was "utterly gone to decay and uninhabitable." Buckley engaged Smart in several lawsuits, but the terrier of 1708 still listed only a small barn as belonging to the living, and in 1712 the incumbent was a pluralist living at Armesby.[4]

Pluralism was the usual answer for parishes without parsonages. The great majority of these livings were among the poorest in the county, and even with parsonages they would probably have been held in plurality; their houseless condition merely assured that they would be served by nonresidents. In 1712, for example, the incumbents of Withcote, Dishley, and Ragdale were living in the parsonages attached to their other livings—Owston, Hathern, and Ratcliffe on the Wreak.[5] Because of pluralism, such incumbents seldom found it necessary to rent a house; however, houseless parishes often went without some church services and were usually deprived of daily spiritual guidance.

Even when a parish did possess a parsonage (and nine out of ten did), there was no guarantee that the incumbent would live in it. In 1712 fully a quarter of Leicestershire's parsonages were either vacant or inhabited by someone other than the incumbent.[6] Usually the reason was pluralism (about two cases out of three), with the pluralist choosing the parsonage best suited to his family's size and desired living standard. Those incumbents with only one parsonage gave various reasons for living elsewhere. The rector of Allexton found his house too small for his family, so he leased it to a tenant and rented another house in the neighborhood. On the other hand, the rector of Skeffington, a bachelor, thought his parsonage much too spacious for his needs, so he turned it over to tenants and lived with his brother in the village. The rector of South Croxton lived in Leicester to keep his children in the free grammar school there, hoping eventually to get them into Winchester on a scholarship. The vicar of Wistow lived with his patron, Sir Richard Halford, as a domestic chaplain at Wistow Hall. Thomas Seagrave, the rector of Leire, had been "annoyed by the incursions of Souldiers in marchings to and fro' all the time of warr" in his parsonage on the great road, so he leased his house to a tenant and moved to a quieter part of the village. Nonresidents generally favored leasing their parsonages to laymen, but sometimes parsonages were turned over to resident curates in partial payment for their services. On other occasions the parsonage would be leased to a layman with one or two rooms reserved for the curate.[7]

THE PARSONS AT HOME

Despite leasing, pluralism, and nonresidence, most incumbents did live in their parsonages, and all but a few Leicestershire parsonages were used as clerical homes at some point during the late-Stuart period. What sort of houses were they? Overwhelmingly they were built with materials immediately at hand. Stone parsonages predominated in the ironstone areas in the northeastern neck of the county and all down the Lincolnshire-Rutland border, merging into half-timbered parsonages in the central lowlands, and back into stone in the rocky Charnwood district.[8] Brick had made con-

Roofing Materials in Leicestershire Parsonages, 1700–1710

(N = 121)

	All parsonages	*Wealthy parsonages*	*Middling parsonages*	*Poor parsonages*
Thatch	48%	5%	64%	73%
Slate or tile	40%	68%	33%	19%
Combination	12%	27%	3%	8%

siderable inroads by the end of the century; though a few examples of brickwork may belong to the prewar period, the use of brick even as infilling was almost entirely a postwar development.[9] The old half-timbered parsonage at Frisby, a poor vicarage worth about £40 a year, was replaced by a larger brick house around 1670, when its hearth tax jumped from three to five.[10] The parson at Ratcliffe on the Wreak also chose brick when he rebuilt his house in the 1690's. The old parsonage had consisted of three half-timbered bays[11] and a separate kitchen-cowhouse; in contrast, the incumbent's new parsonage was a large ten-room house, entirely brick and covered with a slate roof. While the parson was at it, he added three barns, a coalhouse-dairy, and a dovehouse-privy, also built in brick.[12] By 1714, about one parsonage in three was at least partly brick, usually in the form of recent and relatively minor repairs, and all-brick parsonages had been built in one parish out of ten. They do not seem to have been correlated with high clerical incomes, but they were more common in lowland areas where timber had become more expensive and where stone was less available.

Roofing materials clearly did vary with the value of the living, thatch being the usual choice in poor and middling livings worth less than £100 a year. Parsonages were usually slated or tiled when the living's annual value was more than £100, though a quarter had thatch over part of the house with slate or tile over the rest. Slate and tile roofs were becoming more common in Leicestershire village architecture generally,[13] but parsons probably began the transition from thatch to slate earlier than yeomen and had probably carried it further by 1714.

The same is probably true of the transition from packed-earth floors to floors of stone, brick, and wood. Although service rooms in poor parsonages almost always had packed-earth floors, flag-

Number of Bays in Leicestershire Parsonages, 1690-1714[14]

(N = 178)

Bays	*All parsonages*	*Wealthy parsonages*	*Middling parsonages*	*Poor parsonages*
2	3%	0	2%	10%
3	18%	3%	13%	40%
4	24%	10%	25%	35%
5	24%	34%	30%	12%
6	19%	26%	21%	3%
7+	12%	27%	9%	0

Number of Rooms in Leicestershire Parsonages, 1690-1710[15]

(N = 142)

Rooms	*All parsonages*	*Wealthy parsonages*	*Middling parsonages*	*Poor parsonages*
3-5	6%	0	2%	17%
6-9	25%	4%	19%	53%
10-12	46%	48%	60%	28%
13+	23%	48%	19%	2%

stone had become common in the halls along with brick in the kitchens, and poor parsons with boarded parlor floors were not too unusual. In middling parsonages, packed earth had begun to give way to stone and brick even in coalhouses and butteries, and boarding had become almost standard for either the parlor or the best chamber. In rich parsonages, earthen floors had almost entirely disappeared in favor of stone or brick in the backrooms; deal and ash boards were used to floor parlors and one or two chambers. Unboarded chambers in all parsonages were generally floored with limestone plaster.

Parsonages varied considerably in size, as indicated by figures in the tables. Parsonages attached to livings worth less than £50 a year usually contained three or four bays of building and six to nine rooms. Most commonly this meant a hall, a kitchen, a parlor, and a chamber over each. John Kelham's parsonage at Stonesby contained only five rooms, and his estate in 1680 of only £16.11s. 2d. was one of the smallest left by late seventeenth-century Leicestershire parsons; however, he still managed to furnish his rooms in ways that were typical of parsons in the lower income brackets. The hall undoubtedly served as his family's living and dining room. Two tables, nine chairs, and six stools with cushions filled the center of the room, and fire-irons were placed near the hearth. The only other piece of furniture in the room was an inexpensive cupboard containing the family's meager store of tableware: six pewter dishes, a flagon, two cups, four porringers, two candlesticks, and a few other bits of pewter, bringing the value of the room's entire furnishings to about £2. In the adjoining kitchen were kept cooking utensils worth only £1.13s.: a brass pot, a great pan, a frying pan, three small pans, a few tubs and pails, a churn, and a kindle. Kelham's parlor was used as a bedroom, a custom common to two Leicestershire parsonages in three; a bed and bedclothes, three barrels, two coffers, and a few other implements brought the total value of the room's furnishings to just over a pound. The chamber over the hall contained only a bedstead and a few other things worth about 13s. Perhaps Kelham's children slept in the chamber over the parlor, which, besides two beds, was furnished with three coffers in which the family's household linen was stored: eight pairs of sheets, six pillowcases, two tablecloths, and eight napkins. This room's furnishings were valued at just short of £4.[16]

Stonesby had no glebe, so the only outbuilding Kelham required was a small barn of one or two bays for storing his tithes.[17] Here we find ten shillings' worth of hay (perhaps his entire hay tithe for the year[18]), a hog, a bucket and chain for his well, and one or two things the inventory fails to specify, in all amounting to £1.14s.6d. Finally, Kelham left behind ready money, clothing, and books (perhaps kept in his sleeping parlor) worth £5 altogether. One wonders how Kelham lived on Stoneby's poor income of less than £20 a year. Perhaps he received voluntary contributions from his parishioners and his patron, or earned a few pounds by serving as a curate for neighboring incumbents; certainly he was accused three times of picking up extra money through clandestine marriages.[19] But if Kelham's living standards were those of a humble peasant, he was probably himself of humble origins, so he may not have felt unduly deprived.[20]

Living space and household furnishings improved markedly in parsonages belonging to middling livings worth between £50 and £100 a year. Averaging four or five bays of building and ten or twelve rooms, these parsonages were comparable in size and furnishings to the houses of prosperous yeomen and occasionally even those of the smaller gentry, though their inventory values were usually much lower, reflecting smaller investments in farm produce and livestock. Besides the usual hall, parlor, and kitchen, specialized service rooms like brewhouses and coalhouses were standard, and often there was a second parlor as well. Upstairs, five or six chambers afforded more privacy for family members, and garrets occasionally provided rooms for a servant or two. Frequently this extra space enabled a minister to use a chamber or downstairs serving room as a private study, though the "study of books" usually mentioned in inventories in this class sometimes referred to a few shelves set up in a parlor or sleeping chamber.

The parsonage at Houghton typifies this group. Joseph Birkhead, the parish's rector, was the son of a Leicestershire brewer. After his ordination as deacon in 1662, he worked as a schoolmaster in Leicester for several years; he was ordained to the priesthood in 1668, and then served as curate at Welby for ten years more, until he was presented to Houghton by the Bennett family. In a normal year, the living's revenues amounted to about £80, an average income for a late-Stuart Leicestershire incumbent.[21] Houghton parsonage was an old half-timbered house partly plastered over in lime, with a few fairly recent repairs made in brick. Four of its five bays were slated, and the brewhouse, which may have been separated from the main house, was thatched. Like Stonesby, Houghton had no glebe, but seven bays of barns and other outbuildings were available to store tithes taken in kind. Probably Birkhead had been taking money payments instead, for when he died in 1705 his barns contained only some coal and wood, some hay, a few tools, a cow, and a hog. Most of Birkhead's estate of £118.11s.6d. lay in his household goods, his library, and personal savings.[22]

Birkhead's hall was almost as simply furnished as Kelham's, but the individual pieces were more expensive. Two tables rested on the brick floor, and around them could be placed six leather chairs and two stools. The room also held two flag chairs, the usual fire-irons, and a clock, bringing the total value of the room's furnishings to £3. Pots and pans kept in the brick-floored kitchen were valued at a pound, together with a pound's worth of candlesticks and other brass items, and £3 in pewterware, including twenty-four dishes and eighteen plates. In a storage room on the same floor Birkhead kept some barrels and forty-eight bottles, perhaps for storing the ale he concocted in the brewhouse, which held a brewing copper worth £2. The inventory lists the contents of the pantry and the storage chamber together, suggesting that the chamber lay directly over the pantry, and that the two were connected by a narrow flight of steps or a ladder; at any rate, the rooms contained a bedstead, a table, two trunks, and salt, worth in all about a pound. Like Kelham, Birkhead used his parlor as a bedroom, but Birkhead's parlor bed was definitely a soft feather bed with bolsters and valances, worth about £4. Unlike Kelham's parlor, Birkhead's was also used as a comfortable sitting room, with a boarded floor, twelve Turkey-work chairs, three tables, and fire-irons at the hearth.

Upstairs, Birkhead had four sleeping chambers, in addition to the storage chamber already mentioned; their furnishings varied in value from £2 to £13. The least expensively furnished was the maid's chamber, but even she had a feather bed. The next two rooms also had feather beds, and one of them had a mirror. These three bedrooms were all floored with limestone plaster, hard and probably quite cold underfoot in the winter, but the "Best Chamber," where Birkhead himself presumably slept, had a boarded floor partly covered by a rug. Here the feather bed was especially elaborate, with gilt-wrought curtains and silk-lined valances. Beside it was a little turn-up bed with a feather mattress and its own curtains, and against the wall stood a chest of drawers, a table, and six chairs with more gilt-wrought silk. Iron tongs rested near the hearth, curtains hung at the windows, and two mirrors were kept nearby. Birkhead's library, valued at £30, was unusually large for a parson in his income bracket; possibly there was a separate room to house his books, but more probably they were kept in the parlor or the best chamber. Finally, Birkhead died possessed of linen worth about £2, silver worth £15, and clothes and ready money worth an additional £15.

William Paske's inventory at Aylestone (£180 a year) illustrates the way parsonages in the higher income brackets were furnished.[23] Though his estate was valued at £865.4s.9d. in 1670, well over £500 of this lay in ready money and promissory notes, besides £80 in a lease on two houses in Cambridge, £40 in grain still standing in the fields, £25 in silver plate, and £10 in his purse and clothing. Furnishings accounted for about £170 of the estate. A table and frame with five forms stood in the hall, along with a smaller table, a desk, and a clock with weights. The great parlor was used exclusively as a sitting room, its contents including four tables with table carpets, two couch chairs, two wainscoted chairs, ten red leather chairs with Turkey-work cushions for each, three green

Distribution of Houses by Number of Hearths, 1666

	Leicestershire houses (N = 9,650)	*Leicestershire parsonages* (N = 186)
Hearths		
10+	1%	1%
9	.5%	1%
8	.5%	2%
7	1%	5%
6	2%	9%
5	3%	15%
4	5%	24%
3	8%	20%
2	30%	18%
1	49%	5%

Distribution of Houses by Number of Rooms

	Wigston Magna houses, 1675–1725 (N = 55)	*Leicestershire parsonages, 1690–1710* (N = 142)
Rooms		
1–2	29%	0
3–5	45%	6%
6–9	24%	25%
10+	2%	69%

cushions, a wicker chair, and fire-irons for the hearth. The second parlor may have stood vacant, for only the room itself is mentioned; perhaps some of the furniture in the great parlor had been moved from the second parlor to simplify inventory-taking, or perhaps it was here that Paske kept his library, valued at £30. In the kitchen, Paske had £15 worth of brass and pewterware, ranging from eighteen pewter dishes to four brass chamber pots. More cooking utensils were kept in the bakehouse, a cheese press and pots in the dairy, a brewing apparatus in the brewhouse, and a trough in the buttery.

Upstairs, the inventory lists nine chambers and a closet. Two chambers were used for storing wheat and malt, while the men's chamber and the entry chamber probably housed servants and laborers for Aylestone's extensive glebe. Each held two bedsteads, and the other furnishings consisted of a trunk, a chest, a chair, and

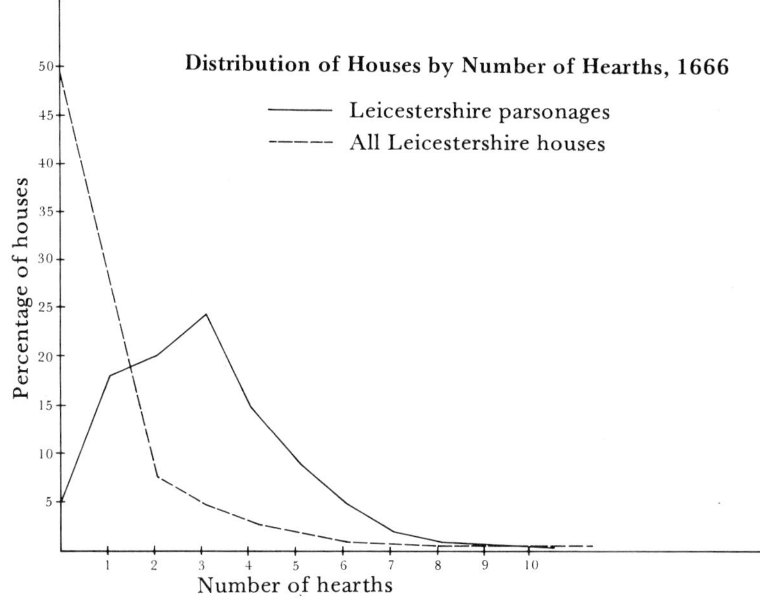

four spinning wheels. Possibly the kitchen chamber housed servants as well, though its three inexpensive beds were accompanied by a rather expensive mirror. All the other bedrooms had feather beds and probably belonged to family members. The one over the great parlor also contained several chairs, two cupboards, and window curtains; the buttery chamber's feather bed was joined by a smaller truckle bed; and the bedroom over the little parlor held three red leather chairs and fire-irons for its hearth. No doubt the great chamber over the hall was where Paske himself slept. Its contents were valued at £18—more than the value of John Kelham's entire estate at Stonesby. Besides the feather bed with its curtains and valances, the room contained a great chair, two lesser chairs, four stools, two stands, a table and frame, curtains at the windows, fire-irons at the hearth, and "one greate lookeing glass." Linen worth £20 was on hand in another chamber to supply the needs of the great house.

As may be apparent, the real gap in household furnishings lay between poor and middling parsons, not between the middling and the rich. Like Paske most wealthy parsons tended to invest extra income in leases and loans, rather than in decorating rooms more lavishly. The Reverend Mr. Gery of Barwell enjoyed an income of over £200 a year, but at his death in 1670 less than one-third of his estate of £222.7s.3d. was invested in household goods; the rest consisted of livestock, crops, and £55 in personal loans.[24] The same was true of William Roberts of Carlton Curlieu, whose household furnishings were valued at only £70 out of an estate of over £1,400, with the balance invested in livestock, plate, promissory notes, and money found hidden in a chest of drawers after his death.[25]

On the other hand, wealthy parsons did have more rooms to furnish, with houses attached to wealthy livings averaging five or six bays and twelve to fourteen rooms. Almost all had two parlors (a few had three), with one parlor usually emerging as a formal sitting room. Formal dining rooms are listed for Norton by Twycross, Lutterworth, and Sapcote; storage rooms and bedrooms were more numerous than in middle-income livings; garret rooms for additional servants were more common and were sometimes replaced by full third floors. Occasionally a "Green Chamber" or a "Red Chamber" occurs, suggesting aesthetic color coordination in window curtains, bed hangings, and chair upholstery.[26] But aside from more rooms and occasional aesthetic refinements, the real gap lay between the bottom and the middle rather than between the middle and the top. Living space and creature comforts improve rapidly as one moves from poor clerics to middling ones, and then begin to stabilize as extra earnings go into leases and loans. Middling and upper-middling parsons tended to live in houses and among furnishings which nearly all late-Stuart parsons would have found satisfactory. Once a parson had reached that level of comfort, he rested relatively content.

THE LOCAL CONTEXT

How did parsonages compare with other late-Stuart houses? Did clergymen live in better houses than most of their parishioners? One answer comes from the hearth tax returns of 1666.[27] For almost every house in Leicestershire, these returns record the number of hearths subject to Parliamentary taxation; they thus provide a rough indication of how houses compared in size. Almost half of Leicestershire's houses were humble cottages with only one taxable hearth; in most cases, these were the homes of outservants, paupers, poor husbandmen, and unskilled laborers. Houses with two hearths (about a third of the county's houses) typically belonged to skilled craftsmen and fairly substantial yeomen—men of better than average standing in their communities.[28] Only a fifth of Leicestershire's houses had three hearths or more; their owners tended to be prosperous merchants, exceptionally wealthy yeomen, and members of the country gentry. Within this context, the clergy's houses were clearly above average: while a few parsonages had one or two hearths, the majority had at least four. Three-quarters of the county's parsonages fell in the top fifth of all of the houses in Leicestershire, and fully a third fell in the top 8 percent. One parsonage in six was the largest house in its village; one in three was either largest or second largest. Much the same picture emerges when we compare the number of rooms in Leicestershire's parsonages with the number of rooms in the houses of Wigston Magna, a Leicestershire village with a sizable yeomanry and a few minor gentlemen. While the typical house in Wigston had three to five rooms, the typical Leicestershire parsonage had ten to twelve rooms. Most parsonages, in fact, were comparable in size to the houses of Wigston's gentry.[29]

Judging from probate inventories, most parsonages were considerably above average in terms of household furnishings as well. Mirrors, for example, were extremely rare in the houses of Wigston Magna. Francis Smith, a Wigston gentleman, owned a mirror in 1677; the next does not occur until 1706, and its owner was likewise a gentleman.[30] In the inventories of parsons, however, mirrors are fairly common items—upper-middling and wealthy clergymen sometimes owned two or three. By the same token, Leicestershire's clergy frequently owned clocks, while Wigston's farmers generally did not. "Dining rooms," though unusual in Leicestershire's parsonages, were still more common in clerical homes than in the houses of Wigston's laymen. George Davenport, a wealthy farmer, had a dining room in 1713, but his was the first to be recorded in Wigston Magna since the death of Queen Elizabeth.[31] Because parsons aspired to gentle status, they usually spent more on household furnishings than yeomen with comparable incomes, and some spent as much as country gentlemen whose incomes were substantially higher.[32]

CONTINUITY AND CHANGE

The late seventeenth century was not a time of rapid change in Leicestershire parsonages: between 1650 and 1720, only about one parsonage in five was rebuilt or extensively renovated.[33]

Market Bosworth's parsonage was among the new ones, and Bishop Wake thought it a "palace" and "one of the finest Parsonage Houses in England." However, the parsonage he described was exceptional both in its newness and its grace, for its builder was the son of the wealthy baronet who was patron of the living.[34] Few incumbents possessed such lofty connections, and the minority who rebuilt their parsonages usually built houses only slightly larger than their old ones. In fact, they tended to rebuild only when neglect by previous incumbents had been so grievous as to make mere repairs impractical. In 1680, for example, the patron of Thurnby sued the nonresident incumbent for dilapidations to the vicarage amounting to over £20. Half the house had completely collapsed, the barn was ready to fall, and additional repairs were needed for the remaining walls, the roof, the floors, and the fences. As a result, the house was almost entirely rebuilt, with only one old half-timbered bay remaining from the original parsonage. The rest had been rebuilt in brick with underground cellars; both parlors now had boarded floors, the floors in the hall and the kitchen were both brick, and the house had a garret.[35]

Periodic repair jobs and minor improvements were more common. About one parsonage in three was reported out of repair at some point during the late-Stuart period, and in a few parishes the condition was chronic.[36] Ashby Magna's parsonage stayed more or less out of repair for a quarter-century; its incumbent was a pluralist who lived at Broughton Astley and leased the parsonage to a neglectful tenant, typically the background of cases like this.[37] But most parsonages were speedily repaired, usually by simply replacing decayed areas with the same materials or the newer brickwork, and with few, if any, structural changes. Inside the houses, the late seventeenth century did bring some improvements in flooring. The use of brick for paving was largely a post-Restoration development, and by Anne's reign almost all of Leicestershire's parsonages had one or more brick-paved rooms. Boarded floors, which began appearing in parsonages in the early seventeenth century, probably became more common under the later Stuarts. In 1708 the rector of Nailstone had recently boarded his parlor with oak "at my own expense," and by 1710 boarded parlors could be found in two-thirds of Leicestershire's parsonages.[38] On the other hand, the period saw few other changes in household furnishings. With the exception of increasing numbers of clocks and a slight tendency for sleeping parlors to turn into sitting rooms, the same range in comfort and expense prevailed at the end of the century as at the middle.

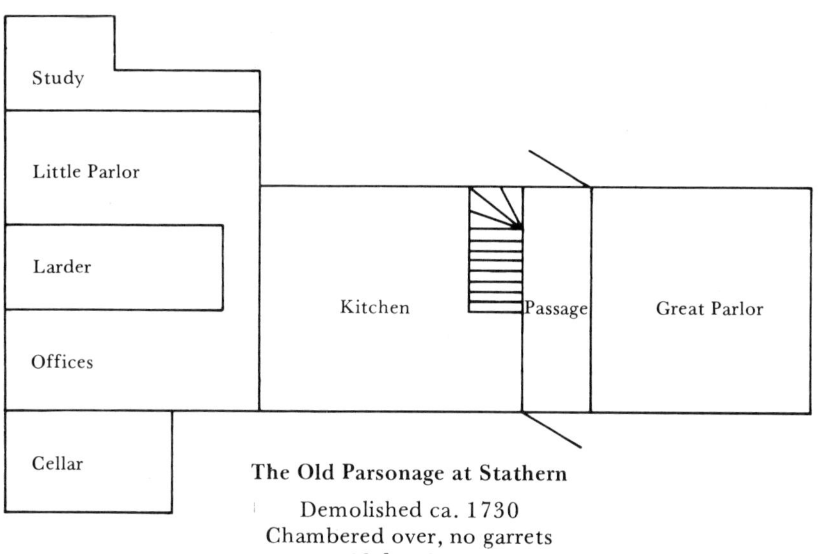

The Old Parsonage at Stathern

Demolished ca. 1730
Chambered over, no garrets
63 feet long

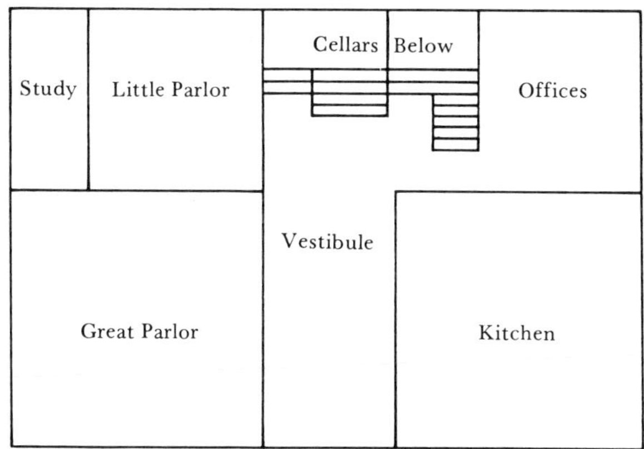

The New Parsonage at Stathern

Built ca. 1730
Chambered over, plus garrets
48 feet long, 34 feet wide

In order to see substantial change, one must look backward and forward. A few parsonages, including those at Claybrook and Sharnford, were wholly rebuilt in the years immediately preceding the Civil War, but terriers are too uninformative to make specific dating possible for most prewar parsonages.[39] Like Cossington rectory, which survived into the twentieth century, many probably began as much smaller late-medieval houses, often with only three or four rooms.[40] During Elizabeth's reign, newly married clergymen found themselves needing additional living space for their offspring, and they began expanding their parsonages one or two rooms at a time. Chambers appeared over halls formerly open to the roof; additional service rooms sprang up at the back and sides; new bays with extra parlors and chambers sprouted. This was often the process involved in the development of Elizabethan and Jacobean village architecture generally, as packed mud walls gave way to half-timber and stone, houses grew in size, and the two-story yeoman farmhouse began to emerge.[41] Certainly several late-Stuart terriers describe parsonages as being "very old" or "ancient," and others describe parsonages as differing from bay to bay in wall and roofing materials, suggesting piecemeal construction. Welham parsonage contained six bays of building, of which three were packed earth and the other three were stone, probably of more recent origin. Galby parsonage was part stone, part half-timbered; five bays were roofed with slate, and the sixth was thatched.[42]

For a few parsonages, detailed records of room-by-room construction and renovation survive for the years after the Civil War, suggesting the sort of changes many Leicestershire parsonages must have undergone in the previous century. Garthorp was a poor living worth only £40 a year, and its parsonage was rated for only one hearth in 1666. A building of two bays, one of which was open to the roof and "little better than a barn," it probably contained a hall, a kitchen, a parlor, and a single upstairs chamber. In 1672 the incumbent, Mr. Truman, added another bay on the east end, and in 1697 his inventory listed seven rooms: kitchen, parlor, hall, brewhouse, dairy, chamber, and storage chamber. James Turner succeeded him as vicar, and in 1706 he apparently rebuilt one of the two original bays. The next year he partitioned the great chamber so that the upper floor now consisted of two chambers and "another small appartment," perhaps used as a study. At the same time, he built a chimney for the parlor, which had formerly been served by "an old tunnel." In 1710 he rebuilt the old west bay, put "conveniences" in it, and tacked on a lean-to to serve as a buttery. He built a stable three years later, put a chamber over it in 1716, and built a new stable and turned the old one into a second parlor in 1722. In 1724 he added another lean-to to the west end of the house, and he rebuilt the barn the following year. When he died in 1730, he was succeeded by his son John, who rebuilt the south wall of the hall in 1733 and put in a new window. The parlor chimney was again rebuilt in 1737, and in 1740 a new flight of stairs was constructed in the kitchen passage.[43]

The parsonage at Stathern probably emerged gradually from similar alterations. In 1730 its spatial irregularities seemed crude and ungainly to its new Georgian incumbent, who found it "very old. . .very low, inconvenient and extended on a great compass of ground." Before he demolished it and erected a new parsonage of fashionably compact symmetry, he drew up floor plans of the old and the new and submitted them to his bishop for approval.[44] (See illustration.) The old parsonage at Stathern, with its haphazard sprawl, odd angles, and probable growth by gradual accretion, must have resembled a great many Leicestershire parsonages of the late seventeenth century. After undergoing physical expansion between 1560 and 1640, most remained relatively unchanged under the later Stuarts, and then slowly succumbed to Georgian and Victorian modernization. Only through inventories and terriers do we know them today.

NOTES

1. Pevsner, *Buildings*, pp. 58, 81, 92, 119, 172, 206.

2. Lincs. Arch. Off., Ter., vol. 23, pp. 105-106; Leics. Museum, 1D41/2/62-64; Wake MSS, CCXXXVII, n.f.: William Floyer to William Wake, October 10, 1715.

3. Buchan, *Poems of Pestell*, p. xliii; Wake MSS, CCLXXVIII, n.f.: Cole Orton.

4. Leics. Museum, 1D41/21 (unnumbered boxes): September, 1679, April, 1676; 1D41/13/80, loose paper at f. 93; 1D41/4/XXXVIII/60-71; Lincs. Arch. Off., Ter., vol. 23, p. 305; Wake MSS, CCLXXVII, n.f.: Fleckney.

5. Wake MSS, CCLXXVII-CCLXXVIII, n.f.

6. *Ibid*.

7. *Ibid*.

8. Generalizations about the materials used to construct, roof, and floor Leicestershire parsonages are based on about 120 terriers of the years 1700-1710. These are found primarily in Lincs. Arch. Off., Ter., vol. 23, pp. 1-1012; others are scattered through boxes of terriers numbered 13, 17, and 18; and several others are found in Leics. Museum, 1D41/2/1-777.

9. Thirsk, ed., *Agrarian History*, IV, 726-727.

10. Lincs. Arch. Off., Ter., vol. 23, p. 325; vol. 8, p. 367; Leics. Museum, 1D41/2/232-237; P.R.O., E 179/251/9, p. 154.

11. "Bay" originally referred to the space between two beams in houses of wooden construction, but by this time it was also being used to describe houses built of brick or stone. When a house had two floors, there were roughly two rooms per bay.

12. Leics. Museum, 1D41/2/538-540; Lincs. Arch. Off., Ter., vol. 23, p. 772; Edward and Young, "Antiquities of Ratcliffe on the Wreak."

13. Hoskins, *Midland Peasant*, p. 304.

14. Lincs. Arch. Off., Ter., vol. 23, pp. 1-1012; boxes 13, 17, 18; Leics. Museum, 1D41/2/1-777, *passim*.

15. *Ibid.*, and probate inventories of Leicestershire parsons' estates taken between those two dates: Leics. Rec. Off., PR/I/--.

16. Leics. Rec. Off., PR/I/82/198.

17. Leics. Museum, 1D41/2/659-662.

18. The entire value of Stonesby's hay tithe in 1707 was 15s.: Lincs. Arch. Off., Ben/8/61.

19. Leics. Museum, 1D41/13/76, ff. 216v., 219v., 226v.

20. He could not have been the John Kelham, D.D., that Venn also makes vicar of Langham, Rutland (*Alumni Cantabrigiensis*, Pt. 1, III, 3). The parson at Stonesby held no degree and was not a pluralist: Lincs. Arch. Off., L.C. VI, f. 191. A thorough check of wills in Leicestershire Record Office has failed to reveal who Kelham's parents might have been. This, his lack of a degree, and his poor income strongly suggest that he was of humble origins.

21. Lincs. Arch. Off., L.C. VIII, f. 92; L.C. IX, f. 164v.; Leics. Rec. Off., PR/1666/20; Venn and Venn, *Alumni Cantabrigiensis*, Pt. 1, I, 158; Fletcher, "Documents relating to Leicestershire," p. 287; Nichols, *Leicester*, I, 512.

22. Lincs. Arch. Off., Ter., vol. 23, pp. 412-418; Leics. Museum, 1D41/2/324-326; Leics. Rec. Off., PR/I/112/100.

23. Leics. Rec. Off., PR/I/70/7; Fletcher, "Documents relating to Leicestershire," p. 234.

24. Leics. Rec. Off., PR/I/70/166.

25. *Ibid.*, PR/I/78/178.

26. *Ibid.*, PR/I: 79/109, 87/212, 83/39, 73/77, 66/3.

27. Leicestershire's hearth tax returns of 1666 are in the Public Record Office, E 179/251/9; I have used the microfilm copies in the Leicestershire Record Office. Philip Styles arrived at somewhat similar findings for Kineton Hundred in Warwickshire, where the gentry's houses averaged 5.66 hearths, the clergy's 4.25, and the yeomen's 2.44. See Styles, "Social Structure of Kineton Hundred," p. 98. See also Howell, "A Short Guide to Records."

28. Hoskins, *Midland Peasant*, pp. 300-302.

29. The figures for Leicestershire's parsonages are the same as those in Tables 17 and 19 (see note 15). The figures for Wigston Magna, which are the same as those in Table 19, are taken from Hoskins, *Midland Peasant*, pp. 300-302.

30. Hoskins, *Midland Peasant*, p. 307.

31. *Ibid.*

32. Judging from Leics. Rec. Off., PR/I/--. I have examined all of the surviving inventories of the estates of parsons who died between 1662 and 1714, as well as approximately one hundred inventories of the estates of husbandmen, yeomen, and gentlemen who died during this period. Clergymen's in-

ventories usually fall below yeomen's inventories in total value, reflecting the clergy's smaller investment in crops, livestock, loans, and farming tools; in the value of household goods, however, clergymen usually exceeded yeomen.

33. Lincs. Arch. Off., Ter., vol. 23, vol. 8, boxes 13, 17, 18; Fac. 1, 2, 9; Leics. Museum, 1D41/2/1-777; Nichols, *Leicester*, passim.

34. Lambeth Palace Library, MS 1770, f. 18v.; Fletcher, "Documents relating to Leicestershire," p. 242; Venn and Venn, *Alumni Cantabrigiensis*, Pt. 1, II, 46.

35. Leics. Museum, 1D41/4/XXXIX/4-7; 1D41/2/716-719.

36. *Ibid.*, 1D41/21 (unnumbered boxes); 1D41/13/67-83.

37. *Ibid.*, 1D41/13/82, ff. 78, 82v., 84, 114v.; 1D41/13/83, f. 14; 1D41/13/77, f. 25; 1D41/13/81, ff. 51v., 105, 109, 123v.; 1D41/21 (unnumbered box): May, 1698.

38. Lincs. Arch. Off., Ter., vol. 23, p. 680; Thirsk, ed., *Agrarian History*, IV, 726-727.

39. Nichols, *Leicester*, IV, 111-113, 920.

40. Herbert, "Cossington Rectory."

41. Barley, *Farmhouse and Cottage*, pp. 95, 124; Hoskins, *Provincial England*, pp. 57-66.

42. Lincs. Arch. Off., Ter., vol. 23, p. 341; Hill, *Parish of Langton*, pp. 334-335.

43. Lincs. Arch. Off., Ter., vol. 23, p. 353; Leics. Museum, 1D41/2/248-249; Leics. Rec. Off., DE 659/17 (Garthorp parish register); PR/I/103/3 (the study of books was probably not a separate room but a collection kept in the parlor or a chamber); P.R.O., E 179/251/9, pp. 9-10 (William Richardson).

44. Lincs. Arch. Off., Fac/9/124.

VI

The Parsons in Politics

From the Restoration to the Jacobite invasion of 1715, the English political community was troubled by one religious crisis after another. Fear of revolution by Puritan radicals in the early 1660's gave way to hysteria over Catholic subversion in the late 1670's, and to an attempt to exclude Charles II's Catholic brother from the line of succession. Heightened persecution of Dissenters in the early 1680's in turn yielded to an abortive effort, in James II's reign, to unite Protestant left and Catholic right against the Anglican middle. Even after the Glorious Revolution of 1688 there remained the problem of the political status of Dissenters, bringing controversies over test acts and occasional conformity. The Revolution itself created two other problems: the threat posed by Jacobites intent on restoring the exiled king, and the clergy's resentment of the Toleration Act of 1689. Meanwhile, during William's reign, English politics were being transformed—from a system of shifting factional interests and Court-Country clashes, into contests between two organized political parties with competing programs and credos. On the whole, the issues that divided Whigs and Tories in the early eighteenth century were more secular than religious: Whigs supported the high taxes and fiscal innovations needed to finance continued hostilities against France by land and sea, while Tories, resentful of heavy land taxes and the moneyed interests in the City which the war had benefited, came to favor either peace or a less expensive naval strategy. But there were strong religious overtones as well. Whiggery meant rapprochement with Dissent and a firm commitment to Anne's Protestant heirs in Hanover, while the Tories stood steadfast behind the Church of England and (somewhat schizophrenically) flirted with a Jacobite restoration.

It was a time when religious issues still agitated the political arena, and when members of the clergy were tempted to influence the course of political events. Although recent works have already treated episcopal dabbling in late-Stuart politics in some detail,[1] the parish clergy's involvement needs more investigation, for even parsons in obscure country districts were important members of the political nation. In most cases they had to exercise their influence out of office and behind the scenes; though bishops wielded considerable power in the House of Lords, the lower clergy seldom even sat on the county commissions of the peace. Few county commissions in this period included more than one or two members of the ordinary parish clergy, and even they were usually distinguished doctors of divinity.[2] In Leicestershire, the county commission of 1680 included the Archbishop of Canterbury, the Bishop of London, the Bishop of Durham, and the Commissary of the Bishop of Lincoln (actually a lawyer); however, these were basically honorary appointees, and the only parish clergyman on the list was George Bright, D.D., rector of Loughborough. John Gery, D.D., rector of Swepstone and Archdeacon of Buckingham, was added by 1685; Dr. Michael Hutchinson, vicar of Packington, gained admission after the accession of George I. These were the only members of the parish clergy who made it onto Leicestershire's commission of the peace during a forty-year period.[3]

But parish parsons were hardly political ciphers. The local clergyman was often the best educated and occasionally the most substantial man in his village, and in a deferential age this gave him considerable influence over his parishioners. "In the character of pastors and teachers," Richard Steele wrote in 1713, "you have an almost irresistible power over us of your congregations," for "circumstances of education and fortune place the minds of the people, from age to age, under your direction."[4] Above all, the clergy possessed the power of the pulpit. Skepticism and scientific rationalism were beginning to undermine the sermon's potency as a political tool, but the pulpit continued to serve as a major political podium for a nation still largely innocent of mass media and still susceptible to religious appeals. Existing political opinions could be justified by scripture and thereby assume an aura of eternal truth, and occasionally political renegades might even be won over by carefully chosen scriptural references. When Sacheverell denounced the Whigs as traitors to the Church in his Oxford sermon of 1702, he proved that the sermon remained at least as important as the secular partisan newsletter in shaping national political opinion.

The Crown had always been aware of the clergy's power, and a late-Stuart royal injunction tactfully reminded them of "how great importance the preaching of sound and discreet doctrine is to our owne safety and the quiet and good of our people."[5] The great majority of the clergy had always been happy to oblige, but during the reign of Charles II their devotion to the person of the King reached new and ultimately dangerous heights. During the Civil War they had seen the Church's fortunes rise and fall with the fortunes of the monarchy, and the restoration of both under Charles II had cemented the bonds that had long joined the two together. More than ever the King had become the Defender of their Faith, and the clergy gratefully responded by becoming, more than ever, the defenders of the Crown. Between the Restoration and the Glorious Revolution, the clergy's sermons unhesitatingly called for perfect loyalty, unstinting obedience, and nonresistance to the royal will. In Nathaniel Alsop's Leicestershire assize sermon of 1682, Charles II assumed the stature of a Moses who had led his people from pagan bondage. Alsop attacked those who had challenged Charles's authority during the Exclusion Crisis, and especially those who had tried "by a most fulsome Flattery of the People to insinuate into them an Opinion that all Sovereignty and Power, all Honour and Authority, as to the first Ownership is theirs." His text was the commandment to "Honour thy Father and thy Mother," and much of his argument that the nation owed perfect obedience to its regal father proceeded straight from Filmer's *Patriarcha*, a debt Alsop specifically acknowledged.[6]

Passive obedience became a major stumbling block in James II's reign, when the clergy were suddenly confronted with a cruel dilemma. How could they preach nonresistance to a monarch who appeared to be subverting the very Church he had sworn to uphold? It was a problem James forced them to face when, in 1688, he ordered his Declaration of Indulgence to be read from every pulpit in the realm. "We are now in a great bustle about reading the king's declaration," Theophilus Brooks wrote his patron, the Earl of Huntingdon, on June 2. "Our Bishop sent it to our several churches, and our gentry very much oppose the reading of it. Mr. Ferrers, as Mr. Burdett told me, swore it would not be read in his church, and I believe it will be read in few churches in Darbyshire, pamphlets being spread amongst the clergy against the reading of it." Brooks was distraught: "I must read it or waive it at my peril," he wrote; "all are so sharp here that it's very difficult to live amongst them." Brooks was a cautious man and asked his patron "how to behave myself in my difficult circumstances." The Earl's reply was apparently to read the Declaration, for on December 19, in the midst of the Glorious Revolution, Brooks reported that "the gentry look evilly upon me, so that I sit uneasily."

But he had partly redeemed himself. While most of the gentry were in Nottingham greeting Princess Anne, a "mighty alarum went from town to town that the Irish were cutting of throats, Lichfield on fire, and Burton attempted upon"; Brooks therefore "ordered our own arms and put our house in some way of defence" and went out "soldier like towards Burton to prevent the Irish massacre. . .being followed by some 60 horse and foot with mighty resolution." When the rumor proved false, Brooks dismissed his men and found himself held in even greater contempt by the gentry, to whom he was still "but a little Papist." Nevertheless, he had become a hero to the "rabble, who I believe upon another such alarum would follow me in hundreds." The Earl may have been pleased with Brooks's actions too, because the next year he appointed him rector of Markfield and vicar of Belton. Furthermore, it was probably through the Earl's influence that Brooks succeeded in 1699 to the Crown's living at Norton by Twycross, worth £100 a year.[7]

John Gery was another Leicestershire parson caught up in the events of 1688. He had begun his career in 1662 as rector of Swepstone, and in 1676 the Earl of Huntingdon presented him to Stoney Stanton, raising his income to over £200 a year. In 1683 he acquired the Archdeaconry of Stow, a preferment he exchanged the next year for the more lucrative post of Archdeacon of Buckingham, and in 1687 he acquired a Lincoln prebend. With all these preferments Gery was potentially one of the most influential parsons in the county, a man whose actions in 1688 would be carefully watched. Though it was reported that many of Leicestershire's clergy were averse to reading the Declaration of Indulgence, Gery read it anyway at both his churches and thereby "met with too much disdain from his brethren of the clergy and others." Friends suggested in August and September that the Earl try to procure a bishopric for Gery to compensate for the unpopularity of his loyal actions. However, James was overthrown before anything came of this, and Gery's career had advanced no further before his death in 1722 than it had by 1688. His name, which had appeared in the lists of Leicestershire justices of the peace from the beginning of James's reign, was apparently dropped during the reign of William and Mary and did not reappear until the reign of Anne.[8]

Only nine Leicestershire parsons carried passive obedience to the point of becoming Non-Jurors and active Jacobites.[9] The others somehow managed to transfer their loyalities to William and Mary, but they soon discovered that the Glorious Revolution called for a complicated revision of the old pieties that their sermons had previously instilled. How could passive obedience to the current monarchs be demanded when the previous monarch had been overthrown? How far could a parson go in preaching loyalty to the Crown without implying a return to the anointed House of Stuart? After 1689, the semantic dividing line between nonresistance and treason became hard to pinpoint, and parsons who still preached passive obedience could easily expose themselves to charges of Jacobitism, even if they really meant something quite different. In 1708 the Reverend Samuel Carte of Eastwell wrote Bishop Wake a letter defending his son, who was also a parson, from charges of having delivered a Jacobite sermon. "Your Lordship well knows," Carte nervously explained, "the difference between representing passive obedience due to the person of the prince, though acting against Law and subverting a constitution, and passive obedience due to the Law and the entire sovereignty wheresoever lodged."[10] His son, he was saying, was not a Jacobite but a constitutional Tory.

The Reverend Thomas Sawbridge hit on a better formula in his Leicestershire assize sermon of 1689. He urged his fellow clergymen to stay out of politics altogether, and not to "meddle in these matters, whereof they are not competent judges." They should in fact leave political issues to the "cognizance and determination of States-men and Lawyers, who best understand the Constitution of the Government and the Force and Effect of the Laws of their Respective Countries." Thus nonresistance shifted into noninvolvement; but in 1689 this advice was aimed primarily at Non-Juring parsons still loyal to James, and Sawbridge himself did not hesitate to imply his own preference for constitutional monarchy and the Protestant succession. Even kings must "govern according to the Laws they have made," he proclaimed, and their judges are bound to uphold the established religion.[11] Most clerics felt more at home with a divinely anointed monarchy than with one that in some fashion or other had been contracted; even so, after 1689, loyalty to Protestantism and fear of Jacobite rebellion prodded them toward contractualism, and toward an emphasis on the obligations of the monarch as much as on the duties of his subjects.

If the Glorious Revolution brought a subtle shift in the political theories expected of loyal parsons, it also marked the beginning of three highly charged decades during which political tensions within the clergy steadily increased. Though the great majority of the clergy were able to accept the Revolution, most ultimately felt cheated by the religious and political developments that followed it. The Toleration Act of 1689 virtually destroyed the ability of the church courts to enforce church attendance and to suppress Dissenting academies and schoolteachers. Then, in 1695, the government allowed the official censorship of scandalous literature to lapse, making possible the publication of virulent attacks on the Church and its doctrines by writers like William Whiston and John Toland.[12] Meanwhile, many of the clergy were finding little to admire in King William. As Gilbert Burnet put it, "his indifference as to the forms of church-government, and his being zealous for toleration, together with his cold behaviour towards the clergy, gave them generally very ill impressions of him."[13] At the same time, Whig politicians, including certain members of the episcopal bench, were calling for rapprochement with Dissent, and in some cases for reforms in the Church's liturgy thoroughgoing enough to accommodate Anglicans and Dissenters within the same church establishment.[14] Most Anglican parsons, trained in universities that had become bastions of conservatism, took a jaundiced view of all this. Little wonder then that in 1697 a Yorkshire parson told his diary the outrage he felt when

> the House of Commons had the impudence to pretend to meddle with the holy things of the church, and would needs have the cross in baptism, the surpless, and the use of the ring in marriage made indifferent things. . . .The House of Commons are commonly a company of irreligious wretches who cares not what they do, nor what becomes of the church and religious things, if they can but get their hawkes, hounds, and whores, and the sacred possessions of the church.[15]

Especially frustrating was the fact that the clergy's official channels of protest were limited, for during much of this period Convocation was effectively muzzled. In 1661 convocations of the clergy of both provinces had met to revise the prayerbook, but three years later an oral agreement between Clarendon and Archbishop Sheldon drastically reduced the role Convocation would play in the Church's direction in the future. Apparently threatened with a new survey of parochial livings that would have greatly increased the clergy's subsidies, first fruits, and tenths, Sheldon gave up the Church's power to tax itself in Convocation and allowed the clergy to be taxed with the rest of the nation by Parliament. The result was that the Crown found it unnecessary to allow sitting convocations after 1664, and Convocation in effect lapsed for the next twenty-five years. In 1689 Convocation was finally summoned and instructed to revise the prayerbook again, this time in a direction that might bring the more moderate Dissenters back into the Church. But when elections to the lower house indicated that the great majority of the parish clergy were hostile to reform, Convocation was again prorogued. Then, in 1697, Francis Atterbury began his vitriolic campaign to restore sitting convocations, and to increase the power of the conservative lower house at the expense of the more moderate bishops in the upper house. At last allowed to meet in 1701, the lower house made an abortive effort to suppress Toland's *Christianity not Mysterious*; and in 1710 Atterbury offered the lower house a drastic program for restoring the power of the church courts over church absenters, tithe defaulters, and blasphemous writers. Convocation was able to accomplish little, however, largely because of the obstructionist tactics of Whigs and moderate Tories in the upper house and in the government.[16]

The clergy could take some consolation in the accession of Queen Anne, for they found in her a woman almost excessively devoted to the Church and genuinely concerned with the poverty of many parochial livings. Most parsons in Anne's reign ardently campaigned for the Tories as supporters of Church and Queen, urging their parishioners to liberate Anne from the Whig politicians who seemed to be subverting the Church and, through heavy land taxes, impoverishing its ministers. One such Tory parson was Humphrey Michel, the incumbent of two of Leicestershire's poorer livings, Blaston and Horninghold. While Whigs and Dissenters were to him nothing but "Scandalous Schismaticks and Hereticks," his devotion toward Anne and her Stuart ancestors verged on idolatry. On January 30, 1712, he registered the birth of his third son and noted that it came on the anniversary of that "direful day whereon the Presbyterians and Independents murdered King Charles, the best of all Kings but one—King Jesus." But rejoicing was still called for, because the child's baptism a week later (as "Charles") fell "in the tenth year of the prosperous reign of our most pious queen Anne; who by act of parliament restored her tenths and first fruits to the poorer Church of England clergymen for their better maintenance."[17] Although Michel was devoted to Anne, the granddaughter of that "ever memorable martyr," he was not a slavish disciple of unchecked monarchy. Monarchs, he believed, were "no more exempted from Obedience to the Laws of Piety and Charity, Equity and Sobriety, than the meanest of their Subjects," and they must rule by "Reason, Law, and Religion." Nor did Michel's affection for the Stuarts imply any loyalty to James II's exiled son, who was currently living in France. Jacobitism struck Michel as both reactionary and unpatriotic: its close association with French tyranny was "enough surely to turn any English stomach."[18]

By following national political developments through the *Monthly Mercury* and other newsletters, Michel became convinced that virtue everywhere was being corrupted by Whiggery. In March, 1709, he recorded in his diary that "Sir Littleton Powis, Judge. . . acquitted one Barrett, though a murderer, being of the Whig party and. . .a briber or somebody for hire. . . .The Whig party causes (they say) generally prevail among the Judges, Justices, &c."[19] To his horror, he discovered that leftist Whigs and reactionary Jacobites were operating even in Leicestershire. He was stunned when a local Whig tried to justify the execution of Charles I; he was equally appalled when, from some casual remarks made by his own sister-in-law, he "perceived she was an obstinate Jacobitess, though she had my two unanswered sermons against Jacobitism." Michel did his best to defend the forces of truth and justice. In April, 1709, he gave "one Mr. Boucher, a Jacobite minister out of place, my two sermons against the Jacobites and my sermon upon the Queen's coronation to convert him." At the same time, he lent Sacheverell's sermon and *Eikon Basilike* to an obstinate Quaker Whig.[20]

Much to Michel's disgust, a minority of the clergy supported the Whigs. According to Burnet, these parsons "did not envy the dissenters the ease that the toleration gave them; they wished for a favourable opportunity of making such alterations, in some few rites and ceremonies, as might bring into the church those who were not at too great distance from it."[21] One of Leicestershire's Whig parsons was the Reverend Thomas Sawbridge. Though he had urged political quietism on his clerical brethren in 1689, he became in Anne's reign an active political agent for the Duke of Rutland and the Duke's Whig allies. According to local tradition,

Sawbridge's relationship with the Manners family had in fact begun on a political note. When he petitioned the Duke in 1690 for the rectory of South Croxton and was told there were only five parishioners to recommend him, Sawbridge retorted that that was "as many as your lordship had when you put up for Knight of parliament." The Duke admitted there was some truth in this and gave Sawbridge the living, promoting him ten years later to the wealthier living at Knaptoft. During the next decade, Sawbridge's correspondence with the Manners family was often political in nature, offering advice in March, 1708, on electioneering tactics should the Marquess of Granby stand for the county, and advising again in July, 1710, concerning Granby's thoughts of giving up the borough of Stamford to run for one of Leicestershire's county seats. In April, 1711, with the Whigs a despised minority in opposition, he lamented the fall from favor of a Whig general ("time will reckon his disgrace our own") but advised the Duchess of Rutland not to despair. "God is no respecter of parties no more than persons," he counseled, "and those who now seem to carry all before them may get so high till they fall the heavier; and those who are now low may be exalted."[22] Sawbridge's political interests were keen and immediate, and he saw a close affinity of interest and principle between himself and the Whig allies of his patron.

Parsons who supported the Whigs naturally met with accusations of treason from the supporters of Church and Queen. The Archdeacon of Bedford reported in early 1715 that "we who were for [the Whig candidates in the recent election], in number about twenty, are loaded with all the opprobrious names to represent us as enemies of the Church of England and friends to the Dissenters."[23] John Rogers, rector of Seagrave and Archdeacon of Leicester, feared in 1714 that if he followed his convictions and supported the Whig candidates he would "undoubtedly have the mob upon me and all my windows broke, which now look into the Castle-Yard where the Poll will be."[24] Sometimes political animosities did go beyond mere name-calling. Michael Hutchinson, the Whig vicar of Packington, complained in 1709 that his taxes had been raised unfairly, adding that "I have been long enough here to know that no Clergyman must looke for any favour in these parts. . .nor justice neither who doth not run headlong into the prevailing party."[25] The Archdeacon of Bedford, another Whig, perhaps had this sort of thing in mind during Anne's reign when he drew up a list of reasons for appointing more clergymen to the county commissions of the peace: one advantage he noted was the "happy opportunity of skreening the poorer Clergy from the insults of faction or oppression."[26] This may have been one reason why the same Whig parson who complained of unfair taxation in 1709 was made a Leicestershire J.P. in the Whig triumph following the accession of George I.[27]

And so the clergy fought among themselves and quarreled with their political opponents in the ranks of the laity. In a non-election year, the Archdeacon of Bedford might report to Bishop Wake that "We are all now very quiet and peaceable as to Whig and Tory among the Clergy," but, he carefully added, "how a new Election for Convocation may ferment us, I know not."[28] His uneasiness was justified when elections were held two years later, for the clergy's own elections to Convocation seemed "at present of no great moment whilst the Clergy are so generally bewitch't with State Politicks." They were "utterly unprepared to promote any Ecclesiastical Reformation," for their attentions were turned instead to "obstructing and traducing the measures of the Ministry, whom they cannot endure to see of that sort they call Whigs."[29] Similarly, the Archdeacon of Leicester complained in November, 1714, that the elections were infected with "such outrageous zeal of the Clergy here as will amaze you." In another letter, perhaps referring to the Tory landslide of 1710, he told how one Leicestershire parson was in "Transports of Joy for the late glorious victories obtained over Presbyterian Bishops, which in his opinion is a deliverance next the Reformation, only it wants a vacancy at Lambeth to perfect it." By December, 1714, the archdeacon was complaining that many of Leicestershire's clergymen were covert political traitors. Omitting prayers for George I was "so common that I dare say much the majority have taken it up, beside all young men out of the universities."[30]

Some of the clergy genuinely regretted their brethren's political activism. The Archdeacon of Bedford believed that parsons seldom "step out of the way of their profession, but they come off with scratcht faces." Far better to "keep the clergy quiet, that during the election they may not run into any extravagant heats, and that when it is over we may meet together as friends and unanimously pursue the great ends of our holy calling."[31] His brother Archdeacon of Leicester entirely agreed, for he feared that "if the Church of England be ever torn to pieces, it will be by the rashness and intemperat zeal of the Clergy beyond any other body of men."[32] Unfortunately, their protestations could not change the fact that conditions had altered since less polarized days in previous reigns. Nor were the two archdeacons willing to follow their own advice. Even while they were lamenting their brethren's political involvement, they were themselves quietly campaigning for Whig candidates for Parliament. In November and December, 1714, Archdeacon Rogers of Leicester was visited by the county leaders of both the Whigs and the Tories. The two Tory incumbents "came to me very early and were very importunate for my vote," he wrote, while the Whig leader came soon afterward with his company of knights and esquires. Rogers quickly excused himself from supporting the Tories, for he wished the Whigs success "with all my heart." But Rogers was timid when it came to politics and feared persecution if he worked too openly for the Whigs. He was relieved when the Whig leader said he "would expect no more from me than that I would not engage against them, which they need not to have asked." Even so, he did engage in a bit of covert electioneering, and he twice hinted to Wake that if he were pressed he would do more, "whatever I suffer for it."[33] Archdeacon Frank of Bedford was cautious, too, and feared that strong exertion for the Whigs would "stir up a nest of Hornets and render myself uncapable of serving my friends." But in 1705 he canvassed the clergy of the county and returned to Wake a list of those whose votes for the Whig candidate were sure, hopeful, uncertain, or clearly beyond reach; the notations beside many of the names show that his soliciting was rather active. The parsons at Bedford, Milton Brian, and Odel had promised him their support, and there was a good chance that Mr. Pulford of Leighton would come across, for "I have spoken to him, and I hope effectually." Mr. Hardacre of Lillingstone was not firmly committed, but again Frank reported that "I have spoken to him, and hope to prevail." And even though Mr. Stonestreet of Eyton Bray could not pledge full support, he had promised "at least to be neuter."[34]

Local candidates of both parties actively competed for the clergy's support, for even though parsons supplied less than 5 percent of the votes in most elections, small clerical voting blocs could not be ignored when elections were frequent and seemed close. Moreover, contemporary politicians realized that the clergy's influence far outweighed their numbers. In their Sunday sermons and in their weekday conversations with their parishioners, they were quite capable of swaying the votes of entire villages. When elections approached, some clergymen in fact assumed it was only right that they should offer their parishioners explicit instructions; they had, after all, been doing so for some time. In 1685 the Dean of Durham, who was also rector of Sedgefield, wrote the following letter to the Dean and Chapter's registrar:

> I earnestly desire you, as soon as possibly you can, to take one journey more both to Easington and Sedgefield. . .to fit and prepare the parishes to be advised by me in reference to the next Election. . . .Remember me kindly to my Curates, and all my loving neighbours, and tell those at Sedgefield that I have so good an opinion of them that I do not suspect any opposition from them when I recommend any Knights of the Shire to their election, which I am like to do very speedily. . . . Captaine Milford, having lost his lieutenant, Stothard, would hardly oppose me now, I guesse, if I were upon the place, and made an addresse to the people, betwixt the Nicene Creed and the Sermon.[35]

Clergymen continued to solicit votes in the reigns of Anne and George I. In 1714, for example, the Archdeacon of Leicester wrote to Bishop Wake that Parson Thomas of Barkby had been "with me this day and interested himself so far as to engage his whole Parish not to promise the Old Members when they come to engage them."[36] Similarly, the Archdeacon of Bedford reported during the campaign of 1707 that he had "already secured a good part of my own Parish for Lord Edward. . .and shall make it my endeavour to confirm them." He had also promised to get "such of my freinds among the clergy as I can trust" to solicit lay votes in their own parishes, but this must be done with enough discretion to avoid "noise and publick controversie." Passions were rising, and Frank feared that such influence would be resented; it went on nevertheless, and the Whig candidate carried the election.[37] Even the act establishing Queen Anne's Bounty may have been passed with an eye to the effect it would have on the clergy's votes and, through the clergy, on the votes of their parishioners. As the Earl of Egmont had it from a friend,

> At the time her Majesty made that grant the Pretender had wrote over that if he came ever to wear the Crown he would restore the first-fruits and tenths to the clergy. This happening when a new Parliament was to be called, the Ministry, apprehending that the clergy would bestir themselves in favour of the disaffected persons to the Government, advised her majesty to do the thing herself.[38]

Meanwhile, Burnet thought that one reason for the Tory landslide of 1710 was the fact that the clergy

> had a great share in this; for besides a course, for some months, of inflaming sermons, they went about from house to house, pressing their people to shew, on this great occasion, their zeal for the church, and

> now or never to save it; they also told them in what ill the Queen had been kept, as in captivity, and that it was a charity, as well as their duty, to free her from the power of the late Ministry.[39]

In 1714 the Archdeacon of Leicester thought that taking the names of those Leicestershire parsons who refused to pray for George I would make the clergy "for the future more cautious" and "would have a good influence upon the Elections."[40]

If parsons were often able to influence their parishioners, to what extent were patrons able to influence their parsons? Several pieces of evidence suggest that the influence exercised by patrons was substantial. A poll division list dated December, 1707, survives for Leicestershire, with George Ashby, the Whig candidate for Parliament, pitted against Sir Geoffrey Palmer, a firm Tory.[41] The manuscript is in the handwriting of the vicar of Syston, who voted Whig, and it lists the choices made by about 4,200 county voters. Of these the clergy numbered 137, roughly 3 percent of the total, and they went Tory by almost three to one. Their Tory sympathies are hardly surprising, but what looks interesting is the extent to which their choices coincided with those of their patrons. A substantial number of the clergy had been presented to their livings by the Crown, by corporate bodies, by patrons living outside the county, or by patrons whose political sympathies are otherwise unknown; in most of these cases no comparison between the parsons and the men responsible for their advancement can be made. But such a comparison can be made for about 40 percent of the voting parsons, and the results are overwhelming: these parsons agreed with their patrons over 80 percent of the time. Of the eleven voting parsons in the Duke of Rutland's livings, for example, ten voted Whig. The exception was the rector of Redmile, whose moral misdemeanors had aroused the Duke's wrath and touched off a bitter patron-parson feud several months before.[42]

Contemporaries in fact seemed to assume that parsons would usually vote with their patrons. When the Archdeacon of Bedford canvassed his county's parsons in 1705, his most common explanation for a parson's anticipated voting behavior was a simple notation of who his patron was. Mr. Cooling of Wootton was listed as a sure vote for the Whig candidate, with a notation which simply said "Sir Philip Monox, Patron." Mr. Rice of Arlsey and Mr. Garden of Astwick could likewise be counted on: "Mr. Brown, Patron." Mr. Fenton of Pulloxhill could not be relied on, for he "tells me that he must vote with his patron, Mr. Coppin." Mr.

Cawne of Wilshamsted was a good prospect: "Sergeant Selby is his Patron, who can determine him, the Sergeant being, as it's said, in my Lord's interest." Mr. Boranskyle of Wrestlingworth was another possibility, for "His Grace's Grandfather procured that Living for him from the Lord Keeper."[43]

Does all of this mean that most parsons slavishly parroted the political choices of their patrons, regardless of their own political principles? The Reverend Samuel Carte implied that this was true of some of the Whig clergy: "Some persons," he wrote Wake in 1708, "seem to endeavour to recommend themselves to their governours, by indiscretely exclaiming against all passive obedience, and it is to be feared advance such notions as may sometime or other be pernicious to this Nation."[44] Parsons may not have been so involved in outright electioneering in the 1670's, when Zachary Cawdrey published his *Discourse of Patronage*; it is interesting to note, however, that Cawdrey thought parsons "must be ready in the service of their Patrons, if there be just occasion for it, to ingage all their abilities of Body and Mind, and all other acquired interests and advantages."[45] Did these acquired interests and advantages include their right to vote Whig or Tory in the early eighteenth century? Some parsons undoubtedly did serve their patrons this way, but it is not necessarily true that all, or even most, did. After all, incumbents enjoyed security of tenure, and a patron could not remove a parson simply because the latter favored a candidate whom the former disliked. If, like the Duke of Rutland, the patron held advowsons to several livings of varying income, he did have one weapon in his arsenal: when a parson proved politically uncooperative, the patron could refuse to advance him to a wealthier living. But the great majority of patrons held only one or two advowsons, and the threat of such career blockage need not apply if, by voting against his patron's candidate, the parson found a political ally in a different patron.

On the other hand, does the political agreement between parsons and patrons imply that the great majority of parsons were politically indifferent, at least to the point of placing gratitude to their patrons and affection for them above political considerations? Again, this was probably true of some. However, in view of the complaints made by the archdeacons of Leicester and Bedford about the clergy's "intemperate zeal," their being "bewitched" by state politics, and their widespread refusal in Leicestershire to pray for George I, this posture seems unlikely for most. Perhaps a better explanation for both the political zeal of the clergy and their tendency to vote with their patrons is that parsons did indeed have strong political views, and that they tended to find patrons whose views they could share.

Certainly there is evidence that in the early eighteenth century, if not before, recommendations of preferment were being made and considered on the basis of party allegiance. When a Leicestershire parson was recommended to Wake in 1705 as a possibility for bishop's commissary, his friend was quite specific about his qualifications. He was not only an excellent preacher and a man of good character, but "at Coventrie in the late reign a zealous Williamite, and still continues so at Leicester." His friend's rival for the post, "though he is otherwise well qualified for his business," was "extremely addicted to a party that I believe you will not care should grow numerous in your Diocese."[46] Similarly, Thomas Sawbridge, the Duke of Rutland's Whiggish political ally among the clergy, was fully aware of his patron's preferences when he solicited a living for his son in 1711. Sawbridge had been "faithful to my principles and for my firmness to his Grace disobliged all the other party," he wrote, while the other candidate the Duke was considering had been known to "magnify his enemies, particularly Lord Nottingham," and was guilty of "terming the Whigs rascals."[47] Meanwhile, the Reverend Willoughby Willey actively campaigned for the Whigs in the elections of 1715, working chiefly with one Mr. Digswell; and Sir Thomas Cave, a Tory gentleman, wrote, "We are under apprehensions of [Mr. Digswell's] presenting the Scandalous Parson Willy to a Benefice in Warwickshire." Though Cave obviously disliked Willey, he never charged him with cooperating with the Whigs simply for the sake of advancement. He was convinced that Willey was genuinely corrupted with Whiggish principles, for he was "Son to a rigid Presbyterian and a Sorry Wretch," and the "young Prig" had seduced one of Cave's own clerical clients into joining the Whig persuasion.[48]

Political considerations extended even to the lowest levels of preferment. In October, 1715, the Reverend Bennet Sherard wrote to a Whig bishop for the name of a reliable curate, bypassing his own bishop, who was a Tory. Sherard was a Nottinghamshire rector from a Whig family and with a strongly Whig patron, and he would be nominated to the rectory of Aylestone in Leicestershire by the Whig Duke of Rutland the following year. "Your Lordship is the best judge of the necessary qualifications of the person," Sherard explained, "and I am satisfied that at this critical juncture your Lordship will think it necessary to have regard to such as are hearty in their affections to the King and his administration. A gentleman so well inclined will be very agreeable to me and suitable to the disposition of my Lord Howe's family and (I thank God I can say) of the Parishioners."[49] And so, if the clergy's voting patterns superficially suggest unprincipled or apathetic mimicry of their patrons, that may not have been the case in practice. With parsons often gravitating toward patrons with compatible political views, the reality may well have been a series of cooperative relationships in which parsons and patrons happily joined together to further their common political ends.

William Paul was one Leicestershire parson for whom the religious and political issues were too significant to be ignored, and his convictions eventually brought him to the scaffold. He was born at Little Ashby in 1678, the son of a grazier with freehold land worth £70 a year. After attending a petty school conducted by the rector of Leire and spending a few years at Rugby, he entered St. John's at Cambridge and took his B.A. in 1701, his M.A. four years later. The Bishop of Peterborough ordained him priest in 1705, and he served for a short time as curate at Carlton Curlieu and as domestic chaplain to Sir Geoffrey Palmer, a staunch Tory. Then, after brief stays in Staffordshire and Warwickshire as a curate and teacher, he was presented in 1709 to the Leicestershire vicarage of Orton on the Hill by the Bishop of Oxford. For the next six years he lived and worked much like any other incumbent of a remote country parish, preaching twice on Sundays, offering communion four times a year, and catechizing the children of his parishioners. But then one Sunday in 1715 he climbed into his pulpit and preached a sermon on the twenty-sixth chapter of Ezekiel: "Thus saith the Lord God, remove the diadem, and take off the crown; exalt him that is low, and abase him that is high: I will overturn, overturn, overturn, and it shall be no more until he comes whose right it is, and I will give it him." A few days later he left for Lancashire to join the forces of the Old Pretender.

Paul's neighbors thought they spotted him in Leicestershire later that year wearing a layman's colored clothes, a laced hat, a long wig, and a sword. However, he was not apprehended until a Leicestershire justice of the peace recognized him in St. James' Park in London and informed the authorities. Paul made a poor showing at his trial for treason the following June. At first pleading not guilty, then admitting his guilt but offering lame excuses for his misconduct, he finally threw himself ignominiously on the mercy of the court. Despite all this, he died well. On July 13 he was dragged on a sled from Newgate to Tyburn wearing his canonical habit, and before he was hanged, cut down still alive, and quartered, he made a most affecting speech. Previous excuses and apologies were cast aside as he proclaimed himself a faithful member of the Non-Juring Church and urged the spectators to "Remember that King James the Third is your only rightful Sovereign, [and that] you are obliged in conscience to do all you can to restore him to the Crown." The crowd became unruly at this point, but Paul was no longer afraid: "I wish I had quarters enough to send to every parish in the Kingdom," he proclaimed, "to testify that a Clergyman of the Church of England was martyred for being loyal to his King."[50]

Between 1688 and 1715, only nine Leicestershire clergymen publicly proclaimed their loyalty to the exiled Stuarts. Paul was the only one who actually took up arms and sacrificed his life; two of the Non-Jurors later recanted, and the others simply retired.[51] But if the Non-Jurors were religious and political eccentrics, they were merely the most extreme examples of how parsons became entangled in politics during and after the Glorious Revolution. In the two-party conflicts of William's and Anne's reigns, the political lives of country parsons were hectic and intense. Their votes were eagerly courted, their sermons were carefully listened to for political allusions, and their allegiance was sought as a means of securing the votes of their parishioners. Some clergymen, like the Archdeacon of Leicester, felt threatened by the forces of division and hesitated to try their hands at full-scale intervention. Others responded with the same candor that Nathaniel Alsop of Carlton Curlieu had used even in 1682: "If any shall except against my meddling with Political Matters in the Pulpit," he shrugged, "they ought to reflect how our People are of late made all Statesmen."[52]

In some ways it was an aberrant situation, and it would not last much beyond the reign of Anne, at least not with the same form and content. As the wars with France came to an end, and as the nation grew more accustomed to official toleration and an elective monarchy, political passions gradually subsided. By 1730, fewer elections were being determined at the polls; many were now being settled in polite drawing rooms, and many parsons discovered that the issues that had formerly excited them had somehow evaporated. In addition, the political nation was coming to rely less on divine writ to formulate its political opinions, and more on the dictates of reason and natural law. Even in 1717 the rector of Cotesbach could see what was happening. His *Forty-Six*

Propositions supporting an elective monarchy were drawn not from the Bible, but from "the plain Dictates of Reason, and the Nature and End of Government in general; or else from the Nature of our Constitution, and the Laws of this Land in particular." In order to satisfy his readers, he even presented his propositions "in a Mathematical Method. . .that may be easily read over in the Space of a Single Hour."[53] The intellectual atmosphere and political system of the mid-eighteenth century would not prove conducive to significant priestly intervention in the affairs of state. The late-Stuart period, however, was a time when clergymen were strongly moved by political developments, and when a parson's opinion on political issues seemed of crucial importance to the people of his parish and to the politicians themselves.

NOTES

1. For example, Sykes, *William Wake*; Sykes, *Church and State*; Hart, *John Sharp*; Holmes, *Politics in the Age of Anne*.

2. Public Record Office, C 193/12/3-5; Crook, ed., *Justices of the Peace*.

3. *A Catalogue of the names of all. . .Justices of the Peace* (British Museum 579.i.2); P.R.O., C 193/12/4-5; Leics. Rec. Off., QS 3/1-14; QS 6/1/1-3.

4. From *The Crisis* (London, 1713). Quoted in Wilson, *Importance of Reign of Queen Anne*, p. 29.

5. Bodleian Library, Tanner MS 80, ff. 116-117.

6. Alsop, *Sermon*, pp. 5-8, 11, 14, 19, 25.

7. *H.M.C. Hastings MSS*, II, 184-185, 211; Lincs. Arch. Off., P.D. 1690/79,84; P.D. 1699/42.

8. *H.M.C. Hastings MSS*, II, 183, 186-187; Leics. Rec. Off., QS 6/1/2, f. 83 ff.; QS 6/1/3, f. 49 ff.; QS 1/1-14; Venn and Venn, *Alumni Cantabrigiensis*, Pt. 1, II, 203.

9. See below, pp. 169-170.

10. Wake MSS, CCXXXIV, f. 180.

11. Sawbridge, *Sermon*, pp. 8-13, 25.

12. Bennett, "Convocation of 1710," 311-312.

13. Burnet, *History*, IV, 564.

14. *Ibid.*, IV, 392.

15. de la Pryme, *Diary*, p. 150.

16. Sykes, *From Sheldon to Secker*, pp. 41-53; Bennett, "Convocation of 1710," pp. 311-319.

17. Wake MSS, CCLXXVII, n.f.: Blaston; Nichols, *Leics.*, II, 450.

18. Michel, *Sovereignty Subject unto Duty*, pp. 8, 13, 15-16.

19. Michel, "Diary," pp. 188, 192, 195.

20. *Ibid.*, pp. 189, 192, 194.

21. Burnet, *History*, IV, 392.

22. Nichols, *Leics.*, III, 237n.; *H.M.C. Rutland MSS*, II, 188, 190-192.

23. Wake MSS, CCXXXVIII, n.f.: Thomas Frank to William Wake, February 18, 1714/15.

24. *Ibid.*, n.f.: John Rogers to William Wake, November 24, 1714.

25. *Ibid.*, CCXXXIV, f. 204.

26. *Ibid.*, CCLI, n.f.: unsigned treatise in the handwriting of Thomas Frank entitled "Reasons why the Queen's Majesty should entrust some of the Clergy in the several parts of this Kingdom with Commissions of the Peace."

27. Leics. Rec. Off., QS 6/1/3, f. 217 ff.

28. Wake MSS, CCXXXIV, f. 344.

29. *Ibid.*, CCXXXVIII, n.f.: Thomas Frank to William Wake, March 26, 1715.

30. *Ibid.*, n.f.: John Rogers to William Wake, November 24, 1714; CCXXXVI, n.f.: John Rogers to William Wake, undated; CCXXXVIII, n.f.: John Rogers to William Wake, December 4, 1714.

31. *Ibid.*, CCXXXIV, f. 132. Quoted in Sykes, *William Wake*, II, 91.

32. Wake MSS, CCXXXVIII, n.f.: John Rogers to William Wake, November 24, 1714.

33. *Ibid.*, and December 4, 1714.

34. *Ibid.*, CCXXXIV, f. 133; CCXXXVI, n.f.: four pages in Thomas Frank's handwriting headed "Votes for Lord Russel," "Votes hopeful," "Votes which appear to be desperate," and "Concerning the inclinations of those underwritten."

35. Granville, "Remains," p. 197.

36. Wake MSS, CCXXXVIII, n.f.: John Rogers to William Wake, November 24, 1714.

37. *Ibid.*, CCXXXIV, f. 133; Sykes, *William Wake*, II, 90–92.

38. *H.M.C. Egmont MSS*, V, 49–50. Quoted in Best, *Temporal Pillars*, p. 32.

39. Burnet, *History*, VI, 16.

40. Wake MSS, CCXXXVIII, n.f.: John Rogers to William Wake, December 4, 1714.

41. Cambridge University Library, MS Mm.vi.61, ff. 200–223.

42. Wake MSS, CCXXXIV, ff. 28, 30, 62.

43. *Ibid.*, CCXXXVI, n.f.: four pages in Thomas Frank's handwriting (see note 34).

44. *Ibid.*, CCXXXIV, f. 180.

45. Cawdrey, *Patronage*, p. 39.

46. Wake MSS, CCXXXIV, f. 4.

47. *H.M.C. Rutland MSS*, II, 191. I thank Dr. Parker of Leicestershire Record Office for transcribing the original document at Belvoir Castle.

48. Verney, ed., *Letters*, I, 330, 333; Bloxsom, "Rectors of Gilmorton."

49. Wake MSS, CCXXXVIII, n.f.: Bennet Sherard to William Wake, October 17, 1715; Lincs. Arch. Off., P.D. 1716/11.

50. Nichols, *Leicester*, IV, 23–24; Venn and Venn, *Alumni Cantabrigiensis*, Pt. 1, III, 320; Fletcher, "Documents relating to Leicestershire," p. 312; Lincs. Arch. Off., Reg. XXXVI, f. 111; *D.N.B.*, XLIV, 77–78.

51. Overton, *Non-Jurors*, pp. 471 ff; Nichols, *Leicester*, II, 162; IV, 933–934; Lincs. Arch. Off., L.T. and D.: William Vincent, June 8, 1688.

52. Alsop, *Sermon*, pp. 3–4.

53. Wells, *Forty-six Propositions*, introduction.

Conclusion

What did it mean to be a typical late-Stuart parson? That ultimately depends on whether one believes that such a creature really existed, for the parish clergy were so diverse socially and economically that only with great reservations can they be considered a coherent social class. On one hand, there were parsons like William Cotton of Broughton Astley (1624-91), the son of Thomas Cotton, Esq., lord of Laughton manor. With his gentle origins, his twelve-room parsonage, and his income from Broughton of £200 a year, Cotton fraternized with Leicestershire's country gentry on terms of virtual equality. His son William married the daughter of Sir Thomas Halford and succeeded him at Broughton rectory in 1692; his daughter Mary married Sir Richard Halford, and through her he became the grandfather of Sir William Halford, Baronet.[1] On the other hand, there was the poor country vicar of £20-60 a year who, according to Swift, "lives like an honest, plain farmer, as his wife is dressed but little better than Goody." If he "is sometimes graciously invited by the Squire," he always "sits at humble distance," for "as to himself, we must let his parentage alone. If he be the son of a farmer it is very sufficient, and his sister may very decently be chambermaid to the Squire's wife."[2]

One such humble clergyman was the Reverend Robert Meeke, curate of a poorly endowed Yorkshire chapelry, and the son of an equally impecunious country parson. Meeke was invited to dine with all sorts of people—local yeomen, fellow clergymen, prosperous merchants, even with Sir John Kaye, M.P. But at Kaye's he found himself shunted off after dinner to share a bedroom with the family chaplain, and he felt ill at ease when required to preach before members of Kaye's social class: "Preached at Denton Chapell," he wrote in 1691, when "Sir John Arderne and his Lady were there. I thought I was not so ready in the forenoon as I would have been; when I would appear better than ordinary, having great persons to be my hearers, oftentimes I am worse, more stammering in the utterance, and more confused in the matter, both in prayer and preaching, though my sermons be noted verbatim."[3]

While Cotton was born into the landed gentry and maintained his connections with it through his children, Meeke confessed that he did not know "how to court or address the great ones of this world."[4] The fact that both men were members of the parish clergy caused some confusion about the precise social standing of the profession as a whole. Swift, for example, could insist that a clergyman was by definition a gentleman, and yet admit that the "mean servile temper" of some of the clergy had "almost rendered the whole order contemptible."[5] If a bit of Cotton's gentility rubbed off on Meeke, a bit of Meeke's servility rubbed off on Cotton, leaving many parsons unsure about where they stood in relation to other social classes, and undecided about the social role their contemporaries expected them to play. In terms of family origins, incomes, and domestic living standards, they in fact covered much the same spectrum as lay society, and they were subject to some of the same class tensions. Humphrey Michel's resentment of his better-born and better-paid clerical neighbors was not simply the product of a sour disposition, and the poorly paid curate of Barwell who left for South Carolina merely acted out the resentment which many other curates must have felt toward their employers.

All of this makes it difficult to generalize about the clergy. Judging from the clergy of Leicestershire, however, one thing does seem clear: late-Stuart writers tended to exaggerate the clergy's social and economic difficulties. Certainly John Eachard did, and so did such prominent churchmen as Stillingfleet, Kennett, and Burnet.[6] Admittedly, they were addressing some very real problems, ones they hoped to prod their countrymen into solving. As they constantly pointed out, many of the nation's livings were grossly under-endowed. The incumbents of these parishes lived little better than the poorest members of their congregations. Such poverty fostered clerical ignorance, undermined the prestige of the entire profession, and thus reduced the Church's ability to perform its appointed mission. By calling the nation's attention to problems such as these, contemporary writers were performing a worthy service. But by stressing the poverty and ignorance of some of the clergy, rather than the prosperity and learning of others, they gave a distorted impression of the parish clergy generally, an incomplete picture which sometimes misled subsequent historians. At the same time, they tended to ignore some significant advances which had occurred since the sixteenth century.

Eachard's complaints about clerical ignorance, for example, obscured a tremendous improvement in the clergy's university credentials, the best objective measure of the clergy's erudition and learning. In the early years of Elizabeth's reign, fewer than a fifth of Leicestershire's parsons were university graduates. In contrast, by the middle of the seventeenth century almost all held bachelor's degrees, and two-thirds of the county's parish incumbents held master's degrees as well. This was a dramatic development, especially for a period in which relatively few laymen advanced beyond a rude sort of literacy. It helped to enhance the clergy's professional standing, and it gave late-Stuart parsons a stronger claim to gentle status than their predecessors of the sixteenth century. Eachard, however, doubted that a university education was adequate preparation for a career in the Church, and to some extent he was correct. As he pointed out, the undergraduate curriculum was more secular than religious; clerical candidates would have profited from a stronger emphasis on theology and English oratory; and some graduates flaunted their learning in pretentious, pedantic sermons—orations designed more to impress than to instruct. Judging from churchwardens' presentments in late-Stuart Leicestershire, however, Eachard's dissatisfaction with the clergy's training was not universally shared. While Leicestershire's churchwardens charged a few parsons with preaching heresy, and others with preaching too seldom, they never accused parsons of ignorance or complained about the general quality of their sermons. Apparently parishioners were less exacting about the clergy's training and effectiveness in preaching than contemporary critics supposed.

Similarly, Eachard's complaints about clerical poverty obscured the fact that most parsons were relatively prosperous. Gregory King guessed that a typical clergyman's income in the 1680's was about £50 a year—an estimate which, according to King, placed parsons within the upper fifth of England's population as a whole.[7] In Leicestershire twenty years later, the typical parson earned about £70 a year—an income slightly greater than that of the average yeoman farmer, almost twice that of the average skilled craftsman, and at least four times that of the unskilled farm laborer.[8] The typical parson was in fact one of the more substantial men of his village, closer in domestic living standards to the local squire than to the majority of his other parishioners. While 80 percent of the parson's neighbors lived in houses with only one or two hearths, his own house had three or four hearths, placing him in the upper 20 percent of his local parish community, and in the same league as men that his contemporaries labeled "gentlemen." Moreover, late-Stuart parsons were better paid than their sixteenth-century predecessors; since most clerical incomes were still tied to farm production, most had profited from inflated food prices, advantageous enclosures, and increased agricultural productivity. Despite the fact that heavy taxation during William's and Anne's wars with France brought a temporary setback after 1690, most parsons' net revenues in 1714 still surpassed the levels of the 1530's, often by a very wide margin. During the Tudor-Stuart period, the clergy also improved their position in comparison with the majority of their parishioners. As the clergy moved forward economically, England's great mass of copyholders and landless laborers fell precipitously behind, hurt by rising rents, declining real wages, and chronic underemployment. The gap between the clergy and most of their parishioners therefore widened considerably—a fact which in turn tended to improve the clergy's social standing.

While this was going on, the clergy's status was further enhanced by a shift in social origins. In the early sixteenth century, most parish parsons were the sons of plebeians. This was probably still the case in Restoration Leicestershire, but social and economic pressures were gradually reducing the plebeians' numbers, and by Anne's reign they were in the minority among the clergy's newest recruits. Of the factors which had combined to thin their ranks, the most important was the system of ecclesiastical patronage. It had always posed problems for plebeians; from time immemorial, gentlemen's sons had had an advantage in competing for the better parish livings. But with the spread of clerical marriages in the sixteenth century, plebeians found themselves confronted with a whole new class of privileged competitors: the sons of the parish clergy. Socially more respectable than the plebeians, and more frequently connected with the advowson-owning elite, clergymen's sons began to elbow the plebeians aside. By the middle of the seventeenth century, they had snapped up a quarter of the nation's parish livings, including many of those with above-average revenues. As pluralism spread and the number of clerical openings declined, prospects for plebeians dimmed even further. A few who developed the right connections still managed to rise to the top, but most had to settle for below-average incomes, and some never found permanent livings at all. Taking note of this, fewer young plebeians came forward to enter the Church. The clergy's social mix increasingly shifted toward the sons of parsons and country gentlemen; by Anne's reign, the clergy were acquiring a more exclusive, genteel social image.

And so for most of the parish clergy, the Tudor-Stuart period was a time of significant advancement. Socially, economically, and academically, the Anglican clergy moved forward, both in absolute terms and in comparison with most of their parishioners. The result was that late-Stuart parsons were not only better educated, better paid, and socially more respectable than the parsons of Elizabeth's day; they were also, to a greater extent than their predecessors, among the best educated, most substantial, most respectable men of their parishes. According to the standards set by John Eachard, this should have enhanced the clergy's ability to further the work of the Church—for, if clerical poverty and ignorance were the Church's greatest ills, then the Church was less afflicted under the later Stuarts than it had been in the sixteenth century. Yet the clergy's rise did not at all seem to increase the Church's power and influence; on the contrary, the late-Stuart Church lost ground, and the late-Stuart clergy seemed strangely unable to reverse the Church's decline.

In 1689, the Church was stripped forever of its monopoly over the nation's religious life, an ancient privilege which Parliament no longer cared to preserve. When toleration enabled the nonreligious to avoid church services of any sort, relatively few laymen really seemed to mind. Contemporaries detected a falling off in religious enthusiasm among Anglicans and Dissenters alike; excommunication became less frightening, and the power of the church courts waned. Even worse, Gilbert Burnet reported that people were beginning to "find it a modish thing, that looks like wit and spirit, to laugh at religion and virtue."[9] Alarmed and appalled by these developments, the clergy tried to rise to the challenge. Crying out that the Church was in danger, they called on their parishioners to rise up with their old-time zeal and to rescue the Church from its enemies. The clergy's efforts did not go entirely unrewarded; during Anne's reign in particular, many of the laity sprang forward in the Church's defense. To most members of the governing classes, however, the clergy's cries soon came to sound shrill, old fashioned, and obstinately unrealistic. Surely the clergy must see that the world was changing: that religious passions were out of place in an enlightened kingdom, that the Church's interests must be subordinated to the interests of the nation as a whole. If this meant tolerating Dissent and irreligion, then so be it—the parish clergy would simply have to understand.

Times had changed indeed. Exhausted by earlier outpourings of religious enthusiasm, many late-Stuart Englishmen were shifting their attention from religious to secular concerns. Less willing than their fathers to disrupt the nation with religious controversies, they were discovering the expediency of religious moderation and compromise. Perhaps long-term social and economic developments played a part as well. Men tend to turn to God during times of trouble, times in which they feel powerless to explain or cure their personal problems and insecurities; and in some ways late-Stuart England was less troubled, less insecure, than the England of Elizabeth and the early Stuarts. Elizabeth's England had been severely jolted by an exploding population, skyrocketing food prices, and rising levels of unemployment—problems which continued into the first decades of the seventeenth century, and which may have heightened the nation's search for divine aid and counsel. But by midcentury the population explosion had ended, price levels had tapered off, and the nation's social tensions had eased considerably; partly for these reasons, perhaps, late-Stuart Englishmen came to feel more confident about the future, less inclined to seek divine assistance, and less interested in religious affairs generally.

Later generations of clergymen would find it easier to accept the nation's altered concerns. But late-Stuart parsons were tragically trapped in an awkward transitional period, one that lay uneasily between the Age of Faith and the Age of Reason; and so, for many of the parish clergy, the closing decades of the Stuart dynasty were a time of confusion, frustration, and bitter resentment. Unable to reverse the secular tide or to preserve all of the Church's ancient privileges, they were forced to serve their parishes as best they could in a time that seemed strangely out of joint.

Judging from Leicestershire, most continued to serve their parishes conscientiously. A few were charged with moral offenses, but they were a small minority. Some held fewer church services than their bishops might have liked, but most held as many as their parishioners would attend, and relatively few were ever charged with neglecting their parochial duties. Ironically, it is the immoral, neglectful minority that we know the most about; the Church's official records tell us much less about other, more typical parsons, the ones who performed their duties satisfactorily and who managed to live in harmony with their neighbors. Yet we occasionally catch glimpses of them, quietly urging their parishioners to come to church, trying to bind up local quarrels. "I was desired," an Anglican parson wrote in 1692, "to make away a difference between two neighbours, and brothers. . . .God grant that I may be an instrument to reconcile sinners unto God; and also, as occasion serveth, to reconcile contentious sinners one to another."[10] Such parsons became intimate, respected members of their local parish communities; they settled into their livings early in their careers, and they served their parishes faithfully until the day they died. Because they were farmers as well as clergymen, deriving part of their incomes from the fruits of their glebes, they understood the day-to-day concerns of their village neighbors, the seasonal rhythms of their parishioners' lives. Together with the members of their congregations, they prayed to their God for a bountiful harvest, and they scanned their skies for signs of rain. The following passages come from the journal of a Yorkshire parson of the 1690's:

15 June. It is now hot weather. Lord, grant us a seasonable harvest for hay and corn. The fields seem now to flourish with plenty.

25 June. We began to mow today: dark and cloudy, but fair. It hath been very seasonable weather, the earth is full of fruit.

27 August. This night we cut down all our corn, and many persons suppered here. It is commonly said that there never was a year in any man's memory when corn was all ripe together, as it is now. Every field is fit for the sickle, and all people are busy reaping.[11]

As the parsons farmed their glebes and ministered to their neighbors' spiritual needs, they came to discover that life itself had a seasonal rhythm, a seedtime and harvest. "I went to see Abraham Broadbent, who continueth very weak," the Yorkshire parson wrote in 1689; "baptized a child, new-born, and buried a corpse. So in this world one generation cometh, another goeth, and those that continue a while are full of trouble."[12] In countless country villages there came a day when the parishioners learned of the death of their parson, an elderly gentleman who had lived among them longer than many could remember, and whose occasional quarrels with his neighbors had been settled peacefully and without recourse to law. And so they laid him to rest in a quiet country churchyard among his neighbors and friends, men and women with whom he had worshipped and farmed and, over the years, pondered the age-old mysteries of life and death.

NOTES

1. Nichols, *Leics.*, IV, 724; Leics. Rec. Off., DG 24/65; Leics. Museum, 1D41/2/104; Lincs. Arch. Off., *Speculum* I.

2. Swift, *Prose Works*, III, 252, 267.

3. Meeke, *Diary*, pp. 8, 42, 45, 47, 51, 67, and *passim*.

4. *Ibid.*, p. 30.

5. Swift, *Prose Works*, III, 30, 37.

6. Eachard, *Grounds and Occasions*, pp. 129-137 and *passim*; Kennett, *Impropriations*, pp. 161-164; Savidge, *Queen Anne's Bounty*, pp. 5-9.

7. Laslett, *World We Have Lost*, pp. 32-33.

8. *Ibid.*, pp. 32-33. King estimated that "Freeholders of the better sort" received about £91 a year, "Freeholders of the lesser sort" £55 a year, "Farmers" £42 10s. a year, "Shopkeepers and Tradesmen" £45 a year, "Artisans and Handicrafts" £38 a year, and "Labouring People and Out Servants" £15 a year.

9. Burnet, *History*, VI, 193.

10. Meeke, *Diary*, p. 48.

11. *Ibid.*, pp. 41, 43, 81.

12. *Ibid.*, pp. 19-20.

Bibliography

MANUSCRIPT SOURCES

Lincolnshire Archives Office	
Reg. XXXI-XXXVIII	Episcopal Registers, 1640-1761
Add. Reg. 3	The Red Book, 1611-93
P.D. 1620/-	Presentation deeds
Sub. I, IIa-VIb	Subscription books, 1660-1723
Resig. 4	Resignations, 1661-1821
Ben/-	Documents connected with benefices
Cor/B/4	Correspondence of the Bishops of Lincoln, late Stuart and early Georgian
Cor/M/3	Miscellaneous correspondence, 1662-1838
L.T. and D., 1660-1720	Letters testimonial and dimissory
Lic/Sch/1	Letters testimonial and licenses for schoolmasters, 1603-1760
For/4,6	Collections of forms and precedents, 1683-1725
Ter., vols. 8, 23; boxes 13, 17, 18	Ecclesiastical terriers, chiefly 1625-40 and 1700-1710
Cj/33-38	Episcopal court books, 1664-1726
Resp. IX-XI	*Responsa personalia*, 1604-1704
Seq/1-2	Documents connected with sequestrations, 1574-1855
Fac/1-2,8-9	Faculty papers, 1525-1829
L.C. V-VI, VIII-XVII	*Libri cleri*, 1662-1739
Specula I and II	Episcopal surveys of the state of the Church in the diocese, 1663-1784

Leicester Museum	
1D41/1/9-11	Clerical subsidy of 1661

1D41/2/1-777	Ecclesiastical terriers, chiefly of the seventeenth and eighteenth centuries
1D41/4/XXVIII-LV	Loose papers connected with court proceedings, 1660-1716
1D41/8/1-2,4-7	Excommunications and caveats, 1660-1714
1D41/11/68,73-78	Instance court act books, 1662-1721
1D41/12/6	*Libri cleri*, 1662
1D41/13/67-83	Correction court act books, 1660-1718
1D41/14/II-IV	Visitation papers, 1662-66
1D41/18/13-20	Church inspections, 1670-92
1D41/21, unnumbered boxes	Churchwardens' presentments, 1662-1715
1D41/28/356-1260	Induction mandates, 1625-1740
1D41/29/1-277	Sequestration bonds, 1686-1740
1D41/31/1	Sequestrators' accounts at Wigston Magna, 1684
1D41/34/1-3	Subscription books, 1661-1749
1D41/35/1-58	Documents connected with Leicestershire schoolmasters, 1730-1818
1D41/40/4-35	Documents connected with procurations, 1670-1750
1D41/41/1-246	Faculty papers, 1668-1841
1D41/51/19-59	Papers of the Reverend Humphrey Haines, ca. 1704-32
Leicestershire Record Office	
PR/-	Probate records: wills and administrations
PR/I/-	Probate records: inventories
EN/A,AX and QS 47	Documents connected with enclosures, chiefly eighteenth century
QS 3/1-14	Letters patent for Leicestershire commissions of the peace, 1688-1715
QS 6/1/1-3	Leicestershire quarter sessions order books
DE 66	Bray papers
DE 108	Tarbutty papers
DE 565	Pochin papers
DG 5	Winstanley papers
DG 24	Halford papers
Other DE- and DG-	Miscellaneous documents, too numerous and varied for detailed listing. All typescript and file-card catalogs available at the record office as of May, 1972, have been checked for documents of the period 1650-1730 connected with tithes, glebes, commutations, advowsons, and enclosures, and all relevant documents have been examined.

Public Record Office

E 179/251/9	Leicestershire hearth tax returns, 1666
P.C.C. Wills	Prerogative Court of Canterbury wills, 1674-1700
C 193/12/3-5	*Libri Pacis*, 1664, 1680, ca. 1685

Cambridge University Library

MS Mm.vi.61, ff. 200-223	Leicestershire election poll, 1707

Lambeth Palace Library

Cod. Misc. 960-965	*Notitia Parochialis*, ca. 1705
MS 1770	Diary of William Wake, early eighteenth century
CommXIIa/3/1-119	Commonwealth surveys of Buckinghamshire livings
CommXIIa/10/210-374	Commonwealth surveys of Huntingdonshire and Hertfordshire livings

Christ Church Library, Oxford

Wake MSS

CCXXXIV-CCXXXVIII	Lincoln letters and documents, 1705-15
CCL-CCLI, CCLVI	Miscellaneous letters and papers, 1683-1726
CCLXVII	*Nomina Dignitatum*
CCLXXVII-CCLXXVIII	*Notitia Archid. Leicester*
CCXCII-CCXCIII	*Notitia Dioecesis Lincoln*
CCCXXIV-CCCXXVI	*Notitia Episcopatus Lincoln*

Bodleian Library, Oxford

Carte MS 77, ff. 112-118v.	Survey of Leicestershire livings, ca. 1603
Tanner MS 80, ff. 114-123v.	Late seventeenth-century documents concerning the clergy

St. Paul's Cathedral Library

MS 17-D-20 MS 17-C-2	Returns to Bishop Gibson's visitation articles, 1718 and 1721 (on microfilm at Leicester Museum)

PUBLISHED SOURCES AND SECONDARY WORKS

Abernathy, George S. *The English Presbyterians and the Stuart Restoration, 1648-1663*. Philadelphia, 1965.

Addison, Joseph. *The Spectator*. Ed. G. Gregory Smith. London, 1897.

Addison, W. *The English Country Parson*. London, 1947.

Allen, W. O. B., and McClure, Edmund. *The History of the Society for Promoting Christian Knowledge, 1698-1898*. New York, 1970.

Alsop, Nathaniel. *A Sermon Preached at the Assizes Held at Leicester*. London, 1682.

Babington, Churchill. *Mr. Macaulay's Character of the Clergy in the Latter Part of the Seventeenth Century Considered*. Cambridge, 1849.

Badcock, J. C. "The History of Fleckney." Unpublished manuscript at Leicestershire Record Office, n.d.

Barley, M. W. *The English Farmhouse and Cottage*. London, 1961.

Barratt, D. M. "The Condition of the Parish Clergy Between the Reformation and 1660." Ph.D. dissertation, Oxford, 1949.

———. *Ecclesiastical Terriers of Warwickshire Parishes*. Oxford, 1955.

Bax, B. A. *The English Country Parsonage*. London, 1964.

Bellairs, Col. "The Accounts of the Churchwardens of St. Mary's, Leicester, 1652-1729," *Transactions of the Leicestershire Architectural and Archaeological Society*, VI (1888), 253-263.

Bennett, G. V. "The Convocation of 1710: An Anglican Attempt at Counter-Revolution." *Studies in Church History*, VII (1971), 311-319.

Beresford, M. W. "Glebe Terriers and Open Field Leicestershire." *Transactions of the Leicestershire Archaeological Society*, XXIV (1948-49), 77-126.

Best, G. F. A. *Temporal Pillars: Queen Anne's Bounty, the Ecclesiastical Commissioners, and the Church of England*. Cambridge, 1964.

Billson, Charles James. *Leicester Memoirs*. Leicester, 1924.

Bloxsom, Martin. *A History of the Parish of Gilmorton*. Lincoln, 1918.

———. "The Rectors of Gilmorton." *Associated Architectural Societies' Reports and Papers*, XXX (1910), 391-462.

Bosher, R. S. *The Making of the Restoration Settlement: The Influence of the Laudians, 1649-1662*. London, 1951.

Bowker, Margaret. *The Secular Clergy in the Diocese of Lincoln, 1495-1520*. Cambridge, 1968.

Bradshaw, H., and Wordsworth, C. *Statutes of Lincoln Cathedral Arranged by the late Henry Bradshaw*. 3 vols. Cambridge, 1892-97.

Brinkworth, E. R. C., ed. *Episcopal Visitation Book for the Archdeaconry of Buckingham*. Buckinghamshire Record Society, 1947.

British Museum General Catalogue of Printed Books. 263 vols. London, 1960-66; and *Supplements*. 76 vols. London, 1968-72.

Brockbank, Thomas. *The Diary and Letter Book of the Rev. Thomas Brockbank, 1671-1709*. Ed. R. Trappes-Lomax. Chetham Society, n.s., LXXXIX (1930).

Brooks, F. W. "The Social Position of the Parson in the Sixteenth Century." *British Archaeological Association Journal*, 3rd ser., X (1945-47), 23-37.

Buchan, Hannah. *The Poems of Thomas Pestell*. Oxford, 1940.

Burke, J. *A Genealogical and Heraldic Dictionary of the Landed Gentry of Great Britain and Ireland*. 2 vols. London, 1848.

———. *A Genealogical and Heraldic History of the Commoners of Great Britain and Ireland*. 4 vols. London, 1834-38.

Burnet, Gilbert. *History of His Own Times*. Ed. Martin Joseph Routh. Hildesheim, 1969.

Burtchaell, G. D., and Sadleir, T. U. *Alumni Dubliniensis, 1505-1905*. 2 vols. London, 1924.

Calendar of State Papers, Domestic: Charles II, 28 vols.; *James II*, 2 vols.; *William and Mary*, 11 vols.; *Anne*, 2 vols. London, 1860-1960.

A Catalogue of the names of all. . .Justices of the Peace. London, 1680.

Cave, J. *King David's Deliverance, and Thanksgiving*. London, 1683.

Cawdrey, Zachary. *A Discourse of Patronage*. London, 1675.

Clay, J. W., ed. *Familiae Minorum Gentium*. 4 vols. London, 1894-96.

Cole, R. E. G., ed. *Speculum Dioeceseos Lincolniensis, Part I.* Lincoln, 1913.

Cooke, H. W. *Bygone Loughborough*. Loughborough, 1934.

Corfe, T. H. *The School on the Hill*. Leicester, 1960.

Crook, Barbara, ed. "Justices of the Peace, 1642-1700." Computer print-out available in the Round Room of the Public Record Office.

Curtis, J. *A Topographical History of the County of Leicester*. Ashby de la Zouch, 1831.

Curtis, M. H. "The Alienated Intellectuals of Early Stuart England." *Past and Present*, XXIII (1962), 25-43.

Davies, J. C. *Bowden to Harborough*. Market Harborough, 1964.

Day, E. H. "The Country Clergy of the Restoration Period." *Theology*, XXXV (1937), 354-360.

de la Pryme, Abraham. *The Diary of Abraham de la Pryme*. Ed. Charles Jackson. Surtees Society, LIV (1870).

Dictionary of National Biography.

Ditchfield, P. H. "The Errors of Lord Macaulay in His Estimation of the Squires and Parsons of the Seventeenth Century." *Transactions of the Royal Historical Society*, 3rd ser., IX (1915), 77-93.

Dowell, S. *A History of Taxes and Taxation in England*. 3rd ed. London, 1965.

Dryden, A., ed. *Memorials of Old Leicestershire*. London, 1911.

Dyson, A. H. *Lutterworth*. London, 1913.

Eachard, J. *The Grounds and Occasions of the Contempt of the Clergy and Religion*. London, 1671.

Ecton, J. *Thesaurus Rerum Ecclesiasticarum*. London, 1742.

Edward, C., and Young, E. "The History and Antiquities of Ratcliffe on the Wreak in the County of Leicester." Unpublished manuscript at Leicestershire Record Office, 1932.

Edwards, K. *The English Secular Cathedrals in the Middle Ages*. Manchester, 1949.

Elliott, B. *A History of Kibworth Beauchamp Grammar School*. Kibworth Beauchamp, 1957.

Evans, E. J. "Tithing Customs and Disputes: the Evidence of Glebe Terriers, 1698-1850." *Agricultural History Review*, XVIII (1970), 17-35.

Evans, R. H. "The Quakers of Leicestershire, 1660-1714." *Transactions of the Leicestershire Archaeological Society*, XXVIII (1952), 63-84.

Fletcher, W. G. D., ed. "Documents relating to Leicestershire, preserved in the Episcopal Registry at Lincoln." *Associated Architectural Societies' Reports and Papers*, XXII (1894), 228-365.

———. *Leicestershire Pedigrees and Royal Descents*. London, 1887.

———. *The Rectors of Loughborough*. Oxford, 1882.

———. "Religious Census of Leicestershire in 1676." *Transactions of the Leicestershire Architectural and Archaeological Society*, VI (1888), 296-306.

Foster, C. W., ed. "Admissions to Benefices and Compositions for First Fruits in the County of Leicester, A.D. 1535-1660," *Associated Architectural Societies' Reports and Papers*, XXXVII, 144-176, 322-336.

———. *The State of the Church in the Reigns of Elizabeth and James I as illustrated by documents relating to the Diocese of Lincoln*. Lincoln, 1926.

Foster, J. *Alumni Oxoniensis*. Parts 1 and 2. 8 vols. Oxford and London, 1888–91.
Francis, H. J. *A History of Hinckley*. Hinckley, 1930.
Fussell, G. E. "Four Centuries of Leicestershire Farming." *Transactions of the Leicestershire Archaeological Society*, XXIV (1948–49), 154-176.
Gill, Harry, and Guilford, Everard L. *The Rector's Book, Clayworth, Notts.* Nottingham, 1910.
Granville, Denis. "The Remains of Denis Granville, D.D." Ed. G. Ornsby. *Surtees Society Publications*, XXXVII (1860), 194-292.
Greaves, R. W. "An Eighteenth-Century High Churchman." *Theology*, XXIX (1934), 272-286.
Guide to the Contents of the Public Record Office. 3 vols. London, 1963–68.
Habakkuk, H. J. "The Market for Monastic Property, 1549-1603." *Economic History Review*, 2nd ser., X (1957–58), 362–380.
Hart, A. Tindal. *Clergy and Society, 1600–1800*. London, 1968.
———. *The Country Priest in English History*. London, 1959.
———. *The Eighteenth-Century Country Parson, 1660–1820*. Shrewsbury, 1955.
———. *The Life and Times of John Sharp, Archbishop of York*. London, 1949.
Hartopp, H. *Calendars of Wills and Administrations Relating to the County of Leicester*. 2 vols. London, 1902–20.
———. *Leicestershire Marriage Licenses, 1570–1729*. London, 1910.
———. *Register of the Freemen of Leicester, 1196–1930*. 2 vols. Leicester, 1927–33.
Herbert, A. "Cossington Rectory." *Transactions of the Leicestershire Archaeological Society*, XIX (1936–37), 27–31.
Hieragonisticon: or Corah's Doom. London, 1672.
Hill, J. E. C. *Economic Problems of the Church from Archbishop Whitgift to the Long Parliament*. Oxford, 1956.
Hill, J. H. *The History of Market Harborough*. Leicester, 1875.
———. *The History of the Parish of Langton*. Leicester, 1867.
———. "The Prebendaries of St. Margaret's, Leicester." *Transactions of the Leicestershire Architectural and Archaeological Society*, III, (1874), 327–331.
Hill, J. W. F. *Georgian Lincoln*. Cambridge, 1966.
———. "The Royalist Clergy of Lincolnshire." *Lincoln Architectural Society Reports and Papers*, n.s., II (1941), 34-127.
———. *Tudor and Stuart Lincoln*. Cambridge, 1956.
Historical Manuscripts Commission:
The Rutland Manuscripts. Ed. H. C. M. Lyte. Vol. II. London, 1889.
The Portland Manuscripts. London, 1893.
The Hastings Manuscripts. Ed. F. Bickley. Vol. II. London, 1930.
Holmes, Geoffrey, ed. *Britain after the Glorious Revolution*. London, 1969.
———. *British Politics in the Age of Anne*. New York, 1967.
Hoskins, W. G. *Essays in Leicestershire History*. Liverpool, 1950.
———. "The Leicestershire Country Parson in the Sixteenth Century." *Transactions of the Leicestershire Archaeological Society*, XXI (1940–41), 90–114.
———. *Leicestershire: An Illustrated Essay on the History of the Landscape*. London, 1957.

_______. *The Midland Peasant: The Economic and Social History of a Leicestershire Village*. London, 1957.

_______. *Provincial England: Essays in Social and Economic History*. London, 1964.

_______. "A Short History of Galby and Frisby." *Transactions of the Leicestershire Archaeological Society*, XXII (1944-45), 173-210.

Houston, J. *Catalogue of Ecclesiastical Records of the Commonwealth, 1643-1660, in the Lambeth Palace Library*. Farnborough, 1968.

Howell, Roger. "A Short Guide to Records: Hearth Tax Returns." *History*, XLIX, no. 165 (February 1964), 42-45.

Hunt, P. E. *The Story of Melton Mowbray*. Grantham, 1957.

Hutton, W. H. *The English Church from the Accession of Charles I to the Death of Anne*. London, 1903.

Index to the Act Books of the Archbishops of Canterbury, 1663-1859. Compiled by E. H. W. Dunkin. Ed. and extended by C. Jenkins and E. A. Fry. 2 vols. London, 1929-38.

Irving, G. *Lutterworth Grammar School*. Leicester, 1956.

Josselin, Ralph. *The Diary of the Rev. Ralph Josselin, 1616-1683*. Ed. E. Hockliffe. Royal Historical Society, 3rd ser., XV (1908).

Kennett, White. *The Case of Impropriations, and of the Augmentation of Vicarages and other Insufficient Cures*. London, 1704.

Laslett, Peter. *The World We Have Lost*. New York, 1965.

Le Neve, John. *Fasti Ecclesiae Anglicanae*. Corrected by T. D. Hardy. 3 vols. Oxford, 1854.

Legg, J. W. *English Church Life from the Restoration to the Tractarian Movement*. London, 1914.

Longden, H. I. *Northamptonshire and Rutland Clergy*. 16 vols. Northampton, 1938-52.

Macaulay, A. *The History and Antiquities of Claybrook*. London, 1791.

Macaulay, T. B. *The History of England from the Accession of James II*. Vol. I. London, 1849.

McClatchey, Diana. *Oxfordshire Clergy, 1777-1869: A Study of the Established Church and of the Role of Its Clergy in Local Society*. Oxford, 1960.

Maddison, A. R., ed. *Lincolnshire Pedigrees*. 4 vols. London. 1902-6.

Major, K. *A Handlist of the Records of the Bishop of Lincoln and of the Archdeacons of Lincoln and Stow*. Oxford, 1953.

Matthews, A. G. *Calamy Revised*. Oxford, 1934.

_______. *Walker Revised*. Oxford, 1947.

Mayo, C. H. "The Social Status of the Clergy in the Seventeenth and Eighteenth Centuries." *English Historical Review*, XXXVII (1922), 258-266.

Meeke, Robert. *Extracts from the Diary of the Rev. Robert Meeke*. Ed. H. J. Morehouse. London, 1874.

Michel, Humphrey. "The Diary of the Rev. Humphrey Michel." Ed. J. H. Hill. *Associated Architectural Societies' Reports and Papers*, V (1859), 187-195.

_______. *Sovereignty Subject unto Duty*. London, 1702.

Moore, A. P., ed. "Leicestershire Livings in the Reign of James I." *Associated Architectural Societies' Reports and Papers*, XXIX (1907), 129-182.

_______. "Subsidies of the Clergy in the Archdeaconry of Leicester in the Seventeenth Century." *Associated Architectural Societies' Reports and Papers*, XXVII (1904), 445-495.

Moore, Giles. "Extracts from the Journal and Account Book of the Rev. Giles Moore." Ed. R. W. Blencowe. *Sussex Archaeological Collections*, I (1848), 65-127.

Nichols, John. *The History and Antiquities of the County of Leicester.* 4 vols. London, 1795-1815.

Overton, J. H. *The Non-Jurors: Their Lives, Principles, and Writings*. London, 1902.

Peile, J. *Biographical Register of Christ's College, 1505-1905.* 2 vols. Cambridge, 1910-13.

Pevsner, Nicholas. *The Buildings of England: Leicestershire and Rutland.* Middlesex, 1960.

Phelps Brown, E. H., and Hopkins, S. V. "Seven Centuries of the Prices of Consumables, Compared with Builders' Wage Rates." *Economica*, XXIII (1956), 311-314.

Phillimore, Robert. *The Ecclesiastical Law of the Church of England*. Vol. I. London, 1873.

Plumb, J. H. *The Growth of Political Stability in England, 1675-1725.* London, 1967.

Portus, G. V. *Caritas Anglicana*. London, 1912.

Potter, S. P. *A History of Wymeswold*. London, 1915.

Prideux, Humphrey. *Letters of Humphrey Prideux*. Ed. E. M. Thompson. Camden Society, n.s., XV (1875).

Savidge, Alan. *The Foundation and Early Years of Queen Anne's Bounty.* London, 1955.

Sawbridge, Thomas. *A Sermon Preached at the Assizes in Ste. Maries Church in Leicester*. London, 1689.

Simon, J. *Education and Society in Tudor England*. Cambridge, 1966.

Statutes of the Realm. 9 vols. 1810-28.

Stieg, Margaret F. "Some Economic Aspects of Parochial Churches in the Diocese of Bath and Wells in the Seventeenth Century." *Albion*, III (1971), 212-222.

Stone, Lawrence. "The Educational Revolution in England, 1560-1640." *Past and Present*, XXVIII (1964), 41-80.

———. "Social Mobility in England, 1500-1700." *Past and Present*, XXXIII (1966), 16-55.

Strawley, J. H. "Michael Honywood, Dean of Lincoln, 1660-81." *Lincoln Minster Pamphlet*, no. 5, 1951.

Styles, Philip. "The Social Structure of Kineton Hundred in the Reign of Charles II." *Birmingham Archaeological Society's Transactions*, LXXVIII (1962), 96-117.

Swift, Jonathan. *The Prose Works of Jonathan Swift*. Ed. Temple Scott. Vol. III. London, 1898.

Sykes, Norman. *Church and State in England in the XVIIIth Century*. Cambridge, 1934.

———. *From Sheldon to Secker: Aspects of English Church History, 1660-1768.* Cambridge, 1959.

———. *William Wake, Archbishop of Canterbury, 1657-1737.* 2 vols. Cambridge, 1957.

Thirsk, Joan, ed. *The Agrarian History of England and Wales.* Vol. IV. Cambridge, 1967.

Thomlinson, John. "The Diary of the Rev. John Thomlinson." *Surtees Society Publications*, CXVIII (1910), 64-167.

Thompson, J. *The History of Leicester from the Time of the Romans to the End of the Seventeenth Century*. 3 vols. Leicester, 1849.

______. *The History of Leicester in the Eighteenth Century*. Leicester, 1871.

Townsend, B. M. "Castle Donington in the Seventeenth Century: A Manorial Society." Castle Donington History Group, 1971.

Trotter, E. *Seventeenth Century Life in the Country Parish*. Cambridge, 1919.

Tyler, Philip. "The Status of the Elizabethan Parochial Clergy." *Studies in Church History*, IV (1967), 76-98.

Valor Ecclesiasticus. Ed. J. Caley. 6 vols. Record Commission, 1810-34.

Venables, E., and Perry, G. *Lincoln*. S.P.C.K. Diocesan Histories, London, 1897.

Venn, J. *Biographical History of Gonville and Caius College, 1349-1897*. 4 vols. Cambridge, 1897-1912.

Venn, J., and Venn, J. A. *Alumni Cantabrigiensis*. Parts 1 and 2. 10 vols. Cambridge, 1922-54.

Verney, Margaret M., ed. *Verney Letters of the Eighteenth Century*. 2 vols. London, 1930.

The Victoria History of the County of Leicester. 5 vols. London and Oxford, 1907-64.

The Victoria History of the County of Wiltshire. 10 vols. Oxford, 1957-70.

Wake, William. *The Bishop of Lincoln's Charge to the Clergy of the Diocese, in his Primary Visitation*. London, 1707.

Walker, G. G. "Dr. Robert Sanderson." *Associated Architectural Societies' Reports and Papers*, XXXI (1911), 19-30.

Ward, J. *Chronological Events in the History of Melton Mowbray*. Melton Mowbray, 1889.

Warne, Arthur. *Church and Society in Eighteenth-Century Devon*. Newton Abbot, 1969.

Wells, E. *Forty-six Propositions Briefly proving, that His Present Majesty King George Is the Only Rightful and Lawful King of Great-Britain*. London, 1717.

White, Anne. *A History of Loughborough Endowed Schools*. Loughborough, 1969.

Whiteman, A. "The Re-establishment of the Church of England, 1660-1663." *Transactions of the Royal Historical Society*, 5th ser., V (1955), 111-131.

Whitley, H. *A History of the Parish of Sapcote*. Leicester, 1853.

Wilshere, J. *Glenfield: A Considerable Village*. Leicester, 1971.

Wilson, F. W. *The Importance of the Reign of Queen Anne in English Church History*. Oxford, 1911.

Wing, D. G. *Short-Title Catalogue of Books Printed in England, Scotland, Ireland, Wales, and British America, and of English Books Printed in Other Countries, 1641-1700*. 3 vols. New York, 1945-51.

Wood, A. *Athenae Oxoniensis*. Ed. P. Bliss. 5 vols. Oxford, 1813-20.

Index

Indexed villages and towns are in Leicestershire, unless otherwise indicated.

THE GUILLOTINE

LUCAS PEDERSON

SEVERED PRESS
HOBART TASMANIA

THE GUILLOTINE

WWW.SEVEREDPRESS.COM

ISBN: 978-1-925840-10-0

ONE

One never forgets the smell of burning bone.

No matter how many times he cuts them out, even through the mask to protect his lungs from the sharp dust, he can smell it. And it's a stench that lingers. One which slithers into the brain and stamps itself on the mind. A reeking stink forever imprinted in memory.

Despite this, Ash hunches into his work. The ground under him trembles. The air-powered bone saw in his hand whirs, then screams as he sinks into the femur. Low rumbling sounds, even through the screaming of the saw. He glances up, frowns, and goes back to cutting the ones out of the stone.

"Ash," Julia shouts. "We need to move. It's getting too close!"

He shakes his head, cuts free the final section of the femur and goes to work on the smaller bones, careful not to break any. If he had more time, he'd cut the stone and lift the slabs out and worry about extracting the bones in the lab. As it is, however, there's no more time.

Sweat drips off the tip of his nose. The heat is getting worse. The ground begins to quake now rather than merely tremble.

He cuts through the bones, collecting small piece after small piece he places in a tub beside him.

"For shit sake, Ash," Julia cries. "Leave it. We need to go now!"

"If I leave them, they'll be destroyed," Ash shouts back, still cutting.

"Better them than us."

"Go, then," he says. "I'll meet up with you guys later. I can't leave these."

"It's just a velociraptor, damn it. Plenty of them around." Julia's voice cracks a bit on the last word.

Shaking his head, he frees more of the smaller bones and places them in the tub. "It's not a raptor."

"I really don't care what it is, Ash. We have like, zero seconds to haul ass out of—"

"Done," he shouts, placing the remaining bones in the tub and standing.

"'Bout damn time, dude," Julia says and grabs one side of the tub. "Startin' to feel like a flame kissed steak right now."

"Yeah, yeah," Ash says, hefting his end. He smiles. "Let's get out of here."

The wall of lava is about ten feet away. Any longer and they would have surely cooked.

They haul the tub of bones to the SUV, strap it into the backseat and get in. He leaves the air-tank and bone saw. No time to drag the damn thing to the vehicle.

Volcanic ash rains down on them and Ash can't help but to think he got lucky. Even a minute longer would've killed them. If not the lava, then the ash. He might've been okay wearing his face mask, but Julia…

No time to dwell on that now.

He slams the SUV into reverse and they shoot backward away from the wall of lava. Gray ash clings to the windshield, obscuring his vision. But he doesn't dare use the wipers. No, the stuff will smear and it won't matter how much windshield fluid he uses. The fallout will just smear more. In the distance, the volcano spews geysers of reddish-orange.

The tub of bones rattle and click as he slides the SUV around and speeds away from the site.

So much for all the funding we begged for, he thinks, sighing.

"They could've told us about the damn volcano," Ash says as the SUV jostles over rocks and the rough tropical terrain. He swerves onto dirt road and things settle a bit.

In the rearview mirror, the volcano continues billowing its hell onto Earth.

"Probably why we got the site so cheap," Julia says. "Bastards." She huffs out a breath. "At least we got one."

"The scans showed hundreds of skeletons. We lost out."

Julia nods. "Well, at least it happened before all the gear and crew got here. There's that."

Ash grunts, focuses on the road ahead.

The sooner they get off this waste of an island, the better. No one on the Board said anything about a possibly active volcano. The mountain, he assumed was but a dead volcano. Long gone the days of its angry rampage. Also, he figured the Board would've mentioned something if it was indeed active.

Assholes…

Julia is right, though. At least the eruption didn't happen with all the gear here. At least it happened now and didn't risk the lives of his crew.

The small carrier they rented for this little excursion rests, ramp settling on the white sand like a gray tongue, at the beach.

Ash guns the SUV through the sand, slowing only when they get close to the carrier.

"Straighten the wheel a bit," Julia says. "Hair to the left."

"I'm fine," he says aiming for the ramp into the carrier.

"Dude, I'm telling you you're—"

The right-side mirror shears off the edge of the opening. A loud squeal of metal scraping metal as the right side of the SUV swipes the carrier.

Then they're inside. He straightens the vehicle a bit and parks.

"Oh, *now* you straighten it out," Julia spouts and opens the door. "Jackass."

He chuckles, shuts the SUV off and climbs out. "I'll strap it up and close the hatch, you get this beast moving. I don't—"

The entire carrier quakes. Metal groans all around them.

Julia shoots him a wide-eyed look. Somewhere floating between fright and confusion. He waves a hand at her and hurries toward the hatch. He needs to bring in the ramp then seal the hatch.

"Go," he shouts. "Get us out of here."

The quaking happens again, this time nearly knocking him off his feet. The carrier's groans are deafening. He holds on to the railing near the hatch, slams a palm onto the blue ramp button. It buzzes as it lifts away from the sand and pulls back into the carrier. And of course, the damn thing is like watching a clock minutes before quitting time at a factory. So slow. It's—

The explosion is so strong it knocks him off his feet. He lands hard on his ass. Pain laces through his tailbone. And there he sits, gaping as the beach thirty feet in front of the carrier opens up and vomits a glut of lava. The glut soon becomes a towering geyser.

It's not the only one, either. There are several smaller geysers shooting hell itself out of the beach.

The ramp clicks into place. Ash scrambles to his feet and slams the side of his fist against the red button. There's an airy whoosh, and the hatch slowly begins to close. Six inches of metal lowers from the ceiling. And like the ramp, it's so damn slow.

A stream of lava inches its way toward the carrier.

Shit.

He wastes no more time and hooks the SUV down, so it doesn't move around in the open ocean. By the time he's done with this, the hatch is just about shut. No matter how much he wants to join Julia in the wheelhouse, he needs to make sure the hatch closes and fully seals. He just hopes with all this time, the lava doesn't reach the carrier and melt through. If that happens, they can't go anywhere without sinking.

The hatch clanks into the floor of the carrier. Several clicks sound, indicating all the locks sliding home. Fifty in all. The rattling noise indicates the hatch being sealed.

Good.

He rushes to the ladder and climbs into the wheelhouse where Julia is muttering a string of curses.

"What's wrong?" he asks, sitting in the seat next to her.

"The stupid software is updating."

"You can't override it? Go full manual?"

Rubbing her temples, she says, "Okay, grandpa, look, there hasn't been a full manual option in the last fifteen years."

"I'm thirty-seven..."

"Like I said, *grandpa*, times be changing. Keep up."

"I don't even have a kid!"

"You don't need a kid to be old as dirt, dude."

He sighs. "Thirty-seven isn't old as dirt."

"Since when?"

He smiles. They've had this very argument/joke for two years now. All because she's five years younger than he is. It's also a thing they do during stressful times.

Somewhere with the minute range, a robotic voice announces, "Software update complete. You may now continue your operations."

"'Bout damn time," Julia says and engages the engines.

The quaking intensifies.

"Hurry," Ash says. "Lava is close."

Her face is stripped of emotions, blank, while she gets the small carrier charter online and running. Sweat beads her temples and Ash nods. He can almost hear her heart crashing her chest. Almost feel the waves of worry washing off her. Something that wriggles over his skin like tiny worms.

The carrier grumbles to life. All the buttons and monitors light up. The panel in front of her opens and a control yoke emerges. She touches a blinking green light on the yoke and a voice says, "Control systems online."

She pushes the throttle forward. The carrier shudders, groans. In less than a minute, they're cruising through the blue waters of what used to be the Caribbean. Like everything after Earth went mad and mixed up its climates, after a large majority of the icecaps melted and drastically rising sea levels, the Caribbean and all its islands were reduced to a scattering on mini islands. Much as good portions of the continents have been submerged.

Ash pulls up the rear camera and watches steam billow as the lava rolls into the ocean. Beyond this, the volcano still shoots its inferno into the air. All the fauna and trees, everything, is engulfed in flames.

He turns the camera off, heart sinking.

It was the greatest find he stumbled upon in years.

Now it's gone.

He wipes sweat from his face with his handkerchief – his grandpa's handkerchief – and stuffs it back in his pocket.

"I think next time," Julia says, "we check out the volcanic activity before we get the funding."

He snorts. "Or just stay the hell away from islands."

She nods, increasing the carrier's speed a bit. "I hate the tropics anyway."

"At least it's not the cold tropics."

Now it's Julia's turn to snort. "I'd rather skate on the ice than swelter to death in all that humidity, dude."

Smiling, he says, "Fair enough."

Funny thing, the cold tropics. A huge swath covering thousands of miles from what used to be the Gulf of Mexico, stretching down to what's left of South America, and spreading as far east as the sunken Florida Keys. The temperatures in this massive region fluctuate between -40 degrees Fahrenheit and 30 degrees Fahrenheit. Only spot on Earth colder is around India.

"Well," Julia says, ripping him from his thoughts. "We have like six hours to the coast. You should get some sleep."

Ash stares out the window, squinting at the open sea. "I'll be fine."

"Like hell. You've been on the go for two days straight." She jerks a thumb over her shoulder. "Hit the bunk and get a few hours."

He almost laughs. He's technically her boss, but he's also her friend. And this is a case of a friend looking out for the other. Besides, she's right.

"Fine," Ash says. "Wake me up when we're close to the coast."

She flicks a hand at him, as if saying, "Be gone."

He lightly pats her shoulder and walks out of the wheelhouse and into a short hall. On either side are three metal doors painted white. They don't have specific rooms to stay in, so he just picks one and steps inside.

At once, he can tell the room hasn't been lived in for a long time. It doesn't smell bad, though has that slightly musty odor of neglect. At least there's no dust and when he unties, kicks off his boots, and lies on the bunk, the mattress feels so damn divine he can't help but sigh relief.

After all the bullshit and near death by volcano, it feels good to just let it all go and let weariness sweep over him in sardonic waves.

Within seconds, he's asleep.

He dreams of running within a world of bright orange trees and something is chasing them. Something big. They crash through the orange foliage, a small cave not far. It's this cave he needs to get them to. The thing chasing them is too big. It can't get them in there.

But Ky stumbles over a protruding tree root and goes sprawling. His baby girl, only nine, he turns to pick her up when the creature bursts through the trees and snatches her from his hands. A Spinosaurus. Its long, pointy teeth stab into his Ky as it lifts its head and swallows her.

He screams and screams and…

TWO

...he sits up screaming and someone is telling him to calm down. Someone tells him it was just a dream and to just take it easy. But all he sees is Ky's body sliding off those long teeth and disappearing down the Spinosaurus' gullet. All he—

The slap makes a sharp crack. Hurts like hell, but...he blinks, coming into the here and now.

"Jesus," Julia says. "What the shit were you dreaming about?"

She's sitting on the bunk next to him as he tries to control his erratic breathing. Sweat slicks his face and dampens his shirt. And he needs to piss like no other right now.

He swipes tears and sweat from his face. "S-Sorry. Just...it was about Ky."

Julia visibly softens. Her brown eyes lower. "It wasn't your fault, you know."

Not wanting to talk about it, he stands from the bunk and walks toward the doorway on legs that feel like pillars of gelatin.

"Where you going?"

He pauses, "Need to piss." He finds his way to the head and unloads his sloshing bladder.

Finished, he washes his hands and steps out, finding Julia standing there, arms crossed over her chest, glowering a bit.

"You should really talk about things like this, you know? Keeping it all in isn't good."

Ash grunts. "Yeah. I know. Someday, maybe." He brushes by her on the way to the wheelhouse.

"It's been four years, Ash."

He spins on her. "Look, I'm not ready to let her go. Why can't you understand that?"

"I know you're not, but you need to. I mean, what do you think Ky would want?"

Shaking his head, he turns away from her. "Ky's dead. She doesn't want anything."

"You—*really*? For shit sake, dude, think about what she'd think if she was still alive about how you're suffering. I know she'd be pretty disappointed in you right now."

Ash stops, hands curling into shaky fists at his sides. Fingernails digging into his palms. He counts down from ten until the anger subsides. His hand unfurls, leaving deep, purple, crescents in his palms.

"You're right," he says. "I…just miss her more and more every day. She's even in my dreams now."

Not far behind him, Julia says, "Ash, none of what happened was your fault. You need to accept that fact. Was it tragic? Hell yeah it was. It hurt me to see you so down. But there's a time you need to let go, dude. Let her rest."

She's right. Of course she is. But…letting go right now, he just can't do it. Almost feels like a betrayal to move on in life without her.

Ky wasn't eaten by a Spinosaurus, of course, that's all a dream, but she might as well have been, given how unlikely things went to shit.

A one in a million crapshoot, really.

"She was taken from me," he says. "Right out of my own house. I should've had more security in place than a locked gate. Alarm system, all that."

He's in the wheelhouse now and Julia isn't far behind, spouting, "No one expects someone to break into their home and kidnap their kid. Especially in small town Iowa. It's just not thought of much. And it's not your fault that bastard picked your house to do all that either. Sometimes shit is just random."

Ash plops into his chair, not sure what to say. Shortly after, Julia sits in the seat beside him.

According to the ETA monitor, they'll be reaching the coast in less than an hour.

Leaning back in his seat, he mutters, "He didn't have to kill her."

Julia doesn't say anything for a while. She stares at the approaching coast. Then, "No. He didn't. Some people, man, no one can understand why they do what they do. Some people are just evil."

He glares at the control panel, too caught up in hate to say anything. It froths inside him, this hate. A froth threatening to boil over each passing year. Every time Ky's bright, smiling face shifts across his mind's eye, the hate gathers. It'll take over if he lets it. If he allows the boil to spill over. Then what? If—

The force of the hit is so strong it lifts the heavy carrier out of the water and spins it about one hundred and eighty degrees. All Ash knows is when everything settles is they're not facing the coast anymore.

During the wild spin, he fell out of his seat.

Now he climbs back in and buckles up. His breathing is erratic, heart trampling through his chest.

Once he gets himself under control, he faces Julia. "Okay, what the hell was that?"

Julia shakes her head. She frowns at one of the monitors. As above, so below, cameras set in the carrier capture what lies under the surf. She doesn't respond.

"Did we hit a sandbar, maybe?" he ventures.

Again, she shakes her head.

"Then what the fuck—"

"My dad said there were monsters in oceans now. Some are prehistoric, some…mutations."

Ash blinks at her. "You mean that shit in the news is real? That…that…leviathan was real?"

Julia nods. "I actually know the daughter of the dude that killed it. Anyway, I didn't see what hit us and I don't think we should stick around to find out."

He gapes at her. She's talked about monsters in the ocean before, but he refused to believe any of it. He thought, surely, it was just the media hyping up what could have been (in the case of the leviathan) something as simple as an accident on an old oil rig. And yet, he knows they didn't hit a sandbar. Something struck them from the side hard enough to spin a ten-on carrier around.

Julia maneuvers the carrier, aiming it back toward the coast and goes full throttle.

Right before she does, though, he catches a glimpse of something on the monitor. From camera nine. Large, glowing red eyes and an open mouth full of jagged, pointy teeth.

Then they're moving. He's not even sure how many knots, though speeding through the water so fast, the coast is directly in front of them in a matter of seconds. Like the Atlantic Ocean is reputed to be, the waters are unruly. They rock the carrier to the point of tipping.

Julia eases back the throttle, then cuts the engines sending them to drift.

But…

Ash tenses. "We're going in too fast. Reverse."

"We're fine."

So she says, but the carrier is approaching the coast second by second without slowing much, he's not so sure. If they hit the beach at this speed…

His hands grip the armrests of the seat. He draws in a breath, readying himself for impact.

Then, just when he's sure shit is about to get real, the carrier slows to a near crawl and they scrape onto the beach a few feet.

He glances at her and she smiles. "Told ya." She unbuckles and slaps him on the arm. "And you're supposed to be my fearless leader. Ha!"

She hurries out of the wheelhouse, leaving him to blink at all the sand and rock of America's east coast.

He doesn't move for a while. He thinks about the thing that hit them not far from the coast. A giant thing with large, glowing red eyes and so many teeth. He thinks about Ky…

It's not until Julia shouts for him when he finally moves.

She's standing near the SUV. A Land Rover.

"Uh, maybe we should turn this thing around so we can get that thing out?"

Julia sighs. "At the time I was trying to save our lives. But yeah. Just hold on to something and I'll turn us around." She rushes out of the cargo hold and he leans against the SUV, desperately wanting a cigarette.

He hasn't truly craved one in a couple years. But now…

No. He promised Ky he wouldn't ever smoke again and he's not about to break that promise now.

Ky's dead, a lurid voice says in his head. *You can go back to being you again.*

How long has it been since he's heard that ugly voice? A year or so after he quit? A voice so unlike his own it scares him a little.

Ash shakes his head to clear both the voice and the craving to have a smoke. It works to dislodge the voice, though not the craving.

He pops a tab of gum into his mouth and chews. A habit he's taken on since he quit, which usually helps.

Not today, though. He still craves the harsh smoke of a cigarette.

The trick is putting it totally out of your mind, he knows. Think about something else or do something else. Anything but light up. Anything but—

The carrier shifts and groans as Julia turns the thing around so they can get the SUV out.

Sand scrapes the bottom. Ash grabs onto the Land Rover, then the carrier jolts to a stop. The engines slow, buzzing to a halt. He walks to the hatch, presses the release button. Air hisses as the seals let go. The hatch splits open to a beach that's more rocks than sand. Tepid air washes over him. Somewhere nearby, seagulls cry. He presses the ramp button. A buzz sounds and the ramp extends to the beach.

"We're not at the right location," Julia says behind him. "Coordinates changed somehow."

He faces her, frowning. "That's not possible."

She shrugs. "Maybe it is. Might've had a glitch during updates."

Ash shakes his head, glances away. "So, where are we?"

"Appalachian Coast. Three hundred miles north of our destination, Lyle's Port."

"I'm not going back out in the water with that…whatever the shit that thing is waiting for us."

Julia snorts. "Same."

"We drive, then. We'll stow a few gas cans, just in case there's no stations on the way."

She nods. "Let's do this then."

THREE

"You couldn't have found a better road?" Ash chokes down the chunks gathering in his throat. The SUV dips and rocks and leaps, churning his stoMach.

"Look," Julia says. "It was either this one or the one with all the vagrants."

He shudders at the thought. Vagrants are the remnants of a past humanity. Although, they're not quite human.

Rumors shiver through the nation about cannibals. Not only cannibals, but cannibals that become something…different. People change into large wolf-like creatures. They ravage and feast and kill anyone nearby. Even if the person isn't a threat. Vagrants remind him of an old story his grandma used to tell. One he barely remembers, though will never forget.

Something about a poor beggar that transforms into something grotesque and kills a lot of people. Something of legend. And although he can't remember what his grandma called the thing, he remembers envisioning a massive wolf-like beast.

Vagrants are said to turn into such beasts. Although he has never seen it in the news or in person. All they're said to be are ruthless cannibals. People who will rip a baby from a mother's arms and eat it in front of her.

"Good call," he says finally, fighting to keep down the vomit as it burns in his throat.

"If you're gonna puke, at least do so out the window, dude."

He closes his eyes, nods.

Motion sickness isn't usually something that gets to him. But then again, he's been through some crazy shit the past twenty-four hours. Hasn't slept much at all. All this combined has created a noxious stew. Even the slightest jostle messes with his equilibrium. Well, at least after they drove out of the carrier. So many jostles going on.

He stares ahead, mainly because looking out the side window and seeing the passing foliage and how it shifts, will force him to vomit.

He swallows, and his throat makes a dry click.

"Need to stop and put some gas in," Julia says. "You gonna make it?"

He nods, not trusting himself to speak, let alone open his mouth right now. She brakes, parks the SUV and turns it off.

"I'll be right back," she says. "Just try to relax." She hands him a bottle of water from the back. "Drink this if you can. A little bit at a time, don't down it."

Again, he nods. She climbs out of the SUV and shuts the door, leaving him alone in the vehicle for now. Without all the motion, his stoMach eases a bit. He manages a few, slow, deep breaths and takes a sip of lukewarm water. The water trickles down his throat and he begins to feel better. He lets it settle a moment as Julia opens the rear hatch and drags out one of the gas cans. Then he drinks a little more. A gulp, rather than a sip this time.

He's about to move onto two gulps of water when Julia shouts, "Ash! The gun!"

Sucking in a sharp breath, Ash glances at the sidemirror just as something large and on all fours darts out the green fauna.

On the backseat, near their sparse collection of bottled water and the tub of ancient bones, rests an assault rifle. Not the latest and greatest model, but it's come in handy to deter various creatures, either mutations or of natural origin. He grabs the rifle and opens the door to Julia screaming.

Shit.

Ash stumbles out of the SUV, turns the safety off, and runs to the rear of the vehicle in time to see the beast leap on top of Julia. She stabs at it with her knife, blood splashes the ground, spatters onto her, but little damage is happening. It pins her arms down with slender, black claws. Its lizard-like head lowers, mouthful of teeth opening.

He lifts the assault rifle, aims at the green, scaly head and pulls the trigger.

A shrill yelp explodes out of the creature. Blood mists the air, parts of its head blow out in chunky strings. It slumps, and Julia shoves it aside where it plops onto its side, twitching. A pool of blood spreads around its reptilian head.

Julia sits, breathing in gaps for a few seconds. A long scratch wells blood along the right side of her face, but otherwise she appears unharmed. Just shaken. Ash doesn't blame her. That thing…

"Took ya long enough," she manages as she stands.

"Was kind of trying not to puke, but you're welcome."

She waves a hand at him and kneels next to the dead creature. "What the hell is it?"

"Looks like a mutation." He sighs, glances around. "We better put gas in this thing and get to Lyle's Port."

Julia doesn't move as she inspects the creature.

This close, the smell of the thing is almost worse than its looks. Reminds him of the musky stink a garter snake leaves behind. And, although its head and claws are very reptilian, the rest of its body is covered in short, black fur, muscular like a panther.

"Like on land," Julia whispers, "So in the sea."

Ash frowns. "What?"

She stands and faces him. "Something my grandpa used to say. 'Like on land, so in the sea', which means there are mutations on land and in the oceans. Like what hit us before reaching the coast."

"I get it," Ash says. "We should keep moving, though." He turns around, searching the area, the woods, then looks at her. "There might be more of these things out here."

"Probably." She drags the gas can to the driver's side of the SUV.

Ash opens the flap and unscrews the cap and helps her lift the eight gallon can and insert the nozzle. Before long, gas glugs into the tank. Finished, they stow the empty can next to the four others and gets back into the vehicle.

"Let's hope we come across a station before we run out of gas completely," Julia says and keys the ignition.

And so, the jostling returns, though this time, it doesn't affect Ash much. He sips his water and waits.

After about one hundred and fifty miles in, and with one gas can left, Ash takes over driving while Julia snoozes in her seat. He yawns, weariness really digging in.

If there's a town up ahead, maybe they'll need to stop for a night to sleep. Recharge.

Until then, however, all that stretches before him is the crumbling road and trees.

FOUR

Almost three hundred miles gone, and they finally roll into a small town.

"Blaxley," he mutters, pulling into a tiny gas station that might as well be a relic like the bones in the tub. He gives Julia a gentle shake. "Hey, I'm going to fill up. Hungry?"

Julia jerks awake, sucks in a breath and blinks at him. She wipes a bit of drool from the corner of her mouth and chin and squints out the windshield. "Looks like a lovely establishment, don't it?"

He chuckles, because it does not. The station is more like a tin shanty than a building at all. The pumps are old, plastic faded and cracked. An elderly, opaque potato chip bag tumbles across the tarmac and catches on a rusty chain-link fence where it flutters in the mild breeze.

It's dusk, sky the color of healing wounds. And in the gloom the shack station shines bright with light from within.

"They look like they're open," Ash says, opening the door.

"Take the gun with you," Julia says, yawns.

"I'll be alright."

"Okay, well, if you get kidnapped by cannibal hillbillies, I'm totally leaving you here."

Ash raises a dark eyebrow. "Well, that's reassuring." He gets out, shuts the door and walks across the small tarmac to the tin shed, shack, shanty, whatever.

There's a window, but it's so slathered in grime he can't see inside. The door is a crooked rectangle of wood with a stainless-steel latch. White light seeps through the varying gaps around the door.

Ash knocks. The door rattles on its hinges. The tin siding creaks.

But no one answers.

He knocks again.

Nothing.

Faint, crackly music plays a tune he hasn't heard before.

He huffs out a breath, cheeks puffing, and opens the door.

He's greeted with a wall of smoke that smells vaguely of something green, bordering mildew. He knows exactly what it is and smiles. Brings back memories of his buddies he used to hang out with as a teenager. He never touched the stuff, but they were all about it.

It always happened in Colin's mom's basement. They'd all sit on the couch, sometimes playing a video game, sometimes watching anthropology documentaries. He'd be drinking beer while they all got stoned out of their minds. And really, he hadn't minded. They were a great group of guys. Good friends. And those memories will last forever.

During these times, he also fell in love with anthropology and later prehistoric anthropology. The latter became his passion. To piece together dinosaurs and figure out not only what they looked like, but how they lived and what they ate and origins…a few years out of college he became the most sought after prehistoric anthropologist and paleontologist. With a mix of archeology, paleontology, and anthropology, he's discovered over fifty new species of dinosaurs in the ten years he's been doing this.

The profession brought him world renown, but it also cost him his beloved daughter Ky.

The man who kidnapped her and eventually killed her…the man was a competitor who lost to Ash more than once. It wasn't Ky the man, Gerard, was after, but she was the closest he could get to Ash. The cowardly bastard shot himself before the police broke down his door.

There are times Ash wishes he could kill the son of a bitch again for what he did.

The wall of smoke clears, and he stands in the doorway watching an elderly woman waltzing by herself in front of a warped counter. The rest of the shack is bare, save for a buzzing cooler to the right where what appears to be bottled water is stored. Although, it could be moonshine for all he knows.

This old woman, her hair dangles in silvery strings, which sways as she turns and bobs and turns. Scrawny arms out, as though she's holding onto an invisible partner. She's smiling, her lips cracked, and oozing blood mixed with pus. A dark, hairy mole mars the center of her forehead. Her eyes are closed and she's smiling, blissing out to the wobbly music coming from the room beyond this one. She's wearing what appears to be a tattered, stained nightgown.

He's about to back away and leave when she blinks. She stops waltzing, arms lowering to her sides and faces him. Her eyes are the color of cornflowers caught in doughy sockets.

She glances over his shoulder, then around the room as though she has no idea where she is right now.

"Hi," Ash says. "I was wondering if your pumps work?"

She starts, eyes wide and stares at him. She stares at him for a very long time.

Then, "Yes. You pay per gallon."

Ash nods. "I know."

She squints at him. "Do I know you?"

He chuckles, "Not likely. Okay, I'll go fill up and come back and pay you."

"You pay now!"

Ash lifts his eyebrows. "Oh. Okay. Um…how much?"

"Ten!"

"Ten dollars?"

The old woman grins, a long, slender finger going toward her hawkish nose. She slips the finger, second knuckle deep, and begins rooting around in there. She pulls out a green glob of snot, inspects it carefully, then sticks her finger in her mouth and sucks it clean.

"Um…" Ash isn't exactly sure what to do here. He's never had to deal with someone this out of it. "So, I'll fill up and pay you ten dollars."

She yanks the finger out of her mouth with a loud smock sound and nods. "Yes, yes. Go, go."

He doesn't think twice and hurries back to the SUV and pumps. Julia is leaning against her side, assault rifle cradled in her arms. "Take it they have gas?"

"We'll see," he says. "The lady is pretty…out of it."

Julia sniffs. "I smell weed. You smell weed?"

He cocks a thumb over his shoulder. "Lady of the Station is a stoner. Among other things. Plus side, we get to fill up and only pay her ten bucks."

Julia sighs. "Must be nice being crazy."

Ash shrugs. "Bet it has its perks." He opens the flap, unscrews the cap and inserts the nozzle. Then he lifts the lever the nozzle had been resting on. The pump clanks. Groans. Then it hums to life.

He squeezes the trigger on the nozzle and gas flows into the tank. It clicks off at a little over thirty gallons.

He replaces the nozzle, brings out a ten-dollar bill and walks back to the shack, shed, station, whatever. But the elderly woman is no longer in the store. The wobbly music still plays, but the woman has vanished, perhaps to the next room.

Instead of looking or calling for her, he places the ten-dollar bill on the counter and walks out.

Julia is already in the SUV. He opens the door, hops in and closes the door.

"Well, that was fast," Julia spouts.

"She was in the other room. I just left the money and walked out."

"You probably could've kept your money. She wouldn't have ever known. If she's as stoned as you think."

Ash keys the ignition. “She’s more than stoned, I’m pretty sure.”

To this, Julia says nothing.

He pulls out of the odd gas station and continues south. They only have about twenty miles until Lyle’s Port.

At least he hopes so.

About five minutes into the drive, Julia falls asleep again.

He sighs and focuses on the broken, dark road ahead.

FIVE

Lyle's Port is just as large and sprawling as he remembers.

A town, not quite a city, is lit up to the point of obliterating most shadows. It's a port town. Where fishermen, or what's left of fishermen these days, deposit their catch. Where deep sea explorers come to rest. Where imports and exports happen.

It's a business town.

It's also a drunk town.

Still, it's where he's supposed to meet with his employer. The safest place to meet his employer, in other words. Lyle's Port has a reputation for not only being the drunkest in the east coast, but also the most protected by biological threats, even mutations. Their gates guarded by highly trained men and women. The streets are routinely patrolled by police who both take care of the crime in town and kill anything that manages to sneak in. The police, they're more like an army.

The walls around Lyle's Port are massive too. Iron reinforced concrete.

"'Bout time," Julia says, sitting up a bit in her seat.

"Got the tablet?" He glances at her as he stops the SUV at the credential check gates. Not as huge as the town's gates, but still impressive.

Eight guards stroll out of flanking bunkers. All are armed and dressed in black tactical gear.

Julia rummages around in the glove compartment and brings out a nearly paper-thin device of plastic and glass. Their credentials tablet.

The shortest of the guards taps Ash's window with a gloved knuckle.

Ash rolls the window down while taking the credentials tablet from Julia. Standing at her door is another guard, assault rifle ready for action.

Ash hands the shorter guard, probably the team's leader, the tablet.

The guard swipes through the information, face an unwavering frown. "What is your purpose in Lyle's Port?"

"Business," Ash replies. "We were to meet Murdock Jones in the harbor, but our coordinates got mixed up and we came ashore three hundred miles n—"

"Shut up."

Ash glares at the guard. "You asked, I answered."

The guard, gray eyes glimmering in the bright lights, shifts from the tablet, and gives Ash a withering gaze. Those eyes tell Ash all he needs to know about the man. He's the alpha, or so he thinks. A tough man, who has seen some shit in his life and in order to counter all the horrors, his heart and mind have turned to iron. He's used to having everything go his way and *only* his way. No gray area with this guy.

Ash sighs. "I apologize. We just need to meet Murdock Jones so—"

"Credential information needs updating," the head guard grumbles and hands Ash back the tablet. He straightens. "Mr. Jones left Lyle's Port two hours ago."

Ash opens his mouth and closes it again.

"Oh, lovely," Julia says. "There goes our financial backing."

He closes his eyes, shakes his head, and opens them again.

The head guard stares at him, arms crossed over his chest. His bald head gleams under all the lights.

"Alright," Ash says. "Thank you, but I guess we no longer need to enter now."

The head guard grunts, nods and backs away from the vehicle. "Word of advice."

Ash frowns.

"Don't be a smartass to someone who can gun you down without penalty." The head guard turns away and returns to the left bunker.

The rest of the guards move away, most also returning to their designated bunkers.

Ash rolls up the window.

"Let's go home, boss," Julia says. "We'll figure the rest out later."

"We need to get ahold of Murdock. Tell him what happened."

Julia nods. "Well, we can do that when we get home."

"No." Ash straightens in his seat. "Get out the phone. I'll call him now."

"He never answers though…"

"He'll answer."

Julia blows out a heavy breath. "Fine."

She rummages around in a black bag, brings out the phone, and hands it to Ash.

Murdock's supposed personal number is in his contacts. He touches the call button, holds the phone to his ear, and waits.

The call is picked up in three rings.

"Barrington? Where the hell are you?"

"Hey," Ash says. "Our coordinates had a glitch and we hit the coast three hundred miles north of the destination. Currently leaving Lyle's Port."

There's a long pause, then… "Did you get it?"

"I think so," Ash says. Because, whatever the bones he managed to collect are, he didn't recognize them.

"You *think*? I pay you to *know*, Barrington."

He draws in a deep breath and slowly. God, he hates this vile man. Still, without Murdock there would be no funding to go on productive digs. He's worked for Murdock for three years now and still doesn't trust the man. The oil tycoon has a reputation for his employees unexpectedly, well, dying.

Take the leviathan debacle not so long ago in the South Pacific for example…

Yet, he says, "Okay. I know. It's definitely not a species I've seen before."

Another long pause from the other end, then Murdock says, "Meet me in Des Moines."

Ash is about to tell the man okay when there's a beep of a call ended. The bastard hung up on him. He tosses the phone into the center counsel and turns the SUV away from Lyle's Port.

"He's pissed, isn't he?"

Ash shrugs. "Maybe. Wants to meet us in Des Moines."

"Close to home, at least."

"Right."

He sets out, taking the clearer roads if they prove safe enough. Most are. The few he avoids are the main interstates, which are crawling with vagrants. Interstates are the easiest and fastest ways anywhere, so of course the assholes want to stalk them. Easy meals.

So, he takes highways and secondary roads.

They have a couple days until they reach Des Moines.

Ash just hopes Murdock Jones accepts the rare find.

SIX

All told, it takes over eighteen hours to get from the east coast to midland Des Moines.

Another half hour to find the hotel where Murdock is staying.

Espiath's Hotel, Murdock's text had read. The newest, most lavish hotel in all of Iowa.

It took a bit of time, but he eventually found the monstrosity.

He parked, not in the parking complex, but across the street in the lot of an abandoned grocery store. There's no way he's paying the fee if he's not staying here.

Together, Ash and Julia haul the tub of bones into the lobby of a hotel made specifically for the wealthy.

Behind the counter, the clerk frowns at them. A tall, lanky man with slicked back gray hair, this clerk watches their every move. And when Ash makes it a point to notice him watching them, the clerk lifts his head a bit, long blade of a nose aimed toward the intricately sculpted ceiling, eyes finding something else to look at.

Making sure the tub of bones is out of the way from foot traffic, Ash approaches the counter. "We have an appointment with Murdock Jones."

The clerk slowly lowers his gaze to Ash, and snorts. "You? I hardly think so."

"Ash Barrington, look it up."

The clerk sniffs, glances away. "I think not."

Anger flares within Ash. "Look, you snobby motherfu—"

"Ah, Ash," a smooth, cultured voice sounds, "There you are."

From deeper into the lobby, a man of average height, dressed head to toe in a brilliantly white suit, Murdock Jones emerges from cool shadows. He casually swipes a small, black comb through his equally black mustache. He tucks the mini-comb into the front pocket of his suit jacket and beams a smile at Ash.

"Your travels were safe, I assume?"

"Fine." Ash cocks a thumb at the clerk. "Well, until *this* douchenozzle, anyway. Almost had an assault charge on my hands."

Murdock chuckles. "Oh, come now, Ash. Quinton is perfectly harmless." Yet, Ash catches the man's dark eyes (*weren't they blue the last time I saw him*?) shift toward the clerk in a cold glare.

Ash doesn't turn to see but can hear the shuffling of feet and someone clear their throat. Apparently, Quinton the Clerk is in trouble.

Murdock, with his oiled black hair and tanned skin, his manicured fingernails, says, "Glad you made it back safely, Ash." Murdock, with his crocodile grin, "Where is it? The skeleton."

Ash steps aside and gestures to where Julia stands near a red sofa. "Over there."

The oil tycoon frowns. "She's a bit on the modern side, isn't she?" He slides a much toothier grin in Ash's direction.

It takes Ash a second to realize the man just told a joke. He chuckles, shakes his head. "No, it's behind her."

The grin melts away, face firming up. "You mean the tub you two lugged in? *That's* the great find? *That's* what I paid for?"

"Um, yeah." Ash sighs. "The Board neglected to tell me about the active volcano."

For almost a minute, Murdock doesn't move, nor does he speak. He simply stares at Julia. She tries to look anywhere but at the man, feet shuffling. Under Murdock's gaze, it's hard not to squirm a bit. The man has the power to give the order to have you killed, body disposed of and your entire identity erased with a mild snap of his slender fingers.

Then Murdock smiles and motions toward Julia and the tub behind her. "Well, then, let's see this discovery."

Ash leads the man to the tub full of fossilized bones.

Again, Murdock frowns. It's deep, edging on irritated, his frown. He hunkers down, carefully sifting through the bones, then shoots Ash a confused expression. "Are some of these…cut?"

"Yeah. Had to cut a few of them. Ran out of time with the lava and all."

Murdock huffs out a breath, but nods and stares at the bones some more. "What do you think it was? And it better not be another damn velociraptor. I can't give those things away these days."

"Honestly," Ash says, "I don't know. The configuration in the rock was odd. I need to take these to my lab and—"

"No need for that," Murdock says. "I have a great team that can connect the bones, even the ones you destroyed. You can assess it after they've done the reconstruction." He stands and claps his hands, startling Ash.

Two large men dressed in gray suits hurry out of the shadows, pick up the tub and haul it to an elevator plated in gold.

"I have a new job for you," Murdock says, running the tiny comb through his black mustache.

"And me?" Julia pipes up.

Murdock waves a dismissive hand without looking at her. “Sure, sure.” His gaze levels on Ash. “It—”

“Whoa, hold up,” Julia spouts and stands beside Ash. “We’re partners. You talk to both of us.”

Murdock rolls his eyes and Ash wants to punch the pompous asshole.

“That’s right,” Ash says. “Both of us.”

“Oh for…” Murdock runs his hands over his shiny, slicked hair. “Fine. Fine. But this job isn’t just some go-dig-it-up-and-give-it-to-me opportunity. It’s bigger than that.”

“What’s the job?” Julia asks.

Ash nods, interested.

Murdock grins. “Are either of you familiar with Lake Superior?”

SEVEN

"This is the dumbest thing you've ever made me do, dude," Julia says as they stop in a large lot which gives way to the Port of Duluth.

Ash shrugs. "He got me with, 'Massive pile of bones at the bottom of a lake'."

"I know, and it's stupid. All of it. I don't trust the bastard."

"I don't either, but the pay we signed for will retire us both."

"I'm thirty..."

He lifts an eyebrow. "You don't want to retire early? Really?"

She stares out through the windshield at the giant lake before them. "This is all I know and all I ever want to do."

He laughs, then manages, "Yeah, see, there's something wrong with you, lady."

Julia punches his shoulder. Hard. Hard enough to jar him a bit. "Fuck off. You can't tell me you wouldn't miss all this. The adventure of it all. The rushes and discoveries..."

He nods. "I'd miss it." He winks. "But who says we can't keep doing this job even after we retire?"

She blinks, finally smiles. "Good point."

They face Lake Superior.

Since the changes Earth took decades ago due to everything from the melting ice caps and nuclear effects to straight up pollution and the gray fogs of biowarfare during the Civil War Two, the once wild Great Lake is now mild, nearly placid. The only Great Lake which remains full of waves and life is, oddly enough, Eerie.

It's just now seven o'clock in the morning and the sky is full of golden roses and soft oranges as the sun rises higher above the horizon. It's quite beautiful. Ky would love it, Ash knows. He smiles a little, thinking about how she would gasp and point at all the colors and tell him how she's going to paint this very scene when they get home and—

"...this."

He shakes his head, blinks. "Huh?"

"I said, we should go do this." Julia opens her door. "If I die on that lake I'm gonna come back and kill you."

"What if I die too?"

"Well, shit, then I'll bring you back to life and kill your ass again." She scoots out of the SUV. "C'mon, man."

He gets out of the vehicle and together they walk toward Port Duluth where, according to Murdock, a specialized team awaits them.

Ash listens to the sound of his old boots clumping over the cracked cement and almost hears the shuffling of small sneakers. Ky's small sneakers.

Ghosts…

He focuses on the harbor ahead. Before long, a small town comes into full view, along with what appears to be hundreds of large docks. The day is already getting hot and he arms sweat from his forehead.

Not long and they're standing on the docks.

"So, uh, who are we supposed to meet here?" Julia asks. "Looks pretty deserted."

And indeed, it does. The docks should be bustling, but they're not. Instead there are places that appear in a need of repair. Warped planks and entire docks slathered in green moss and black mold. One of the farther docks slants downward and appears to lead directly into the lake.

Once, these docks bustled with fishermen and the buildings behind him were like processing warehouses for the fish. At least by all the stories his grandparents told him.

Not anymore.

Now, it's like a ghost harbor. It's simply void of life.

Except…

"On your knees!"

Ash catches a glimpse of two men in black gear, carbines pointed at him, and does as he's told. Julia follows suit.

"Who are you?" A woman, shouts. "Names. Credential info. I want everything you have."

"I'm Ash Barrington and this is my partner, Julia Evers. Murdock Jones sent us to aid in the exploration."

There's a long pause, and the muzzle of a gun presses against the back of his head. "Do you have a credential tablet?"

"Yes. In the glove compartment of the Land Rover in the parking lot."

Another long pause, then, "A direct call to Murdock Jones has been initialized. Stand fast."

The minutes pass like hours and Ash desperately needs to piss.

Finally, the woman says, "Stand up. You've been cleared."

Ash and Julia do. Ash turns, coming nearly face to face with a stony-faced woman.

"Master Chief Green. US Navy Seals." She holds out a hand, smiling a bit. Dark skin glistening gorgeously in the rising sunlight. "Sorry about the inconvenience, Dr. Barrington."

He shakes her hand. "No worries." He hasn't been called Dr. Barrington for years. "I take it you're the team we're supposed to meet up with?"

"Team Talonshank," Master Chief Green says, nodding. "Yes." She points at the vessel bobbing near a dock to the far right. He hadn't even noticed it until now. "We'll escort you to the facility."

Ash cocks his head a bit. "Facility?"

Green smiles. "That's classified."

He smirks, thinking, *And this is why I hate working with the military.*

The military always give tiny flakes of information, barely enough to go on, no matter how crucial information is needed. They follow orders and do what they're told. Like they don't really have minds of their own.

The Talonshanks escort Ash and Julia to the object bobbing in the water. To Ash, it resembles the tall topside hatch on submarines, only much stouter.

The hatch opens and a thin man, bald head gleaming, pops out like a damn gopher. He smiles a nearly toothless smile. "Watch'yer step, folks."

Ash helps Julia balance while she steps onto a small, metal platform fixed to the protruding hatch. The bald man nods and disappears down the passage as Julia swings her leg over. She too disappears into whatever awaits below. A min-sub, maybe?

Heart thudding heavily, he steps onto the platform and climbs down the narrow passage.

When his boots clomp on the bottom, he turns and finds himself face to face with the bald, nearly toothless man. He's smiling. And it's not a very pleasant smile, though Ash does see friendliness in the man's blue eyes.

"Welcome aboard!" He steps aside. "I'm Merlek, your host on this dive. Please find a seat and buckle in. We—"

"Oh, for shit sake, Merlek," Green says as she thumps to the floor. "This ain't royalty we're escorting. Get to your station. We dive in five minutes."

Buckling in, Ash catches Green's attention. "We were never told of a facility."

Green plops in a seat directly across from Ash, sighs. "What were you told?"

Ash glances at Julia. She shrugs, then gestures for him to spill it. "Just that we'd be a part of a team collecting dinosaur fossils and piecing them together for shipment to collectors." He frowns. "Which makes little sense because very few dinosaur fossils have been recovered in this region due to erosion."

A corner of Green's mouth quirks in a slight, crooked smile. "That's all?"

"Yeah."

Green leans back, buckles in as the rest of her team follow suit. "Well, most of that's true. You'll be assisting and sharing your expertise with everyone. But it's not some cakewalk piece the bones together and go home mission. It's—"

All the lights dim to red, an alarm brays and the bald man's voice says, "Prepare to dive. Prepare to dive."

Green rolls her eyes and says, "Just sit back and relax. We'll bring you up to speed as we go along."

Last time Ash heard those very words from a military official, he almost died.

The mini-sub, because that's exactly what this vessel is he comes to realize, shifts. Air hisses, stabilizing the core of the vessel. Metal groans.

Next to him, Julia says, "Yup. We're going to die."

He laughs a little, shakes his head, and yet…what if she's right?

What if this is all a trick? Murdock wasn't pleased with the tub of bones and now…

EIGHT

No one really talks as the mini-sub dives deeper and deeper into Lake Superior. And as the vessel groans and creaks around them from the pressure, Julia begins to squirm.

Ash pats her knees, trying to comfort his good friend as much as possible. She grabs his hand in her own before he can move it away. She grips his hand. Hard. Like his beloved wife, Willow, had during Ky's birth. He squeezes back just enough to show her he's here for her.

A couple of the Seals and Green all share the same cocked eyebrow expression watching Julia.

"She doesn't like tight spaces," Ash explains to them.

Green nods and looks away, but the other two – both women – continue staring at Julia as though she's some new exotic species. Like they don't have phobias of their own.

"Docking in ten minutes," Merek, the bald man says through the speakers.

Ash watches the Seals all grip the armrests of their seats and makes sure Julia is doing the same, peeling out of her grip and placing her hand on the armrest between them. She gasps and just to make sure she knows he's still there for her, Ash rests his hand over hers. He holds onto the other armrest with his free hand.

"Gonna get bumpy," Green says.

In a few minutes, his teeth click, body shaking and bouncing in his seat as the mini-sub docks. The entire vessel screeches around them and he'd say "bumpy" is the worst understatement ever right now. It's more like a goddamn earthquake.

Then there's a loud clunk and everything is still. Well, everything besides his stoMach anyway. But this too eventually settles.

"Prepare to board Infinity Moon," Merek says.

The Seals unbuckle. Ash and Julia follow suit.

Green stretches her back, pulls Ash and Julia aside. "There will be changes in pressure as you step through the hold. Ears popping and all that. You will also be sanitized. I advise you both to keep your mouths shut, eyes closed and don't breathe until the beep sounds." Then she hurries toward the rear of the vessel where the others stand near what Ash assumes is a cargo hatch. Much like the carrier him and Julia took to the island.

Also, like the carrier, the hatch hisses as the seal releases. The doors slide open and Ash is instantly blinded by bright light. He half-turns, blinking.

"Well," Julia says. "She could've warned us about the bright lights of death too. Jeez."

"Agreed," he says and then they follow the others out of the mini-sub and into a white, shiny room.

In front of them are a set of sealed doors.

All around, a voice says, "Welcome. You are about to board explorer facility Infinity Moon. Please step through the doors single file and do as instructed. Thank you."

"Closed underwater facility," Merek whispers behind Ash, startling him a bit. "Gotta scrub the outside world off ya. Illnesses spread fast down here."

Ash nods and slowly follows behind Julia through the open doors and into a long, mirrored hall. The doors swish shut behind them.

"Stop." The voice is firm, though not human, Ash assumes. Too monotone. "Pressurizing."

There's no sound, but his ears do indeed pop and crackle like he's on an airplane lifting into the clouds. His stoMach drops a little and he has this sudden urge to find the nearest restroom. Eventually, though, everything stabilizes and he's feeling fine. As for Julia, he's not so sure. She groans a few times, head lowering every few seconds.

Ash places a gentle hand on her shoulder. "You alright?"

"Y-Yeah," she says without looking over her shoulder at him. "Just too much too soon, I think."

"I hear ya."

"Please move forward into the sanitizing tank," the robotic monotone voice says.

The tank is large, round and smooth. The ceiling, a mirrored dome and all seven people fit without issue. Although, Ash's heart whip-cracks against his ribs. Because this feels wrong. Like those vile death showers in the Concentration Camps long ago. He can't shake it and for one godless minute, he almost tries to break out of the tank and return to the mini-sub. But…

"Prepare for sanitization."

Everyone around him closes their eyes and holds their breath. He makes sure Julia follows their lead and does likewise.

The moment his breath is held, he's sprayed with a mist of cold liquid. And it keeps coming. He needs to breathe, and the spray just keeps covering him from top to bottom and back up again. Up and down. His chest burns. How long has it been? He's not used to holding his breath long. Next to him, Julia moans deep in her throat. He reaches out blindly, finds her hand and holds it. Giving each other strength.

And still, the spraying continues. His lungs are on fire. His body quakes. His lips twist, wanting to part, expel the old air and suck in fresh. His eyelids clamp down tighter, face pinched.

He's about to give up, let be what will be, then the spraying stops.

The robotic voice says, "You may open your eyes in three, two, one. Now."

Ash's eyes and mouth pop open. He whooshes out dead breath and sucks in air that reeks like lighter fluid and tastes like rotten bananas. He coughs, gags and shoves his way through the Seals to the door opening across the tank, dragging Julia with him, who is also coughing. They burst into a small square room, everything painted sterile white.

He drops to his knees. Julia leans against a nearby wall, hacking.

And somewhere amongst all the coughing and hacking, Green says, "Deep, slow breaths. You inhaled too quickly and might have gotten a bit of the disinfectant in your throats. Just keep it slow. You'll both be fine here in a few seconds."

Ash tries to do what she says, but it's the hardest thing he's ever had to do. Well, as far as he can remember anyway. He's had a crazy life full of dangers, but this…

Yet, as his mind spins through the various jobs he's been on, his breathing increases and the coughing lessens. His stoMach quivers, though not bad enough for nausea to set in. Eventually, just as Green said, everything eases, and he feels alright again.

And by the sound of it, Julia is coming around too. She's no longer hacking and sputtering.

Ash stands, wobbles a bit and a woman steadies him. She's shorter than him, but the fierceness in her green eyes tells him she'd kill him before he knew he was dead.

Regardless, she gives him a thin smile. Beautiful on her deeply bronzed face.

"Thanks," he says.

"No problem," the woman Seal says, pats his back and joins the rest of her team.

The others kind of blink at her, even Green, then that monotone voice says, "You are clear to enter Infinity Moon. Someone will be greeting you."

"Dude," Julia mutters. "This shit is messed up. So not worth retirement. Also, Infinity Moon? Sounds like a damn spaceship."

Ash snorts. "The price we pay…"

She lightly kicks him in the shin. It's not painful but he acts like it is. "Hey, what the—"

"That's for being a smartass." She kicks him again. Harder. "That's for dragging me to this underwater hellhole."

"I—"

"If you two are done bickering," Green booms. "We're about to enter the facility. From here on out, you'll see little of us unless there's trouble. For what it's worth…" Her gaze lingers on Ash for a moment. "It's been a pleasure to meet both of you. Your discoveries have given scientists new ways to approach things, especially in medicine."

Ash knows what she's referring to.

An unexpected and extremely rare find in Iowa. A partially preserved triceratops found deep in limestone caves. Only the head was preserved, having been frozen in a sheath of thick ice. With this, scientists were able to find the cure for diabetes and drastically slow the progression of ALS. All this found in the blood and brain of the triceratops head. It's the big find that truly put him and Julia on the map.

A door slides open, Green gives Ash and Julia a nod, spins and hurries out of the room, her team in tow.

"Well," Julia says, "I think she has the hots for you. Congrats, dude."

Ash chuckles, waves her away. "There's something wrong with you."

"We've known this for like fifteen years, man."

"Seventeen."

"Whatever. We gonna see what's beyond this room, or just kinda stand here forever?"

Ash shakes his head, steps toward the doorway. "Says the woman who wants to go back."

"Dude," Julia says. "Not so loud. They're probably recording us."

"Probably. You coming?"

Her footsteps fall in behind him as he walks through the doorway and into a corridor split in a T-intersection. It's empty.

"Um," Julia says, "Didn't that robot say something about someone greeting u—"

A short, portly man with tufts of red hair sprouting above his ears and around his otherwise bald head, steps around the corner. His face is wide, all smile, beady blue eyes shining under the bright lights. His forehead and stubby nose glistens with sweat. His cheeks are rosy, a sign of high blood pressure, Ash assumes.

"Dr. Barrington. Dr. Remus. So glad to finally meet you both!" He holds out a small, chubby hand and Ash shakes it. Julia steps forward and also shakes the man's hand.

Once this is done, he says, "I'm Dr. Giles. Head of Invertebrate Discoveries."

Ash nods. "Finding anything worthwhile?"

Giles shrugs his narrow shoulders. "A few interesting specimens, but nothing to call home about." He sighs. "I chose the wrong profession." He smiles at Ash. "Should've studied anthropology."

Ash chuckles. "Yeah, well, it's not as fun as it seems sometimes."

"But that triceratops in Iowa...and the mastodon in Texas. Your name is a big one, Dr. Barrington."

All this time, and he's still not used to being semi-famous. So, he's not really sure how to react to such praise. In public, usually a thank you and a smile works, but here, right now with a colleague...? It's not so easy. Especially if said colleague looks up to him.

Julia clears her throat. "Um, I was there too."

Giles smiles bright. "I know, Dr. Remus. I was just about to tell you how your finds in Wisconsin changed the way I approach digs. From the side, not top to bottom. That Spinosaurus you uncovered...well, to say the least is the rarest of the rare. They were said to have only be found in North Africa. But..."

Julia slaps her arms. "Right? That find was unexpected. I thought I was uncovering a T-Rex until I saw the longer snout and spines."

"And if you had gone from top to bottom you might've damaged those crucial specifics."

Julia grins. "Right on, dude."

They chat a bit more about certain finds, as well as Giles' research into curing lung cancer using rare prehistoric plankton.

When the conversation flags, Ash points down the hall. "So, what's down there?"

Giles glances behind him, then beams a smile at Ash. "One of the places I'm supposed to show you. The Research and Reconstruction Department."

The corridor isn't long and stops at a set of silver doors with no windows.

Curious, Ash starts toward the doors.

Giles steps in front of him. "Allow me, Doctor." He bustles ahead, and all Ash can do is smile. The small, portly man is like their biggest fan. Bringing them into the department is a big honor to him.

Giles taps a narrow, black pad nearby and the doors slip open, giving way to a slightly dimmer room boasting several tables with bones sprawled over them. A few men and women decked out in white sort the bones into bins. They look beyond bored.

"This is where we sort the bones we find, if you haven't figured that out already," Giles says, leading them down a narrow aisle between sets of tables.

"I have," Ash says, eyeing the bones as they pass. "They're all pretty small. Raptors?"

Giles doesn't turn around, keeps walking, though nods his head. "A few have been found here, surprisingly, but a majority of our finds until the scans came in a few days ago aren't even dinosaurs. That's why we separate them. Mammals, fish, dinosaurs."

"How many dinosaur fossils have you uncovered so far?"

To this, Giles stops a couple feet from the next set of doors. He faces Ash. "Full skeletons, or frags?"

Ash shrugs. "Let's go with full."

"Five."

"*Five*? In region said to not boast dinosaurs…that's not a bad haul."

Giles nods, chuckles. "Yeah, well, they aren't a preserved triceratops head. Two raptors. A young stegosaurus. Two hadrosaurs."

The raptors and hadrosaurs don't surprise him as much as the stegosaurus. Those have only been found in the west around California and far east in parts of Asia.

"What about the scans?" Julia steps beside Ash. "You think there's more than just what you've found already? Or are we all just wasting time here?"

Giles smiles. "Let me show you." He turns and pushes through the set of doors.

Ash and Julia follow him into a long hall and stop.

"Whoa," Julia manages, eyes wide, neck craning.

Ash smiles, gaze drifting.

The hall they stand in is not a hall, but a large, clear tube. In every direction, they can see into Lake Superior. A murky wonderland…

"Oh," Giles says. "Forgot about these. Once you've been down here a few months, you kind of get used to them."

Julia knocks on her side of the tube. "Is this glass?"

"About six percent, yes. Micro reinforced plemeria glass."

Julia blinks. "What the shit is plemeria glass?"

"Friend of mine invented it. Sam Rogers. Made from composites of actual glass, plastic, metals, and various other minerals I can't remember right now."

Frowning, Ash crosses his arms over his chest. "How much pressure can it take before breaking?"

Giles waves a small, chubby hand. "Plenty. We're perfectly safe down here." He continues on, loafer flapping the polished, steel floor.

As they follow, Julia leans close to Ash and whispers, "He doesn't know."

"I know," Ash says and looks around at the composite tube they walk through. Weeds from the floor sway around the tube, giving the murkiness an even greater creepy factor. He's been diving in the ocean a couple times, and that's plenty creepy, but this…it's just dead. The gloom. The swaying weeds. The cold depths of America's greatest lake. All of it sends shiver after shiver over his skin.

"Can we go back home now?" Julia hugs herself, hands stroking her arms as if she's cold. Even though it's perfectly comfortable in the tube. "I'm getting a seriously bad feeling about this."

"We're here," Ash says. "Might as well see what there is to see. If I think it's bogus, we request to be taken back. Cool?"

"Fine," Julia says. "But I doubt this is the huge find Murdock or anyone here thinks it is. You know damn well this region has no dinosaur fossils. If it did, it's all been eroded away with the glaciers and all."

"That's the claim," Ash says. "But you never expected to find a Spinosaurus in Alaska, did you?"

"Touché." Julia blows out a breath too heavy to be a sigh. "Guess we'll see."

Ash nudges her. "Come on, you like this. Admit it. Better than an island spewing lava, right?"

She laughs a little. "Right. Still hate the feeling of being trapped under a thousand feet of water though."

"You've been in *oceans*," Ash says.

"Yeah, but in a mini-sub a few times and never below five hundred feet."

"We'll be fine."

Julia snorts. "I don't plan on staying here long enough to feel fine, dude."

Ash nods. "Fair enough."

They follow Giles out of the tube and into another room. This one, it's so massive, Ash has trouble taking it all in. Not only is it huge, there's so many things going on and people milling about.

Over an intercom, a woman says, "Lunch is in ten minutes. Stage your stations for time of rest."

More than a few people, Ash notes, visibly sigh relief. They work on setting up their tables with whatever they're working on for when they, presumably, return from lunch. Others tap away on computers. The people across the room, he can't really tell what they're doing, but assumes they're preparing as well.

This room, it smells a little like vanilla and onions. Onions equals body odor in his mind. From personal experience anyway. If these people have been down here for months, he's willing to bet more than one ran out of deodorant.

"This," Giles says, "is the Nerve Center. Where all data is examined, collected and recorded. This is also where explorations are recoded and documented."

"You really need all these people, with so little finds?" Ash shoots Giles a frown. "Doesn't make sense."

"We process more than just dinosaur fossils. There's the sediments of the lake. There are the fish species we encounter. Rocks and whatever we come across. We process it all."

"What purpose does it even serve to know the sediments of the lake?" Julia asks.

"Pollution, mostly. If we can provide enough data, the Government will change pollution laws."

Julia laughs. "Like that's gonna do a shit-ton of good now. Earth is pretty fucked, dude."

Giles blinks. "There are some who say the standing negative can be reversed. I'm absolutely shocked, Dr. Remus, you of all people would feel otherwise."

"Yeah, well, I've been out there a while and seen some shit. Changes perspectives a bit."

"So, you truly believe there is no hope at saving Earth?" Giles ventures, challenging Julia now. Which, in Ash's experience, isn't a very wise move. "There's absolutely nothing we can do to reverse what's going on?"

Julia steps closer to the short, portly man. His jowls jitter a bit as she approaches. "I'll tell you what I *believe*. I believe we already fucked this planet up beyond all repair. I believe it's healing itself, but not in the way we want. It's changing. Shifting. Maybe even going back to an earlier form of itself before humans were even a thought. *That's* what I believe. Earth is purging us to make way for greater species to evolve."

Deep red burns through Giles' cheeks. His eyes are wide, unblinking. His mouth opens a little.

Ash clears his throat, taps Giles on the shoulder and the man lets out a small yelp. He faces Ash.

"Shall we continue on?"

Giles gives Julia a wide-eyed glance, nods and bustles off toward a set of yellow doors.

Julia sighs. "I did it again, didn't I." Not a question, because of course she knows she did it again.

"Yup," Ash says.

They follow Giles to the yellow doors as the employees of Infinity Moon gawk in their lunch hour.

"Well, it's true, dude, and you know it. There's evidence everywhere Earth is changing, maybe even reverting."

"I know that, but going all out on a colleague who respects you…"

Again, she sighs. "Yeah. I just…yeah."

As they come upon Giles, he's standing close to a scanner set beside the doors. There's a short beep, then, "Retinal scan complete. Welcome, Dr. Giles."

The doors whisper open and Giles motions for Ash and Julia to hurry.

They rush through a second before the doors slip shut and seal.

"This," Giles says, "is Gathering Department." Floor to wall, the room is packed with carts, tubs, shelves crammed with bags full of what Ash guesses is sediment samples.

"So technical," Julia says. "Lemme guess, they're gathering things."

Giles doesn't look at her, barely acknowledges her comment. "Here, we hold and store what we recover from the lake bed for further processing."

As he finishes, a tall woman bursts through swinging doors to the right, pushing a heaping cart dripping brownish water.

She tosses a red disc onto the heap and glowers at Giles. "Looks like more partial mammoths and a hadrosaur. Your sediments and shit are on the bottom." She blows out a breath, nods at Ash and Julia and hurries out.

"That's Fern," Giles says, "my assistant."

"She seems nice," Julia says.

Ash chuckles, he can't help it. When he's able, he taps the cart. "Finding a lot of hadrosaurs here. Didn't think this region would boast so many, actually."

"Well," Giles says. "These fossils are below the lakebed, so they were spared during the glaciers erosion. Same with the raptors we found."

"How far have you dug below the bed?"

Giles strokes his nubby chin, frowns, then snaps his fingers. "We're at sixty feet now."

"All in the same spot?"

"Oh, no. Not at all. Our teams move around." He places a hand on the cart. "This haul is about two miles north of the facility."

Ash steps toward the swinging doors. "So why are we here? You mentioned scans. If we're here to help with whatever cause you're after, we're not interested. Murdock Jones hired us for a special job. If that's not the case, I request we be taken back to the surface."

Giles grins and to Ash it's the oddest grin he's ever seen. Including Murdock Jones. "I have such sights to show you…"

Julia and Ash exchange a glance and Julia says, "Okay, that's creepy, dude. Stop."

Giles' grin droops. He puffs out a breath. "I wanted to give you two a mini tour of the facility, but yes, might as well get to business, right? Follow me."

The change in Giles is gradual. From being a mystified fan to a dower, sarcastic ass. Julia's comments no doubt aided in this change too. As often happens to almost everyone who meets her. Great person as she is, she just has no filter. Colleagues or not. She doesn't care, and that's a small part of why he likes her so much. Unlike Julia, Ash does have a filter. He can't help it. It's just his personality.

Giles walks to a single metal door. Here, there is no scanning. He simply pulls the latch and opens it. Then waits for Ash and Julia to join him.

When they do, he says, "Beyond this point, the facility is a bunch of glass composite corridors like the one you two awed over. There's the living quarters also, but I guess we'll get to that later. But, we're going straight into Scan and Retrieve, since you both want to know why you're here." His tone is almost smug, Ash notes.

Neither Ash, nor Julia says anything and follow Giles down another clear corridor. This one, Ash realizes, isn't all murk and weeds, though. It's actually fairly clear. A large sturgeon thumps the glass composite, flutters a bit, then swims away. Close to prehistoric, sturgeons. Besides crocodiles, sandhill cranes, and jellyfish, sturgeons are right up there with animals still living these days. Though, evolution has altered all of them in many ways, especially size, they remain basically the same.

He can see other clear corridors to the right, dotted with white. Are those the living quarters? Doesn't matter. If Giles can't show him some real results, him and Julia are out of here.

Murdock can go suck an egg.

The corridor is long and curves to the left a bit until they come to yet another set of yellow doors. Giles scans his retina and the doors open. The next room they step into is just as large as the Processing Department. Only difference, besides all the people and computers and table, is the large pool dominating the room.

"This," Giles says, "is Scan and Retrieve and—"

"Giles! For Christ sake. You know you need to call ahead if you..." A stout woman in maybe her middle thirties stops near the pool. Her face wrinkles in a frown. "Is that...?"

"Yes," Giles says. "Murdock sent them. I'll leave you all alone to get acquainted."

Before Ash can stop him, the small, portly man leaves.

Ash faces the woman.

Her brown eyes look him up and down as she slowly approaches. "So, he's sending *experts* now." She glances at Julia then turns her full attention on Ash. "I know who you are, Dr. Barrington. I know of Dr. Remus too." She stops approaching merely a foot away. "Well, let me tell you both something. We don't need you. We have a team of top-notch people right here doing their best."

"Nice to meet you too," Julia says and looks at Ash. "Everyone is so darn friendly down here. I can hardly contain my love for them all."

Ash waves a hand at her and addresses the woman. "Look, we don't want to be here anymore than you want us. Just show us the scans and we'll go from there."

The woman looks from Ash to Julia and back again. "So, why are you here?"

"To look at the important scan taken yesterday," Ash says.

"So, Murdock thinks we're incompetent now?"

"Excuse me," Julia spouts. "Who are you? Didn't catch your name."

The woman shoots Julia a sharp glare. "Because I didn't give it."

Ash, rubbing his temples, sighs. He says, "No one said you or your crew are incompetent. We've just been sent to assist, that's all."

The woman, she deflates a little. Her face softens the tiniest bit. "Okay, listen, the last 'experts' Murdock sent down here were complete morons he must have thought were geniuses. Seriously. The moment they arrived, they tried to take over the entire operation we have going. *My* operation. In the process, they nearly dumped all the data we had saved over the months when one of them tried copying it all onto his tablet. I about killed them both. Would have, if Green hadn't intervened and taken those two bastards topside."

"Well, holy shit," Julia says. "But we're not them."

"Never said you were."

"Then stop treating us like shit."

The woman visibly hardens, gaze growing cold. But this lasts only a few seconds before she softens again. Her shoulders slump a bit. "Okay. Okay. I'm Quinn, Head of Scans and Retrieves." She motions to the pool beside her. "This is the Moon Pool."

Julia snaps her fingers. "Now I get it. *Moon* Pool. Infinity *Moon*."

Quinn's gaze rolls in Ash's direction. "She's not the brightest crayon in the box, is she?"

Ash snorts.

"*Hey*," Julia says. "I'm right here, lady."

A ghost of a smile touches Quinn's lips. "You remind me a lot of my sister."

Julia chuckles. "Must be a good thing, then."

"She had schizophrenia. Killed her husband and chewed her wrists open."

"I…" Julia looks at Ash, then back at Quinn. "That's messed up."

Quinn nods solemnly. Her face darkens some. "Indeed. Forgot to take her meds and continued forgetting until…well…"

"Wait," Julia says. "How the hell do I remind you of your crazy sister?"

"She was a jokester too."

Julia swipes a hand across her forehead, exaggerating wiping off sweat. "Good. I thought I was crazy."

"Oh," Quinn says, winks, "You are, but I promise, if you start talking to the walls and trying to kill people, I'll shoot you."

This, for the first time since Ash has known her, leaves Julia speechless.

Quinn laughs, claps her hands and points at Julia. "Oh, you're going to be fun. Come on, I'll show you those scans."

Ash pats Julia's shoulder as he passes. She's staring at Quinn, wide-eyed, mouth opening and closing.

Behind him, she says, "I think I just met my new best friend."

Ash chuckles, following Quinn across the large room to a narrow, silver door.

NINE

The room Quinn leads Ash and Julia into is considerably smaller than any of the others they've stood in. Every wall is adorned with monitors, three men tapping away on computers. But it's the far wall Quinn leads them to.

Here, the wall carries only one large monitor. Protruding from the wall are various panels and a large, glowing, blue dome. Ash recognizes some of the equipment. Like the seismograph and depth finders, but the rest...he's utterly lost.

Quinn taps a blinking green light next to the glowing blue dome. It flickers to red. She types something on a flat keyboard resting on the opposite side of the dome.

"This is the main hub of all the scans ever taken during the thirteen months this project has been funded," Quinn says. "Every scan is closely inspected before any orders are given."

She taps another button and steps away from the dome.

"Um," Julia says. "Is something supposed to happen? Because—"

Before she can finish, an image manifests above the blue dome. For a moment, it's nothing but blurry waves, then Ash is staring at the lakebed. In the right corner is: 1,300 feet.

The image flickers, revealing an ultrasound view. In the right corner, it reads: 1,350 feet. An image itself...

"Holy shit," Ash manages, heart stuttering.

"Are those...?" Julia leans closer.

"We estimate between five hundred to two thousand different species of dinosaurs," Quinn says.

The image flickers again. Clearer this time. Ash blinks at a fully intact tyrannosaurus rex skull.

Barely able to breathe, he points at the images, shaking his head. "No. Not possible."

Quinn smiles. "The T-Rex skull? Agreed. But here it is. If you look closely, there's also a brachiosaurus skull and partial spine. As you know, the sauropods did not roam in this region as far as science knows. Stuck mostly to the west according to fossils. Although, those were never considered a real brachiosaurus, of course."

"Juvenile brontosaurus," Ash says. "Only true brachiosaurus found in North America, and only the skull was in Georgia. Many confused brontosaurus with brachiosaurus. They still do."

"Which is dumb," Julia says, "because their skulls are totally different."

"Brontosaurus has a broader snout, and overall skull, yes," Ash says. "But compared, that's the only real difference, besides the ridge between the brachiosaurus' eyes. Sometimes that ridge gets broken off over time, so…"

Quinn waves a hand. "Yeah, yeah, we all know that much. But there's an entire trove in this cave. Could be the finds of a lifetime."

There's a long pause, before Julia ventures, "Then why haven't you exhumed the bones?"

"We plan to in…" She glances at her wristwatch. "Two hours."

Both of Ash's eyebrows lift. "You've already breached the cave? According to this, it's under the lake bed."

"Last report from my dig team leader out there is we have about ten feet to go. Most of it solid rock."

Ash nods. He stares at the T-Rex skull for a long time and straightens. "I want to join the dive team to exhume the bones."

"You want to…" Julia says. "Dude, you're terrified of water!"

He faces her. "Have to get over that fear sometime, right?"

"Sounds more like you want to take credit for the finds," Quinn says.

Ash shakes his head. "No. I just like to see everything first hand."

"Yep," Julia says. "Doesn't matter where or how dangerous, he's all up in everything all the time. Crazy bastard. Annoying as shit too."

Quinn taps one of the buttons and the image dissolves. "We have a highly trained team who go on these excavation dives. How much training have either of you had on deep dives?"

Ash and Julia exchange glances.

"I went snorkeling once," Julia says. "Does that count?"

"Mini-sub involved?" Ash asks.

"A modified sub, yes. Equipped with claws to help collect and heavy lifting, but most of the netting is done by hand and divers."

Ash faces Quinn fully. "So, get me trained. I want to help."

She frowns. "Why? Because if you think—"

"No. This is your find. Full credit. I just want to be there. I want to help."

Leaning close, Julia whispers, "What the hell are you doing, dude?"

"The right thing," he says and looks at Quinn. "I'll even sign a waiver or whatever you need. Get me trained so I can help."

Quinn glances away for a moment, takes a breath, and looks at Ash. Her eyes are cold again. Stony. "Fine. But I swear, if you take any credit for any of this and belittle my crew, I'll shoot you."

"She's really into shooting people, man," Julia tosses out.

"You have my word," Ash says. "This is your find. I'm only here to assist."

Quinn shakes her head, but motions for them to leave the room.

Back in the Moon Pool room, another woman is inspecting dive gear. It's only now Ash notices the modified mini-sub suspended above the pool.

"Well, here we go," Quinn says as she brushes by Ash. "Hi Kayla."

The other woman, Kayla, she favors Quinn with a brief smile, then returns to inspecting the gear lined up against the wall. She doesn't acknowledge Ash or Julia, just keeps going on about her job.

Quinn turns to Ash. "This is Kayla. She's our marine biologist and deep dive expert. She's the one who found the real Flying Dutchman ship six years ago."

Ash sucks in a breath, gaze drifting to Kayla as she tests air tanks and makes sure there's no cracks in the hoses. At least, that's what he thinks she's doing.

He blows out pent up breath, and manages, "This is Kayla Fivewinds?"

"The very same," Quinn says.

"You know," Kayla says. "I do speak English, right?"

Julia giggles. "Oh, I like her already."

Ash clears his throat and steps forward a bit. He hunkers down beside her. "I'm Ash Barrington." He extends a hand.

Kayla frowns at the hand. "I know." She winks at him, then goes on about checking the diving gear again.

"Kayla," Quinn says. "I need you to train Ash about diving."

For a long time, the woman doesn't answer. Finally, though, "This isn't some amateur dive. We have two hours. Not days to train."

Ash says, "I'm a fast learner."

Without looking at him, Kayla says, "Everyone says that until they're eight hundred feet underwater and their tank is running low."

"Kayla," Quinn says, tone firm.

The other woman sighs and finally gives Ash her full attention. "Alright, look. Deep diving isn't just something you learn overnight, let alone in less than two hours. Letting you dive without proper training would possibly kill you."

"I can handle it," he says.

"Ash…" Julia says, placing a hand on his shoulder. "If she thinks you can't then—"

"I'll be fine." He shoots a glare over his shoulder at her.

Julia rolls her eyes and flaps her arms in exasperation. "Fine. Whatever, dude."

"Give him the best possible training," Quinn says. "He'll just be there to help, nothing more."

"I have enough help."

"Kayla…" Quinn with her firm tone again.

"Fine," Kayla says and jabs Ash in his chest. "You want to learn how to dive? Then let's learn how to dive."

"Don't kill him," Quinn says quickly.

Kayla chuckles as she stands. "No promises, Boss."

"Oh, that makes me feel so much better about letting my partner go into the water with you," Julia says.

"Then maybe he should have already been trained before volunteering."

"Look, you little—"

"Enough," Ash shouts. He stands, gives Julia a simmer-down gesture, then faces Kayla. "Teach me the basics. That's all I ask."

Kayla lowers her gaze, lets out a long breath too heavy to be a sigh. "Okay." Her hazel eyes meet his blue ones. "As long as you stay out of the way and remember I'm the boss out there. Do as I say and do it right away. A single false move and it jeopardizes not only the operation, but the lives of my dive team too. Understand?"

Ash nods. "Understood."

She shakes her head, chuckles humorlessly. "You're one crazy son of a bitch."

Grinning, Ash says, "Not by choice."

"You should see him standoff a river of lava," Julia spouts. "Now that's crazy."

For the first time, Kayla beams a genuine smile. It brightens up her entire face and Ash can't help but notice how beautiful the woman is.

She bends, picks up a black vest with a long, thin rectangular tank fixed to the back. "Good thing for you, Mr. Jones funded us well and we have the latest in dive gear. Top notch tech." She taps the rectangular object on the back. "We don't use oxygen tanks here. Instead, we have this."

After a few seconds of silence, Julia says, "Um…what is it?"

"The latest in oxygen filtration, the X-600 Shark. It draws the water in through it, harvests the oxygen produced by the flow and natural oxygen all water has." She runs a finger over a thick, black tube fixed to a modified helmet. "Air goes through here, filters into a regulator in the side of the helmet and dispenses into the mask."

"So," Ash says, "you never run out of air during a dive?"

Kayla nods. "Only problem you might face with the Shark are the water intakes. Sediment tends to clog the valves if things get stirred up too much out there."

No one says anything for a while.

Ash stares at the dive vest and helmet. "Are there techniques to clear the intakes if they do get clogged?"

Kayla points at a blue button built into the vest. "There is. You push this button. Before you do, though, hold your breath until you hear the beep. The Shark uses the air in the mask to blow out the intakes in a reversal of flow." She lowers the vest. "But there's some risk doing this. Sometimes it's not enough to clear the clogs and no more oxygen can be produced through the Shark, leaving you without air until either help arrives, or you die."

"And if I don't push the button?"

"You'll have enough air in your mask and in the tube, so if you breathe normally you can return to the Moon Pool. We're a close team, so if one of us is in trouble, there's always someone nearby to help too." Her face hardens some. "Since you won't have the experience and full training one should have before going on a deep dive like this, I'll assign someone to stay by your side at all times."

Ash holds out a hand and this time Kayla shakes it. Her grip is firm. Strong. "Thank you."

Kayla nods. "For what it's worth, I'm really honored to meet you…and Dr. Remus."

"Holy hell," Julia says, sounding all aghast. "You *do* know who I am."

"Of course. You have a following."

"I…do?"

Kayla laughs, holds the X-600 Shark up for Ash. "Ready to do the quickest deep dive training known to man?"

TEN

Through the helmet's earpiece, Kayla's voice is firm, yet gentle. "We're going to dive below the Moon Pool. Sixty feet to the lake bed. We're one thousand feet deep, so the pressure will be the first thing you notice. The suit you're wearing decreases the pressure, but you'll still be able to feel some of it. I want you to find a clam and bring it back to the surface of the Moon Pool. Remember, if you get disorientated or something feels wrong, call me. I'll be close."

Ash nods. They tread water in the center of the Moon Pool. It's been a little over an hour since they began training. The greatest obstacle, at least for Ash, was not holding his breath when he went under water. A natural reaction. Humans aren't made to breathe underwater, after all. But the more he practiced, the more he learned to breathe normally. The air in the mask has an odd minerally odor, though not unlike standing near a lake on a breezy day. Nothing unpleasant. Eventually Kayla made him stay under and swim around the Pool for half an hour until he felt completely comfortable breathing in the modified helmet.

Now is the true test, though, and Kayla told him if doesn't pass it she can't let him go on the dig, and he agreed.

"Okay," Kayla says. "Just dive to the lake floor, find a clam and bring it back up. Ready?"

"Yeah," Ash says, hearing both his own voice and breathing through the mask like a tiny echo chamber. Another little quirk he needs to get used to. Good thing he's not claustrophobic.

"Dive," she tells him, and he does as he's told, bending at the waist and sinking downward. He kicks and in seconds he's cruising toward the bottom opening of the Moon Pool.

The room above, according to Quinn, is pressurized to keep the rest of Lake Superior from flooding the facility. Which hadn't boded well for Julia, but, in usual Julia fashion, she snarked it off.

He dives to the bottom of the Moon Pool, remembering to keep his breathing steady. Already he feels the pressure of being one thousand feet underwater. And as Kayla mentioned, it's a bit uncomfortable. He waits a moment, holding onto the lip of the hole at the bottom of the Pool, letting himself get at least a little used to the slightly crushing feeling. He wonders why they don't just use dive-mechs? Would definitely make things easier. And hadn't Murdock funded something a few years ago involving dive-mechs? Ash vaguely remembers reading something about an old oil rig in the South Pacific. Also, about the leviathan creature. The very creature Julia mentioned before.

"Everything okay, Ash?" Kayla, sounding calm.

"Yeah. Just getting used to the pressure thing right now."

"No one ever gets used to it, but I promise, you won't be crushed."

"Why don't you have mechs to do this?" Asking the very thought slipping through his mind.

"Mr. Jones felt that, since we're in a lake, the mechs would be a useless expense."

"This is just as deep as some parts of oceans, though."

Kayla grunts. "We know this, so does he, but apparently it's not enough to convince him."

Ash shakes his head, positions himself toward the lake's floor, and pushes off. The floor is about twenty feet from the bottom of the Moon Pool. He swims to the lake floor, lake bed, whatever, and spares a look around. The water isn't entirely murky and to the right, a couple of clawed mini-subs dig into a slight rise in the floor, collecting specimens and whatever else might be there. They stir up silt and other sediments, but they're too far away to affect visibility much.

By all accounts, the water is rather clear. Another sturgeon, this one almost as long as he is tall, swims by.

Enough gawking. Get the clam.

A patch of thick weeds sway below him. Rocks stick out here and there like brown, rotten teeth. Ash lowers himself into the weed patch, parting them carefully so not to stir up any silt or sand. He's more afraid of the silt clogging the intakes of the Shark than being able to see. Still, he searches, eventually pulling weeds out of his way.

Nothing in the weed patch, he moves on to the rocks. Beyond the scattering of large rock is a gradually rising hill, ragged with more rock. No weeds grow on the hill.

He frowns at this, shakes his head, and continues his search for a clam. Not that he'll ever find one, but...

There. Right beside one of the brown rocks. A smile spreads over his face behind the clear mask. He swims toward an unsuspecting clam, arm reaching, fingers splayed—

Something smacks the back of his head hard enough to shove him into the silty, sandy floor of the lake. Pain blooms, spreading over his skull, and all he sees is darkness. On his back, whatever struck him is now shaking him. He's flung, tumbling over and over in a storm of silt.

When he finally comes to a stop and catches his balance with a few firm kicks, all he sees is a swirling wall of dark brown and tiny bits of debris.

"Ash?" Kayla, her tone calm. And when all he can do is try to control his out of control breathing, she says, "What's wrong?"

Once he catches his breath, he manages, "Something attacked me."

There's a long pause, then, "There's nothing in this lake that will attack humans, nor pose a threat, Ash."

"Tell that to the back of my head and whatever tossed me around like a fucking ragdoll."

"Ash, it might've just been a sturgeon. They sometimes bump into divers, but—"

"Since when do sturgeon have teeth? Because whatever attacked me shook me like a shark shakes a damn seal."

Another long pause. "Get back up here."

"When I can see. It shoved me into the lake floor. Too much silt right now."

"Okay. Swim backward. Don't let it get in the intakes."

Ash snorts. "No shit."

"Ash, I really need you to stop and think. Profanity and sarcasm doesn't help. Can you see the opening of the Moon Pool?"

He cranes his neck. There's faint light above, surrounded by the high-density lights set around to light up the area clear as day. Well, unless there's a storm of silt obscuring everything, of course. Still, that faint light is wide. Has to be the Moon Pool.

"Yeah," Ash says. "I see it."

"Okay. Swim for it and—no, wait. Stay right there."

"Huh? What? What's wrong?"

Kayla, very quiet, says, "Quinn just came out with lifeform scans. Just...don't move."

All around, save for above, walls of swirling darkness.

"What do you mean, 'lifeform' scans? What's out here with me?"

"I...don't know. Something big. Scans aren't detailed enough, but Quinn and Julia are working on it. Just don't move."

Heart galloping, he opens his mouth, then closes it, not really sure what to say. All at once, his mouth feels way too dry. His stoMach churns. A shiver trickles over his skin. The special suit he's wearing cuts out most of the chill due to the depth, but this isn't a shiver caused by the outside. No, this is the chill of fear.

Something big is here with him. Not a sturgeon. Something...else...

Something with teeth.

"Okay," Kayla says in his earpiece, startling him. "Looks like we have a shark."

Ash blinks. "A…wait, what? *Shark*? In Lake *Superior*?"

"The waters aren't as cold as they once were before the climate changes. You're swimming in forty-six degrees right now. Bull sharks have been found here before, just not at this depth."

"Whoa, whoa, there's a *bull* shark down here with me?"

"Looks like it. Bigger than average though…"

"Oh, that makes me feel *so* much better," he says.

"Just stay put. I'm coming down to clear the silt and get you back up here."

"Well, hurry up, then."

He's walled off, can't see anything in any direction except for up. Christ, why does it take so long for silt to settle? Then again maybe—

It bursts through the dark wall in front of him, mouth gaping and lined with pointy teeth. He swims to the side. A pectoral fin clips his arm hard enough to send pain into his shoulder. He's turning when…

Hands grip his shoulders and shove him downward with so much force he's buried into the silt and sand again. All is darkness. The hands on his shoulders squeeze, agony shoots through him and he screams.

"Ash? You alright?"

He screams again when whatever is attacking shakes him again.

Can't be a shark. Sharks don't have hands.

"I'm on my way, Ash," Kayla says.

Too late, he thinks. *It'll kill me before she even gets out of the Moon Pool. It'll—*

He's turned around yet again and from out of the stormy silt emerges a gaping mouth filled with so many pointy, jagged teeth he's damn sure it's not a bull shark. Gray arms protrude from just in front of the gills. Arms attached to the hands gripping him.

"Wha…what the fuck?"

The mouth is broad, like a tiger shark. The teeth, a dead giveaway. He's seen plenty over the years. Whatever the hell else it is, the mouth and head is that of a tiger shark.

Mutation, his mind wails. *It's a damn mutation.*

The hands and arms pull him closer and closer to the snapping mouth. With no way to stop it, Ash simply closes his eyes and waits for the inevitable. Soon those massive jaws will clamp down over his head. Soon all those sharp teeth will puncture his skull and neck. Soon…it'll shake and saw his head off. Soon—

The hands release his shoulders.

A loud roar blasts through his earpiece and when he opens his eyes, blood mingles in the swirling stew of silt. The shark mutation is gone.

His breathing whooshes in his ears as he tries to look everywhere at once.

An arm and hand shoot out of the bloody silt, grasp his vest and pull him forward until he's face to face with Kayla.

"Swim," she says. "Fast as you can."

In her other hand, she holds some kind of slender gun.

He does as she says and kicks his legs as fast as they can go until he's at the opening of the Moon Pool. Here, he stops and looks down in time to see the large mutant shark glide by directly under him.

"Go," Kayla says as she speeds toward him.

Ash wastes no more time and enters the Moon Pool. He swims hard, kicking and stroking his arms until he breaches the surface.

A few seconds later, Kayla pops up beside him.

Both of them are breathing too heavily to speak. They simply stare at each other through the clear masks.

Finally, Kayla says, "Gotta call Green and get an extermination crew out there."

"H...How?" It's all Ash can manage between breaths.

"River channels from the Mississippi, I guess. Only way, really."

"We're doing an entire lake scan right now," Quinn says as she approaches the Pool.

"You alright, dude?" Julia asks, kneeling. Her face is drawn, eyes somewhere between tearing up and stony.

He gives her a thumbs-up. Although, now, he's beginning to feel the effects of the attack more. Pain laces around both shoulders and slices down his back.

Kayla, drifting toward the ladder to climb out, says, "I shot it in the back but—"

Gray arms shoot out of the water, hands clamp onto her Shark vest and yank her down.

Quinn screams. Julia scrambles away from the edge.

Ash sucks in a breath. For a moment, he's lost.

Stop being a weak ass, his mind says. *Save her*.

He takes a few slow breaths and tuck dives. As the bubbles clear, he gapes at the scene not far below.

Kayla struggles against the thing holding her. The toothy mouth opens wide behind her head. Through the mask, he marks how wide her eyes are.

Ash darts downward, shoving terror aside, grabs the slender gun from Kayla, jams the muzzle into the creature's mouth, and pulls the trigger.

The sound is a muffled whoosh.

Blood billows, consuming Kayla as she kicks and writhes in the creature's grip.

Then she's there, dragging him away from the creature and back to the surface. The breach, and she wastes no time, shoving Ash toward the ladder.

"Get out of the water," she shouts.

Ash, struggling with the flippers on his feet, climbs the ladder a foot to the edge of the Moon Pool and flops out. In an instant, Julia is there. She strips off the flippers and unbuckles the helmet from the vest. Then she carefully pulls the helmet off. Her face is full of worry. To Ash, she looks to be on the verge of vomiting.

"You okay?"

He manages a nod before Kayla bursts out of the Pool and crawls away. Quinn's right there to help her out of her gear.

"Call…Green…" Kayla breathes once the helmet is off.

"Scans are still incoming," Quinn says. "Will have them in five minutes. Tops."

Kayla nods, repeats, "Call Green."

Quinn pats Kayla's leg and sprints to the Scan and Retrieve office.

Ash rolls onto his back, catching his breath and stares at the mirrored ceiling. Stares at himself staring back.

"Thank you," Kayla says.

He turns his head, smiles wanly, and shoots her a thumbs-up. "Anytime."

"Jesus…" Julia says, her voice brimming with both awe and horror.

Ash sits. She's standing near the Moon Pool, hugging herself, hands stroking her arms as though she's cold.

Kayla rolls onto her side, sits, also facing Julia. "Stay away from there."

Julia flinches likes she's just been slapped and stumbles away from the edge of the Pool.

Gaining his feet, Ash catches her before she trips over her own boots and falls.

"Easy," he says.

Her eyes are wide. "Let's go home. Can we go home now?"

"Why…?" He spares a glance at the Pool and his blood turns to ice water.

Floating, white belly up and gray arms sprawled on either side, is the creature that nearly killed him and Kayla. The entire pool is scarlet with the thing's blood. Small waves sway the creature back and forth, back and forth, sloshing against the sides of the Pool.

"Okay," Quinn announces as she rushes out of the office. "Green and team are on their way and—holy scuttle shit, what's that?"

"That," Kayla says, standing. "That is what attacked us."

Quinn shuffles closer to the Pool, stops. "Are those…*arms*?"

"It seems," Ash says, leading Julia away, "a mutation made its way into Lake Superior. Or maybe these lakes have mutations like the ocean. I don't know. All I know is my shoulders hurt like hell and I need coffee for my friend here."

Quinn blinks at him, nods and bustles off. Not to the office but through a small door next to it.

"That's the kitchen for this area, by the way," Kayla mutters, waving a hand at the door. She clears her throat, straightens. "The dig is postponed until Green and her team clear the area. Might be more than one down there."

Ash nods. "Good call." He leads Julia to the office and helps her into a chair.

She stares at him. "I…I never saw an actual mutation before."

"But your grandpa—"

"Told me stories of mutations and monsters in the sea. I've read about them. Saw reports on the news. But I've never actually seen one. The closest I came to one before that…thing, was whatever hit us on our way to the east coast."

He hunkers down in front of her, a hand on her knee. "Same here. This is my first time."

"How are you dealing so well, dude?"

He chuckles. "I'm not. Inside I'm a ball of knots. I want to call the job off and get transported back to the surface and onto land."

"Then why don't you?"

Ash stands, rubs the back of his sore neck. "Because this job is it. This is the last one we do professionally, if Murdock pays the agreed amount."

Julia rolls her eyes. "That's a big if, dude."

He smiles. Julia is coming back to herself. "We signed contracts. I have copies. If he tries to back out, we take him to court."

Still, Julia shakes her head. "I have a really bad feeling about this, Ash."

"There's nothing big enough to damage this facility, not even that mutation. We're safe in here."

Julia slams a fist on her knee. "Yeah. In *here*, not out *there* where you want to go!"

"I'll be fine."

She makes a pshhh sound and glowers at him. "Just like you thought you'd be fine diving for a fucking *clam*?"

"They're taking precautions now. Scans and a sweep. Plus, I'll be with a group of professional divers. I'll be okay out there."

Julia, shaking her head, turns away from him. "I'd take being on an island oozing with lava than here. At least there we knew what the threat was."

He walks to the scans Quinn had set-up. They blink on a monitor set in the wall. Almost eyelevel.

"The scans of the lake came back. Nothing larger than a sturgeon out there now." He faces her. "That thing floating in the Moon Pool, it was an accident. It's not a part of the lake. Must've swam all the way up the Mississippi for whatever reason. Like those bull sharks about twenty years back."

"That was Lake Michigan," Julia says, though she sighs. "Okay. Fine. Go out and play. Whatever. Just promise me, as soon as you're back, we get out of here. Okay?"

Ash nods. "Promise."

Although, the other part of the job is to figure out the deaths of the dinosaurs, he agrees. He'll deal with her when the time comes for that.

For now…

"Okay," Quinn says hurrying into the office. "It's black, but I brought a packet of cream and sugar."

Julia takes the cup of coffee from Quinn, smiles. "Thanks."

Quinn smiles back, though her gaze pings on the monitor behind Ash. The scan results. Obviously noticing the lack of rare lifeforms, Quinn returns her attention to Julia. "Are you hungry?"

Ash leaves the office, finding Kayla glaring at the edge of the Moon Pool.

"It shouldn't have been here," she says as he approaches.

"Accidents happen," he says, frowning at the dead creature in the Moon Pool.

"Yeah, but there's not supposed to be any accidents here. This is a relatively controlled environment. It's supposed to be as safe as possible. Someone was sleeping at their post, apparently, if they didn't catch this thing on any scans."

"Well," Ash says. "Maybe it just recently entered the lake?"

"Maybe," Kayla says, glaring at the dead creature. "Might've been planted too."

Ash turns to her. "Planted? By who?"

Without looking at him, she says, "Murdock. Who do you think?"

"Murdock?" He moves closer to Kayla. "What makes you think it's him?"

She laughs. Its tone is clipped and length short. "Because he's a sadistic asshole."

He's heard some things, sure, but…

"Why would he put his own people in jeopardy with god knows how many millions he's put into this facility?"

Kayla flashes a grin at him. "Because he's a sadistic asshole."

Ash stares at the dead creature, not sure what else to say.

She turns away from the Pool. "You know he was behind the tragedy on that old rig in the south Pacific years ago, right? I met the guy who survived. Bracken. Good man. His daughter is expanding his mech business into finding water. Anyway, he told me all about how there was a botched drop off of gear. How a mutated Mosasaurus infected his crew. How they had two monsters to deal with and then everyone just…" Kayla shakes her head.

"I've heard the stories," he says after a moment.

"Right. So, you understand what I'm worried about."

Ash peels off his vest. "No. But I think at the end of the day we all get paid."

"What if I told you," Kayla says, "We're never getting paid."

He pauses, sends his sight to her. "What do you mean?"

She blows out a long, heavy breath. "We've been down here for almost a year and my bank account is still zero. So is everyone else's, as far as I know."

Ash frowns, not sure what to say.

"The longer we're here, the more I'm beginning to believe we'll die here. The only ones who are allowed to go to the surface are Green and her team. And it's very rare they get the clearance at all. I think it's been at least two months until you arrived since they've been topside. Maybe longer."

He shakes his head. "No vacations or time off?"

"None."

Ash glances at the dead creature. "That's a long time for so many people to be cooped up like this. I mean, after a while, people go—"

"Insane," Kayla finishes for him, nodding. "Green had to put a couple down about a week ago. Cabin fever got to them. Those guys, they were going from room to room killing and eating people."

"Jesus…"

She nods gravely. "Yeah. It was pretty bad, but I'm seeing declines, even in my dive team now. Periods of being…off. Hell, even I get this really low feeling from time to time and being shut in for long periods usually never bothers me." She turns toward the office. "Even Quinn is showing signs. For one, she's never gotten anyone coffee before. She's the boss in this department, not me."

Ash stares at the dead creature as it slowly begins to sink, as most sharks do. He's actually a little surprised it floated at all. "So, you think Murdock is purposely keeping everyone locked in here for…what? Why would he do that? Why risk such an expensive investment and operation?"

A short pause, then, "Maybe we're an experiment."

He turns, face furrowing in a deep frown, toward her. "An experiment? For what?"

She shakes her head, still staring at the office. "I don't know, but every day I spend down here the closer I feel to my death. Maybe it amuses him to see us scurrying around like rats in glass tubes. See how long it takes before we break." She faces him. "All the data gets leaked out to him every other month, so he could cut us off from everything at any time without losing anything vital. Hell, for all I know, he has bombs set-up everywhere and all he needs to do is push a button."

Again, he's struck silent for a moment. What does one say to that kind of theory? And that's exactly what it is. A theory. Even if he can almost imagine Murdock setting this all up as some sadistic rattrap, it just doesn't make sense to Ash's brain. There has to be millions dropped into the facility and crew, not to mention all the tech.

Doors at the other end of the Moon Pool room crash open. Master Chief Green and her team of six march in, faces utterly blank, armed and geared in black from head to toe. Each of them carry black flippers and air tanks slung over their shoulders.

Kayla faces Green as the Master Chief approaches. She gives Green a respectful nod. Green nods back, eyes shifting toward the Moon Pool.

"What are the scans showing?"

"All clear," Ash says, though shrugs. "But who knows."

"Scans didn't pick this thing up until it attacked Ash," Kayla says. She smiles at him. "Who would have thought he'd save me, but he did. Blew the thing's head off."

Green gives Ash a firm nod, though her face remains stony. "Good. What are we dealing with, if you know?"

"Mutant," Ash spouts. "A shark with human-like arms and hands."

Finally, Green's face softens, though just barely. "A mutant? Here?"

Both Kayla and Ash blink in unison.

"Must've traveled all the way up the Mississippi," Ash says.

After some thought, Green shakes her head. "It's possible, of course, but all this time, there have never been reports of mutants in the Mississippi."

"So," Kayla says, "how do you think it got here?"

"Planted." Green steps closer to the edge of the Moon Pool, grimacing at the dead thing a few feet below the scarlet surface now. "Someone is trying to jeopardize the operation."

Ash blinks. "But who? Murdock?"

"No," Green says. "It'd make sense, but no. Could be our competitors from the Government."

"Roskie's group?" Kayla asks.

"The very same." She faces Kayla and Ash. "They want this lake. They've tried to get it before. What better way than to plant a few mutants in the lake to scare off the competition?"

It makes sense to Ash, but…

"Seems kind of extreme, don't you think?"

Green favors Ash with a weary smile. "Yes. They tried pushing us out a couple months ago. It didn't work. So, I assume, they decided to take extreme measures."

Ash nods, though watches Green carefully. What if, after being down here so long, despite being able to go topside from time to time, she's beginning to go a bit bonkers? Maybe even delusional?

Even so, he can see how some competitors might go the extreme route.

And yet…why, unless they know about the cache of dinosaur bones?

"We'll dispose of this thing," Green says, "and do an eighty-meter sweep. Keep the scanners running and keep in contact. You see anything, let me know right away." She gives her team a nod and they strap on their tanks.

"Why aren't they using the Sharks?" Ash asks Kayla.

"Because," Green answers, "I don't want my shit clogging up on me every ten minutes."

"Master Chief Green doesn't like the Sharks," Kayla says.

"Didn't I just say that?"

Kayla smiles at Green. "You did."

Both women exchange a warm glance, then Green sits near the Pool and pulls on her flippers. The rest of her team follow suit. She tests her oxygen through the mouthpiece, fits in an earpiece, and slips down her goggles. "Be back soon. Keep those scanners running and keep me informed."

With this, she enters the pool. Her team follows.

Ash watches them pull the dead mutation toward the bottom of the Moon Pool.

"We better get on those scans," Kayla says and hurries to the office.

Ash lingers, sight fixing on the disrupted scarlet water of the Moon Pool.

Never in his life has he felt so trapped.

Never has he felt a true pang of terror.

Until now…

ELEVEN

It takes over two hours before Green and her team gives up and returns to Infinity Moon.

Nothing on the scans indicates a threat.

Exiting the pool, Green announces an all clear. She doesn't even wait for conversation. Instead she storms out of the Moon Pool room, her six-member team quickly in tow.

"She's never been one for conversation," Kayla says.

"She's an asshole," Quinn adds.

Kayla snorts, nods. "She's that too. But without her we'd be in trouble."

"Whatever," Quinn says in a low voice, nearly a whisper.

Kayla appears to ignore her and looks at Ash. "My dive team will be here in about five minutes. Suit up, if you're still joining us."

Ash blinks. "Wait, I passed?"

"You saved my life. Yes, you passed."

He doesn't waste time and snugs on a Shark vest.

"Remember," Kayla says. "Try to stay out of our way and keep your intakes clear. Keep your back away from the stirring silt and sand as we dig."

Ash nods. "Okay." He buckles the vest tight.

Kayla smiles, gives him a thumbs-up, and begins gearing up. A minute or so later, ten men and women stroll into the Moon Pool room.

To Ash, they all look tired. Faces haggard, bags hanging under their eyes. Their movements are slow while they suit up for the dive.

Julia steps in front of Ash, checking the buckles of his vest. "You don't have to do this, you know."

"Yes. I do."

She frowns. "You know, I'm supposed to be the stubborn one, right?"

"You still are," he says. "If I can help these people in any way, I'm going to at least try."

"I know. Just be damn careful down there, okay?" She rolls her eyes. "Christ, I sound like a damn nagging wife."

He chuckles and places a hand on her shoulder. "I love you too, dear."

Julia mocks gagging and shrugs his hand off. "Do you want to see a girl puke? Because this is how you see a girl puke."

Kayla and her team sit around the Moon Pool. Humming sounds lead to thc clawed mini-sub lowering.

"Bryce," Kayla says. "Man the sub. Dig to where we need to be. Everything should be uploaded to the sub's computer."

A younger man stands, nods and waits for the mini-sub to lower a few more feet before climbing on and getting inside.

The mini-sub sinks into the pool in a flurry of bubbles, then disappears.

Once the bubbling is over, Kayla says, "Okay, team. Let's uncover some history." She looks at Ash as he makes his way closer to the Pool. "You ready?"

"Yeah," he says, siting beside her on the edge of the Moon Pool. His heart is a hammering mess, but he tries to ignore it. He smells the remnants of Julia's coffee. Coffee would be amazing right about now.

Her team jumps into the Pool as Kayla and Ash secure their helmets.

In his ear, Kayla says. "Just stay close to me."

Before he can respond, she slips into the Pool and dives.

Ash sighs, pushes off into the Pool and follows Kayla down to the bottom. The dig site isn't far from the Moon Pool, as he noted from the scans. In fact, it's the ragged, rocky hill he noticed before the mutation attacked.

The mini-sub, using a large drill Ash hadn't really noticed before, digs through the rock and sand of Lake Superior. All kinds of debris spews everywhere, clouding the water black. Ash drifts back up into the Moon Pool to avoid clogging the intakes. How the others are faring, he's not sure. Somehow, though, they seem to be doing just fine. Maybe he's just being too paranoid.

Suck it up, jackass.

He takes a breath and returns to Kayla's side.

A storm of debris and dirt storm into them.

"Just keep breathing," Kayla says. "Slow and easy to keep those intakes working."

"And if they clog?"

"Do like I told you. Go to the Moon Pool."

Ash sighs and forces himself to regulate his breathing until it's slow and steady. In front of him there's nothing but a moving, black wall.

"Fulk," Kayla says. "Clear some of this debris, will ya?"

"On it," a gruff voice replies.

There's a wavery, muffled whirring sound, and in a few seconds the black, stormy cloud of filth dissipates. Or rather, is blown out of the way. A smaller man swims by, a wide nozzle attached to a squat, black cylinder object that reminds Ash of a small Shop-Vac. He swims back and forth, blowing the debris and sand away from the team as the mini-sub continues digging.

"It's only fifty or so feet," Ash says.

"I know."

"Probably ease up around forty-five feet just in case it caves."

"Ash," Kayla says. "Relax. We've been doing this a while."

"For almost a year, I know." He watches the mini-sub disappear into the foot of the hill. "But I have years of experience and—"

"For shit sake," Kayla says. "Stop. Bryce was drilling underwater with his dad long before he joined this operation. He knows exactly what he's doing. Relax."

But he can't relax. If there's a thin crust layer before the opening where all the bones are...everything around could collapse, further burying and destroying the trove.

He wants to tell her this, but decides to let whatever happens, happen. He has no control here, and it's driving him nuts, but he also needs to learn to trust others more. Trust has been a difficult thing all his life. Especially after Ky's murder.

Ky...

No. He shakes his head, trying to clear all the bombarding memories before they manifest before his mind's eye. Memories of pushing her on the swings at the park. Memories of laughter and love. Even older memories of holding her for the first time while his wife lay dying on a hospital bed. Cruel memories. He—

"We're through," a man's voice says. "Stay clear as I back out. You guys need to see this."

"Thank you, Bryce," Kayla says.

The rest of the team swim back a few more feet as the mini-sub emerges from the hole and anchors into the lake floor. Less than a minute later, a hatch on the side opens and Bryce swims out. The hatch shuts behind him.

"Won't we need the sub for the heavy lifting?" Ash asks.

"Not until we see what we really have here," Kayla replies. "Might not be as big as the scans show. Happens a lot."

"It does?"

"Yep. Now, come on. Stay close. Let's see what there is to see."

She swims off to the large hole made by the min-sub and Ash follows. They're the first ones into the drill passage. Here, there's no flow or current or a man named Fulk to clear the water. It's murky. Bits of rocky debris obscure his vision and the stir Kayla's flippers make creates a disorientating stew.

It's not long before Kayla whispers, "Holy…shit…"

"What?" Ash tries to see through all the murk, but it's hopeless.

Then the passage opens up a few feet. He glides in beside her. Here, all he can do is gape.

Below them, no more than two feet, is a large underwater cave of bones. He spots the brachiosaurus skull immediately. The scans weren't wrong at all, from what he's seeing now. Although, the scans didn't show the complete massiveness of the bone trove.

"I don't even know what half of these are," Kayla says, tone brimming with awe.

"I do," Ash says. "This is it. This is the dig every paleontologist dreams of."

"Jackpot, then?"

He smiles. "Jackpot."

Kayla inspects the rocky walls of the passageway. "Too narrow to get everyone in here. The trove is plenty wide down there, but might need to open the passage up a bit more."

Ash nearly chokes on his own saliva. He coughs, shakes his head. "That could be bad. It might all collapse."

"*Might*," Kayla says and swims to the trove of bones. "We have a few tricks up our sleeves, Dr. Barrington."

"Ugh," Ash says. "That sounds so…old. Just call me Ash."

She snorts in his earpiece. "How old are you, anyway?"

"Thirty-six."

"Well, that's almost forty, so…"

"I—shut up."

Kayla chuckles.

Ash laughs a bit and says, "How about we focus on getting these bones out, hmm? That would be fantastic."

"Oh, hush, ya ol'fart. I'm getting to it."

He laughs some more. Can't help it.

From out of a sack attached to her belt, Kayla brings out what appears to be folded, blue cloth. A silver cylinder is fixed to it. Carefully, she unfolds the blue thing. The more she does, however, it looks more like a tarp than paper.

"When I set this," Kayla says, "we have three minutes to evacuate the passage."

"What happens if we don't make it?"

Kayla humphs. “Then we don’t make it.” She spreads the blue tarp-like thing over as much of the bone trove as she can. In her right hand, she holds the silver cylinder.

“What is that thing?”

“This,” Kayla says, “is what will protect the fossils when we widen the passage.”

Ash frowns. “How in the name shit is a tarp going to protect anything?”

“Get the hell out of here in, three, two…one…” She presses a button on the cylinder and swims frantically toward him. “I said get the hell out! *Go*!”

Ash, not really sure how to maneuver in such a tight space, tucks, turns and swims toward the mouth of the passage.

“Gogogogo,” Kayla shouts.

He pushes himself to swim faster and in less than a minute he bursts out of the passage mouth and into the lake. He stops, though not for long. Kayla emerges, grabs his belt and pulls him away from the passageway and hill.

“Don’t stop,” she says. “It—”

There’s a muffled, though deep thudding sound. Then a force shoves him hard from behind. He spins, head over flippers. Kayla says something, though he’s not sure what. He’s trying not to puke as he tumbles through the water in a flurry of madness.

When he’s finally able to stop the momentum, Ash rights himself, choking down hot bile. Once the sensation of vomiting passes, he gapes at the hill as it cracks and silt swirls in the water creating a sickening stew.

The debris is quickly blown away and all Ash can think of is that the trove is gone. Whatever Kayla used, it created the collapse he feared would happen. His heart bashes itself against the walls of his chest like a mad-ape as the last of the silt and debris swirls to the side like a filthy curtain.

He blows out a long sigh of relief. The hillside is cracked, yet still intact.

“Okay, Bryce,” Kayla says. “We need to widen the passageway.”

“On it,” Bryce says. The mini-sub moves into position and does its thing.

“And you thought it’d collapse,” Kayla says direct link, swimming close to him. “Oh, what little faith you have.”

“Yeah, well, it *should* have collapsed,” Ash says, trying not to chuckle too much.

“Ah, but it didn’t. You ready to make history?”

Ash laughs. When it subsides, he says, "Not really. Just can't wait to see what species are here."

"Spoken like a true nerd."

"Hey now."

They both laugh a little and face the hill as Bryce widens the passage.

Via direct link from Julia, "You know we can hear everything up here even if you're talking through direct link, right?"

He blinks.

"By the way, *barf*. You two need to get a damn room."

"We're just joking around like we do," Ash says, not sure if he believes that or not.

"Stop it,' Julia says. "That was all grade A flirting right there. She—"

"You know," Kayla says, "being the dig team's leader has its perks. Wanna know what one of those perks is? Anyone?"

Ash, bobbing in the water waves his arms to turn and look at her.

She winks through the clear glass composite of her mask. "No takers? Well, one of the perks is the ability to hear all communications, just like up in the office. Hi, Dr. Remus."

Very tentative, "Hey, Kayla."

Again, Kayla winks at Ash. "Oh, I just want you to know I'm not hitting on your boyfriend. I'm not into men."

"You—I—he's not my boyfriend."

Kayla giggles, waves a hand at Ash. "I know, but see how it feels when one assumes?"

Through Ash's earpiece, Julia sighs.

Kayla shoots Ash a thumbs-up and swims toward Bryce and the mini-sub.

"Ash…you're not my boyfriend."

He snorts. "That'd be weird, considering you're not into men either."

Kayla, obviously hearing this, pauses her strokes for a couple heartbeats, then continues to the mini-sub. "Let me see how we're doing, Bryce."

"Anyway, Quinn and I are listening and recording as the dig progresses. Just a heads up on that."

"I kind of figured," Ash says. "I'll give as much description as I can."

"Rock on. Be careful, dude."

"Always, lady." He swims, soon joining Kayla at the opening of a much wider passage.

“Not complete yet,” Kayla says. “But I think this diameter will do. About seven feet.”

Ash nods. “Looks good to me too.”

They back away and Kayla tells Bryce to finish up, keeping the seven-foot diameter. As Bryce does his thing, the other guy (Ash forgets his name) swims near, blowing the debris, silt and sand away from the dig site. The remaining eight of Kayla’s team swim around, more then five have what appear to be rifles of some kind. They’re lookouts, he realizes. Just incase of any dangers, they’re the first line of defense. And with the mutation coming out of nowhere…

Ash watches and waits as Bryce uses the laser drill of the mini-sub to widen the passage.

He waits, though inside his nerves are a tangle of electric wire.

TWLEVE

It takes almost ten minutes for the passage to widen completely and as soon as the mini-sub is ordered to moved aside and await further instructions, Kayla leads Ash, the debris blower guy, and four others down to the trove.

Like all the others, Ash is given a high-density mesh bag. He can't help but wonder if they find bones too large to fit into the bags? Then what? The mini-sub, maybe? Probably.

"At the bone trove," Kayla says, relaying to the office recording equipment. "Here with Dr. Barrington, world renown prehistoric anthropologist and paleontologist, and…what else?"

Ash chuckles. "Archeologist, but that one is typically ignored."

Kayla nods. "Archeologist too. In any case, we have dug a passageway into the foot of what we've all dubbed History Hill, over one thousand feet under the surface of Lake Superior. And now we enter the trove of presumably prehistoric bones and fossils previously indicated in deepening our floor scans. What follows, is the discovery as it happens."

She gives Ash a nod and points at the trove of bones no more than three feet below him.

He clears his throat. "Dr. Ashton Barrington, about to exhume the first skull of the trove." He swims the short distance, right hand plunging through the empty eye socket of the brachiosaurus skull. It's a young one, judging by the size. He carefully pulls the skull away from the rest of the large mound.

"A young brachiosaurus skull." He holds it up as bits of debris float by. "Fully intact and, except…" His sight lingers on the deep gouge along the right side of the skull. "There is a long gouge on the right side. By the look, it appears to have been made by a sharp tooth."

He places the skull in his bag and reaches for a random bone. They're all very well preserved being locked in this cave for millions of years under the floor of Lake Superior. No air. Still, considering they are all bones, either the dinosaurs were picked clean by scavenger fish, or something stripped the flesh right off to consume. But what kind of creature could do such a thing? What would actually bother with peeling the flesh off its prey?

Breath whooshing through his helmet and mask, Ash pulls free what appears to be a femur. He swims backward, bumping into a few of

Kayla's team as he does. The femur is at least six feet long. Too big to stow in the bag.

"It appears," Ash says, "I have the femur of the same juvenile brachiosaurus." He turns it back and forth. "There are more of the same deep gouges as on the skull." Which concerns him a bit. What could have made those marks? His brain tries to click through all the possible species that might've been in the area millions of years ago, but draws a long, white blank. "Too large to place in my bag, so transferring out of the passage to Bryce." At least he thinks Bryce will retrieve it. Hopes so, anyway.

The team hands it out of the passage and he returns his attention to the trove again.

Little by little, him and Kayla pull apart the tangle of bones. Only a few fit in their bags. Then…

"No," Ash says, barely able to breathe as they come upon the last of the trove.

"What?" Kayla asks. She even nudges him.

Ash shakes his head, blinking at the sight below him. "There's no way."

He's vaguely aware of Kayla swimming closer to him. She glances at Ash, then follows his sightline. She doesn't say anything.

Ash swallows down a thick thump in his throat, heart thudding. "That…that's a carnotaurus skull." He observes the short skull adorned with a pair of knubby horns over the hollow sockets of its eyes. Dead giveaways of this species. "They have only ever been found in South America. Very rare."

"So," Kayla says, "why do you think its skull is here when…wait, is that a tyrannosaurus rex under it?"

Ash squints, and holy shit…

"Yes," he says. "T-Rex." The skull is just barely under the carnotaurus and twice as large. The closest a tyrannosaurus has been found in this area is Sue, discovered in South Dakota. She is also the largest recorded. Though, various species of tyrannosauruses have been considered an invasive species from Asia.

"Dr. Barrington," Kayla says. "Are you alright?"

He shakes it off. "Y-Yeah. Sorry. We just already have more species here than we should, if science is right. Tyrannosaurus' might have been an invasive species to this region. But the carnotaurus…" He shakes his head.

"How do you suppose those species got here, Dr. Barrington?" Julia chiming in, like always. "Ash, how do all these fossils end up in one place? Because it's not making sense to my brain."

All he can do is shake his head.

And for some reason, his mind drifts to his daughter Ky. Her bright, smiling face under the warm summer sun as she picks tiger lilies outside the entrance of Maker's Woods before their weekly hike to Ghost Rock. Wondering, as he often does, what his beloved wife would have thought about their beautiful, smart daughter? Their daughter who poured her heart into everything she did. Their Ky, who would rather hug someone than hold a grudge. Not saying she didn't have her moments, like all children, but her moments were few and far between. His memories shift to them fishing on the beach of their Minnesota campsite, watching the sun dip lower and lower across the lake. Golds and pinks and reds and purples, all shimmering over the surface of the nearly placid water as far as the eye could see.

And what was it Ky turned to him and said? Something he hadn't expected, but…

"Mom's watching us," Ash says now as the memory fades.

"What?" Kayla waves a hand in front of him. Bits of lake debris swirl. "Dr. Barrington are you alright?"

He blinks, shakes his head, hating himself for letting the memories override reality again. "Y-Yeah. Sorry."

"Ky?" Julia asks in his earpiece.

He sighs. "Yeah."

"Who's Ky?" Kayla frowns at him and adds, "I hope you've stopped recording."

"I have," Julia says. "Ash, just breathe. She's in your heart, always remember that."

"Who's Ky?" Kayla asks.

"I know," Ash says. "Just sometimes—"

"*Whoa,*" Kayla shouts. "Who the *hell* is Ky?"

Ash wants to tell her, but his mouth doesn't work right and instead of telling her Ky is his daughter, all he manages is a mumbling, "A-ghter."

Julia swings in for the rescue. "His daughter. She was murdered over a year ago."

Kayla mutters something Ash can't make out. Then, "Sorry for your loss, Ash. Really. But I need you to focus here. With you naming off the bones we pull from this place it adds more validity. Murdock will actually do something. And I, for one, want nothing more than to get the fuck out of here. This will be enough to shut Infinity Moon down and Murdock can swim in the spoils, which will be billions judging by all the rare finds here. So, suck it up and finish your damn job."

A long moment of silence, then Julia says, "Well, holy shit. Now that's a speech."

"When you haven't seen the surface in almost a year, so yeah, I'm a little pissed. We all want out of here. We *need* to get out of here."

Julia says nothing, as Ash figured. She knows just how right Kayla is and any other argument is moot. Ash knows Julia is smart enough to recognize this.

"Okay," Ash says, managing a few breaths. The memories of Ky, those ghosts, stowed away for now. "Let's finish this and get everyone back home." He pulls the carnotaurus skull out of the bundle and passes it up the chain. Too large to fit into his bag.

"Recommencing recording…now," Julia says, her tone cold and dry.

"The discovery of the carnotaurus skull, a species only found in South America," Ash says, "has me more stumped than ever. The brachiosaurus, now the carnotaurus. Why are they here? How are they here? And even though there's a young T-Rex skull, tyrannosauruses were invasive species that roamed and hunted widely." With Kayla's help, they pull the T-Rex skull from the trove, turn it and…

He gasps, and for the longest moment, cannot speak.

"What…what happened to it?" Kayla asks, frowning at the skull, which is nearly as long as she is tall.

"It…" Ash swallows down a hard lump in his throat. "Appears something took a bite out of its head."

"A *bite*?" Kayla points at the skull. "Half the skull is missing."

"Something very big took a bite," Ash corrects, not really sure what to say, but saying something. He clears his throat and says, "It appears some rather large animal bit a majority of the young T-Rex's skull off. Perhaps an attack by a larger T-Rex, or…"

"Or what, Dr. Barrington?" Kayla asks.

His gaze slips over the clean cuts in the bone. It doesn't look like the skull was bitten into but…sheared.

"I'll need to examine it more to be sure, but it appears that whatever bit through the skull, there's more of a shear than a bite."

"Dr. Barrington, can you explain a bit more what you mean?"

He shakes his head. "Not at this time."

Kayla and Ash hand the partial T-Rex skull over to her team. It takes four of them to swim it out of the passageway to the lake.

Ash places a few more smaller skulls in his bag. A couple velociraptors, skulls no larger than a horse or cow. He gathers smaller femurs and various other bones. The larger ones, he passes to Kayla's team. The trove is huge, he realizes as they dig in. Much larger than he at first realized. And deep. It feels like the more they dig, the more bones appear. It's almost maddening.

He's about to have Kayla net a bunch of the bones and just pull them out with the mini-sub when something more unusual than either the brachiosaurus or carnotaurus catches his eye. It's partially buried, but…

He swims to it, pulling away various other bones. Then he just sort of floats there staring at the new skull.

"What is it, Dr. Barrington?" Kayla asks.

He shakes his head. "I don't know. But it was a herbivore, judging by the teeth."

The skull isn't small, either. Larger than himself and maybe another person. Something between a brontosaurus and a triceratops. Kayla loops a strap through its eye sockets and orders Bryce to back up slowly. As the skull is pulled from out of the trove, other bones and skulls tumble into the hole it creates, though fall straight through. He frowns, peering into the hole.

"There seems to be some kind of tunnel below the trove," he says.

"What?" Kayla joins him, also looking into the hole. "Holy shit, you're right. How come our scans never picked this up?"

All Ash can do is shrug.

Kayla sighs. "Julia, hun, please stop recording."

"Done," Julia says.

Kayla shines light into the hole, revealing a very large tunnel leading down into absolute darkness.

"I think we're done for the day," Kayla says. "We've collected a lot and it'll take you a while to do your thing."

Ash grunts. "Sometimes it only takes a couple of seconds."

"Right. Okay. But I'd rather you take this a piece at a time and be accurate rather than flying through and getting things wrong."

"Alright," Ash says, giving the hole in the bone trove another long glance. He really wants to see what's down there. Then he waves Kayla. "After you."

Kayla nods and swims up the passageway with her team.

Ash stops, once more stares at the hole and dark tunnel beyond.

After a while, he sighs and joins the team out of the passageway.

THIRTEEN

For millions of years, the water has never been so warm.

The cold water of the tunnel mingles with the much warmer waters of the upper-waters. And as the warm water flows in, it pushes deeper into the tunnel. Deeper and deeper. Another fifty feet. Another hundred feet. Deeper still.

All flowing in through the hole in the barricade.

Like invisible tentacles, the warmer water slithers through the tunnel, branching off to other tunnels. It writhes against the ice, melting it. Not so slow, though not extremely fast either. A moderate melt. Thin cracks slither through the ice.

And, as the hours pass, something within the pocket of ice begins to stir…

FOURTEEN

Giles shakes his head and pats Ash on the back. "Well done."

"I didn't find these," Ash says. "Kayla, Quinn, and their team did. Give them the credit, they've more than earned it."

Giles nods, though his face has gone all sour looking. Pursing lips and all. Like he just bit into a lemon. "Perhaps I will."

If Ash didn't like the portly man before, he kind of despises him now. The sexist bastard. He turns away from Giles and joins Kayla, Julia and Quinn as they help sort the haul. The partial T-Rex skull rests, dripping on its own metal table. Placed on a separate table are the young brachiosaurus and carnotaurus skulls. Lake water pools on the floor. And, glaring with its massive, empty sockets on a larger table is the skull to a species Ash has yet to identify. The brontosaurus/ triceratops hybrid. Or at least he assumes it's some kind of hybrid.

"Lots of hadrosaurs here," Julia mutters as she places a duckbilled skull on the table in front of her. "Woolly Mammoths too, or at least bits and pieces of them. So far, I'm not finding any whole skeletons of anything, though."

"There's still tons of bones down there," Kayla says.

Ash nods. "It'll take a couple days to exhume them."

Kayla, she gives Ash a tentative glance. "Sorry about your daughter, by the way."

He chokes down all the emotions threatening to boil over, blows out a long breath. "Yeah. Thanks." He looks away. "Anyway, let me know if you find anything unusual."

At his back, Kayla says, "You need to let her go."

A flicker of rage. He can't even remember how many times people have told him this very same thing. Mostly Julia. The same shit. Let her go. Let her go? How the fuck is he supposed to do that? *How*? He never got a chance to say goodbye. She was just…taken from him. Taken and murdered by the lowest of scum. Jealous of Ash's success, the monster stole Ky away. Stole her from him and left her lying in a swampy ditch outside of town.

Ash shivers, forcing himself not to spin on Kayla and unload all the pain and anger and sorrow flooding him. He manages a few shuddery breaths.

At his side, Julia whispers. "Easy. She doesn't know how it is. Just—"

"But I do," Kayla says, her tone firm. "I know more than you both can even imagine. My entire family was slaughtered one night while I was at work. Wife and two daughters just…mutilated."

Ash turns, facing her, heart trip-hammering.

Kayla's eyes swim in tears. Tears which soon trickle down the sides of her face. "Do you know what it's like stepping into your home and finding their blood all over and…their…their…" She slams a fist down on the table. A few smaller bones clack onto the floor. "My *wife* was cut out from groin to sternum for fuck sake!"

"Oh…" Julia says. "Oh, hun." She starts toward Kayla, but Kayla holds up a stopping hand.

"No." She wipes tears away, sniffs, shakes her head. "No. I don't want pity. I don't want condolences. I've said my goodbyes. But don't you *ever* assume I don't know how it is to lose someone to a killer. Something in me died that night." She glances away. "They never did find the bastard."

Ash, oddly feeling better, straightens. "I'm sorry for your losses. And thank you."

Kayla blinks, still wiping away tears. "Thank you for what?"

"For your condolences and for helping me to feel not so alone." All the truth, because suddenly, he's not the only one with a murdered son or daughter haunting them. He's not the only one carrying around all the pain. Oddly, Kayla's horrific story eases the storm pounding through his soul.

Kayla laughs a bit, wipes a stray tear, nods. "Good to know you're not alone, eh?"

"Yeah. It does."

What follows is a very long, very awkward silence finally broken by Julia.

"Okie dokie, then. Glad you two are kindred spirits now. You're both awesome and all and have my love and condolences, but can we get this done so we can eat? My stoMach has resorted to gnawing on itself already."

To this, both Ash and Kayla burst into gales of laughter. The loud, raucous kind. The kind that's more relief than triggered by humor. Of release. Of letting go…

Once the laughter subsides and Ash is pretty sure everyone around them is thinking they've both fallen off the nut-wagon in Crazytown, Julia says, "You know they lock people up in padded cells who laugh for no reason, right?"

It's enough to get Ash giggling again and he has to cough it out before laughter invades again. After a few seconds, he regains his composure. "Okay. Yeah, let's get these sorted. Eat something and I'll burn some midnight oil investigating."

"I bet it wouldn't help to know it's already passed midnight," Julia quips.

"Wait, what?"

"Look, dude, it's not my fault you don't know how to read clocks." She grins, winks.

Chuckling, he waves her away and heads to his own pile of bones to sort.

As he sorts, something gradually comes to his attention. A very subtle thing at first, then he can't not see it. He stops, face contorting into a frown. Running a finger along the ridged surface of a rib bone, his stoMach churns a bit. He drops the rib bone and hurries to Kayla's table, sifting through the bones she's already sorted.

"Ash? You okay?"

He doesn't answer Kayla. He can't. His mind is a maelstrom as he inspects a few bones from Kayla's pile.

"Dude, you're scaring the natives," Julia spouts.

"Something is wrong with the bones," is all he can manage as he lowers the large, attached magnifying glass to a femur.

"Other than mysteriously being tucked away under Lake Superior?" He can almost taste Julia's sarcasm.

"Come here," he says, staring into the magnifying glass.

Julia nudges him. "What is it?"

"Tell me what you see." He steps away from the magnifying glass.

She bends, peering through the glass. She stands this way for a minute or so. Then…

"Are these…acid erosions?"

"Yes."

She straightens. "StoMach acid…"

"A very high-powered kind too," Ash says. "Whatever ate these dinosaurs, it regurgitated their bones."

"Like an owl?" Kayla ventures.

Ash nods. "Very close, yeah. So, whatever ate these dinosaurs, it swallowed them in large chunks. The stoMach acid dissolved the flesh and nutrients, leaving only the bones, which it regurgitated instead fully digested." He looks at a few more bones. "Also, if you notice, several of the bones are sheared off. Meaning, whatever ate the dinosaurs here chomped and swallowed instead of biting and ripping away flesh. This thing took bones and all."

"What kind of thing could do such a thing?" Kayla asks.

Ash, drawing a blank, shakes his head. "Something very big and powerful."

"Thanks, Dr. Obvious," Julia says.

He ignores this and walks to the T-Rex skull. A juvenile nearing adulthood. The scrapes on the skull where it was chomped in two. The scrapes are slight. It literally appears a sharp blade just cut the skull in half. Like a snapping turtle…

There's something he's missing. A final piece to the puzzle. But he just can't pin it down. No matter how much he looks, there's simply not enough clues to go on.

Eventually he wanders to the brontosaurus/ triceratops skull, or whatever it is. The thing is huge and…

He leans close, eyes widening. A long gouge cuts down the center of the skull. This is something, but what traps his attention is a piece of whiter bone lodged into the gouge near the left eye socket. Something broken off that almost resembles a great white tooth. A very large great white. The tooth, if that's what it really is, was snapped cleanly off whatever predator killed this strange dinosaur.

Ash turns. "Anyone have some pliers?"

There are eight workers in the Moon Pool room sorting, not including Kayla, Julia and Quinn. All of them stop and stare at him like deer caught in the headlights. Frozen.

Quinn says, "Hold on, might have something in the office."

The eight workers glance at each other, shrug, almost in unison, and go about sorting. Well, more like a pre-sort so he can go through the bones more efficiently before sending them to be marked, recorded and stored.

"What is it?" Julia asks, walking over to him.

He points at the tooth, or shard of bone, or whatever it is. "Not sure. Looks like a tooth."

She carefully inspects it. "It's not a shark tooth, at least."

"How do you know?"

Julia straightens, an eyebrow lifting. "You get hit in the head down there? Come on. You know when sharks lose their teeth they lose them at the root and another one replaces the missing one. They don't break off."

He nods. Of course he knows that. The information just hadn't managed to swim through everything swirling around in his head.

"So, what do you think it is?" He taps the object. It's cold.

"Whoa, dude, that's your area. I'm just here for the whacky adventures." Julia holds up her hands, spins and hurries back to the table beside Kayla and Quinn.

With a grunt, Ash returns his attention to the huge skull and that infuriating object lodged in the bone.

Finally, Quinn bustles up to him and places a pair of needle nose pliers on the table. "These okay?"

He withers a bit, but, "Yeah. Hopefully."

"Good," she says and bustles away. Because, apparently, she's the bustling type.

Ash picks the pliers up and clamps the narrow jaws onto the bony object. It's almost too wide to get a grip on it. He adjusts the jaws a bit, opening, sliding around, before finally clamping down once more. He gives the pliers a firm wiggle, but the object stuck in the skull doesn't budge. He tries again, a little harder this time. Still, nothing.

"Maybe it's part of the skull?" Julia ventures.

"It's not part of the skull," he says.

"Whatever, dude. You're the boss."

He rolls his eyes, sighs and continues trying to pull the shard of whatever from the skull. It just won't move. It can't be part of the skull. That makes no damn sense. Unless it's some kind of bone growth. But if it's a bone growth, whatever cut the gouge through the skull would have taken that imperfection with it. Would've scraped it right off.

"I need something with wider jaws," he says and storms toward the office.

"There aren't any other tools in there besides a screwdriver," Quinn says.

He stops, takes a couple breaths and asks, "Okay, so where the hell can I find tools in this godless place?"

"Whoa," Kayla says.

"Agreed," Julia says. "Calm down, dude."

"I'll calm down when I get that fragment out of the skull. Now, someone tell me where the hell all the tools are kept."

There's a long pause, then Kayla says, "Maintenance. Those old grease monkeys have everything."

"Great. Where is maintenance?"

"Through the doors there. Take a right and it's the first door on the left." Kayla shoots him a smile. "Just don't get pissy with those guys. They'll probably make you squeal like a pig."

He leaves the Moon Pool room, not really sure what the hell Kayla is referencing. Sounds familiar though.

When he opens the door to maintenance, he's assaulted by the reek of oil and what might be ammonia. Or ether. Shit, he doesn't know. All he knows is it makes him gag a little. He tries breathing through his mouth and steps into a large room. Across the room is a large bay door. Dominating the center of the room are two mini-subs. The one closest to him is mostly in pieces. Rusty chains sway from the ceiling. The floor appears to be slathered with oil.

With a few careful steps deeper into the room, Ash says, "Hello? I need a pair of channel locks if you have them."

Only silence greets him.

Not far to his right is a rolling tool box. Red paint faded to pink and peeling, there are roughly a million drawers. He shrugs and walks over to the toolbox. He'll borrow a pair of channel locks, dislodge the object and return the plier before anyone knows it's missing. Ash opens one of the top middle drawers. It's full of grinding pads and god knows what else. He closes it and opens the drawer to the right. Screws, bolts, nuts and washers. He slams the drawer shut, quickly moving to the next. Nails. Next. Coils of wire. Next.

He blinks. "Chalk?"

Ash shakes his head and moves to the next drawer, this one reveals small screwdrivers.

Good, we're getting somewhere now.

On to the next drawer and—

"What the shit crawlin' through the belly of hell is goin' on here? Git away from m'stuff!"

A tall, scrawny man with a reddish tuft of hair sprouting above his big ears, comes shambling out of the shadows. In his hand is a silver flask. His face is covered in freckles, skin otherwise utterly pale. Like a tall glass of milk. His green eyes narrow on Ash. The grimy blue jean overalls draped over his thin frame flaps as he motions toward the toolbox.

"The jackshit ya doin' in m'toolbox, boy?"

"I just need a pair of channel locks," Ash says.

"Channel locks, he says," another, much deeper voice sounds behind Ash.

He turns to see a massive man lumber by the bay door. In his hand, there's a toque wrench. His jowls quiver with every step. The reddish-purple bulb of his nose tells Ash all he needs to know about the man's stance on drinking. Indeed, an old alcoholic. His considerable belly sways as he lumbers closer.

Ash holds up his hands, showing he means no threat. "Kayla in the Moon Pool sent me to get channel lock pliers."

"Din't think to ask?" The scrawny man asks, takes a swig from his flask.

"I didn't see anyone so I—"

"So ya thought ya could just waltz in here and take whatever the fuck ya want? That it?" The fat man brandishes the torque wrench at him. "We don't want your kind in here, snotnose."

"Snotno—hey, look, I'm just here to help. All I need are some channel locks. Wide jaws."

"They all adjust, stupid," the tall, scrawny man says and bursts into cackles.

"Yeah, yeah," the fat man says. "Stupid."

He sighs, knowing he's trapped by a couple of drunk idiots. A couple of…

Then he gets Kayla's joke.

Squeal like a pig.

It's a line from a demented film many decades ago about a few guys being terrorized by hillbillies. As the thought jiggles like gelatin, he almost hears the sound of dueling banjos…

A slice of fear cuts through him and all at once, he can't find the strength to move, let alone talk.

The tall, scrawny man shuffles closer, cloudy gaze narrowing into a glare. "Who are you?"

"Um, I'm…" And for some reason he can't remember his damn name. And it's like the more he tries the more it evades him.

The fat man blinks wildly for a moment. "You're…what?"

"Why, Clam," says the tall man, "I do think he's lost his tongue."

"Must be from the south."

Ash shakes his head, clears his throat. "I'm Dr. Ash Barrington."

"Oh, well hell, lookie here," the fat men, Clam says. "Got ourselves another doctor." He places a large, chubby hand on Ash's shoulder. "Tell me Doc…do you like games?"

"Games?"

The tall man steps beside Clam. They're both grinning.

"Games," the tall man says, grin barely faltering.

Ash looks from Clam to the tall man and back again.

FIFTEEN

The layer of ice is thin. So thin, it's as though nothing is there at all.

Tiny holes let in more of the warmer water.

Flesh twitches, that has not twitched in millions of years.

A heart long frozen, thumps heavily. Muscles stiff from time and ice, quiver and stretch.

Massive jaws open and snap shut. A groan rumbles through the chamber it has been trapped in for centuries and the old monster awakens.

The holes in the ice widen, spilling in more warm water. Water that thaws its gills. Water which melts the ice sheathing its giant fins. Another groan quakes the chamber and a large piece of the ice wall breaks free and floats away.

Its tail slaps into the side of the chamber. Rocks crumble, chunks of ice bust loose and drift out.

The groan becomes a roar and with another swipe of its huge tail, it breaks through the ice wall of the chamber and into a wide tunnel. The old monster's stoMach aches. A dull, though irritating pain. Food. Food is what it needs and it surges upward through the tunnel. Above, there is food. Its instincts spark. It fed from the waters above many times. There will be food.

Its boulder-like head crashes through the deposit of bones it left behind so many, many, years ago, shattering almost all of them. With a few sharp flicks of its tail, tilting its pectoral fins just right, this monster swims up through the widened passage. Something smells...different, but that doesn't still the raging hunger curling around its stoMach like a serpent.

This old monster of the deep, it blasts out of the passageway, rocks and silt and sand flying.

There's so much light here. Too much. It doesn't even stop when it sees the strange new thing in front of it. It can't stop. Only hunger drives it now. How will this new thing in its waters taste?

Its massive head plows into the thing. Its huge jaws open and snap onto one of the thing's legs. The thing clanks and creaks and these are new noises that don't make sense to the old monster. They are not the sounds of injured prey.

Still, it swims, circling, and rams its head into the thing again and again and…

SIXTEEN

It happens so fast he's not even sure if he's still alive or not until the fat man, Clam, helps him to his feet.

"Goddamn," the tall scrawny man spouts. "The hell was that?"

"Earthquake?" Clam ventures.

Ash, still trying to regain his bearings, shakes his head. "Fault lines aren't large enough here."

"Huh?" Scrawny tall man says. "I don't—"

The force of the quake is so intense it knocks all three men off their feet again. Ash lands hard on his ass, teeth clicking, somehow managing not to shear off the tip of his tongue. The toolbox topples over, spilling various tools and even an old, greasy porn magazine over the floor. The mini-subs break loose of their harnesses and fall from the jacks with deafening crashes. Shelves holding various parts break apart. Something hard bounces off Ash's right shoulder. Jarring agony spreads through his arm and neck. He tries standing, but another quake knocks him back down.

"This place can't take anymore," Clam shouts over the creaks and groans and crunching noises.

Then, as soon as it began, the quaking stops.

Even so, Ash waits. His shoulder stings from whatever bounced off it. Stiff when he tries to move it. Guess he should feel lucky nothing is broken as intense as the quaking was.

All three men help each other up and just sort of blink at one another.

"Sorry 'bout given ya a hard time earlier, by the way," the scrawny tall man says. "My name's Ben."

"We get a lot of holier than thou folks in here demanding this'n'that," Clam says. "So, we've come to messin' with folks before we decide to help. You seem alright."

Ash waves a hand, wincing at the dull pain in his shoulder. "It's fine. You said this place can't take much more of those...well whatever they were. Are there escape pods or anything in case we need to evacuate?"

Ben nods. "'Course there is. One hundred pods all in tip-top shape. I check'em out every other day or so to be sure."

"Good." Knowing this eases his mind a bit. "I—"

"Ash? Ash, you okay?" Julia bursts into the maintenance room, face flushed, eyes like golf balls.

"I'm fine," he says. "You alright?"

Julia blinks, glances around, finally nods. "Y-Yeah. What the hell was that, do you think?"

"I don't know."

"Quinn is doing scans. Bunch of water sloshed into the Moon Pool room and we lost a few of the bones." Julia visibly shivers. "We need to get out of here. Like yesterday, dude."

"I think we better see what's going on before making any decisions," Ash says.

"Did you not *feel* any of that?" Julia, her eyes once more bulging.

Ash stretches his shoulder, grunts. "Yeah. I felt it alright."

"Something weird is going on, we all need to get out of this thing before it collapses."

"She won't collapse, darlin'," Ben says. "Clam'n'I, we keep this rig tip-top. Gonna take more than a few shakes to break'er."

Clam says, "If those quakes kept on, though…"

Ben nods. "Ya, but they didn't. No alarms goin' off. We're fine."

Julia, eyes still wide, flaps her arms and paces. "I counted six of these quakes, or whatever. *Six*. In my experience if there's that many, shit is about to get real."

"Right," Ash says. "But let's see what the scans tell us, okay? Before we abandon ship for no reason. Reasonable?"

She shakes her head, blows out a harsh, hissing breath and storms out of the room.

Silence takes her place.

Ben straightens a little. "Say, your girlfriend on that meth? "Cause I had an uncle once who was on the meth and *he—*"

"She's not on meth," Ash says, walking toward the doorway. "Just scared."

Neither Ben, nor Clam, say anything as he leaves and breaks into a light jog to the Moon Pool room. People are gathering bones. People are standing around the Moon Pool watching the water lightly slosh into the sides. And Giles is here barking orders no one is paying any attention to. Shouting at people to return to their stations. Ordering folks to calm down and follow protocols. No one is listening. All of them appear in some sort of shock. Neither here nor there.

He finds Julia, Kayla and Quinn in the office.

"Hey," he says. "I was thinking you should do some deep scans just in case of a…"

He notices their stiff postures. The way they all don't acknowledge his presence. He notes, as he steps beside them, a similar expression of terror crawling over each of their faces.

Ash frowns, trying to see what has all three women so scared. Something on the scan monitor, no doubt, but they're so crowded around it, he can't see what it is. Finally, he nudges Julia. She makes a shrill cry, stumbles away from the monitor, glances at Ash before gaping at the monitor again. She's trembling all over. Her mouth opens and closes, opens and closes. Never in his life has he ever seen her so terrified. So brimming with fear she can't even speak, only stare and shiver.

He faces the monitor, and all the air wheezes out of his lungs. Blood turns to ice water. A thin whine seeps from his open mouth.

"W...What is it?" Quinn asks, her voice distant, as if speaking through the fog of dreams.

Or nightmares.

He knows exactly what it is and instantly everything they've found makes sense. He knows, though he can't find air enough in his lungs to say so. Hell, he can't even move. Frozen like a damn statue gaping at the monstrosity swimming around no more than two hundred feet from the facility.

Finally, he manages a few breaths and says, "We need to get out of here."

Kayla and Quinn tear their gazes away from the monitor to look at him.

"What is it?" Kayla asks. "Another mutation?"

Ash shakes his head, still staring at the image on the monitor. "No. I think...we woke something up."

"What?" Kayla brushes by Quinn, facing Ash fully. "What did we wake up?"

A shuddery breath blows out of him. He looks away from the monitor, heart bashing against his ribs. "It all makes sense now." He walks away from the women, pacing slowly, thinking. "All the skulls. The shattered bones..." He paces and paces and—

"*Ash,*" Julia shouts. "For fuck sake, what is it?"

He stops, turns to them. "A dunkleosteus. Placoderm fish." His gaze drifts to the monitor. "Nicknamed, Dunk or...The Guillotine. It doesn't have teeth, really, but bony plates that extend into sharpened fangs in the front of its massive mouth. Between the bony fangs is another plate, which is like a razorblade or...when the jaws close, a guillotine."

"I...huh?" Julia manages, her face void of terror, dripping with confusion. "I've read about these, but...how the hell is there one right here, right now? They existed over three-hundred and fifty million years ago."

"I don't know, but maybe that trove of bones…maybe they kept the warmer water from reaching whatever ice pocket this thing had been frozen in. In theory. I don't know for sure. All I know is it makes sense we found more skulls than other bones. It's said the dunkleosteus often decapitated its prey."

No one says anything for a long time, then Kayla straightens. "I'll get Green out there to kill it."

Ash thinks this over for a moment. "That fish is over thirty feet long. Has to weigh tons. Does Green have the right artillery to take down such a monster? Even without the thick armor, it'd take a tank or large bomb to kill it."

Kayla sighs. "I don't know. I can ask her."

"Why don't we just get in the pods and leave?" Quinn asks. She appears on the verge of some nervous breakdown. Eyes twitchy, sporadic shivers. Uneven voice.

A moment of thought is all it takes Ash for an answer. "We could. But I'm not sure how many would make it to the surface. After being frozen for so long, I'm betting that thing is ravenous. It'll eat any thing it sees or senses. And it won't stop until its hunger is sated."

"I'm calling Green," Kayla says. "She might have something." She goes to phone and in seconds is asking to speak with Master Chief Green.

Julia pulls Ash aside. "This fish isn't supposed to exist anymore."

"I know."

"It's in a habitat very different and smaller than it's used to."

"I know."

"There's not enough food in this lake to keep it satisfied."

"I know."

She sighs. "Why didn't you just listen to me earlier when I said to get the hell out of here?"

"Because this is the discovery of a lifetime."

"And now," Giles says, strolling into the office. "It'll be the capture of a lifetime."

Everyone spins and gapes at the short, portly man.

Giles smiles thinly. "Seismic readings set by Murdock revealed something under the lake bed. Something massive and whole. We didn't really know what it was but figured we should find out."

"You…" Quinn says. "What the hell are you talking about? This is a fossil dig."

Giles chuckles, nods. "Indeed. But everything changed after those scans, which also revealed the bone trove you all dig into. Who would've thought taking a few bones out would unthaw the creature ten meters below you."

Ash, hands curling into tight fists at his side, says, "You knew about it this whole time?" He steps closer to the portly man. "You just helped release a prehistoric fish large enough to demolish this facility and kill everyone in it." He moves closer yet. "And capture it? How the hell are we supposed to capture a fish that size, jackass?"

Shrugging, Giles says, "Nets, of course. Can't be any worse than a sperm whale."

"Oh," Ash says, lifting a fist to Giles' face. "It can be much worse. This creature just woke up. It's starving. It doesn't know this new environment. Capturing it will—"

Giles holds up a phone, grinning. From the phone's speaker, Murdock's cultured voice. "Dr. Barrington. How are you? I'm sure you're a bit perplexed by it all but think of the brighter future here. Think of all we can learn from this magnificent creature. For all we know, there's a cure for ALS and cancer in its blood. We could save *lives*, boy."

Ash grits his teeth, and finally manages, "No, you just want to have it stuffed and put on a wall of your many mansions. This fish is out of time. It's starving. It'll react in unexpected ways and trying to capture it, I'm telling you, is a mistake."

"You don't have a choice, Ash. I hired you to gather and identify any fossils found in the trove. The Dunk is one of those fossils. Now, I want you to gather it for me and I don't want any bullshit about it. You'll get paid handsomely when this is all over."

Ash snorts. "Yeah. Okay." He glares at the phone. "Say we manage to capture the thing, then what? How the fuck do we haul it or keep it contained?"

"I have teams above you ready for such a task," says Murdock. "All you have to do is net it and bring it to the surface to get it removed from the lake."

"And how the hell am I supposed to do that? A dunkleosteus is said to have the most powerful jaws ever. Like a souped-up snapping turtle."

"The nets are titanium weave. Nothing can bite through them, not even this thing. Net it, drag it to the surface and you won't ever have to worry about money again. You might even be able to afford to bring your daughter back."

This…this has crossed his mind more and more over the last couple years since they found a way to bring back the dead. No one beyond a certain age, of course. But doctors and scientists collaborated in actually reviving a corpse. All the memories still intact. All organs are in working order. Any damage repaired. Everything is restored. They are like gods, the way they bring back loved ones. And the price is in the millions to do so too.

Ash sucks in a breath, as if slapped, and says, "What is the pay now?" All through numb lips.

"Two billion. Not a penny more."

He can't speak. Can't think. That number is far beyond the previous amount of six million for the fossil job.

"Ash," Julia says, drawing him out of the proverbial clouds. "Ash, dude, think about this. I mean, really think. This is a *living* prehistoric fish. How do you think it'll do in captivity?"

Before he can respond, Murdock spouts, "Were you not all talking about killing it?"

The man had them all there. Yes, killing the Guillotine seems appropriate, though having it suffer in a half-assed habitat…? Which would be worse? Ending it now so the thing won't spend months dying and in pain or kill it now and return order to this region of the world. Extinct is extinct for a reason.

The dunkleosteus isn't supposed to exist in this time. At all.

"No," Ash says. "We kill it so it doesn't hurt anyone, then I'll bring it to the surface for you to haul away."

"This is non-negotiable, Ash," Murdock says. "You either collect that fish alive, or you lose everything. Your money, reputation. All of it. And you'll never see your daughter again."

Ash manages a few breaths and says, "I see her every day."

"Ah, but you can't touch her. You can't tuck her in at night like you used to. You—"

"Enough," Ash says. "This is how it's going to be. We'll kill it and bring it to the surface. You don't even have to pay, except for our original deal."

"The original deal is void as of this conversation," Murdock says, sounding more than a little irritated. The man isn't used to being challenged. "Complete this simple mission and you'll have two billion in your bank account tomorrow."

"Ash…" Julia says. Her face is one of worry.

He stows everything and says, "Then don't pay me at all. This fish is not meant to be in this time and having it here is a risk to everyone on the Infinity Moon."

"You really think I give a flying *fuck* about…" Murdock audibly clears his throat. "Look, Ash, you do this and you'll be rich. You'll have your daughter back. Isn't that worth saving the life of a prehistoric creature that could save *human* lives? You'll be a hero."

He glares at the phone. "Being a hero is doing what's right when the odds are stacked against them. Being a hero doesn't involve money."

For a moment, Murdock Jones says nothing. Giles shifts from one foot to the other.

Finally, "If you kill it, I'll have you and your partner killed." Murdock's tone is stony, cold, genuine.

Ash grabs the phone from Giles' chubby hand and says, "Then you'll have to kill us." He throws the phone against the nearest wall where it shatters into a few pieces.

"Oh, you son of a bitch," Giles spews. "You're a dead man."

Ash punches the portly man square in the face, dropping him instantly.

"Oooo," Giles shrieks. "You broke my nose!"

"Lucky I didn't kill you too." Ash looks up as Green and two of her soldiers appear in the doorway.

"What now?" Green asks, barely acknowledging Giles kneeling on the floor holding his nose. Blood seeps from between his sausage-like fingers.

Ash points at the monitor. So far, the dunkleosteus hasn't strayed too far from the initial sighting.

A few seconds later, Green looks at Ash. "What is it?"

"Dunkleosteus," Ash repeats.

"Thanks. And how do we kill it?"

Ash looks at the monitor. "Use the biggest guns you have. The armor is thick."

Green steps closer to the monitor examining her prey. "It's not a mutation?"

"No. The real thing."

She watches the giant fish swim for a bit, then nods. "I think I have enough firepower to take her down."

"Good," Ash says. "Murdock wants us to take the corpse to the surface, but I say we return it to its grave."

"Are you insane?" Giles steps between Ash and Green. "He'll have you all killed."

Ash shrugs. "Not if he can't find us."

Giles blinks. "What?"

"Never mind. Get out of here."

Giles ruffles. "You can't tell me what to do on my facility."

"It's not yours," Ash says and faces Green. "I'll help any way I can."

Green nods. Firm, eyes like chips of sapphire. "Just feed me info if what we're doing isn't working. But I think if we hit the belly, that should do her in."

"Okay." Ash smiles. "Let's put her back where she belongs before she decides to eat the facility."

"You're all mad," Giles says. "Two billion dollars...are you stupid?"

Ash grunts. "Not as stupid as you." He drags the portly man by his shirt collar out of the office. "Either get out of here, or I'll have Green shoot you."

Sputtering, Giles says, "Y-Y-You can't *do* that!"

"Wrong," Ash says, looming over Giles. "I can. That's where you underestimate the power I have down here."

"I'm in command!"

Ash give Giles a kick. "Not anymore. To let that thing suffer in captivity..." He sighs. "Can't let that happen. It doesn't deserve to die like that."

"Have you seen that thing?" Giles' jowls quiver. "It's a monster! Its blood will save lives. Think of all the advances in medicine and science that big, stupid fish will bring. Think about all the money it'll—"

"There it is," Ash says. "Money. That's the real reason you want it captured. How much is Murdock paying you?"

Giles glances away. "That doesn't matter." He returns his gaze to Ash. "What matters are the giant leaps in saving lives the thing will bring."

Ash chuckles, hands unfurling. He claps Giles hard on the shoulder. "You're a piss-poor liar, Giles." He leans close enough to smell the sour stench of the portly man's sweat. "We're putting the dunkleosteus back in its grave, where it belongs. Not because I want it dead, god no. I'd love to see it live and thrive. But it can't live in the world it came back to. Not this world. And in captivity it would die slowly as you bastards poke and prod and take your fucking samples."

"You're insane," Giles utters. He glances at Green, Kayla, Quinn and Julia. "You all are. It doesn't need to die just because it was accidently unthawed. That's not the fish's fault. What you want to do...it's inhumane, for god sake!"

"What's inhumane," Ash says, "is keeping it locked up in a tank. What's inhumane is letting it die one day at a time or until its uselessness is no longer required. What's inhumane is not capturing it to save human lives, but to line your pockets with money."

"Um," Julia says. "He kind of makes sense, though, Ash."

He shoots a glare at her. "We'll talk later." To Giles he says, "Get the fuck out of my sight, you sick bastard. Or I'll rearrange your fat face for you."

Giles gasps, stumbles back a few steps, spins and hurries out of the office.

Ash watches the portly man stumble and bustle toward the doors at the far end, and smiles.

"Ash," Julia says behind him. "What the hell has gotten into you? I mean, yeah he's—"

"We're not going to kill it." The thought had formed the moment they decided to kill it. An idea though it didn't manifest itself fully until Giles started his spiel.

"We aren't—wait, what?" Julia grabs his shoulders and turns him to face her. "What are you talking about?"

Green frowns at him. "What do you mean we're not going to kill it? We can't let that thing terrorize the lake."

"Yeah," Kayla says. "And you said so yourself that it wouldn't be able to live in the world as it is now."

Grinning, Ash says, "I lied." He steps away from Julia a bit. "I think the South Pacific Ocean is warm enough for it. North Atlantic is closer though."

They all blink at him. Then Kayla ventures, "How are we going to get that *thing* to an ocean?"

This, he hadn't thought over very well. How, indeed? Then another idea pops into his head.

"Tunnels," he whispers to himself, frowning at the monitor. The dunkleosteus hasn't swum much farther from the facility. Instead, it appears to be just floating there.

"Huh?" Julia nudges him. "Dude, are you going nutty on me?"

He smiles. "I wish." He looks at Kayla. "Under the bone trove, there was a tunnel."

"Yeah? So?"

"So, that's where it came from. Where it got stuck and frozen, or whatever happened. It was in that tunnel, why?"

Kayla shrugs.

"Consider all the different species of dinosaurs," Ash says, cocking a thumb over his shoulder at the Moon Pool room. "What if it travelled through deep tunnels under the ground to the oceans? That's how it got all those different species. It brought some of them or regurgitated them here."

"But why?" Julia asks. "That doesn't make sense. Why would it bring its prey here? Why not just keep to the oceans?"

He shakes his head. "I don't know. Maybe it spawned here? Hard to say, but considering all the baby dunkleosteus skulls found in this region..."

Everyone fell quiet for a moment.

Green clears her throat. "So, you didn't answer the question. How do we get it to an ocean? But more importantly, why? Won't it disrupt the ecosystem?"

Julia snorts. "There are so many monstrous mutations and other things in the oceans these days...I doubt a prehistoric fish will affect anything."

Crossing her arms, Kayla says, "Then we get it to the ocean. Fine. I still don't see how we're going to do that."

"We need to run a deep scan and see if that's really a tunnel under the trove or just a long cave." Ash nods to Quinn. "Think we can?"

Quinn sighs. "I think so. It'll be pushing the boundaries a bit, but I think if I tweak a few things we'll see a good five hundred feet below the lake floor and outward."

"Focus on the south. If the tunnels lead to the oceans, that's the most likely direction."

Quinn nods and goes to work on the scanner.

Ash points at Kayla and Green. "Gather your teams. We need to plan this and plan it right."

"And if there aren't any tunnels?" Green asks.

"Then...I don't know." His sight flicks to the monitor. The dunkleosteus is gone. "Where'd it go?"

Both Green and Kayla face the monitor. Julia steps beside Ash.

Silence ticks by without a glimpse of the old fish.

"Shit," Julia says. "We lost it."

"Just swam out of range," Quinn mutters, still working on the deep scanner. "I have it set at one thousand feet, but we've been talking a while so I'm sure it—"

The quake is so strong it slams all of them off their feet. Green manages to crouch to save herself from falling, but everyone else...

Ash tries to grab onto something, anything, but it's no use. He goes down hard, luckily getting his arms under him before cracking his skull on the metal floor. All around him, the sounds of bending, rattling, creaking metal. A loud, metallic pang, like a thick cable snapping, assaults his ears.

Then everything is still again.

He gets to his feet.

"That's not an earthquake," Julia says, "is it?"

"Nope." Ash stares at the monitor, watches the massive fish swim about three hundred feet out. "It's trying to eat the facility. That's how hungry it is."

"So, what are we going to do?" Kayla, she's glaring at him a bit. "I'm not sending any of my team out there with that thing. You can forget that shit right now."

"There'll be no persuading it into the tunnels," Green says. "It's mad with hunger."

"Maybe," Ash says, "that's exactly what we need. It's hungry as all hell and if it sees us going into the tunnels, or even a mini-sub…"

"It'll follow," Quinn quips, still messing with the scanner.

"Right."

Julia punches his arm hard enough to hurt. "That's the stupidest idea of all the stupidest ideas you've ever had, man. Seriously? You want to go swimming with that thing?"

"Not exactly. We need a decoy after we enter the tunnel. It should follow the decoy all the way to an ocean."

Green smiles a bit. "Good plan. But who's our decoy? Giles?"

Ash laughs, he can't help it. That's funny shit right there. Sad thing is, he almost considers it. Strap Giles in a suit and drop him in.

Once the laughter eases, he says, "As great as that'd be, no. We need something that can swim faster than that thing and also appear irresistibly tasty. Do we have any seeker bots?"

Kayla glances at Green who in turn focuses on Quinn.

Quinn sighs, not looking up from her work. "Yes. We have a seeker bot. Doubt it swims faster than that fish though."

"Can we fix that problem?" Ash, heart sinking.

"I doubt it. Ben in maintenance is a miracle worker, but I don't think even he can make that thing move faster than fifty knots."

"It's gone again," Julia says, groping for something to hold on to. "Might wanna bear down, kids."

No one questions it and finds something stable to hold on to.

The dunkleosteus rams into the facility again. The force, the quaking that results from it, jars Ash from the inside out. He grips onto the mounted table at the center of the room as Infinity Moon groans around him.

Once everything stops vibrating and squealing, Ash steps away from the table. "Get the seeker bot. We're going to give this a shot, regardless."

It's Green who steps in front of him. "And if it doesn't work?"

"Then we think of something better."

Green, she stares at him for the longest time before finally nodding and walking out of the office. "I'll gather my team."

"The seeker bot is in maintenance," Quinn says.

Ash starts toward the doorway.

"This isn't going to work, Ash," Julia says. "We both know it."

He barely pauses before stepping through the doorway. "We've got to try."

SEVENTEEN

It won't die.

No matter what the old monster tries, the creature in its waters barely bends. So it smashes into it. It bites the thing. Maybe its skin is tough. Need to keep trying.

It snatched and ate a few morsels of food, but it's not enough. The giant creature the old monster can't kill, that's what it needs. There's enough meat to feed on for a very long time. Just need to find a way to kill it.

The old monster fears it must go back to the big waters.

But not without a few more tries…

EIGHTEEN

The dunkleosteus is bound and determined to break this facility open and suck out the marrow.

Ash slams into the maintenance room door when another strike from the fish shakes everything. He waits for the quaking to subside, opens the door.

“Hey Doc,” Clam says, hefting himself up off the floor. “These quakes. They ain’t quakes, are they?”

“No. A giant, prehistoric fish. Hey, do you happen to know where the seeker bot is?”

Clam’s broad face pinches in thought. He snaps his fingers. “Over here, man. She’s buried a bit on account of not bein’ used’n all, but she still works, I’m sure.”

Ash follows Clam away from the main room of maintenance and through a set of swinging double doors. They step into a small room, which is heaped with various parts, some rusty, some not and old tools.

“Ben went to check on the pods, just makin’ sure they’ll shoot out no problem,” Clam says as he shoves an oily crate of wires and god knows what else out of the way. “With all the quakin’ goin’ on, he wanted to be extra sure.”

“Don’t blame him there,” Ash says.

“Ayah.” Clam kicks aside a mound of greasy shop rags.

The place reeks of oil, gasoline, and possibly some exotic form of mold. For all Ash knows, he’s gotten ten forms of cancer by just stepping into the room. It’s dark, filthy. His boots slip and slide on the floor, as though it’s made of Crisco.

“She’s ‘round here somewheres,” Clam mutters. “Put’er right…ah-ha!” He bends, clears away a couple smaller crates and a jar of suspicious black fluid Ash cares never to know it’s origin. Under all the junk, there’s a blue tarp. Clam opens the tarp and nods. He beams a bushy, bearded grin at Ash. “Found’er. She’s heavy. Gonna take both of us to haul’er out.”

Ash frowns at the seeker bot. It’s sleek, shiny black and about six feet long.

“Not so much heavy, ya know.” Clam playfully slaps Ash’s arm. “Just awkward as all hell.”

They carry the seeker out of the foul, filthy room and into the main room, placing it on a cart.

"There ya go. Anything more I can help'ya with Doc?"

"Actually, yeah…is there a way to make it go faster?"

Clam puts on his squinting thinking face again. Eventually, though, he shakes his head. "I'm not good with this really new stuff. Ben could though."

"When do you think he'll be back?"

Clam bites his bottom lip, eyes rolling up a bit. "Oh, 'bout ten minutes."

Too long.

"Is there a way to call him here? We're pretty pressed for time."

"'Cus'o'the big ol'fish, right?"

"Yep."

"I'll get'im through the talkie. Hold tight."

Ash smiles. "Try to hurry."

Clam nods and shuffles to a white, grease stained door. The office, Ash assumes. Clam disappears inside, and the waiting begins.

Even so, Ben spills into the maintenance room five minutes after Clam calls him. His eyes are huge, shifting wildly in their sockets. He stumbles over a fallen shelf and skids to a stop in front of Ash. Sweat sheens his narrow, oil smudged face. His greasy hair is a mix of crazy corkscrews and cowlicks.

"Where's the seeker?"

Ash points at the long, shiny black thing shaped like a rocket. "Right there. You think you can make it go faster?"

"Sure as hell can. How fast ya want her? Goes one hundred knots right now."

"Pick it up to about one hundred and fifty knots."

Ben nods. "Can do. Be just a couple minutes."

"That all?"

"Yupper," Ben says, hunkering down beside the seeker bot. "These things, they're all computerized. Motor is plenty capable of goin' four hundred knots, just not rec'mended." He frowns. "Not sure why anyone would want'er to go that fast in the first place."

Using a flathead screwdriver, Ben pries a curved panel out of the seeker. "Clam. Git me the controller, would ya?"

"On it." Clam thunders away toward the filthy room where they got the seeker bot.

"All she needs is a reprogram. Nothin' big. Just switch around a few numbers." He taps a screen, which lights up with numbers. He taps in 3376.

The screen prompts: SETTINGS?

Ben taps the settings icon and goes into engine adjustments. There, he bumps the speed up to one-hundred and fifty knots. Then he replaces the panel and gives Ash a wink. "All ready, bud."

Ash grabs the handle of the cart. "Thank you. You guys might want to come to the Moon Pool room."

"What for? We got tons to do, man."

"To see what's going on. It's a giant, prehistoric fish attacking us, not earthquakes."

"A *fish*?" Ben shakes his head. "Ain't no fish big enough to do that."

"Now there is. You're welcome to come look at the streaming scans in the office."

After a moment, Ben shakes his head. "Nah. I believe ya. We gotta prepare for the worst, makin' sure everything will work when the time comes without a hitch, ya know."

"Got it," Clam announces as he bursts through the double doors. He hands the controller to Ben.

It's basically a tablet only not as thin.

Ben hands it over to Ash. "Has cameras back and front. Can see through both of'em on that and steer'er around. Can also lower'n'increase speed."

Ash nods. "Good." He wheels the cart toward the door and pauses once more. "You're both still welcome to join us in the Moon Pool room."

Ben waves him away. "Nah, man. We're better behind the scenes. Go get that fish."

Ash nods, smiles and hurries out.

A really bad sensation toils in his gut. If this plan doesn't work, then they'll have to try and kill it. If that doesn't work they'll need to take their chances in the pods before it destroys the facility, Infinity Moon.

In the Moon Pool room, Quinn catches him by the arm and swings him to the side. Her face is aglow, eyes wide, smile even wider. "There's an entire tunnel system. They branch off at various points, but you were right. There are tunnels under the continent. That's how it travelled. Maybe how other things travel from the ocean to here too."

He sighs relief. "Fantastic. Were you able to pin-point a tunnel leading toward the Atlantic?"

"Of course. It's the largest tunnel too. Wide, I mean. A freight train could fit through it easily."

Ash nods. "That's what we need, for sure." He pats the seeker bot. "It's all ready to go. Ben upped the speed up to one hundred and fifty knots."

Quinn smiles. "That Ben. He really is a diamond in the rough genius. Wouldn't know that to look at him, or even talk to him, but the man can work mechanical and digital magic."

"Appears so." He glances around. "Now we need this thing to look and smell tasty."

"Might be some meats in the kitchen. Could strap a net to the boy and tie the meat to it. Think there's a couple large salmon in there too. Maybe—"

"Absolutely not," Giles bellows, storming toward them, jowls jiggling. "We are not wasting valuable food to entertain this crackpot scheme."

"If we don't entertain it," Ash says, "it'll keep bashing itself into us until the facility buckles. Now, I don't know about you, but I'd rather not drown."

The chubby scientist visibly ruffles. "This facility is built with the highest-grade steel. It's indestructible."

Ash moves closer to Giles, gaze narrowing. "And I suppose it was tested against, roughly, a ten-ton dunkleosteus with a bite force of over eight thousand pounds?"

Giles stutters, not really saying anything.

Ash grins. "That's what I thought. Now get the fuck out of here so we can save this place and the fish."

"You said you were going to kill it…"

"I lied. Something you're no doubt good at. As I'm sure you're wired so everything we say here gets directly fed to Murdock."

Again, Giles ruffles. His chest puffs out a bit. "I most certainly wouldn't—"

Ash rips the man's coat off and right there strapped to his shirt is a blinking red light with a tiny microphone set on top.

Ash grunts. "Low move, even for you Murdock."

"You're finished after this," Giles says, face flushed red. "Your career, everything. You'll be stripped of any credibility and all your finds will be revealed to be found by someone…lesser known."

"Murdock says this?"

Giles nods. "He does. Told me so over the phone no more than a few minutes ago. He has the power to do all that and more, you know."

Ash, nodding, turns away from Giles. "Maybe. Good thing I've been recording everything going on here." He stops to glance over his shoulder. "Even the conversations. Blackmailing and threats…not going to look good for Mr. Jones." He returns to Quinn. Kayla and Julia are in the office working on something he can't really see.

"Is that true?" Quinn whispers.

He winks. "Could you take a couple of people with you to get some of that meat?"

Quinn smiles, snags a couple of the workers and they hurry off.

Ash stares at the seeker bot, sighs, gaze wandering to the Moon Pool.

It's almost time.

NINETEEN

With all kinds of meats tied securely to the seeker bot, Ash gives Green and her team a nod. "This is like rounding up a stray cow. Need to keep it from trying to go elsewhere. We need to have it fully focused on the bot."

"Easier said than done," Green says.

"If it veers off course, all I need you to do is shoot it in the head. The armor will be too thick to really hurt it but should scare it enough to keep it on track."

"And you're absolutely sure about that?"

Shaking his head, Ash says, "Not at all. But it's what I've got. You can keep your team in here if you want."

Green's face darkens. "We're not here to just sit. My team and I are with you."

"Thank you." He faces Kayla's dive/ drill team. "I want you to flank its other side leading to the tunnel. Once it's in there, it won't be able to back up if it thinks something is wrong. It'll have no choice but to follow the seeker bot."

Julia steps beside Kayla, arms crossed. "I'm going to just put this out there, once again. Dude, are you fucking crazy?"

He chuckles. "Apparently. But we'll give it a shot. Fish run on pure instincts, right? We tap into this one's instincts and we'll get it where we want it."

Using a small hoist, Quinn lowers the seeker bot into the water.

Ash holds up the control tablet, signaling Quinn. "This thing waterproof?"

"Yes," she says.

Ash nods, gets into his suit while Julia curses at him from every direction.

"You can stay in here and control that thing, damn it." Her face is simmering in anger and worry.

"I need to be able to see what it's doing so I can try to predict its movements." He straps on the Shark. "I'll stick close to the Moon Pool."

Julia huffs out a breath. "Like that's supposed to make me feel better? Damn it, Ash, why don't you ever listen to me? You know, putting yourself in danger all the time isn't healthy, right?"

"Is what it is," he says, inspecting his helmet and mask. "I don't have a death wish, just trying to keep us all alive while we're stuck in here."

Julia shakes her head. "Whatever. You just make sure you call things off and get your ass back up here if shit goes wrong. Don't try to be the fucking hero."

"Promise," Ash says and snugs on the helmet.

He jumps into the Moon Pool with the others and snaps Julia a salute. She rolls her eyes and walks away.

So now she thinks he's suicidal. Lovely.

Quinn lowers the seeker bot the rest of the way into the Pool. Ash taps the power button on the tablet and the bot whirs to life. Green and Kayla unstrap it. It bobs in the water.

"Okay," Ash says. "Quinn will give us a play by play where the fish is. Quinn? Location?"

There's a brief pause and Quinn says into their earpieces, "It's swimming back and forth, about three hundred feet from the Infinity Moon."

"Thank you," Ash says, then to the two teams. "We have one shot at this. You all know what to do?"

"My team has been briefed," Green says.

"I told them," Kayla says. "Everyone knows their job."

"Good. Let's round us up a prehistoric fish."

Kayla sighs, rolls her eyes. "That was probably the dumbest thing I've ever heard from you."

"Oh, just wait…" Ash winks. "I get even better."

"Joy…"

With this, they dive toward the bottom of the Moon Pool. It takes Ash a few failed attempts, but he finally manages to get the seeker bot moving and going in the right direction. He keeps it at a very slow five miles per hour.

In his earpiece, Green orders her team to move out into flanking position and hold.

Kayla tells her team to flank opposite Green's team.

The men and women all do as they're told and Ash watches in wonder at the efficient way they all move. The Seals are faster, but Kayla's team moves in a fluid motion that reminds him of a stingray. The way they sort of glide, rather than swim. Everyone has a gun.

Ash maneuvers the seeker bot into the open lake. "Status?"

Quinn comes back right away. "Moving toward you at about five knots. Two hundred feet and closing from the east."

Ash's heart thuds in his chest as he back swims so he's directly under the Moon Pool. Then he turns the seeker bot right to the east and watches the camera feed on the tablet screen as the bot goes to greet the dunkleosteus. He kicks the speed up to twenty knots.

Soon he should see the giant fish through the bot's camera.

"It increased its speed to twenty knots," Quinn say. "Less than one hundred feet."

Soon. Very soon…

"Moving faster now," Quinn nearly shouts. "Thirty…forty knots. You guys better brace yourselves."

And there it is. A huge mass that's all brutal, giant jaws and little else. It appears to pause a moment, perhaps catching the bot's scent.

Ash swings the seeker bot around and increases the speed to sixty knots.

From the back camera, he watches the dunkleosteus almost jump, then its massive jaws open wide and the chase is on.

"Seventy knots," Quinn says.

Ash bumps the bot up to ninety knots. In no time it'll be at the passageway leading to the tunnels.

"Eight. Eighty-five. Ninety knots."

"Everyone," Ash says. "Be ready."

"Roger that," Green says.

"Gotcha," Kayla says.

The bot streams by, closely followed by the dunkleosteus, which entirely obscures Green's team and everything else as huge as it is. A gargantuan thing, every sweep of its tail shoves Ash backward. He fights to remain under the Moon Pool and keep an eye on the seeker bot's location.

Almost to the passageway opening. Maybe twenty feet and—

The dunkleosteus' tail swats sharply, creating a force so great it knocks Ash spinning head over flippers away from the Moon Pool. And all he hears through his earpieces are shouts and screams.

Once the spinning stops, he rights himself, blinking. The force of the tail sends him at least thirty feet away from the Moon Pool. Directly behind him is one of the facility's anchor pillars. If he'd gone another couple of feet…

Quinn is shouting something, but it's lost in a maelstrom of screams and barking orders. Chaos in his ears.

He shakes his head, checks the tablet, but the seeker bot's screen is black. So, it either went head first into the dirt, or the massive fish ate it. Heart hammering, Ash swims back to the Moon Pool, and is bombarded by other divers. He's not even sure who they are. If they're Green's or

Kayla's. All he knows is they're scrambling to get back into the facility. And even in the water, Ash can feel the terror.

He drifts away from the Moon Pool a bit to allow the scared divers easier access, and his breath catches in his throat like a rusty fishhook.

No more than ten feet away, the dunkleosteus bites the head off a diver trying to escape. Blood clouds the water scarlet and before the twitching body can float away, the beast swallows it whole.

Gives its nickname, the Guillotine, a bit more relevance.

Pectoral fins rotating, the monster faces Ash head on. All he can do is gape at this monstrosity. This prehistoric monster. Face to face with living history…

He's more fascinated than scared and he forces himself not to reach out and pet it. To make sure it's real.

Its huge jaws open and close. Open, and close. It's like staring into the mouth of a cave. It wouldn't need to bite off his head to kill him. Just suck him in and that'd be it.

"Ash?" It's Julia, but he can't find his voice to speak. "Ash, just sit tight. Green is…"

A series of thump-thump-thump's and the dunkleosteus' jaws open wide. A rumbling roar vibrates Ash from the inside out. Those guillotine jaws snap shut like a giant snapping turtle and the fish lashes around. In a blink, Ash notices Green and a couple of other Seals. His heart sinks a bit. She just put her and her team into the sights of a ravenous tank. Still, they shoot the creature.

In his ear, Green shouts, "Move out, Dr. Barrington! Get topside!"

"I'm not leaving you down here—"

"Get the fuck into the facility, Ash," Green commands.

He wastes no more time and swims into the Moon Pool while more screams fill his ears.

TWENTY

Julia is helping him out of his suit when, through his earpiece, Green says, "I'm crammed into a narrow crevasse in the hillside. It's bashing at the rocks and will get to me soon. Dr. Barrington, Dr. Remus, Kayla, Quinn, everyone, it has been an honor to serve you and my country. Bullets don't hurt this thing. If you can, Ash, use the LZ-missile launcher I keep in my cabin. If any of my team make it up there, have them show you how to use it. Might be the only—"

Harsh static roars in his ear a second before Julia pulls the helmet off.

Ash, gasping, rolls onto his side. Chill after icy chill shivers through his body.

"Ash?" Julia, sounding more than a little freaked out.

"G-Green's dead," he manages between breaths.

"I know," Quinn says, stepping out of the office, Kayla following closely behind.

He's glad to see Kayla made it out and sits. The Moon Pool is about three feet to his left. He scoots away from it a bit and stands on legs like thin pillars of gelatin. He wobbles some, then gains his balance.

"Any of Green's team make it back?"

"No," Julia says before anyone else. "Ash, I think we should—"

A crash of doors and, "See! Now see what you did!" Giles bustles in. Behind him are a few fellow scientists and workers.

The little, portly man is a couple feet away when Ash points at him. "Any closer and I'll break your nose."

Giles skids to a stop, looks around almost sheepishly, then clears his throat and stands ramrod straight. "Well, Dr. Barrington, you successfully led an entire Seal team to their deaths. Want to reconsider Mr. Jones' offer now?"

"How many do you think will die trying to capture that thing?" Ash walks to the Moon Pool and points. "That fish can't be coaxed or tricked as easily as you think. It's intelligent. I saw that much staring it face to face. It's aware, at least to some degree, what's going on. Attempting a capture would lead to many more lives." He shakes his head, not believing what he's about to say, but saying it anyway. "We have to kill it. If we don't, we'll be stuck down here forever. Or until it decides to tear Infinity Moon apart. If we don't, more lives could be taken, not to mention a total upheaval of Lake Superior's ecosystem."

Giles is grinning.

Ash frowns. "What?"

"Mr. Jones foresaw this happening, so he added extra measures to take place the moment you broke my phone."

Ash moves toward the little man, stops. "What measures?"

Hands clasped behind his back, Giles chuckles. "Let's just say...I hope you're used to wearing a mech."

Ash blinks. "Come again? Did you say mechs?"

"Submersible mechs don't exist," Kayla says. "Only time I've ever heard of the things is during that oil rig craziness that happened years ago."

"The leviathan..." Julia muses.

"Yeah," Kayla says. "That thing. The survivor said something about sub-mechs in an interview. But that's not possible because sub-mechs haven't been invented or tested yet. Trust me, I looked into it for this job."

Giles, he's giggling. A high-pitched, ugly clown-like giggle.

"What's so funny, jackass?" Julia asks.

"All of you," Giles manages around giggles. He takes a few breaths, and says, "That survivor, he invented the sub-mech, and Mr. Jones made it a reality. Mr. Jones' sub-mechs have been in full production for three years."

Ash shakes his head, looks at the Moon Pool. "Secrets."

"Mr. Jones is a genius and he has a plan to capture that beast. He also requires all of you to assist."

"Fuck off," Julia spouts. "He can't do that."

Giles grins. "He just did."

A few workers push shiny, blue mechs through the doors behind Giles.

"He sent six of them," the portly man says, grin barely faltering.

Lying on their backs, the sub-mechs are lined up behind Giles.

"Dr. Barrington, Dr. Remus, Kayla. You three get in the mechs and will be accompanied by three others of Mr. Jones' choosing."

"Three others?" Ash steps away from the Moon Pool toward Giles. "Who are the three others?"

As though perfectly timed, the doors crash open again and three men stride in. "Us," the one in the lead says. Tall, blond, a chiseled face Ash wants to punch.

The two behind him are shorter, though every bit as punchable as their leader.

"And who the hell are you?" Ash's hands curl into tight fists, fingernails biting into his palm.

"Captain Riley Frost," the tall, blond, douche says. He stops beside Giles. "I train people to use these mechs, Dr. Barrington. And I can tell by that little glint in your eye that you hate me already, well…you gotta hate someone. But hating me will only work against you on this mission."

"And," one of the shorter men steps around Frost. "I can assure you, we've been given full clearance to dispatch any and all threats, including you."

Ash glares at the man. "Is that so?"

"Yup. You wanna try us, asshole? We'll—"

"That's enough Corporal," Frost says. "We're here to work together, not bicker."

The Corporal rolls his eyes and darts back behind his Captain.

"Anyway," Frost says. "This is a simple seize and transport operation. Our supplied nets are strong enough to take over ten thousand pounds of pressure. We net it, drag it to the boats above, and that's it."

"And," Ash says, "I suppose you've captured hundreds of prehistoric fish…"

Frost smirks. "You got me there, Dr. Barrington. Though, I suppose it wouldn't matter to you how many giant mutations I've captured in the last three years? No, it wouldn't, because you not only hate me, but fear me and anything I say won't matter." He steps closer, hands clasped behind his back, very much like Giles. "I've been given a full file of you, Dr. Barrington. Very impressive resume. Even more impressive finds and theories on deaths and what those old fossils might've looked like in their day. I had the utmost respect for you…until I met you."

Ash, not really sure what to say, shrugs. Maybe he was wrong about Frost. Maybe there's more honor than douchery.

"Point is," Giles says, "you all will comply. If you don't…further extreme measures will be enforced."

"Like what, you fucking weasel?" Julia, she looks like she's about to start hitting people. Her entire body quakes.

"Oh, I don't know…I have Captain Frost and his men shoot you? Fair enough?"

"What the actual fuck, dude?" Ash has to stop Julia from charging at the small man. "You can't do that!"

Frost clears his throat. "It has been ordered, yes. But, if you all comply, and follow my instructions, I don't see why anyone should be hurt. We can all work together on this and be on our separate ways in less than five hours."

At his side, Julia says, "I don't trust them."

"Me either," Ash says.

But, what if Murdock can indeed keep the fish alive? Despite everything, maybe it really can help humanity. Maybe it really can cure diseases and cancers. Maybe it can stop ALS and Alzheimer's too.

Maybe it can do all those things…but to what end?

Why does it even matter when humanity keeps killing itself anyway?

Why save a species that clearly doesn't want to be saved?

And, yet…what other choice does he have? Get the missile launcher from Green's cabin and go at it man to giant, ravenous fish? And what if he misses or missiles don't hurt it much? Then what? He'd probably be dead and it'd break apart the facility anyway.

But, really, is this the best choice…?

Is there even a choice now?

He sighs. "Let's do it."

"*What*?" Julia nearly shoves him into the Moon Pool.

"It's the only way, right now," he tells her.

"What about that missile thingy Green was talking about?"

He shakes his head. "I wouldn't even know how to shoot it. Probably blow up the damn place."

She steps away from him, frowning. "So, you're giving up? You'd rather it suffer?"

"Maybe it won't suffer. Maybe Murdock will have what it takes to keep it alive."

"He does," Frost interjects. "The best habitat has been constructed just for this fish. They want to keep it alive for a very long time, Dr. Barrington and Dr. Remus. If I thought otherwise, I wouldn't have accepted this mission."

"So," Ash says. "You actually care about this creature? Besides getting paid, you really want what's best for it?"

Frost nods, smiling. "Believe it or not, I wanted to be a paleontologist before I became a Marine."

Julia blows out a harsh breath, flaps her arms. "Of course you did. Of course! How fucking convenient."

"I know it sounds convenient, but it really isn't." When Julia makes a humph sound, Frost walks over to one of the tables with a few bones still on it. He picks up a small skull, turns it over in his hands and lifts it for both Ash and Julia to see. "Infant hadrosaur. Duckbill species."

"Anyone could know that with a little research about the region," Ash says.

Frost places the skull back onto the table and picks up another skull. This one slightly larger. "Velociraptor. Not yet fully grown. Probably a juvenile."

Julia clears her throat. "Lucky guess."

Frost chuckles, replaces the raptor skull and holds up a long, thick bone. A femur. It takes Ash a few seconds to recognize what species it is.

Frost, waggling the femur at Julia and Ash, still smiling, says, "This one. This one is probably so rare, you didn't even realize what you had. Until now anyway." He holds the femur up. "Ladies and gentlemen, I present you with the femur of a juvenile minotaurasaurus. So rare, only a single skull from the Gobi Desert and scatter of bones here and there have ever been found. Well, until now."

Ash glances at Julia. She's glowering at Frost. But, eventually, she sighs, rolls her eyes and says, "Fine. So you were into dinosaurs when you were a kid. Why should we believe you're not just in this for the money?"

With a shrug, Frost says, "You'll have to trust me."

"Heh, yeah, okay, dude." Julia waves Frost away, grabs Kayla and Quinn, and walks to the office, leaving Ash alone with the men.

He sighs. "Alright. We'll try this. I don't trust any of you. No matter how much knowledge of dinosaurs you have." He shoots a glare at Frost. "And when I say we'll try it. That's all. We try. If it doesn't work, we go back to Plan B."

"There was a Plan A?" Frost asks.

"They thought they could lead it back to the ocean," Giles quips, chuckling.

Frost glowers and the small man withers. "Sounds like a fine plan. Why didn't it work out, Dr. Barrington?"

"The dunkleosteus decided it didn't want to be made a fool and ate everyone. Almost"

"Ah," Frost says, nodding. "Noted."

"You all need to realize," Ash says. "We're not dealing with some dumb fish. Does it run on instincts? Of course. But does it think? Does it reason? Yes, I think so. I also think it makes plans too. Just like us."

"That's nothing more than a theory," Giles says. "You don't know that for sure."

"Oh," Ash says, "I know. I was face to face with it. I saw intelligence in its eyes and actions. It figured out exactly what we were trying to pull and called our bluff."

Silence drapes between him and them like thick gauze for the longest time, then Frost steps away from the table. The femur is back on the table. "Then we need to outsmart it. These mechs will give us an advantage."

"They might," Ash agrees. "But those jaws deliver over eight thousand psi. Maybe even ten thousand. How will those mechs hold up to that kind of bite force?"

"Look," Frost says, stepping closer to Ash, eyes firm. "I'll be honest. I don't know if they were ever tested on bite force, but I do know one of these very same mechs was eaten by that leviathan creature a few years ago. If they can withstand that…"

"Was it chewed on by the leviathan?"

Frost shakes his head. "No clue, man."

Ash glances from Frost to Giles, then back again. "Okay. So, what's this plan of yours? And like I said, if it doesn't work…we have to kill it."

"Agreed," Frost says. "The plan is simple, though. We lure it into our nets, tie it up and bring it to the surface where another team will take over. That's it."

Turning back to the Moon Pool, Ash says, "Then let's get it over with."

TWENTY-ONE

Frost helps Ash into one of the mechs. "Now, it'll move when you move." Frost clicks the harness on. "In the arms are joysticks and triggers. Those are your weapons and laser cutter. There are four speed settings that have been altered from the original design. Slow. Jog. Rapid. And max rapid. All you have to do is tell it which one." He grumbles under his breath, looks away. "Wish I had more time to properly train you guys in these. They're difficult to work with and get used to at first."

"And they're airtight?" Ash, heart slamming against his ribs.

"Yep. Like those Sharks over there, they draw in oxygen through the water."

"What do you need me to do out there?"

"Hold the net. Once it's in, help tie it up and haul it to the surface."

It sounds simple enough, almost easy, though he's not so sure about that.

Still, it's worth a shot. He doesn't trust any of them. Frost, maybe a little more than Giles. But, like Julia said, it just feels too convenient.

"I'll tell you what to do when the time comes," Frost says.

"Okay."

"I'm going to close the hatch. There will be a bunch of noises. Hisses and beeps. You'll feel some pressure as everything stabilizes. All of this is normal. But once I shut this, there's no turning back. Are you sure you're ready?"

"Yeah," Ash says.

Frost nods. "Just follow my lead and it'll be over with in no time."

"Famous last words," Ash says.

Chuckling, Frost lowers the hatch.

He's never been claustrophobic, but being sealed inside this tin can…

He worries most about Julia. How will she react? As the hisses and beeps assault his ears, he wonders if Julia can do this? She has always had a hard time with tight spaces and the mechs are as tight as one can get without being crushed.

Still, he doesn't hear her voice through the comms. So, either she opted out, or she's sucking it up and showing everyone what a true warrior she is.

As the pressure stabilizes in the sub-mech, Frost's voice says, "These mechs are designed to leech from your brainwaves. Every motor thought, the mech will mimic. You sit up. It sits up with you. Every mech is equipped with a three-foot knife, laser cutter, and a fifty-caliber gun with limited ammo. If all goes well, we won't be using any of those. We'll be relying on the mechs' strength to haul the thing to the surface." A pause. "On my command, sit up and then stand."

Ash glances around, not really sure what to think, then Frost's voice blares, "Sit up."

He follows orders and sits. The mech makes a hissing sound. In fact, he barely has to move at all. The mech does most of the work.

"Stand."

He stands without issue. Through the mech's visor he sees everything in full, vivid color. Everything is in startling detail, almost beautiful. Nearby, Julia favors him with a weak smile. He smiles back. They're at least ten feet tall right now.

This isn't her thing, he thinks. *She shouldn't be in a mech.*

There's no choice in the matter, he knows this, but he doesn't want Julia facing the pressures of being underwater. Hopefully the mech will give her some comfort, though he doubts it.

Spilling through the mech, Frost's voice. "You give the mech an order, and it will follow. You tell it slow, fast, rapid speed, it will do that. You can engage your weapons and cutting tool using the buttons and toggles in the right and left arms. Time is short. My team will provide the netting. All you have to do is hold it and help us drag the thing topside."

"This is bullshit," Julia spouts through the speakers. "But whatever."

Ah, the good old passive aggressive Julia. Soon they'll all see the very aggressive Julia. The pissed off Julia he's a little afraid of. If things go shitty quick, anyway.

"On my command," Frost says, "I want you all to jump into the Moon Pool, my team included. Stay near the Pool's bottom opening until I arrive. Orders will follow thereafter."

Ash waits and when Frost gives the command, he walks to the side of the Moon Pool, draws in a breath, and steps off the edge. He's instantly submerged, sinking fast.

"Um," he says. "I'm going to crash, Frost. Sinking too fast."

"Tell the mech, 'Slow pulse'."

"Slow pulse."

A thin whine and the mech's descent slows to a near stop.

"At the bottom of the Moon Pool, tell it to hold," Frost says.

Ash slips out the bottom of the Moon Pool. The lake floor is maybe thirty feet under the mech's shiny, blue legs. Another mech shoots by him, in his ears, someone screams.

"Julia?" He tries to maneuver the mech so he can see, but the other mech crashes into the floor of the lake, shooting up a geyser of sand that obliterates any view.

He finally gets the mech to point head first toward the floor. "Um…fast pulse?"

The mech beeps and suddenly he's cruising downward at a rate he's not at all comfortable with. Through the cloud of sand and whatever else and—

"Hold!"

The mech stops so suddenly, Ash's forehead smacks the visor. Pain laces around his head.

"Dr. Barrington? Dr. Remus?" Frost, sounding a bit alarmed.

"I…I'm here, but Julia…she came down too fast and—"

"I'm looking right down at you, dude. That was Kayla, I think."

Ash sucks in a breath and as the sand settles, he gapes at the rounded top of the mech's head.

"Kayla? Can you hear me?"

"She's probably been knocked cold from impact," Frost says and another mech glides down. A quick glance and Ash sees Frost's face through the visor. "Help me dig her out before the intakes get clogged."

Heart bashing against his ribs, there's a godless minute where he can't control the mech, then, finally, Ash helps dig Kayla out enough to pull her free of the lake floor. Frost brushes away sand from the intakes.

"Kayla? This is Frost. Can you hear me?"

No answer.

Frost taps Ash's visor. "Get her back into the facility and meet us here."

Ash nods, grapples onto Kayla and her mech and says, "Fast." He surges upward toward the Moon Pool.

"There was a time you'd have to say rapid pulse," Frost says. "But the mechs have since been updated."

"Thanks for the history lesson," Julia quips.

"As I've told everyone, there are three settings to these mechs. Four, if you include hold. But once more, it's slow, fast and Mach. You don't have to say pulse after each, either."

Ash sighs, feeling dumb. He's so lost on technology these days. He breaches the surface of the Moon Pool and hauls Kayla out. He gets out, inspecting the suit until he finds the emergency tab near the right armpit.

Using his mech's giant fingers, he grips onto the tab and pulls. In an instant, Kayla's mech opens up.

"The hell happened to her?" Giles kneels beside Kayla, checking her pulse. So…the little asshole isn't without regard to human life after all. "Pulse is strong. Looks like she got a nasty bump on the head though."

"Can you look after her while we're gone? Please?"

Giles rolls his eyes, but nods. "Yes. Just go get that thing."

Ash turns and jumps back into the Moon Pool.

"Slow," he says and the mech's descent eases. His heart still hammers hard, but at least he's able to keep his breathing under control as he sinks below the Moon Pool's bottom. Under him, the others wait.

"Good job, Dr. Barrington," Frost says.

"Ash. It's just Ash."

"Okay, Ash. You ready to catch a prehistoric fish?"

"Not really."

"Oh c'mon, Ash," Julia spouts. "These mechs are awesome."

"Thought you'd be freaking out by now," Ash says.

"You know…me too, but it's like being in a mini-sub. Weird, but not uncomfortable."

"Okay," Frost says. "Quinn, can you hear us?"

"Yes."

"Location of the fish, please?"

"Four hundred yards from you to the east," Quinn says. "Looks like it's close to the surface."

"Not good," Ash says. "If it's preying on humans…"

"We need to attract it," Frost says. "Get it closer to us."

Ash frowns, thinking. How does one attract a dunkleosteus? Is there a way? He figured it'd be at the facility non-stop until it broke it apart. If it's as intelligent as he knows it is, why is it so far away? It's starving. It wants food. And it's going to get food no matter what. Fishermen. Anyone. Anything. It's going to feed regardless of how strange the world has become around it.

So…how the hell do they get it back to the facility?

It takes a few minutes, but an idea finally surfaces.

"Blood and lots of noise."

"What?" He can practically hear the horror in Julia's tone.

"We need blood and a lot of noise. Something so loud it'll catch its attention. Maybe need a spotlight to attract the vision senses of the fish too. Need all three to attract a fish. Vision, smell, sound. The sound will create vibrations in the water too."

"Light and sound," Frost says. "Good. But how are we going to get blood?"

"That," Ash says, "I don't know."

"Can we try the other two and see if it works?"

"We can, but you have to remember, this fish has been stuck in ice for millions of years. It's practically starving. The scent of blood will get it moving faster than light and sound."

"How much blood do we need?"

"A shark can smell blood over a mile..." Someone says, though Ash isn't sure who. One of Frost's men.

"At least a pint," Ash says, though he has no idea, really.

There's a long pause. He lowers himself to be among the group. Julia is directly across from him. She winks.

Frost is to his left. The man nods inside his mech, though the mech doesn't nod with him. So, maybe mechs don't mimic everything...

"And where the hell are we going to get a pint of blood?" One of Frost's men asks.

"I don't know," Ash says.

"How about we draw from a few of us up here?" Quinn asks.

Ash smiles. "Yes! If you can, that would be perfect. Is there a nurse to draw the blood?"

"No, but I've done it a time or two interning. Give me a few minutes."

"Well, hell," Julia says. "How 'bout that."

"So," Frost says. "We sit tight until we get the blood. Any ideas on noises and lights?"

Silence trails after this and all Ash can think about are the tunnels leading under America. How many are there? Where do they all go? If it's true, then it also explains, at least in part, the monster in Lake Champlain. Champ, or Champy. And if one wants to go further, maybe it even explains the Lochness Monster. Maybe some of those sightings weren't fake. Maybe they were an actual liopleurodon or something else finally thawing out after millions of years. Maybe all those myths are real...

"An explosion," Julia says.

Everyone gives her the same, "Huh?"

"A gas tank, or something, I don't know. But an explosion is loud enough, right?"

"Yeah," Ash says, heart galloping now. Excitement is mounting. Another step closer to getting the beast back in their area.

"So," Frost says. "What are we going to blow up?"

"Quinn," Ash says. "If you're listening, get Ben to bring four hydrogen tanks to the Moon Pool, please."

It takes her a few seconds, but, "On it. I have almost a pint of blood now."

"Good. Thanks. I'll grab that and the tanks." Ash, feeling like everything is either moving too fast or not fast enough, tells his mech to go fast. He aims himself for the Moon Pool.

"What about the light?" Frost asks.

"Can the facility use high beams?"

Quinn says, "Yes. Kind of. I can flash them on and off."

"Rock on," Ash says as he enters the Moon Pool. "I'm almost to the surface, has Ben brought the tanks yet?"

"Rolling the last one in now."

"Good. How's the blood coming along?"

"I have it. Just getting it ready for you. Ben is strapping the tanks together."

Ash smiles. "Thank you, Quinn."

"Shush. Just don't die out there."

"I'll try not to." He surfaces, pulls himself out of the water and towers over everyone standing near the Moon Pool. The mech reads everyone's blood pressure and body heat. Giles is the highest in everything. Especially blood pressure.

"The blood is taped to one of the tanks," Quinn says. "Let me know when you want me to start flashing the lights."

"I will," Ash says. "Thank you." He grabs the strap of the tanks, lowers them into the Moon Pool, and steps in.

"Slow," he says, and the mech stops its instant plunge. Gradually, he pulls the tanks and bag of blood down the Moon Pool to the open lake.

When he reaches the bottom, two other mechs slam into him and latch on.

"What…?"

"I was right," Julia says. "They're assholes."

"From now on," Frost says. "You will both do as I say. This isn't a matter of control, as it's for your own safety and the safety of my team. Follow orders and we all get out of this alive."

"We're doing as you say anyway," Ash says as Frost's men take the tanks away from him. "Why act like we won't?"

Frost's mech rises up, only a few inches from Ash. "Because I know your tendencies to stray from plans. To toss aside protocol. I want this operation to run as smoothly as possible. I know my team will do exactly what's expected of them. I can't trust you or your partner."

"Oh," Ash says, "That's lovely. Just when I started to trust you…"

"You can trust me, Ash. I just need you to realize I will not be made a fool of. It's my way now, or you're dead. Understand?"

Ash glares at the man. "We'll see how this ends up."

Frost chuckles, nods. "Yes. We will." He turns away from Ash and announces, "We'll blow up the tanks first, blood bag attached to one of them. With the explosion the blood will travel farther. On my command, Quinn, you start flashing those lights. When the fish is close, team, you get the net ready."

"Oo-rah," Frost's team booms.

"Ash and Julia," Frost says. "All I need you two to do is help secure the net and help pull the fish to the surface. You have my word, once that's finished, you are free to go along as you please. Murdock will compensate you as he deems fit."

"Sounds peachy," Julia says. "Thanks for cementing the fact that you're an asshole."

"This is a job, Dr. Remus," Frost says. "Please note that I do hold the highest respect for you and Dr, Barrington. This is not personal, and do not make it so."

Ash can't find the right words to say, so he remains silent.

"Let's get those tanks out about one hundred feet and blow them," Frost commands. "Time to see what this big fish is made of."

TWENTY-TWO

Two of Frost's team pull the four tanks out. In a minute or two, they return.

"I have a lock on the tanks," Frost says. "Sending laser pulse in three, two, one…"

A red flash bursts from Frost's mech's left hand. No more than a second later, a loud yet muffled boom sounds, followed by enough force to push everyone back a few feet. Through the detailed visor of the mech, Ash notes the cloud of red.

Blood…

"Quinn," Frost says. "Flash those lights, please."

Lights along the side of the Moon Pool tube flicker on. Then they flash sporadically.

"Good, good," Frost says. "Now we wait. I want the net ready, team."

"Yes, Sir," Frost's team booms in unison.

About thirty yards out, Frost's team deploy the net. Six men and women in all. Three on each side of the net, pulling it taut.

"Before it touches the net, I want you all to turn your fast pulses on. That should keep you from being jostled too much."

"Yes, Sir," they all say.

"Ash and Julia," Frost adds. "As soon as it's in the net, I want you to seal it in using the mechs' lasers. Melt the mesh together. Once that's done, transport should be fairly easy."

"You really think melted plastic is going to hold that thing?" Ash asks. "I don't think you've been paying attention. This fish is massive."

"I've caught many giant fish this way, Dr. Barrington. I know what I'm doing."

Ash chuckles humorlessly. "Let's hope you do, then."

Several minutes pass, then…

"It's on the move," Quinn says. "Two hundred yards and closing."

"Tighten the net," Frost shouts. "Prepare for impact!"

His team follows orders, all of them stretching the net tight.

Ash backs way, pulling Julia with him. He propels them closer to the Moon Pool. A bad feeling worms its way into his chest. She glances at him and he shakes his head, wanting her to keep quiet.

"One hundred yards," Quinn says. "Eighty."

A massive shadow looms to the east.

Smaller fish dart by Ash.

"Is that the biggest net you have?" Ash asks. "Because—"

"When I need your opinion, Dr. Barrington," Frost says, "I'll ask you. Until then—"

"Sixty feet," Quinn says.

Small features are picked out by the flashing lights, giving the giant shadow substance. Large eyes glint.

"Pull them back," Ash shouts. "It's—"

Monstrous jaws unhinge, opening in a dark, cavernous maw. The blades of its mouth gleam.

"Holy shit," someone manages. "It's…it's…"

Before they can finish, those massive jaws, wider and higher than the net, snap shut, cutting through everything, even a few of Frost's men. Even through the mechs. Blood clouds the water.

Ash shoves Julia to the Moon Pool. "I'll be up in a second."

"Like hell," Julia shouts. "Get your ass up here!"

"I'll be up in a second."

"Leave them! They'd leave you."

Ash snorts. "I might be an asshole, but I'm not that kind of asshole. Now get up there and help me out when I surface."

"Fine! But if that thing eats you, I'll gut it and kill you again."

"Fair enough. Just—"

Screaming cuts through his words, spilling out of the mech's speakers. Somewhere through all the screaming, Ash thinks he can hear Frost barking orders. Without making sure Julia gets topside, he moves away from the facility. In front of him is a storm of red and sand and silt and…body parts…

A severed arm thumps against his visor. Blood forces everything through a scarlet filter.

"Slow," Ash says. "Frost? Where are you?"

No answer.

Heart whip-cracking against his ribs, he cruises forward into the storm. Bits and pieces of other mechs clink and clank against his. A severed foot thumps his visor, pinwheels away.

"Jesus," he mutters. "Frost? Hey, are you…"

From out of the storm of debris and blood, another mech crashes into Ash hard enough to shove him backward, despite the slow pulsations.

Visor to visor, he stares directly into Frost's wide-eyed face. "Monster," Frost manages, and that's all he manages.

In a blink, he's yanked away from Ash, screaming.

"S-Stop," Ash says. The mech stops.

And all he can do is gape as the dunkleosteus, the Guillotine, tosses Frost up, then snaps its sharp jaws down, chomping Frost in half. His lower half disappears into the old fish, but the top half flounders. Frost coughs, splattering blood over the inside of his visor.

In the speakers, Ash is plagued to listen to the man gag and gasp.

It's not long, though, the dunkleosteus chomps through him again and again, swallowing the chunks. There's so much blood in the water, Ash isn't even sure where the Moon Pool is anymore. Everything is just...red...

"Reverse?" He tries and to his surprise the mech actually begins propelling itself backward.

As the swirling blood dissipates a bit, Ash finds himself once more face to face with the monstrous fish. It doesn't attack. Instead, it simply stares with those silvery eyes.

"Ash? Are you alright?"

"Y-Yeah. It's...in front of me. Maybe ten feet. Looking right at me."

"Oh, shit...and Frost?"

"Fish food."

There's a short pause, then, "You think you can go Mach and get to the Moon Pool?"

"I don't know. Maybe. It might chomp me to bits before then, though."

"I love it when you talk dirty," Julia says, laughing a little. "Seriously, though, maybe give it a try?"

Ash, trying to remember how far behind him the Moon Pool is, steals himself. The Guillotine can dart out and cut him into pieces at any second. One false move...

"You on your way yet?" Julia, sounding more than a little scared.

"If I move, it'll have me," he says. "I need a distraction."

Several seconds pass, then Julia says, "Going to give the lights a few pulses. Think that will work?"

"I don't know, give it a shot."

The lights to the left of the Moon Pool flicker.

It takes a full minute, but finally the old fish shifts its attention and starts toward the flickering lights.

He slowly positions himself to face the Moon Pool and says, "Mach."

Before there's time to think, he's shooting through the water toward the Moon Pool. Then he's in the Moon Pool surging upward. And there's no time. No time to think or breathe before he bursts out of the Pool and crashes onto the floor in a fit of scrapes and screeches.

Ash rolls onto his back, sits, heart jackhammering.

"You okay?" Julia kneels beside him. She's still in her mech.

"I…yeah. Just…holy hell that was fast."

Julia laughs. "You were up here in like two seconds."

He stands and together they stare at the Moon Pool.

"Well, another plan failed," Julia says. "Which one was this? Plan C?"

"Plan B," he says. "I think."

"Maybe we need to figure out something, I dunno, more effective?"

Ash chuckles. "This one wasn't my doing. But yeah, something…"

"What about the missile launcher thing Green was talking about?"

Ash backs away from the Moon Pool. "Worth a shot. Anything right now is better than nothing. We deploy those escape pods it'll snatch as many up as possible, then surely come to the surface to finish off those it couldn't catch."

"Agreed. So…it's Green's missile launcher then."

"Yeah, I think—"

A mini tsunami explodes out of the Moon Pool, followed by all too familiar jaws. The floor cracks, breaking open as the dunkleosteus thrashes in the tube of the Moon Pool.

"How the hell did it even fit in there?" Julia, she's stumbling backward.

"It didn't," Ash says. "It's breaking everything."

The floor, thick cracks snake in every direction, radiating from the Moon Pool. Cracks that zig-zag up the walls to the ceiling.

The Guillotine thrashes, widening the cracks. Its massive jaws snap, creating thick booms like the heavy beats of amplified bass drums.

Ash and Julia stumble away, mechs beeping so many warnings Ash can't pin-point why his is freaking out. Maybe the changes in pressure? And if the pressure is changing…how stable is the Moon Pool room right now?

Still backing away as the dunkleosteus snaps its maws and writhes in the constrictive Moon Pool tube. A tube it'll break apart in no time.

"We need to evacuate and seal off this room," Ash says.

"It's tearing the hell out of everything," Julia shouts.

He turns to her, staring at her through the mech's visor. "Get everyone out of here. Seal the doors, if possible."

She blinks. "What about you?"

"I'm going to try and kill it while it's trapped."

She gives him a withering look that makes him shiver. "You're doing that hero thing again. You know I hate that hero thing, right?"

"Yeah, well…you'll be a hero too. Just get them out of here and seal everything up. The mech will stop me from drowning and any pressure issues."

She points at the thrashing dunkleosteus. "And what if that gets you?"

"Then I'm fish food too."

Julia rolls her eyes, shakes her head. "Whatever. Just don't die."

She goes to the office, quickly gathers Quinn and herds everyone out of the room, even Giles. The portly man sputters and spits a bit, but in the end, flees the room. The doors shut. Ash waits for some kind of sign, anything, indicating the doors are sealed.

Finally, a red light blinks above the doors.

"Sealed," Julia says through the speakers. "Kill the thing and let's go home."

"I'll try," he says, facing the monster struggling in the Moon Pool. Part of the floor breaks away as the thing widens the pool more and more.

The facility groans, visibly bending around him. He stands watching the massive fish thrash. *What arm is the gun in? How do I shoot it*? Questions with no answers at first.

Then…

He lifts his left arm and points it at the dunkleosteus. "Gun?"

From out of the forearm, a five inch tube arises.

"Well," he says, "How about that…"

He aims the tube at the belly of the prehistoric fish he thinks of as the Guillotine and says, "Fire?"

Nothing happens.

"Um…shoot?"

Still…nothing.

Then, before he can spout something else, a female's voice says, "If you wish to send an order, please speak clearly, firmly, and in an acoustic environment."

He frowns, staring at the dunkleosteus. How the hell…the tip of his index finger brushes what feels like a toggle switch in the mech's hand. No, not a toggle, but…

"A trigger," he whispers.

The giant, prehistoric fish thrashes, pieces of the floor break free, pelting his mech. Water surges up through the widening cracks. Soon, the pressure in the room will fail. Soon, this entire part of the facility will flood and—

"Holy hell!"

Ash blinks and turns around. Standing in the doorway to the maintenance hall, is Ben. He gapes at the monsters stuck in the Moon Pool.

"Shit," Ash says. "Julia?"

"You kill it yet?"

"No, but you forgot Ben."

"What? The maintenance dude?"

"Yeah. Can you let him in with you quick?"

There's a long pause, then, "Apparently I can't open the doors once they're sealed."

"Damn." Ash towers over Ben, manages to open the mech's helmet. "This room is compromised."

"Heh…no shit," Ben says.

"Can you get to the main facility and seal the doors?"

"I…uh…yeah. Yeah, I think so."

"Okay, get—"

The floor quakes, knocking Ben off his feet. The mech stabilizes Ash's balance. He helps Ben up and sends the man away. He then faces the dunkleosteus, the Guillotine, the underwater tank. A monster lost in time. He closes the helmet, waits for it to seal, then points his left arm at the struggling beast. The barrel of the gun aimed at the presumably softer flesh below the jaws, Ash pulls the trigger.

Blood sprays a few inches below the jaws of the monster fish. It roars, thrashing harder and—

It happens fast.

A loud popping noise and suddenly Lake Superior explodes through the floor of the Moon Pool room. The force of the water slams Ash against the ceiling until the room is completely submerged.

"Fast," he says. The mech cruises away from the ceiling, dodging various debris, stray dinosaur bones, tables and chunks of the pulverized floor of the room.

Heart hitching, he moves forward.

And out of the chaos and drifting debris, the monster emerges.

"Hold!"

The mech jolts to a stop as the massive fish floats toward him. Ash's stoMach twists like a nest of snakes. Air wheezes out his lungs. The thing is so huge and it's not until he notes that only half the fish is in the broken room, just how huge.

Its maw opens a foot or two, snaps shut, opens…

Icy chill after icy chill shivers through Ash and he can't think. His brain stutters, unable to latch onto any constructive thought. Now he knows the meaning behind frozen in fear. He literally can't move or think.

Those eyes. Those large, silvery eyes. They watch him carefully, as though debating if it should eat him or not. It's the same face to face intelligence he noticed the first time where it simply stared at him.

A deep growl rumbles, vibrating into the sub-mech.

"Ash?"

He manages a weak breath, nothing more.

"Ash, what's going on?"

He wants to tell Julia something, anything, but terror grips him in its cold claws so tight he can't do anything but blink at the monster no more than fifteen feet in front of him. Just floating there, maw opening and closing…opening and closing. Just floating there…staring at him.

"I'm coming in."

His heart stutters. "N-No! Stay there. It's…staring at me right now."

"Can you shoot it?" Julia asks.

"I already did. Only pissed it off."

"So, what are you going to do?"

The very question that circles his thawing brain. Round and round and…

An idea strikes, maybe the only option now.

"The tunnels," he says.

"Huh?"

"I'm going make it chase me to those tunnels."

"So, like your original plan but now you're the bait?"

"Yes."

"Have I told you recently how dumb you are?"

Ash smiles. "In so many ways."

"Because it's true, jackass. My god, that's even more suicidal than any of your other hair-brained ideas."

"It's the only way. I think. I don't know. If I don't come back, thank you for sticking by me all these years. You're like my sister. Love you, Jules. Over and out." He shuts off the mech's comms before she can say anything, then draws in a deep breath, glaring at the dunkleosteus. "Okay, Dunky, let's see what you got."

Ash ducks and says, "Mach."

He catches a glimpse of the mouth opening wide, then he's speeding under the thing to the broken opening that used to be the Moon Pool floor. The fish writhes, wriggling as it tries to get him. He shoots into the open water outside the facility and aims for the passageway. The trove of bones…god, it feels like that happened days ago, rather than hours.

"Slow." The mech slows as he approaches the passageway. He turns and…

It's not there. It's not in the giant hole where the Moon Pool room used to be. It's not anywhere.

"Hold." The sub-mech stops.

"What the hell…?" He doesn't know much about the mech, and wishes it had some kind of scanning system. Maybe it has one. He just doesn't know how to access it.

Relying on sight alone, despite the enhanced visor, isn't good. He needs to know where the dunkleosteus is so he can maneuver without being caught unaware.

But the waters are still. Quiet. Maybe it decided him and the facility were too much work?

No. Not that thing. It's starving. And it knows where a bunch of food is. The people in Infinity Moon might not fill it up, but they'll at least sustain its ravenous hunger for a bit. Maybe that's all it wants. To get enough food to last through the tunnels. Makes sense. That way, once it reaches an ocean, it's not half mad with hunger and won't do something rash, like taking on a family of orcas or something. Despite its size, a large pod of orcas might be able to subdue the beast.

Maybe…

But these waters, there's nothing. And if it's near, he can't spot it through the murk. So, he waits. He waits, fighting the urge to turn the comms back on. The last thing he wants to hear right now is Julia freaking out. It'll distract him when he needs to be fully alert. The Guillotine can strike at any time and he needs to be on his toes.

Minutes inch by like hours and his mind drifts to his beloved Ky. His baby girl taken from him not so long ago.

He had planned on taking her to see her first ocean right before that bastard kidnapped her. Before he…he…

Ash growls, shakes his head and glares out the mech's visor.

Letting go is harder than people say it is. He knows that if he lets go, he won't be releasing her memories like a cluster of balloons in a mild breeze. He knows he'll always have the memories. But there's too much anger. A score he feels he needs to settle with the sick son of a bitch who took her life, even if he blew his own brains out. Perhaps that's exactly why he can't let go. No closure, or something. Or is it more like he doesn't get to watch the sick bastard rot in prison or see the life drain from his eyes as the lethal injection takes hold. Smile as his eyelids droop shut forever…

"You needed to suffer," he says, voice choked within the mech. "You deserved to suffer."

Tears trickle down his cheeks. Tears he can't wipe away.

Ky's face drifts before his mind's eye. He sighs. "I miss you, K-Bear. I'm sorry I couldn't protect you. I'm sorry I—"

It rams through one of the pillars holding the facility up, snapping it like it's nothing, and speeds directly for him, maw open wide.

Ash sucks in a breath. Tries to turn and enter the passageway, but the mech merely flails.

"F-*Fast*!"

The mech responds immediately. He spins, to the passageway, glances over his shoulder. Shit, not enough time to get in there and safely hide. Instead of entering the passage, he surges straight up seconds before the dunkleosteus collides into the side of the small hill. Sand and dirt and rocks explode through the water under him.

Using his arms like pectoral fins, Ash glides above the massive, old fish as it chomps away at the hill. Doing this, a random idea strikes.

"Laser."

The armor of the mech parts and a thin barrel rises out. He points the barrel at the dunkleosteus' back…and squeezes the trigger.

A bright, red stream slices through the water and cuts deep into the monster's back, shearing off a portion of its dorsal fin. Its tail whips, entire body bucking. Rumbling shakes the water. The dunkleosteus bashes itself against the hill, spins and goes after the facility. It bites into the side of Infinity Moon, ripping through the metal. Bubbles erupt as it breaches the inside.

"No," Ash says. Julia and Kayla and everyone in there. God, he hopes they're sealed away from the area it just penetrated.

Ash aims the laser and pulls the trigger again. The beam stabs into its side, though he aimed for its head. The monster fish bats away, shakes, then attacks the facility again.

"You son of a…" He aims both laser and gun at the bastard and pulls the triggers. Both bullet and laser beam strike the monster at about the same time.

It rears, maw wide. It bashes its head into the facility over and over then stops. For the longest time, it simply stares at the damage it created. Watching the fish, it's as though the thing is just waking up from a horrible nightmare and trying to figure out where it is. And, in all reality, that's probably close to the truth. It woke up to a changed world and has yet to adapt.

He can't blame it for going a little mad. In fact, he can't blame it for any of its actions. Everything is so different from what it knew. He'd be just as messed up.

Even so…it needs to either find an ocean where it will be more at home…or die.

The last thing he wants to do is kill it, even though it should be. The oceans are great for such a beast, but what will it do to the ecosystem? Maybe it won't affect it at all. Maybe it'll be eaten by a gargantuan mutation like the leviathan from years back. At least it has a chance in an ocean rather than starving to death in Lake Superior.

Then, very slowly, very deliberately, the dunkleosteus pivots, turns, and glares directly up at Ash. And, even from this distance, he can almost feel the beast's rage. He can feel it like bright, hot lava geyser. Lava that completely spills over and consumes him.

He aims both the gun and laser at the massive underwater tank.

Shoot it, he thinks. *Before it moves. Shoot it right in the eye.*

But as much as this makes sense, he can't force himself to pull the triggers. As it bobs, glaring and snapping its jaws, he can't kill it. Even if killing it will end the nightmare. They can all go home…

No. He has to play out his plan fully first.

Has to make sure he gives it all the chances. He…

The old monster rushes upward.

"Mach," Ash says and the sub-mech jolts into action. He's thrown forward many feet before gaining control and soaring by the dunkleosteus. It snaps at him, misses. He barrel-rolls without meaning to around the beast and finds himself directly under it. Merely three feet from its belly. It crosses his mind to slice its belly open with the laser, but he just can't. Instead he darts in front of the creature. It lunges and misses him once again with those guillotine jaws.

Need to get it into the passage…

Ash turns, aiming directly for the passageway's opening. If he can get inside and find a place to hide so the dunkleosteus passes by without noticing…it'll all be over. It will continue on through the tunnels and either die or make it through. Not enough room to back up. It'll be stuck.

It's the most humane way he can think of.

Hell, it's the only—

Pressure crushes his right leg. He glances back in horror, seeing his leg pinched between those guillotine jaws. In the next instant his world is a tumbling mess of confusion.

He cries, "Hold," dozens of times before finally the tumbling stops and he's bobbing in the water not even sure if he's still alive or not.

Finally, everything stabilizes and he blinks at the dunkleosteus as it rams into the passageway. Before long, Ash watches the tip of its tail slither into the old caverns, no doubt on its way into the tunnels.

It's over.

A heavy breath blows out of Ash. He turns on the comms, catching Julia in mid-rant.

"—the fuck is going on? I swear to all the gods that were ever made up I'll kill him if he dies! Thc son of a—"

"Hey, Jules."

The comms are so clear, he actually hears her draw in a sharp breath, as if slapped.

"You...*you*! Don't you *ever* cut me off like that again!"

He chuckles. "Love you too."

"Don't even try buttering me up with that love you crap." She sighs. "But ditto. Did you kill it yet?"

"No. It's in the tunnels. I'm heading back. How's Kayla?"

"Um...we can't find her."

"What do you mean you can't find her? She was with you."

Julia clears her throat. "I know. And up until a few minutes ago, she was here. Maybe she had to pee or something."

"You've checked all over?"

"Yeah. Well, kinda. I'm sure she'll be around here somewhere."

He nods. "She took a hard hit, just want to make sure she's not suffering from amnesia, you know?"

"She seemed okay earlier. A little bruised and shaken, but nothing serious."

"Okay. I'm heading back now. Does anyone there know a way in?"

There's a short pause. "Ben says there's a docking station on the north side for incoming materials. He'll meet you there."

"Good. I'll be—"

Something slams into him so hard he knows absolutely nothing but the darkness that consumes him.

TWENTY-THREE

"Ash?" Static crackles in his ears. "Ash? You okay?" Static…so much static.

He groans, eyelids fluttering.

And somewhere in the static, there are two voices.

"Ash? Talk to me, dude! Damn it, can we figure out how to run scans? I want to know where he is." Julia…yes, that's Julia. But…

"Just stay still for a few seconds. There's more going on here than a prehistoric fish."

Who is that? For the longest time, he can't pin a face to the voice. Then…gradually it comes to him.

Kayla.

But what's she doing out here? She couldn't even pilot the sub-mech. Or…maybe she did know how. What if…she buried herself on purpose? But why? Why injure herself? Doesn't make any damn sense.

"We're direct link," Kayla says. "No one else can hear us."

Ash swallows, dry throat clicking with the effort. He can't even remember the last time he drank some water. His eyes open and he blinks up at Kayla through the mech's visor. They're both still in their mechs. Both still in the water. But…

"What's…what's going on?" His voice is nothing more than a dry croak.

Kayla glances around, then bends over Ash again. "I saw it on the thousand feet scans earlier but didn't say anything because I wasn't totally sure. I saw it again right before we had to evacuate the Moon Pool."

Ash frowns. "Saw what?"

Her face twitches, eyes wide in apparent fright. "I don't think the dunkleosteus was the only thing that got thawed out."

Heart thudding, he sits. "What—"

It happens so fast, all Ash sees is a flash of sharp teeth and a smear of blue as Kayla is ripped away from him.

In his ears, Kayla screams.

Ash sucks in a breath, standing. And when he turns…

"Oh my god…"

"Ash? Ash is that you?" Julia, but he can't talk to her right now, let alone move as the thing that has Kayla in its mouth shakes its crocodile-like head.

It's long, sinuous body is like some absurd mongrelized version of a whale/snake hybrid. The way it swims and moves is very serpent-like, but the way it tries to tear Kayla apart is very much like a shark, or even a crocodile as it rolls through the water near the facility.

"Ash! Goddamn it! Answer me!"

"Uh…I'll get back to you in a second. There's something else out here."

"What? What the hell do you mean there's something else out there?"

He lifts his left arm, aiming the gun at the creature. "It's trying to eat Kayla."

"Wait, she's out *there*? What is? I thought the dunk was in the tunnels!"

"This isn't that."

"Then what the hell is it, for Christ sake?"

His finger finds the trigger as he finally recognizes the creature. "It's a basilosaurus."

"A basilo—Those crocodile-snake-whale things?"

"Yeah."

He aims at the space between the basilosaurus' head and body, finger tightening on the trigger and—

It surges out the murk, massive jaws slicing down like a guillotine, consuming all but the basilosaurus' head. The head spasms, releasing Kayla as the dunkleosteus returns to the murk, disappearing once more. Blood swirls, clouding the waters.

Kayla, grunting, speeds back to Ash. Her thrusters, or whatever propels the mechs, sputter and she half crashes, half lands beside Ash. Her mech is dented, the paint scraped off in most places, but otherwise she appears unharmed.

"Holy hell," she says. "I feel like a milkshake. What the hell was that?"

"Basilosaurus," Ash says, frowning into the murk where the dunkleosteus disappeared.

"Well, thanks for blowing it up. I thought I was going to die."

"I didn't blow it up," He points at the basilosaurus' head as it sinks to the bottom of the lake. "Our old friend ate it."

"Wait, the dunkleosteus? I thought it was in the tunnels?"

"Apparently not."

"So…what do we do now?"

Ash shakes his head, not sure if there's anything they can do.

"You still alive?" Julia asks. "Did it eat Kayla?"

"We're both fine," Ash says to her. "The dunk ate the basilosaurus and saved Kayla."

"I thought that thing was in the tunnels!"

He grunts. "I guess it missed us."

"You know no one likes your jokes but you, right?"

"Yeah, yeah. How's our little buddy, Giles?"

"You know…I haven't seen him in a while."

His heart thumps. "You might want to find him and keep him away from any comms."

"You think he might get Murdock to send more people here?"

"Or Murdock will have an alternate plan and simply blow the facility up and kill everyone in it."

"I've told you your jokes aren't funny, right?"

"Not joking right now. Find him, if you can. Hold him down if you have to. I don't trust that son of a bitch at all."

"Me either. I'll go find him. What's the plan now?"

He sighs. "So far, there is no plan. I'm thinking."

"Gotcha. Let me know."

"Will do, Jules. Be careful."

"You too, jackass."

He faces Kayla. "So, were you faking it when you dive bombed the lake floor?"

"Nope. I sank so fast, my brain kind of stopped working. Trust me, I wouldn't do that shit on purpose. Hurt like hell."

"I bet." He turns back to the murky lake. "Any ideas on how to stop this thing?"

"Not at all. You?"

"Nope."

"Well, look at us," Kayla says, "A couple of geniuses."

Ash chuckles. "You wouldn't think it'd be so hard to stop a prehistoric fish, but…"

"Yeah, it's like it—oh shit!"

He glances at her, then in the direction she's staring.

His breath catches in his throat as the dunkleosteus emerges from the darkness once more and crashes into the facility. It chomps through one of the composite glass tunnels. It beats its juggernaut head into everything around it. It bites into walls, ripping away strips and chunks of metal.

Ash, breathing in shallow gasps, manages, "Jules?"

"Hold on, Ash, things are kind of nuts right now."

"Get to the escape pods," he says. "You hear me? Get everyone to the pods."

Static fills his ears.

"Jules? You there? If you can hear me, get the hell out of there!"

Only static greets him.

"Jules?" Tears blur his vision. "*Julia*!"

"Ash, she's probably already moving everyone to the pods. She's busy. Now…what the hell are we going to do about that thing?"

He forces the tears away and tries to focus. His sight drifts away from the monster attacking the facility. Neither the gun nor laser did much to hurt the thing. So, what else is there? The sub-mechs aren't equipped with rockets or missiles. Another flaw Murdock must've forgotten to upgrade.

Ash sighs, shakes his head. "The tunnels. Give it another try."

"Why can't we both shoot at the thing?" Kayla gestures at the Guillotine. "I mean it's armored, but it has to have a damn weakness, right?"

"The belly, probably. But we need to really bombard it and don't let up until it's dead."

"Either or, we should probably get it away from Infinity Moon."

"Good call." He points his gun at the rampaging dunkleosteus and pulls the trigger.

The old monster doesn't even flinch and continues trying to destroy the facility.

"Fuck," he says. "We need to shoot it together. Aim for the belly."

"It's moving around so much. I don't know if I'll hit it."

"We need to try," Ash says, aiming both the gun and laser at the thing. "On three."

"And if it comes for us?"

"Then we Mach to the tunnels. Ready?"

"Ugh. Yeah, whatever."

"One. Two." He takes a deep breath. "Three."

He pulls the trigger for both gun and laser and watches as his beam is joined by Kayla's. Both beams and bullets strike the dunkleosteus near the belly and this time it actually rears, mouth gaping. It dives toward the lake floor, then surges upward at the last minute until it's above the facility. Here, blood clouding around it, the monster floats. It doesn't move.

"Should we…um…shoot it again?"

Ash frowns. "It's trying to figure out what hurt it. Once it does, it won't stop until we're fish food."

"It knows vengeance?"

"This fish…it's intelligent. I saw that in its eyes. If it spots us, it'll stop at nothing to get us. I feel it."

"Well, we better get to the tunnels then, eh?"

"Yeah, we better…uh-oh. Too late."

The dunkleosteus turns and stops as soon as it's facing them.

"You think we can make it to the tunnels before it gets us?"

Ash shakes his head. "It's what…about a hundred feet away?" He mulls it over. "We might make it. Use the fastest feature the mech offers. Directly to the tunnels, which are somewhere under us, I think."

"It's not moving. Maybe it doesn't see us?"

"Oh," Ash says. "It sees us."

"Why isn't it moving?"

"Calculating an attack, maybe? How am I supposed to know?"

Kayla points at the massive fish. "Well, shit. I thought you two were linked or something."

"Hardly. Just thinking how a smart fish might."

"How smart are we talking?"

He rolls this over in his mind a bit, then, "I'd say almost human level."

"Oh, that's just perfect. No wonder it's been so difficult."

"Exactly. We need to outsmart it."

"Why does that feel easier said than done?"

Ash sighs. "Because it is. But in the end, it's a fish. A creature driven mostly by instincts." As the dunkleosteus glares at him, a sliver of an idea rises through the maelstrom of thoughts. "The tunnels. It has to be the tunnels. Get it in there, then close the passageway off."

"Um…how are we going to—oh shit, here it comes!"

TWENTY-FOUR

Everything hurts, and it's their fault.

Those…creatures. Things the old monster hasn't encountered before with their sharp bites and all the pain they bring. They don't even taste good.

Chomp them to bits. Destroy them. It's the only way to stop the pain.

The old monster, rage flaring through its massive body, whips its great tail faster and faster. An inferno of rage fueling every movement, every thought.

It rushes through the water, water so different, yet the same, barreling toward these new monsters. Its jaws unhinge, ready to devour. Ready to end the pain once and for all. To be free to feed without these new creatures interfering.

The old monster roars a rooster-tail of bubbles as it blasts forward like a living torpedo.

It ends now…

TWENTY-FIVE

Using the Mach setting, they race to the passageway opening dug into the side of the hill.

They slow, then hold.

Ash turns as the dunkleosteus rushes by the remains of the Moon Pool.

"This is insane," Kayla says, voice trembling. "You know that right?"

Ash releases a pent-up breath he hadn't known he'd been holding and manages, "Yeah. When I say, Mach away from the opening."

"But if it's as smart as you say…"

"Now!"

Ash and Kayla shout Mach at about the same time, blasting away in separate directions three seconds before the monster barreling at them crashes into the passage's opening in an explosion of rock and sand.

He's about thirty feet away when he tells the mech to slow and hold. Facing the passageway. Is it in there? How deep did its momentum take it? Questions with no answers as the debris creates a dark cloud around the area.

Can't wait for it to clear, he thinks. *Do it.*

"Ash?"

Kayla floats about the length of a school bus above the passageway.

"Cave it in," he says. "Shoot above the passage with everything you have. We'll trap the fish in there so it has no choice but to swim to the ocean."

"But—"

"Now!" He aims at where he assumes is the top of the passage and shoots both gun and laser. He pulls the triggers as fast as he can.

A few seconds later, Kayla follows suit.

More rock and dirt and sand cloud the water, creating a thick, dark wall. And still, he keeps pulling the triggers.

He doesn't stop until the mech beeps at him that the laser barrel is too hot and at its melting point. It glows red on the mech's arm.

"Okay," he says. "Let's see if it worked."

"It's going to take an hour for all that to clear on its own," Kayla says. "Maybe we—"

It erupts from the wall of debris, mouth open wide, like a demon unleashed from Hell.

"Kay—"

It's all he manages before those sharp bone plates shear her in two. Blood spills, mixing with the dark cloud wall, creating a morbid stew.

In his ears, he listens to Kayla gurgling her final breaths, the top half of her body tumbling, the mech's arms flailing and jerking.

Ash screams, points the gun at the monstrous fish and pulls the trigger. Several bullets plunge into its side as it snaps up the rest of Kayla. He keeps shooting at it until it darts into the deeper murk of the lake.

"Get back here you motherfucker!" He's roaring, tears washing over his vision. "Mach!"

He jets forward in a spray of bubbles, both arms out like a flying superhero, fingers curled around the triggers. Rage is liquid fire running through his veins like magma. All he sees through the blur of tears is red. Red that soon morphs into an image of the man who murdered his beloved Ky. The man who stole everything from him.

The murk clears just enough and he comes upon the dunkleosteus in mid-turn. No doubt it wanted to get great speed before taking him out too. And when it notices Ash jetting at it, the old monster almost appears to be surprised. Its tail whips, its maw snaps, silvery eyes roll in their bony sockets.

Ash, still roaring, pulls the triggers.

TWENTY-SIX

This is not how it's supposed to go.

The old monster was always the largest of its kind. The strongest. It could sneak up to beaches, pretend it's a boulder, then snatch its land-prey right off the sand and drag them into its world to feed. It has lived a long time. Longer than most.

And never in its long years has it encountered such prey as this new creature.

Never before has the prey fought back.

As tiny things plunge into its flank, as something cuts off a portion of its pectoral fin, the world is nothing but pain. Pain never ending. Its own blood swirls, getting thicker as more and more spills out of its body.

No.

It has survived much and will not let this small, evil creature keep creating agony.

It will not be defeated by its food.

TWENTY-SEVEN

Gun and laser blasting, Ash grins. *I got it now. I got this son of a—*

The dunkleosteus dives so suddenly, Ash speeds right by, blinking. Its blood still swirls where it once was.

"Slow," he says and the mech slows gradually while he turns, looking down. But he's at least two hundred feet from the floor now and the water is too murky. He can't see a damn thing. "Hold."

As the mech stops moving, Ash stares into the abyss below him.

"Where are you…?" He keeps the mech's arms pointed into the murk, fingers on the triggers. He's not sure how many bullets are left. Next shots need to be aimed better. He hurt it this time, he knows. Saw the pain practically ripple through the giant fish. And now that it's in pain, maybe he can get the upper hand and kill it.

You went a little crazy back there, man, a low voice whispers in his head. *Need to be careful of that.*

Static crackles in his ears and he hisses with how loud it is. But…very faint, "Ash? You there? Ash?"

He blows out a long sigh of relief recognizing Julia's voice. "I'm here. Kayla's dead. I'm…hunting it now."

Static crackles, then, "Got the people in the pods. I'm coming to help you."

"No," he says. "I can't risk losing you."

"Too bad." A wall of static crashes into his ears. Then…nothing.

"Julia? Jules? You better not—"

It's like being hit by a damn train when the dunk emerges from the side and slams into him. He spins, tumbling and turning through the water. Pain laces around his chest and the mech blares some kind of wobbly alarm.

"Slow," he manages and the mech quickly stabilizes him. Just in time to gape into the maw of a biological guillotine.

Screaming, Ash lifts his right arm and blasts the beam into the dunkleosteus' wide mouth.

The monster thrashes away, jaws snapping shut.

Its tail smacks into Ash, though not hard enough to do much damage. Not saying his chest still doesn't hurt though. And the mech still blaring that annoying alarm. On the right inside of the visor is a flickering diagram of the sub-mech. The chest blinks red. Under the diagram he frowns at the short message there.

MECH COMPROMISED.

On the left inside of the visor is another message: MECH FAILURE IMMINENT IN FIVE MINUTES.

What the hell does that mean? Will the mech shutdown? And if it shuts down, does that mean the intakes will stop working too? For shit sake, why didn't he at least ask a few questions while Frost was around?

The alarm whines and wobbles and he can't think. He doesn't know what to do, nor even if the dunkleosteus is dead or not.

The facility isn't far. Maybe one hundred yards or so. If he can make it there, strip the mech off and join Julia in a pod then everything should be okay. Should be…

"Fast," he tells the mech, not wanting to push the thing too much now that it's damaged badly. Even so, the pulses sputter. He dips. The mech shakes. Something behind him rattles.

By all accounts, it's like being inside a 1960's truck with all its rust and rattling panels and coughing exhaust. Maybe with a broken tie-rod too. And clunky wheel bearings.

The fish hit him damn hard to create such damage.

He's around seventy feet—telling the mech to slow down—from the facility when a tendril of scarlet snakes in front of him.

"H-Hold."

Very slowly, he looks down, and his bladder lets go because directly below him, pacing him, is the dunkleosteus. Barely six feet under the mech's feet. Six feet and, perhaps sensing he stopped, swishes its tail and darts forward until it's at the facility. It makes a lazy turn and swims back to him. Level to him. This old monster. And for the fourth time, they stare at each other face to face. No more than seven feet away.

It dwarfs him so severely, he knows what an ant must feel like when a mouse stumbles into its path.

It's much larger than what he assumed a dunkleosteus to be. Comparable to a juvenile sperm whale, perhaps.

This close, his gaze slips over all the scars, both old and newer, and the fresh grooves his bullets left in its heavy armor. Blood seeps from its right side. Its guillotine maw opens and closes, those bone plates serving as teeth sharpening themselves as they scissor together. It's brownish in color, with streaks of heavy, black scales.

And its eyes, silvery, as they reflect the light spewing from the lights fixed in the mech.

A shrill beep startles him and across the visor is this warning: 60 SECONDS TO TOTAL MECH FAILURE.

He sighs as the warning flickers away and smiles at the giant prehistoric fish. "Well, bud, at least you got to see the future, right?"

The dunkleosteus stares at him.

"If it's any consolation to you, it was an honor to see you alive. Typically, all I get are bones."

The old monster's mouth opens, closes, opens, closes.

Before he can say anything more, that massive mouth springs open wide. He closes his eyes, accepting his fate.

A rumble shakes the mech. Slight pressure. The alarm wavers and—

"Ash…can you hear me…go!"

He opens his eyes to a deep, storming cloud of crimson.

"I got it! C'mon, dude!"

"J-Jules?"

"Yeah…can't…something…hurry."

"What? You're cutting out."

Only static answers him.

The mech brays, sending his heart into an instant rampage in his chest. He sucks in a breath as all kinds of light flash along the visor, each with a different symbol. He tries to pick out the symbol that might mean the oxygen intakes, but they flash a couple seconds then disappear. The bray whirrs down to a low groan. Something clicks.

Finally catching his breath, Ash says, "Fast!"

The mech sputters forward a few feet, stops. The suit jitters and for one godless second, he fears it's about to rip itself apart. But then it stills and surges forward a few more feet before quaking so hard he has to choke down vomit.

"You…help?"

"Yes," he says, sweat trickling down his face as the cooling system in the mech begins to fail. "Help!"

Then she's there. Julia smiles through her visor at him. "Gotcha."

He smiles back as she turns and pulls him to the facility, then around the ruins of the Moon Pool to the other side.

"…hatch…" is all that comes through when Julia speaks.

And soon enough, he sees a small docking station. He's not sure what it would have been used as before all this, but it's the way to salvation. Already it's getting harder to breathe. A strange pressure leans against his body. So, either it's the pressure or the intakes have quit as to why he can't breathe very well. Or maybe…

"Shit!"

She spins him just as it swims out of the gloom, half of its face wavering in bloody tatters.

"No," Julia says. "I…it…I…blew it up!"

Blood swirls around the monster and Julia shoves him toward the docking station. Her face through her visor is one of sorrow…and love.

"Slow," he says, but the mech doesn't move. "Fuck."

Julia lifts what looks like a grenade launcher and he suddenly realizes it's not a grenade launcher, but the missile launcher Green was talking about. The one in her cabin…

Julia found it!

But…

He clunks against the dock's door.

"Press the red button, dude," Julia says, clear as day. "See ya in the next life."

"What? No, Jul—"

The world is a fiery explosion so bright Ash has to look away.

When he's able to look again, all he sees are floating pieces of blue mech and blood and shreds of brownish flesh and black scales.

It makes no sense, but somehow Julia blew herself up killing the dunkleosteus.

"No," he cries, reaching out for the shards of mech. He catches an arm with her arm still inside.

With a scream, he tosses it away. Tears cascade down his cheeks. He cries for Julia. He cries for Kayla. He cries for Green. He cries for his long-lost daughter, Ky. He cries for all the fallen. All the dead.

He cries for Julia and Ky the most. Those he loved.

Still crying, he turns to the docking station and finds the red button near the door. Floating nearby is the missile launcher, he grabs it on impulse. Not like he needs it. But it's kind of like a reminder. It's the last thing Julia touched.

The mech stutters, so heavy as he grits his teeth to lift his free arm and slam his hand against the button. The door slides open and he spills inside with god knows how many gallons of water. The door doesn't shut. Stomach a ball of knots, Ash manages to crawl toward the door. There's another button on this side. A green one. Red is open. Green is close. At least…he hopes so.

Ash, grunting, drawing in weak breaths as he pulls the heavy, nearly dead mech along, reaches for the green button.

It crashes through the doorway, sharp maw snapping. Ash tumbles away, though not far enough. Those guillotine jaws clamp down on his right leg. The pain is instantaneous. The pressure so great he screams.

It thrashes, slamming him into the walls.

"You…motherfucker," he breathes and points the missile launcher at the old monster.

Its mouth opens just enough. He yanks his leg out, jams the launcher into its mouth, and pulls the trigger.

All is bright. All is blood.

He blinks at the mess where the monster's head used to be…then collapses. He doesn't have enough strength to kick the rest of the fish out of the bent doorway. Doesn't have enough strength to breathe.

Gray fog seeps into him while he lies on the floor of the docking station.

He gasps, struggling to breathe.

This is it.

This is…

TWENTY-EIGHT

"…breathe."

Ash's eyelids open to blurriness, then close.

"Just breathe, Dr. Barrington."

Why does he know that voice? And why does he hate it?

"We're getting you into a pod. Just breathe. Slow breaths. I have an IV going, you're dehydrated."

His head lolls from side to side as he realizes he's being rolled on either a gurney or table.

He tries to tell the familiar voice to be careful because the monster might not really be dead…but all that comes out is a thin whine.

"We'll get you some medical attention, Dr. Barrington. Here we are. Escape pod. There's a team waiting for us at the surface. Murdock has taken care of everything."

Murdock…

Ash's eyes open, vision clearing from a gray blur to full, vivid color. And the first thing he sees is Giles' chubby, wide-eyed face. This close, he notices the broken veins in the man's bulbous nose. A hard drinker…

Something Ash hadn't picked up before, though should have.

Ash swallows down a thick lump in his throat, coughs. "He's going to kill us."

Giles frowns. "Now, why would he do that? We have provided unprecedented evidence and data for a year."

"You've…been made a fool, Dr. Giles."

Still, the chubby man shakes his head. "No. Mr. Jones wouldn't betray me like that."

Ash doesn't have the strength to laugh.

He's not sure how much long after, he's being strapped into a pod and Giles is telling him not to worry about anything. He tells Ash he's a hero. He saved most of the crew. For that, Murdock will reward him.

If only the portly man knew how that bastard Murdock Jones works…

He's too weak to do anything and so he's strapped in and the pod deployed. It's a mere five minutes to breach the surface.

Still strapped into the chair of the pod, still hooked up to an IV, the pod hisses open as a skiff approaches.

Ash sighs. Everything hurts.

His vision blurs, weariness steals over him.

The last thing he sees are two men in black uniforms reaching into the pod.

TWENTY-NINE

It's not your fault, Daddy…

His eyes open to a white so brilliant he's forced to close his eyes again.

"Congratulations, Dr. Barrington," Murdock says in his smooth voice. "You made it out alive."

I love you, Daddy…

"Ky," Ash manages.

There's a long pause, then Murdock says, very near, "You're not close enough to death to talk to your dead daughter, Ash."

He tries opening his eyes again, this time succeeding as his eyes adjust to the bright light. Not only this, he soon notes he's in a room that's starkly white.

"You have been through an ordeal, Ash. Rest now and we can talk later."

Ash rolls onto his side, grimacing as his body cries in pain. "N-No…now."

Murdock is almost to the door to whatever room Ash is being kept in when he stops and faces Ash. "You need your rest, son. I will come back in a few hours."

"My partner died saving me," Ash shouts, albeit weakly. "You owe me, you bastard."

Murdock chuckles a bit, though nods and gestures for Ash to speak.

"You knew about the dunkleosteus, didn't you." Not a question.

"Of course I did. Why do you think I sent you down there? If anyone could figure out a way to capture it, it was you." He looks away, shakes his head. "I haven't been so wrong since Bracken and that leviathan debacle."

"You knew how big it was. You set us up to fail."

"Wrong," Murdock says, moving toward the bed. "I gave you every opportunity to succeed and you failed. All you had to do was capture it and bring it to me. That's it. Instead you wanted to set it free, or kill it? Come now…what good would come from any of that? I would have retired you with the amount of money I was willing to pay you and your partner."

"It was a prehistoric fish," Ash says, managing to sit. "A couple of blood samples then sending it to live in the oceans would have been sufficient."

Murdock chuckles. "Samples? We needed *everything*. Imagine what that thing could have taught us. Imagine how many lives it could have saved…" Murdock sighs. "All lost. Thanks to you."

"So," Ash says, "I guess you're going to kill me now."

Murdock blinks, then full out laughs. As the laughter eases, he says, "K-Kill you? No. I have plans for you. Huge plans."

"What kind of plans?"

The man, with his slicked back black hair and black mustache, winks. "You'll know soon enough, Ash. Very soon."

Ash starts to jump out of bed when his arms snag. He frowns, gaze dropping to his right arm. A padded leather cuff holds his arm to the bed. Same with his left. Another strap rests along his lap.

Ash yanks on the restraints. "The fuck is this?"

Murdock grins. "Like I said, Ash. I have big plans for you."

"You can't do this!"

Turning toward the door and opening it, Murdock glances over his shoulder. "I already have." He opens the door fully, and steps out.

The door shuts, leaving Ash alone in the stark, white room.

He pulls on the cuffs, tries to wiggle out of them. For a second or two, he thinks he might just slip out of the cuffs, but that doesn't happen. They're too tight. Not only this, there's faint pain in his wrists every time he pulls.

Small drops of blood stain the white sheet under his right cuff.

"You son of a bitch," Ash says.

The insides of the cuffs aren't just padding but embedded with what seems to be razors. The more he pulls and struggles, the deeper the razors cut. And if he struggles too hard…

Fighting to control the rage, Ash lies back down on the bed.

Across the room is a slim TV. It's blank, though a nice contrast to all the damn white.

It's this Ash focuses on. This black rectangle mounted to the wall.

This small TV, representing his sanity, one might say.

But to Ash, it's a grounding point amongst all the white. If his gaze strays too long, perhaps madness will take over.

So, he stares at the blank TV.

He stares, and he waits.

Because, sooner or later, that door will open again.

And when it does…he wants to be ready…

CHECK OUT OTHER GREAT DEEP SEA THRILLERS

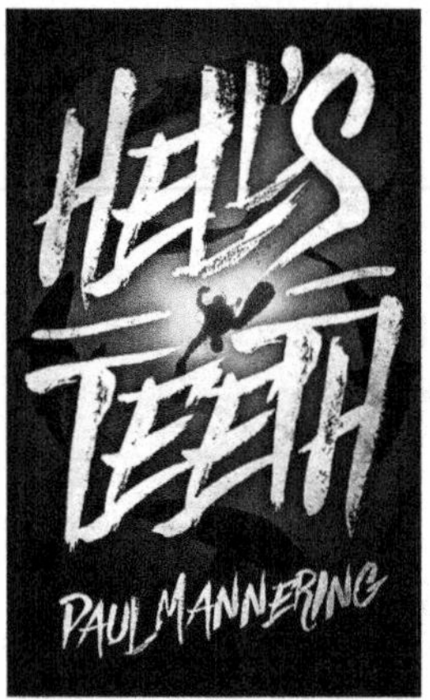

HELL'S TEETH
by Paul Mannering

In the cold South Pacific waters off the coast of New Zealand, a team of divers and scientists are preparing for three days in a specially designed habitat 1300 feet below the surface.

In this alien and savage world, the mysterious great white sharks gather to hunt and to breed.

When the dive team's only link to the surface is destroyed, they find themselves in a desperate battle for survival. With the air running out, and no hope of rescue, they must use their wits to survive against sharks, each other, and a terrifying nightmare of legend.

MONSTERS IN OUR WAKE
by J.H. Moncrieff

In the idyllic waters of the South Pacific lurks a dangerous and insatiable predator; a monster whose bloodlust and greed threatens the very survival of our planet...the oil industry. Thousands of miles from the nearest human settlement, deep on the ocean floor, ancient creatures have lived peacefully for millennia. But when an oil drill bursts through their lair, Nøkken attacks, damaging the drilling ship's engine and trapping the desperate crew. The longer the humans remain in Nøkken's territory, struggling to repair their ailing ship, the more confrontations occur between the two species. When the death toll rises, the crew turns on each other, and marine geologist Flora Duchovney realizes the scariest monsters aren't below the surface.

CHECK OUT OTHER GREAT DEEP SEA THRILLERS

LAMPREYS
by Alan Spencer

A secret government tactical team is sent to perform a clean sweep of a private research installation. Horrible atrocities lurk within the abandoned corridors. Mutated sea creatures with insane killing abilities are waiting to suck the blood and meat from their prey.
Unemployed college professor Conrad Garfield is forced to assist and is soon separated from the team. Alone and afraid, Conrad must use his wits to battle mutated lampreys, infected scientists and go head-to-head with the biggest monstrosity of all.
Can Conrad survive, or will the deadly monsters suck the very life from his body?

DEEP DEVOTION
by M.C. Norris

Rising from the depths, a mind-bending monster unleashes a wave of terror across the American heartland. Kate Browning, a Kansas City EMT confronts her paralyzing fear of water when she traces the source of a deadly parasitic affliction to the Gulf of Mexico. Cooperating with a marine biologist, she travels to Florida in an effort to save the life of one very special patient, but the source of the epidemic happens to be the nest of a terrifying monster, one that last rose from the depths to annihilate the lost continent of Atlantis.

Leviathan, destroyer, devoted lifemate and parent, the abomination is not going to take the extermination of its brood well.

CHECK OUT OTHER GREAT DEEP SEA THRILLERS

THEY RISE
by Hunter Shea

Some call them ghost sharks, the oldest and strangest looking creatures in the sea.

Marine biologist Brad Whitley has studied chimaera fish all his life. He thought he knew everything about them. He was wrong. Warming ocean temperatures free legions of prehistoric chimaera fish from their methane ice suspended animation. Now, in a corner of the Bermuda Triangle, the ocean waters run red. The 400 million year old massive killing machines know no mercy, destroying everything in their path. It will take Whitley, his climatologist ex-wife and the entire US Navy to stop them in the bloodiest battle ever seen on the high seas.

SERPENTINE
by Barry Napier

Clarkton Lake is a picturesque vacation spot located in rural Virginia, great for fishing, skiing, and wasting summer days away.

But this summer, something is different. When butchered bodies are discovered in the water and along the muddy banks of Clarkton Lake, what starts out as a typical summer on the lake quickly turns into a nightmare.

This summer, something new lives in the lake...something that was born in the darkest depths of the ocean and accidentally brought to these typically peaceful waters.

It's getting bigger, it's getting smarter...and it's always hungry.

Printed in Great Britain
by Amazon

A QUESTION OF

MUSIC

GUY ROBERTS AND EILEEN ZABET

A QUESTION OF

MUSIC

foulsham

LONDON • NEW YORK • TORONTO • SYDNEY

foulsham

The Publishing House, Bennetts Close, Cippenham, Slough, Berkshire, SL1 5AP, England

ISBN 0-572-02308-1

Printed in Great Britain by St Edmundsbury Press, Bury St Edmunds, Suffolk

CONTENTS

INTRODUCTION

We all tend to confine our musical appreciation to little 'boxes' labelled 'rock', 'classics', 'opera', etc., even 'all sorts of music from heavy metal to Whitney Houston' or 'all sorts of music from Tchaikovsky to Beethoven'. Because we feel comfortable with our boxes of music, we don't open up to listen to what is outside them. If, however, we do listen, we may find we like what we hear – even if the composer has an unpronouncable name or the performer is pop-oriented. So, why not give it a try?

This book has been compiled from the drawersful of musical 'snippets' that we have, individually, amassed over many years. Our hope is that it will tempt you to 'open up' to music and that you will try listening to music that you have, until now, considered to be outside the range of what you would like; not forsaking the familiar, but 'crossing over' to include new musical territory.

About this book

We have chosen a 'questions and answers' format so that we can cover a wide range of music without – we hope – getting boring. The questions are far from trivial and from most you will be able to pick up new bits of information. Additional notes are given with many of the answers.

There are six sections (Opus 1 to Opus 6), each with 100 questions, some of which are brief, others extended. There are also informative anecdotes, and puzzles that you may like to try.

We have tried to make things as uncomplicated as possible and we hope this will not too annoy much the purists among our readers. We have simplified the spelling of foreign names and, where questions involve musical extracts, these have also been simplified so that non-performers can 'pick out' the tunes on a keyboard or a recorder with little effort, or just hum them. Some questions will help readers who have no instrument-playing experience to grasp the very basics of reading music and to understand the terminology; who knows, perhaps they may open up to playing as well as listening.

We are only too aware that we have scarcely skimmed the surface of a vast subject. Dates have been given and, where appropriate, we have put in references to world events of the time. Of course, we cannot guarantee that everything in this book is the absolute truth. After all, for all we know, Elvis *may* still be alive, Vivaldi *may* have had green hair, Beethoven's last words *could* have been: 'I wish I'd been a baker!'. We can only tell you what others have assured us is so – and we gratefully acknowledge the help of the many who have provided us with pieces of interesting information over the years.

Our thanks go to Philip Carter, Norma Clemson, Joy ffoulkes, Robin Gatcomb, Charles Jarvis and the editors and staff of W Foulsham for all their help with this book.

How you might use this book

- You could read it from cover to cover. The content and the depth of treatment do develop as the book goes along, so we hope it will provide an interesting 'read'.

- You could use it as a 'quiz' book. A range of types of music is covered under each broad heading, so you should find something about which you know a little – or even a great deal – wherever you open the book. If you wish to award points, we would suggest one for a correct (or justifiable) answer or part answer, plus one for any additional piece of relevant information supplied. You may find the 'One-liners' (questions 71–100 for each Opus), particularly useful for quiz sessions.

- You could (and we would like to think that most readers will) find interest and enjoyment by just dipping into the book – either at random or by reference to the Contents list and the Index of People.

Finally, if you would care to try out the 'Recapitulation' and 'Coda' sections at the end of the 'Opuses', we hope you will find that you have, indeed, taken the first steps in crossing over and opening up to music. We trust it proves a pleasurable and rewarding experience for you.

PART ONE

OPUS 1

CROSSING OVER

He sang as a baritone in his parents' *zarzuela* company. His first major operatic role was as a tenor in *La Traviata* in 1961. Now acclaimed as one of 'The Three Tenors', he is also making a name for himself as a conductor. Who is he?

Belle Silverman was born in Brooklyn in 1929. As a child, her voice was heard on one of the first radio 'singing commercials'. Under what name did she later achieve fame as an operatic coloratura soprano?

He was an American-born clarinettist and band leader. He recorded an excellent performance of Mozart's Clarinet Concerto in A major and Paul Hindemith, Aaron Copland, Darius Milhaud and Béla Bartók all wrote works for him. Known as 'The King of Swing', can you name him?

In the 1920s he was principal violinist with Jack Hylton's Orchestra, excelling in solo jazz performances. Later he was conductor of the Liverpool Philharmonic Orchestra and the Covent Garden Orchestra. He died in 1976. Who was he?

He and his father, Ross McManus, co-wrote the ditty 'I'm a Secret Lemonade Drinker' for a well-known 1970s TV advertisement. He had hits with 'Oliver's Army' and 'I Can't Stand Up for Falling Down', in 1979 and 1980. He joined – in 1992 – with the Brodsky Quartet, a chamber ensemble, to write and perform *The Juliet Letters*. Can you name him?

This American composer and viola player worked, in the 1920s, as a symphonic jazz arranger for the band leader, Paul Whiteman. A few years later, he orchestrated George Gershwin's *Rhapsody in Blue*. His own best-known composition is the *Grand Canyon Suite*. Who was he?

Which actor, singer and director had hits in the late 1950s with such as 'Singing the Blues', 'Little White Bull' and 'Water Water', performed at the Old Vic in 1960, and played Jack Point in *The Yeoman of the Guard* (by Gilbert and Sullivan) at the City of London Festival in 1978?

A popular singer of the 1950s, he had a brief charts entry with 'By the Fountains of Rome'. He turned to opera in the 1960s, singing at Glyndebourne and with the Welsh National Opera. Can you name him?

Can you name this 'Bennett'? He was an American (1894–1981) and studied with Carl Busch and Nadia Boulanger. Among his compositions were an opera, *Maria Malibran*, and *The Abraham Lincoln Symphony*. As an orchestrator of stage musicals, he had great success with such as *South Pacific*, *My Fair Lady* and *The Sound of Music*.

And, can you name this 'Bennett'? English, born in 1936, he studied with Pierre Boulez. He has written orchestral and chamber works and several operas, including *The Mines of Sulphur* and (for children) *All the King's Men*. His jazz works include *Jazz Calendar* and *Jazz Pastoral* and his many film scores include *Billy Liar*, *Equus*, and *Murder on the Orient Express*.

Vladimir Dukelsky (1903–69) was born in Russia and studied under Glière. He settled in the USA in 1922. He wrote symphonies and an operetta, and Diaghilev commissioned a ballet from him. He is better known today as Vernon Duke, the name he used when writing popular songs. These included 'April in Paris' and the Bunny Berigan hit, 'I Can't Get Started'.

NOTATION

What is the staff (or stave)? And what are leger lines?

To the right, the same note is shown, but at different pitches. What is the note?

In the diagram for Question 12, the two symbols on the left are known as clefs. What do they indicate?

Can you name each of the clefs and say how its shape and position is significant?

What, respectively, are the signs ♭ and ♯ called?

When, as on the right, such signs follow the clef, this gives the key signature. What does this mean?

What do the numbers **2** above **4**, and the letter **C**, on the right, indicate? And, do you know how this **C** came to be used in the notation?

TV ADS

Featured in the James Bond film *The Spy Who Loved Me*, Carly Simon's version of 'Nobody Does It Better' was a Top Ten record in 1977. B&Q later used it for a TV commercial. Who wrote the song?

The *Steptoe and Son* theme, *Old Ned*, being about a horse (hoarse!) was used, appropriately, to advertise Zubes throat lozenges. Who wrote the theme?

20

The hit song 'Time After Time' was used for a TV commercial by Silvikrin Hair Shampoo. Who was the singer?

21

The 1972 hit song by Roberta Flack was used to promote Oil of Ulay in a TV commercial. What was its title and who wrote it?

22

A Russell-Scott song was a hit for the Hollies in 1969. Featured in a Miller-Lite commercial, it again became a big hit more than 20 years later. Can you name the song?

In 1972, one of the big sellers was the New Seekers' 'I'd Like to Teach the World to Sing'. Where did it originate?

24

'Let's Twist Again' was a huge hit for Chubby Checker in 1961, 1962 and 1975. Intercity used it for a TV commercial. Who wrote the number?

A TV commercial for Lurpak Danish Butter featured Sting singing 'Spread a Little Happiness', a number he had revived in the 1982 film *Brimstone and Treacle*. We say 'revived' because the song was written in 1929, for the first big stage success of the composer and writer, **Vivian Ellis**. Since then he has had countless successes with such as *The Fleet's Lit Up*, *Water Gipsies* and *Bless the Bride*. He was still composing in 1996 when he died at the age of 91.

OPERA

25

It is no great secret that the works of William Shakespeare have been a great inspiration to operatic composers. But, how many operas do you think have been based on his plays? ...42? ...74? ...More?

26

In Handel's *Serses*, the eponymous leading character (usually sung by a mezzo-soprano) extols the beauty of a tree – in which aria?

27

Munich, 1909, saw the first production of Ermanno Wolf-Ferrari's one-act opera *Il Segretto di Susanna*. What was Susanna's secret?

28

Which of these years is generally regarded as being that of the start of Opera ...1597? ...1600? ...1643?

29

Alexander Sergeievich Dargomizhsky died in 1869 with the greater part of an opera incomplete. *The Stone Guest* was based on a poem by Pushkin about Don Juan and is, basically, the same story as that of Mozart's *Don Giovanni*. The opera was first performed in 1872. Who completed it?

30

The great German operatic composer, Carl Maria von Weber, wrote his last work, *Oberon*, to English words. How did that come about?

31

What was the family connection between Weber and Wolfgang Amadeus Mozart?

32

'Nessun Dorma' gained the No 2 chart spot for Luciano Pavarotti when it was chosen as the Italia 90 theme. The aria is from the opera *Turandot*, by which composer?

When translated to 'None Shall Sleep', the aria seems a strange choice for the promotion of football! Why was it, in fact, particularly appropriate?

In the opera, it is announced that 'none shall sleep' until Turandot has discovered the name of a mysterious prince. He will die if she finds out his name but she will marry him if she doesn't. The prince's name is Calaf, but the opera ends with Turandot announcing that his name is … what?

The composer died before completing the last act. Who completed the opera?

At the 1926 première, at La Scala, Milan, the conductor put down his baton and, turning to the audience said, 'At this point, the Maestro laid down his pen.' A tearful Italian audience departed quietly. Who was this conductor?

A railway station just outside Rome was named after the heroine of a 1760 opera by Niccolo Piccini, *La Buona Figliuola* (*The Good Daughter*). What was her name?

The Budapest railway station, Szép Ilona, was named after which operetta by Jacques Offenbach?

The London Underground station, Swiss Cottage, was named after which opera by Adolphe Adam?

The tragic opera *Der Kaiser von Atlantis* (*The Emperor of Atlantis*) was written in 1944 by Viktor Ullman and Peter Kien. It was rehearsed, but not premièred until 1975. What real-life tragedy happened after its 1944 rehearsal?

BALLET

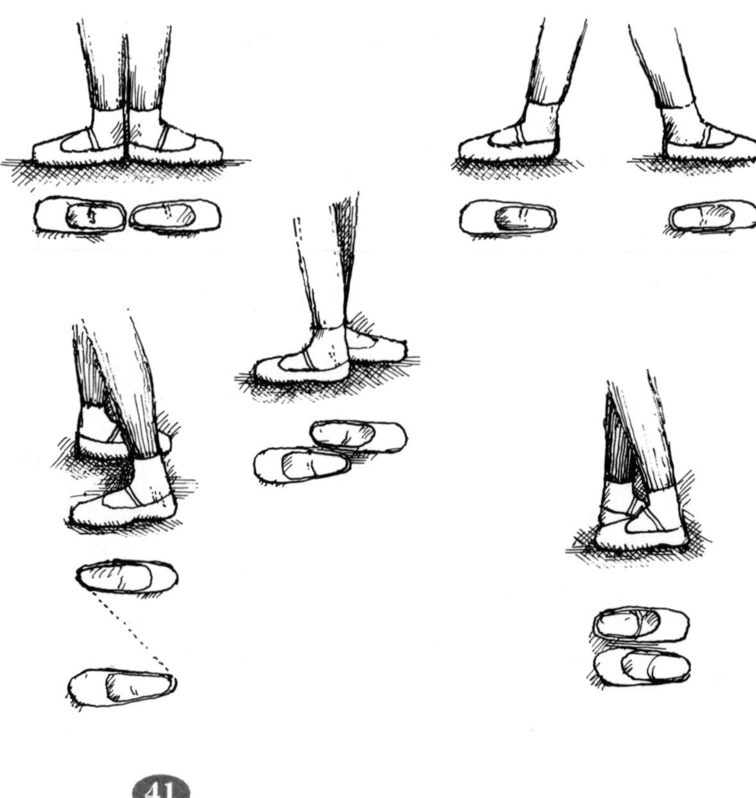

The Five Positions, above, show the basic positions of the feet, from which all movements in strict classical ballet start. Who, more than 300 years ago, defined these and where was he at the time?

Which ballet star created a sensation by removing his mask when performing in Paris in 1770?

43

It is said that the first true developer of ballet as we know it today, was Jean-George Noverre (1727–1810). Can you name some of the changes he brought about?

In 1934, George Balanchine founded the American Ballet of New York and choreographed their first ballet, *Serenade*. On which music was it based?

Léonide Massine choreographed ballets to the music of several symphonies. Which symphony was used for *Choreartium* and which for *Rouge et Noire*?

Which well-known ballet includes singing by a 'choir'?

Which ballet score includes 'cowboy music' such as 'The Old Chisholm Trail' and 'Git Along Little Dogies'? And by whom?

Philippe Taglioni's *La Sylphide*, to music by Jean Schneitzhöffer, was, in 1832, the first 'white ballet'. *Les Sylphides*, also a white ballet, was conceived by Michel Fokine more than 70 years later. On whose music was this based and what was Fokine's original title for the ballet?

Marie Taglioni (1804–84) was born in Stockholm of a Swedish mother and Italian father. She became one of the greats of nineteenth-century ballet. Her dress and her hair-style, at first thought revolutionary, soon became standard in Romantic ballets. In 1832, thanks to special slippers and to the choreography of her father, Philippe, she captivated the audience at the Paris Opera production of *La Sylphide* by dancing *'sur les pointes'* (on the tips of her toes), another ballet 'first'. Taglioni had competition (and rivalry) from three superb ballerinas – Fanny Cerrito, Lucile Grahn and Carlotta Grisi.

In 1845, in London and at the express wish of Queen Victoria, they appeared together in a never-to-be-forgotten performance of Jules Perrot's *Pas de Quatre*, with music by Cesare Pugni, the resident ballet composer at Her Majesty's Theatre, London.

Taglioni ended her career in reduced circumstances. She taught deportment in London, and among her pupils was a young princess destined to become Queen Consort – the future Queen Mary.

FAMILIES

Between 1600 and 1900, more than 60 members of the Bach family took up music as a profession. Some were eminent in their time, a few are eminent today. The first really important Bach was Johann Sebastian (1685–1750). He had 20 children. Now, it is usual in music circles to refer to some of his sons by the centres they mostly worked in. For example, his first son, Wilhelm Friedemann (1710–1784) is known as the 'Hallé' Bach. Can you name J S Bach's third, ninth and eleventh sons, who are known as, respectively, the 'Berlin' or 'Hamburg' Bach, the 'Bückeburg' Bach, and the 'English' Bach?

Do you know the name of the father who wrote 'Hark the Herald Angels Sing' and his son, whose first oratorio, *Ruth*, was written in 1774, when he was eight years old?

Which Czech composer wrote an E minor symphony, subtitled *From the New World*? And who was his son-in-law, whose C minor symphony is subtitled *Asrael*?

Can you name these prolific composers? The father was born in Sicily in 1660, married in 1678, and gained the patronage of Queen Christina of Sweden with his first opera. He went on to write over a hundred more during his lifetime. His son (the sixth of ten children) was born in Naples in 1685 and, in 1709, became official composer to the Queen of Poland. He was a great friend of Handel and during his lifetime he wrote over 600 harpsichord sonatas.

Which singer first took the role of Abigaille in *Nabucco* in 1842? And who was her husband-to-be, who wrote the opera?

PASTICCIO

Pasticcio is the Italian word for a pie. In music, it usually means a 'medley', and that is how we shall use it in this book – for a medley of questions. The French word *pastiche* comes from the same root. But what, musically, does 'pastiche' mean?

In the earliest years of the twentieth century, a boy baby was born in Tacoma, Washington State, USA. He was to become perhaps the most popular (and successful) singer of popular songs there has ever been. He was given the baptismal names, Harry Lillis. Who was he?

56

The year 1876 was the centenary of American independence. Which composer was commissioned to write a march for the celebrations (reportedly earning him $5,000)?

Composer and pianist, he was born in 'the year of the great comet' (1811) and it has been said that the phenomenon presaged a career of equal brilliance. Who was he?

In which Gilbert and Sullivan operetta do peers of the realm (including the Lord Chancellor) marry fairies?

In 1880, after *The Pirates of Penzance* and before *Patience*, Sullivan was invited to write a religious cantata for the Leeds Festival. He and Gilbert were not 'getting on', but Sullivan asked him to write a verse-version based on a poem by Henry Hart Milman about the martyrdom of St Margaret of Antioch. The resulting *The Martyr of Antioch* was dedicated to the Prince of Wales and was very well received. It was to be **Gilbert and Sullivan's** only joint serious work.

THEMES

59

Originally an old Irish air known firstly as *Castle Hyde*, then *The Groves of Blarney*, Thomas Moore adapted it and wrote new words. Here are a few bars. How do we know the song, and in which opera is it featured?

60

In the 1780s, a young Irishman, Leonard McNally, wrote a poem extolling the virtues of the lady he was courting. It was set to music by James Hook and was first performed in the Vauxhall Gardens, London, in 1789. Do you recognise the song?

61

It has been said that, at rehearsals of a work by César Franck, orchestras have been known to sing along to a certain theme with the words 'Get your hair cut! Get your hair cut!' This is the theme. What is the work?

62

Here is a short section from a Mendelssohn overture, composed in 1833. Some years later, Wagner used the same theme in the Rhine daughters' motif of *Das Rheingold*. What did Mendelssohn call his overture?

Note: The four extracts above have been simplified.

NICKNAMES

63

Many of Haydn's symphonies bear nicknames. No 101 in D is known as 'The Clock'. Why?

64

Giuseppe Tartini was one of the most brilliant of eighteenth-century violinists. His most famous sonata is known as 'The Devil's Trill'. How did it come by that name?

65

What was Steveland Morris's nickname in the early 1960s?

66

In 1977, that same young man had, among many hits, 'Sir Duke', a tribute to four Big Band leaders. Which four? And, which of the four was nicknamed 'Satchelmouth'?

67

Schubert's Quintet in A for piano and strings is known as 'The Trout Quintet'. Why?

68

Haydn's Symphony No 45 is often known as 'The Farewell' (or 'Abschieds-symphonie'). How did this come about?

69

And, why does 'The Toy Symphony' , which often appears at the end of a list of Haydn symphonies, have no number allocated to it?

70

Which Italian composer, a contemporary of Haydn, was known, unkindly, as 'Haydn's wife'?

ONE-LINERS

71 Can you name Gilbert and Sullivan's first collaboration?
72 Where, and when, was Handel's *Messiah* first performed?
73 Who was 'The Girl with the Enamel Eyes'?
74 Wagner's second wife was called Cosima. Who was her father?
75 Which singer had hits with 'I Will Survive' in 1979 and 1993?
76 *Adagio; arpeggio; allegro*. Which is the odd one out?
77 Who is the patron saint of music?
78 Who was Napoleon Bonaparte's favourite composer of opera?
79 What is meant by the expression *a cappella*?
80 … And by *alla zingarese*?
81 Which four female vocalists had a 1977 hit with 'OK'?
82 Which Lloyd Webber song was a 1976/78 hit for one of them?
83 … From which musical? And who wrote the lyrics?
84 Who is known as 'The Father of the String Quartet'?
85 With which instrument do you associate the name Boehm?
86 Who made 'One-o'clock Jump' a hit?
87 How many symphonies did Sibelius complete?
88 What is a passing note?
89 What (in about 1840) did Adolph Sax invent?
90 Whose fourth symphony is known as 'The Inextinguishable'?
91 Who founded Motown Records?
92 Who brought the YMCA into the charts in 1978?
93 Where is 'The Dawning of the Age of Aquarius' celebrated?
94 Who was Cavaradossi?
95 Which 1941 film featured *The Warsaw Concerto*?
96 … And who was the composer?
97 Who wrote the music for the ballet *Giselle*?
98 Whose first three releases, in 1963, all topped the charts?
99 What are 'Mother Goose Songs'?
100 Who urged us to 'Stop the Cavalry' in his 1980 'protest' hit?

SAD ENDS

A macabre tale of a 'Skull for Scandal'

On 31 May 1809, the great **Joseph Haydn** died. He was buried in the church of Hundsturm, outside the boundary of Eisenstadt, on 15 June.

In November 1820, Prince Esterhazy decreed that the remains be exhumed and reburied in Eisenstadt but, when the coffin was opened, it was seen that the great man's head was missing. It transpired that the head had been stolen two days after the funeral.

A great fuss resulted and, eventually, the Prince received (anonymously) a skull. This was then interred with the rest of Haydn.

But it wasn't the skull of the composer! Many years later the real skull was given to the *Gesellschaft der Musikfreunde* (the Society of Music-lovers) in Vienna, and there it remained until 1954. Only then, nearly 150 years late, were Haydn's head and body reunited.

The end of Lully

On January 18, 1687, a Te Deum was performed at the Palace of Versailles for the recovery of Louis XIV from a serious illness. The proceedings were 'conducted' (in the manner of the period) by **Jean-Baptiste Lully**, who beat time on the floor with a long stick, rather in the way of a modern-day drum major.

Part-way through, Lully inadvertently struck himself on the foot. The injury developed an abscess.

Following complications (and somewhat incompetent medical treatment), Lully died on March 22. The Italian-born master of French ballet and opera was only 54 years old.

Another 1687 end

Michael Wise was a talented organist and composer. He once offended Charles II by interrupting a church service attended by the king, by playing an organ voluntary – because he thought the sermon was too long.

Later, under James II, he was appointed Master of the Choristers at St Paul's Cathedral.

One evening, at home in Salisbury, he quarrelled with his wife and, rushing from the house, he struck down a night-watchman who was in his path. The watchman rose and, fracturing the organist's skull with a bill-hook, killed him. Wise was 39 years of age.

Meanwhile, in Italy ...

... there was **Alessandro Stradella**, a singer, violinist and composer – said to have influenced Handel, Purcell and Scarlatti. Tradition has it that he eloped with a Venetian nobleman's lady and that assassins were sent after him. They found him directing his new oratorio, *St John the Baptist*, and were, supposedly, so moved by the music that they spared him. A subsequent assassination attempt, in 1682, was successful. Stradella was 39 years old.

The story has led to various published literary works and at least two operas, one of them being by Friedrich von Flotow.

... And an end by fungi ...

Johann Schobert was a talented harpsichordist and a popular composer of chamber music. In 1767, in Paris, he and his entire household died after a meal of mushrooms – which proved to be toadstools. Schobert was 47 years old.

An unsolved end

Jean Marie Leclair was a ballet master, then a successful violinist, and finally a composer of considerable importance.

In 1764, at the age of 67, he was murdered in Paris – virtually on his own doorstep. No one has ever discovered why, or by whom.

A victim of war

Albéric Magnard was born in Paris but received much of his education in Ramsgate. He studied music under Vincent D'Indy (and so was a once-removed disciple of César Franck). His first opera, *Yolande*, was produced in 1892.

He was a wealthy man, living on his own estate in France, when World War One broke out. He tried to enlist in the army but, since he was approaching his fiftieth birthday, he was turned down.

As the invaders advanced, he sent the womenfolk away from his house at Baron, Oise, and waited with his stepson. The house was surrounded and Magnard's stepson was captured. The composer opened fire, killing one German soldier and wounding another.

Eventually, Magnard was, himself, shot. His house and its contents (including many manuscripts) were burned. As a further reprisal, the mayor of the nearby town of Senlis was executed and the town razed.

But, some of Magnard's music survives. Maybe it will never appeal to more than a small discerning public. Who knows! It's well worth the effort of seeking out, though.

OPERA HOSPITALITY

Below, is a list of ten operas. The list of the composers of these operas and the list of the dates of their first performance are mixed up. Can you put them in order? To start you off: *La Bohème* was composed by Giacomo Puccini and was first performed in 1896.

Now, each of the operas features an inn, a café or a tavern. These are listed opposite with clues to help you locate the correct opera. See how far you can get with a correct list of the place of hospitality, in which opera, by which composer, and date.

Opera	*Composer*	*Date first performed*
Carmen	Giacomo Puccini	1825
The Journey to Reims	Jacques Offenbach	1849
The Girl of the Golden West	Gioacchino Rossini	1868
The Merry Wives of Windsor	Leoš Janáček	1875
The Adventures of Mr Brouček	Giacomo Puccini	1881
Peter Grimes	Otto Nicolai	1896
La Bohème	Benjamin Britten	1910
The Tales of Hoffman	Jacques Offenbach	1920
Elegy for Young Lovers	Hans Werner Henze	1945
Le Périchole	Georges Bizet	1961

The Polka Inn, owned by Minnie who loves Dick Johnson, a bandit.

The Café Momus, in Paris, where Schaunard, Marcello and Colline dine on Christmas Eve, whilst Rudolfo is warming Mimi's tiny hand.

The café of The Three Cousins in Lima, where the Viceroy, incognito, first meets the eponymous heroine.

The Tavern of Lillas Pastia, in Seville, not far from the cigarette factory.

Luther's Tavern in Nuremberg, next to the opera house, where the clientèle forgo the second act of *Don Giovanni* to listen to the tales of a poet's three loves.

The Garter Inn in Windsor.

The Inn of the Golden Fleur de Lys in Burgundy, where the whole company meets up on its way to the coronation of Charles X.

The Boar Inn, in The Borough, an east coast fishing village, where the landlady is known as 'Auntie' and her two 'nieces' are the main attractions.

The Black Eagle, in the Austrian Alps, where Hilda Mack has lived for her forty years of widowhood, knitting.

The Vikárka Inn, in Prague, where the hero goes to the moon in Part I and to the fifteenth century – where he is burnt in a barrel – in Part II.

POP

Can you name three chart entries that had the titles of plays by Shakespeare?

The song 'Misty' was a hit for Johnny Mathis in 1960 and Ray Stevens in 1975. Who wrote it?

In January 1966, 'These Boots Were Made for Walkin'' reached the No 1 spot in the singles charts. Who was the artist?

Just over a year later, 'Somethin' Stupid' held the No 1 position. Who were the singers on this recording?

Can you name the Beatles' first single to credit another and additional player? And, can you name this player?

Who, in 1971, 'drove the fastest milk cart in the West'?

Who produced the Righteous Brothers' big hit single of 1965, 1969 and 1977, 'You've Lost that Lovin' Feelin''? …

… which held the No 1 position on the charts for some ten weeks. At the same time, a recording of the same number by an English vocalist held the No 2 spot. Can you name the vocalist?

Issued at about the same time (that is, late 1964), the Righteous Brothers' album, *You've Lost that Lovin' Feelin'*, featured 10 tracks other than the title number. How many of these can you list?

Who wrote 'Annie's Song', which gave John Denver a No 1 hit single in 1974? …

… and which Irish instrumentalist had a hit with this number in 1978?

In the 1976 Eurovision Song Contest, the UK won (for the third time). The winning group was the Brotherhood of Man. What was the song?

13

Can you name the UK winning songs and performers in 1967 and 1969? What was unusual about the result in 1969?

14

In 1992, 'Deeply Dippy' reached the top, performed by a group calling itself after a hit of 1962. What was the group's name? …

15

… and who had the hit with that 1962 recording?

16

Which singer had a No 1 hit in 1976 with 'When a Child is Born' (also known as 'Soleado')?

17

Which legendary skiffler had Top Ten singles with such as: 'Rock Island Line'; 'Lost John'; 'Cumberland Gap'; 'Tom Dooley'; 'Battle of New Orleans'; 'I Wanna Go Home'? … We could go on and on with his hits from the late 50s and early 60s!

HOME-GROWN

In one of his choral works, Sir Edward Elgar quotes from several of his own compositions including both of his symphonies, his violin concerto, *The Dream of Gerontius* and the *Enigma Variations*. First performed at the Birmingham Festival of 1912, what is the work?

On 30 March 1907, a new comic opera based on Henry Fielding's novel *Tom Jones* was first heard in Manchester. Who wrote the music?

Which composer of music for films and television wrote *Cavatina*, played by the guitarist John Williams as the main theme music for the film *The Deerhunter*?

Who wrote the *Spitfire Prelude and Fugue* as part of the score for the film *The First of the Few*?

Two oratorio-length works of the late Victorian period enjoyed considerable vogue for many years. They were *The Daughter of Jairus* (1878) and *The Crucifixion* (1887). Who was the composer?

The music for the ballet *Love in Bath* was arranged by Sir Thomas Beecham. Whose music did he use?

24

For the 1993 Rugby Union 'World Cup' series, TV presentation was heralded by a much-loved tune to which new words had been written by Charles Skarbek. Dame Kiri Te Kanawa sang this as 'The World in Unison'. The English team chose the tune as its own anthem. But who wrote the tune?

In 1851, the Australian conductor (Sir) Charles Mackerras adapted and arranged some music for the Sadler's Wells Ballet as *Pineapple Poll.* Who wrote the music?

In 1917, a composer was inspired to write a tone-poem by a visit to Tintagel in Cornwall. Who was he?

Which twentieth-century composer wrote an opera (first produced in London in 1972) based on the life of a sixteenth-century English composer? And, can you name the opera?

In July 1993, the Wigmore Hall, London, saw the first performance of a work entitled *The Last Sleep of the Virgin (In Memory of Margot Fonteyn)*. Some 20 years earlier, the composer wrote *Ultimos Ritos*, which required the orchestra to sit in the shape of a cross. Can you name him?

During World War One, Elgar set some verses by Kipling to music: '... for lifeboatmen and those manning minesweepers'. The work calls for four baritone voices. What was it called?

Not to be confused with the popular Lloyd Webber/Stilgoe musical on roller skates, Elgar's ***The Starlight Express*** was first produced in 1915. It was written as incidental music to an adaptation of Algernon Blackwood's *A Prisoner in Fairyland.*

Charles Mott (who had an incredibly beautiful voice) sang in the production and recorded some of the songs. He also sang in the Elgar work of question 29, above. Soon after, Mott was called up and sent to France, where, tragically, he was killed.

Over the years, little has been heard of *The Starlight Express*. However, in the early 1990s, some of the songs were recorded, and delightful they proved to be.

The beautiful baritone voice, this time, belonged to Bryn Terfel. He had been awarded the Lieder prize at the 1989 Cardiff Singer of the World Contest. At the last night of the 1994 Proms – after singing the solo part in William Walton's oratorio *Belshazzar's Feast* – Terfel donned Welsh rugby kit for 'Rule Britannia!', one verse of which he sang in Welsh.

NOTATION

30

What is the difference between a minim, a crochet, and a quaver? And why is a minim so called?

31

What is a chromatic scale?

32

Assuming the key is C major, what does the notation below show?

33

Here are six examples of key signatures for different major keys. Can you name these keys?

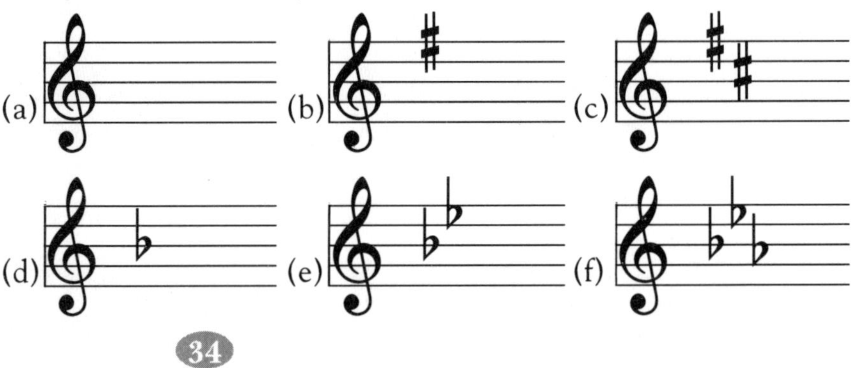

34

For each of the above key signatures, can you list which notes are sharpened and which flattened?

35

Now, can you name the relative minor keys for the six key signatures shown above?

INSTRUMENTS

What is a xylophone? And which 1874 work of Saint-Saëns introduced it into Western European orchestras?

What is, or was, an ophicleide, for which Mendelssohn and Berlioz (among others) wrote parts in their orchestral scores?

Drawing (a) shows an ancient string instrument. Can you name it? (Clue: it is generally known by its Welsh name.)

Drawings (b), (c) and (d) show (not to the same scale) three modern instruments. Can you name them and say in which sections of the orchestra they would be found?

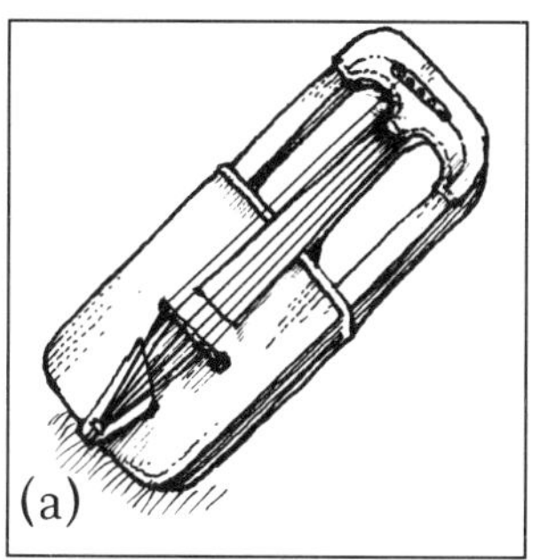
(a)

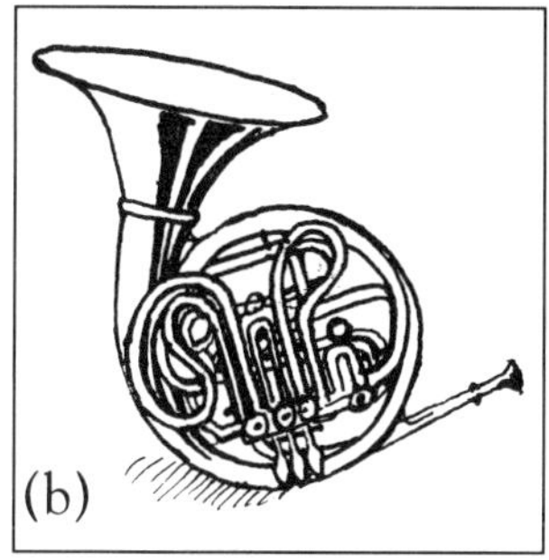
(b)

(c)

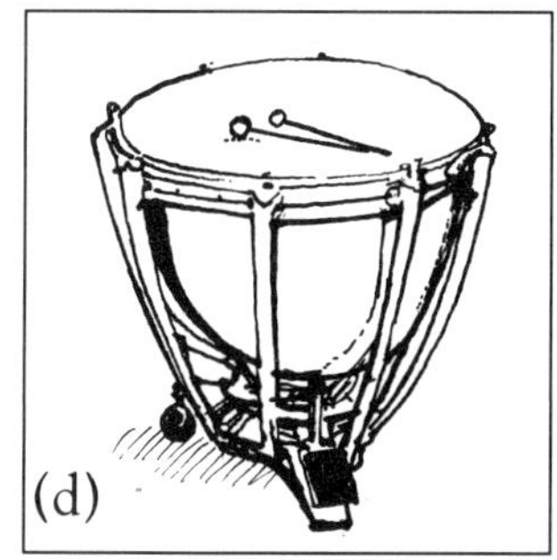
(d)

WHAT HAPPENED ...

In 1828 the French composer, Daniel Auber's opera *La Muette de Portici (The Dumb Girl of Portici)* had its first performance in Paris. It was an early, if not the first, French Grand Opera. With a revolutionary libretto based on a seventeenth-century uprising of Naples against oppression, and having an eponymous heroine who uttered no sound and dived into Vesuvius as the curtain fell, the opera was a huge success. Two years later it was performed in Brussels. What happened then?

At the end of a performance of Haydn's Symphony No 102, in 1794, the audience surged forward, applauding so intensely that a chandelier fell to the ground. Since everyone had moved towards the stage, no one was hurt. What was the outcome?

In 1897, Frederick Delius was commissioned to write incidental music for a political play by Gunnar Heiberg. His treatment of the Norwegian National Anthem (satirical, but correct in the context of the play) caused great resentment when the play, *Folkeraadet*, was first produced in Christiania (now, Oslo). What happened?

In 1806, Ludwig van Beethoven was asked by a talented young violinist named Franz Clement to write a concerto for the violin for him to play in Vienna later that year. As was usual with Beethoven, he didn't finish with work until, literally, the last moment. There wasn't even time for the orchestra to rehearse. What happened at the first performance of Beethoven's Concerto in D major for Violin and Orchestra, Opus 61?

Sir Malcolm Sargent very much loved and revered Elgar's *The Dream of Gerontius* and each time he conducted the work, audiences and critics alike were full of praise. On 11 May 1941, Sir Malcolm conducted *Gerontius* at the Queen's Hall in London. What happened afterwards?

... NEXT?

Enrique Granados, the Spanish pianist and composer, wrote a set of piano pieces, *Goyescas*, inspired by the paintings of Goya, and then created an opera from the piano pieces. The opera was premièred at the Metropolitan Opera House, New York in 1916. Despite his fear of sea travel, Granados made the trip to New York, along with his wife. The opera was well received and the composer was honoured by being invited to play at a presidential reception. But, in doing so, Granados missed his boat home. What was the result?

In October 1993, the Royal Opera House, Covent Garden, staged a not-often-performed opera by Mozart, *Mitridate, Rè di Ponto (Mithradates, King of Pontus)*. Perched on-stage, and making his debut, was a buzzard named Jesse. He listened with interest to a soprano aria. What happened next?

In Toronto, in 1927, a young singer stood in the wings as Duke Ellington and his Orchestra played 'Creole Love Call'. She sang, quietly and wordlessly, along with the orchestra. Her name was Adelaide Hall. What happened then, and what was the 'finale', in London, 45 years later?

Ludwig (known as Louis) Spohr was a Brunswick-born composer and violinist, much esteemed in the music world of the early nineteenth century. In 1820 he arrived in England to introduce his D minor Symphony (he wrote nine, in all). To the astonishment of the orchestra, he scorned the piano from which he was expected to direct the music and ... what happened next?

The story goes that, in early 1958, the singer Connie Francis was attending a last recording session before being sacked by the recording company. Rather dispirited, she found she had a little time left, and tried one last 'take'. What was the result?

NAMES AND ...

50

Who, in about 1925, wrote *Overture to the Flying Dutchman as Sight-read by a Bad Spa Band at the Spring at 7 o'clock in the Morning*?

51

The Lindy Hop, a popular dance of the late 1920s, was named after the achievements of whom?

52

What was the subtitle of the radio cantata *1929* written by Kurt Weill in an early collaboration with Berthold Brecht? And what inspired the work?

53

Heitor Villa-Lobos (1887–1959) was a Brazilian composer. He wrote several works which, generically, he called *Bachianas Brasileiras*. Why did he decide on that name?

54

The *Toccata* of the second of these *Bachianas Brasileiras* is subtitled *The Little Train of Caipira*. How is this realised orchestrally? And, do you know what *toccata* means?

55

The contemporary composer Jan Sandstrom's Concerto for Trombone and Orchestra requires incredible virtuosity in its performance. The work is described as a musical representation of what?

56

In the late 1920s, a young Russian composer produced a then astonishing symphonic poem. This, he said, was in the name of socialist realism, but it did not make him too popular at home. Known as *Iron Foundry* or *The Music of Machines*, the work simulated the noises of a foundry and its machinery, with orchestration calling for such as 'Metal sheets being shaken'. Can you name the composer?

... NOTIONS

One of Paul McCartney's songs was called 'Scrambled Eggs'. Later, he changed the title (and words) and the Beatles' version became a hit single in 1976, six years after the group broke up. What was the title of the hit version?

58

Which work is known as 'The Symphony of a Thousand', and why?

59

Can you name this contemporary composer? He wrote *Shaker Loops*, inspired by the religious sect, the Shakers, and *The Chairman Dances*, which was based on a fictitious scene when President Nixon visited Chairman Mao.

60

Which American composer wrote, in 1915, an orchestral suite, *Adventures in a Perambulator*, and later – influenced by jazz, a ballet, *Skyscrapers* and a pantomime, *Krazy Kat*?

61

Who wrote *Elegy for JFK* and *In Memoriam Dylan Thomas*?

62

Whose new opera, *The Second Mrs Kong*, was premièred in 1994 by Glyndebourne Touring Opera? Its characters included the Idea of King Kong, Vermeer, and Pearl (from Vermeer's painting, *The Girl with a Pearl Earring*).

You too can be a concert pianist! In 1952, **John Cage** wrote a piece in three movements for the piano, entitled *4′ 33″*. For this work, you, the pianist, sit without touching the keyboard for exactly four minutes and thirty-three seconds. You might then try, as a quick encore, another piece by Cage, his *0′ 00″*. The composer does say the work is available to be performed in any way, by anyone!

Slightly more difficult, your concluding piece requires you to have a basic sense of rhythm. It is called *In C*. We are not sure of the composer, but believe him to be Scandinavian. The work has been performed in concert already. All you have to do is play the note C, repeatedly, for 26 minutes.

PASTICCIO

When Schumann heard a particular work for piano and orchestra by a young composer in 1829, he wrote, 'Hats off gentlemen – a genius!' Of whom and what was he writing?

Who, in 1937, wrote the music for a ballet based on a game of chess?

The soundtrack of the Oliver Stone film, *The Doors*, included extracts from *Carmina Burana*, a work by a German composer, produced in 1937. Can you name the composer and give the meaning of *Carmina Burana*?

There are many legends of being able to hear bells from churches sunk, long ago, beneath the waves. Who, in 1910, wrote a piano piece based on such a legend?

What have these works in common? *The Firebird* ballet, the opera *The Rake's Progress* and *Ebony Concerto* for clarinet and swing band.

This Austrian composer (1870–1954) wrote operettas, including *The Chocolate Soldier* and *A Waltz Dream*, and music for the film *La Ronde*. He is often confused with members of a musical family with a similar name. Who was he?

In his latter years, Frederick Delius was both blind and paralysed. Under the most incredible circumstances, a young Yorkshire-born musician helped Delius to complete seven works. Who was he?

During World War One, an eminent English composer served as a special constable in Hampstead. Can you name him?

ONE-LINERS

71 What is a pavanne (or pavan)?
72 Who founded the Royal Choral Society?
73 Ray Charles and Cleo Laine recorded what together in 1976?
74 In which country did the rumba originate?
75 Which singer recorded the first 'million-seller'?
76 … And what did he sing so successfully?
77 What are f-holes?
78 Which instrument did Tommy Dorsey play?
79 Who wrote two poems about his favourite dog, Music?
80 What is the origin of the name Sadler's Wells?
81 What happened to Sadler's Wells Royal Ballet in October 1990?
82 Whose Opus 8 was *The Champagne Galop*?
83 Whose Opus 211 was *The Champagne Polka*?
84 Who, in the 1730s, wrote *The Coffee Cantata*?
85 Who wrote the music for the film *Picnic at Hanging Rock*?
86 What is a sympathetic tone?
87 Which great pianist became Prime Minister of his native land?
88 Which British ex-Prime Minister is an organist and conductor?
89 What was Rossini's last work for the stage?
90 After this, to what did he largely devote his life?
91 What was the first opera specifically written for television?
92 Which rock band's album, *Mass in F minor*, had Latin 'vocals'?
93 Who wrote the song 'Keep the Home Fires Burning'?
94 Which 'siffleur' had a hit with 'I Was Kaiser Bill's Batman'?
95 Who, in the 1950s, was known as 'The King of Skiffle'?
96 Who wrote the operetta *Die Fledermaus* (*The Bat*)?
97 Which of Mozart's symphonies is known as 'The Jupiter'?
98 What is a plectrum?
99 Which Country singer is known as 'The Man in Black'?
100 … And in 1969 had a hit with 'A Boy Named ___' – what?

O MR PORTA!

The Entry of the Queen of Sheba, by Handel, was one of Sir Thomas Beecham's favourite 'lollipops' (encores). Indeed, it may well have been Sir Thomas who gave the above name to the piece. Today, it is often played as a bride progresses down the aisle (although the rhythm can present the occasional problem).

As written, it was the orchestral introduction to the third part of Handel's oratorio *Solomon* and was entitled, simply, *Sinfonia*. That was in 1749. The truth is, however, that the piece was not Handel's at all. It started life as an aria in the opera *Il Numitore*, by the Venetian-born composer, Giovanni Porta, which was first performed at the opening of the King's Theatre, in the Haymarket, London, in 1720.

Handel had left the Duke of Chandos in 1719 and, with others, set up the Royal Academy of Music, a company dedicated to bringing Italian opera to London, centring around the King's Theatre. At the order of the King (a subscriber to the company), Handel travelled Europe to gather up the best Italian composers and singers.

After the opening with Porta's opera, Handel produced one of his own, *Radamisto*. Then, many years, compositions and companies later, he wrote *Solomon*, with its *Sinfonia*.

As for Porta – he worked in London for some years before becoming Court Kapellmeister in Munich, where he died in 1755. One writer has suggested he wrote about 32 operas 'as far as can be ascertained'.

Poor Porta! It is sad that the sole surviving piece of his music is attributed to the man who 'lifted' it.

It must be said that Handel was one of the greatest musical plagiarists, ever. But, it should be added that he did 'recycle' as much of his own music as that of others.

MISTAKEN IDENTITY

Once upon a time (well, in the late eighteenth, early nineteenth centuries), there lived a string-bass player named Franz Anton Schubert. He did compose a little music, but would have passed into oblivion but for one incident.

On 18 April 1817, Franz Anton wrote a letter to the music publishers, Breitkopf and Härtel of Leipzig:

> '... I received ... a letter ... from you in which you enclosed the manuscript of Goethe's "Erlkönig" alleged to be set by me ... I beg to state that this ... was never composed by me.
>
> 'I shall retain the same in my possession in order to learn, if possible, who sent that sort of trash (and who) has thus misused my name ...'

Franz Anton thus described as 'trash' one of the early flowerings of a (then) teenage genius. And, that same setting of Goethe's *Erl-king* is still, after close on 200 years, one of the most performed and best received of the extensive lieder output of the great ... Franz Peter Schubert.

MUSICAL ACROSTIC

Write your answers to the clues, opposite, in the Answers Grid, below. Now transfer the letters that lie in the squares coded A1 to F4 to their appropriate positions in the Quotation Grid, opposite, to spell out some words of wisdom. The author's name can be found by reading down the initial letters in the Answers Grid.

Answers Grid

1	P	E	R	D7 C	U	A3 S	D10 S	B5 I	D5 O	C8 N	
2	B3	F4		F2		B11	E6				
3	C7				D9	C11					
4	B8				A8						
5			A1	F1	C5	E3	B10		B9	C10	F3
6	A7							D4	A2		
7	E10	E7			E4				B2		C1
8			B4	A4			D2		D1		
9		C3	E11		C9	D8					
10	B1			C4		E1					
11			C2			B6		A5			
12		E5		A10	E9			E8			
13		D6				B7					

Clues

1 Family of instruments, tuned or untuned, played by being struck.

2 Composer of *The Warsaw Concerto*.

3 Four-stringed guitar played by George Formby.

4 Charpentier's opera about a poor Parisian dressmaker.

5 Lyricist of such as *Carousel* and *The King and I*.

6 The song 'I'm Always Chasing Rainbows' was based on Chopin's Fantasie- _____ in C sharp minor.

7 A type of juke box.

8 Italian composer of more than 70 operas, including *Lucia di Lammermoor* and *Don Pasquale*.

9 Beethoven's penultimate symphony.

10 French composer of the massive *Turangalila Symphony* which uses Indian themes and rhythms.

11 Having equal tones; a simple system of notation.

12 Russian composer of the ballet *The Sleeping Beauty*.

13 An obsolete stringed instrument; colloquially, a barrel organ.

Quotation Grid

TOM DULA

In the Blue Ridge Mountains of North Carolina (across the border from the Trail of the Lonesome Pine), there stands a roadside plaque erected by the United States National Park Service. It bears these words:

> '... Hang down your head ...'

In 1868, in neighbouring Wilkes County NC, the newspaper printed the following:

> 'Thomas C Dula suffered the extreme penalty of the law by hanging convicted of murder ...'

During his last days in jail, tradition says he composed his tragic and still popular song in which he confessed to stabbing his sweetheart. But the song did not reveal the other woman who may have done the deed.

> 'Poor boy, you're bound to die.'

WHICH JOHN WILLIAMS?

Two musicians, both named John Williams, are often confused, one for the other. So, which is which?

The 'American John Williams' was born in New York, in 1932. As a boy he played piano, trombone, trumpet and clarinet, before studying piano and composition at the Juilliard School.

In the 1960s, he started composing theme music for films, gaining his first Oscar nomination for *The Valley of the Dolls*. Since then he has gone on from success to success. You've probably thrilled to his music for Steven Spielberg's *Jaws*, *Close Encounters of the Third Kind* and *ET*.

From 1980 to 1993, he was conductor of the Boston Pops, often performing his film themes. He has also composed two symphonies and two concertos.

The 'Australian John Williams' was born in Melbourne, in 1941, moving to England when he was 11 years old. His father taught him guitar. A colleague of the authors recalled painfully struggling with chords after weeks of lessons, when in came the teacher's son – a very young John. He picked up the guitar and played through a difficult piece with perfection.

John went on to study, firstly with Segovia, then in Siena and London. His debut as a guitarist at the Wigmore Hall, whilst still in his teens, led to concerts all over the world. Performances in duo with the renowned Julian Bream were particularly acclaimed.

Branching out into rock music in the late 1970s, John co-founded the highly successful band, Sky.

He has performed on several film soundtracks, notably *The Deerhunter* and *Stevie* (but **not** *Star Wars* or *Schindler's List*; the music for those came from the American John Williams!).

MUSICALS

In 1946, Irving Berlin completed what is possibly his best score for a stage musical, *Annie Get Your Gun*. But who was originally commissioned to write the music?

Who wrote the lyrics for *Annie Get Your Gun*?

In a 1951 musical about the Californian Gold Rush, the heroine has two husbands. One sings 'I Talk to the Trees' and the other sings 'Wand'rin' Star'. Can you name the musical and say who wrote the lyrics and who the music?

Which English composer and lyricist wrote the scores for *Fings Ain't Wot They Used T'Be* in 1959 and *Oliver* in 1960, following his success with the lyrics of *Lock Up Your Daughters*?

Who wrote the music for *Lock Up Your Daughters*, and where was it launched in London?

In June/July 1991, Jason Donovan reached the top of the charts with 'Any Dream Will Do'. From which musical did the song come, and who wrote it?

Between 1943 and 1945, Oscar Hammerstein II wrote the lyrics for three hugely successful musicals. These were *Carmen Jones*, *Oklahoma!*, and *Carousel*. Who wrote the music?

'Night and Day', in 1932; 'Ev'ry Time We Say Goodbye' in 1944; 'So in Love' in 1948; 'I Love Paris' in 1953. Just four of the many 'standards' to come from this composer and lyricist. Can you name him? And, can you name the shows from which the songs came?

'Manhattan', from *Garrick Gaieties*, was their first popular success in 1925. *Pal Joey*, with show-stoppers such as 'I Could Write a Book' and 'Bewitched, Bothered and Bewildered', was, in 1940, their last real success. Can you name this composer and lyricist team?

'How are Things in Glocca Morra?' and' Old Devil Moon' were songs from the 1947 musical play, *Finian's Rainbow*. The composer and lyricist had worked together in 1940 on *Hold on to Your Hats*. Who were they?

Can you name this musical play? During World War One it had its debut at His Majesty's Theatre and went on to break all records, running for 2,238 performances. It was written by (and starred) the Australian-born playwright and theatrical manager, Oscar Asche, with music by Frederick Norton.

At about the same time, H(arold) Fraser-Simson, whilst serving with the French Red Cross, was asked to write the music for a new show, with the star of Daly's Theatre, Josie Collins, in mind. Harry Graham was to write the lyrics and Oscar Asche would direct. It became London's second longest-running musical and one song in particular, 'Love Will Find a Way', was a hit. What was the musical called?

H. Fraser-Simson (1872–1944) ...wrote many other musicals, numerous songs, and ballet scores. In 1924, there began a fascinating collaboration between him and the author AA Milne, to set to music the *When We Were Very Young* stories and poems. Perhaps best remembered now are 'Vespers' ('Little Boy Kneels ...') and 'They're Changing Guard at Buckingham Palace'. And there was, of course, the Muppets' 1977 hit record of a delightful version of 'Halfway Down the Stairs'.

ON SCORE

13

On a musical score you see the instruction 'Da Capo' (or sometimes 'D.C.'). What should you do?

14

Elsewhere in the score you find the word 'Fine'. What do you do then?

15

A composer or arranger may mark a passage of music *p* (or *piano*) or *pp* (or *pianissimo*), even, occasionally, *ppppp*. What do these different directions mean to the player?

16

Rallentando is an instruction for the performer to do what?

17

Suppose you are in the string section of an orchestra. On the score you see the instruction '*col legno*'. What are you expected to do?

18

Minore
Marcato
Maestoso

Two of the above terms are indications of the composer's wishes or intentions for the piece of music. The third term is more of a warning to the player. Can you sort out the terms and say what they mean?

19

'Animato' is written at the head of a score. What does it mean?

INSTRUMENTS

Name the three string instruments shown above.

What is a celesta? In which work was the instrument first used in an orchestra?

What type of musical instrument was found in Tutankhamun's tomb?

What is the difference between a kit and a pochette?

When a string of one of the instruments illustrated above is tightened, what happens to the pitch of a note played on it?

25

Hautboy was the English corruption of the French *haut-bois* and, in Handel's time, it became spelt 'hoboy'. All of these names refer to the same musical instrument. Which instrument? And, in which section of the orchestra will it be found?

FROM RUSSIA

The composer often referred to as 'The Father of Russian Opera', actually completed only two such works: *A Life for the Tsar* (sometimes known as *Ivan Susanin*) in 1836 and *Russlan and Ludmilla* in 1842. Who was he?

There were considerable problems with the libretto of *Russlan and Ludmilla*. Do you know what caused these?

Earlier we mentioned that Rimsky-Korsakov and Cui were members of the group of 'The Five'. Can you name the other three?

'The Five' were none of them professional musicians. Can you give the profession of any of them?

He was born in Russia in 1899 and studied under Glazounov. As a piano virtuoso he travelled widely but, after settling in the USA, he made his name with the composition of film scores, of which he wrote well over a hundred. He gained Academy Awards for *High Noon*, *The High and the Mighty* and *The Old Man and the Sea*. Who was he?

He was a pupil of Rimsky-Korsakov. After the Revolution, he became a 'People's Artist of the Republic'. He wrote six operas and pieces such as *Hymn to Labour* and *Song to Stalin*. However, today he is remembered for one early work, *Caucasian Sketches*, and his tongue-twisting name – which is a challenge to radio announcers! Who was he?

One of the most popular piano concertos of this century was dedicated to a doctor (who specialised in psychiatry and treatment by hypnotism). Which work, by whom?

33

Whose Symphony No 7, composed in 1941 during the siege of the city, is known as 'The Leningrad'? And of which tune from an operetta does the march theme invariably remind listeners to the symphony?

Which composer died, in circumstances as yet unresolved, after drinking unboiled water in St Petersburg during a cholera epidemic?

... And by what name is his sixth and last symphony – thought to presage his death – known to us? Why is this name somewhat misleading as to the composer's feelings?

Which prolific composer wrote symphonies, concertos and operas, *Seven Merry Songs* based on English nursery rhymes, and an orchestral suite, *The Comedians*?

Alexander Scriabin (1872–1915) was a talented pianist and composer. He devised new harmonies based on a 'mystic chord' of fourths. He became preoccupied with mysticism, in fact, attempting to 'fuse' all the arts and the senses, leading to some ideal state of existence.

His symphony *Prometheus* has a part for a keyboard of light which he devised to play changing colours on a screen during a performance.

In his last months he planned a great *Mysterium* of music, dance, drama, perfume, colour, etc. to express his philosophy through 2,000 performers.

He died, suddenly, of septicaemia which developed from a tumour of the lip. He had just returned to Moscow after giving recitals in England and had hardly begun to write his great work.

HYMNS ...

A metrical psalm is one rewritten to be singable to an ordinary hymn tune. Bearing that in mind, the hymn that begins 'All people that on earth do dwell,' is often sung to a tune known as 'The Old Hundredth' (the first line is shown). Why is it known by that name?

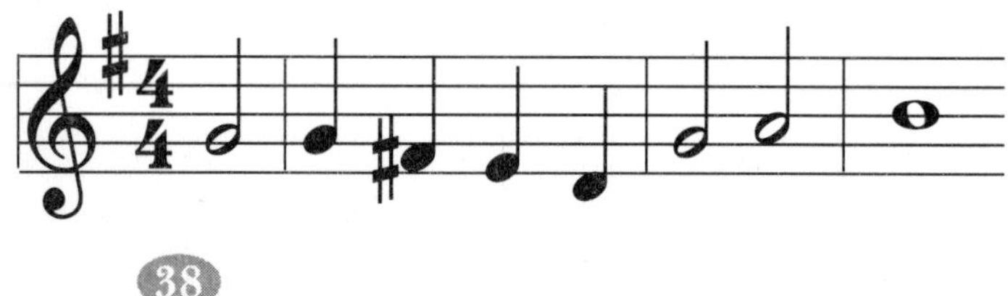

38

In 1708, when William Croft was organist at Westminster Abbey, a hymn tune by him, now known as 'St Anne' was published. Here is the opening. What are the words of the first line?

39

Probably the most popular of our time, it is 'Trad' and in few hymnals. It's been in the charts on several occasions, was the inspiration of the extra-terrestrial pod people in the film *Invasion of the Bodysnatchers*, is a sacred theme of some North American Indians and ... well, here's the opening: can you name the hymn?

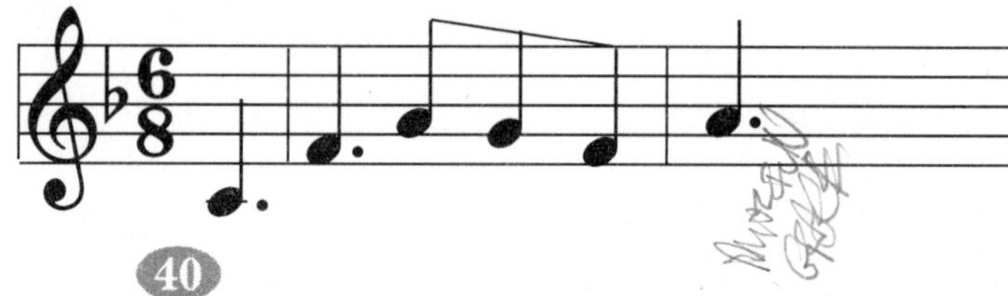

40

The hymn tune 'St Gertrude' is often sung with great fervour as 'Onward Christian Soldiers' or 'Forward! Be Our Watchword'. Who wrote the tune?

Note: The extracts above and opposite have been simplified.

… AND CAROLS

The Christmas carol 'We Three Kings of Orient Are' is often regarded as being traditional. This is not so. Can you say in which country it originated as an important 'first'?

A very beautiful carol, 'O Holy Night', was sung by Luciano Pavarotti in Montreal, and by Dionne Warwick in Vienna, at Christmas concerts in the early 1990s. Do you know who wrote the carol?

This hymn tune, from *Cheetham's Psalmody*, has been used for many years for the carol, 'While Shepherds Watched'. Can you name the tune? (And, should it seem otherwise familiar to you, the note below may explain.)

'It was in Coronation year,' the man said. He was possibly the last surviving member of a group of choristers who had attended a particular carol concert rehearsal (we worked out) in 1911. On a cold December evening, the group was trudging back home to Baildon, Yorkshire.

To amuse themselves, they made up a song as they trudged. It was all about the dire consequences of going out on Baildon Moor without a hat, and they sang it to the tune of the carol they had just rehearsed – 'While Shepherds Watched'.

Their song was to become the so-called 'Yorkshire Anthem', **'On Ilkla Moor Baht 'At',** but somehow Baildon Moor got taken over by nearby Ilkley Moor. So, are traditions born!

JAZZ

Lil Hardin was the pianist with King Oliver's band. Whom did she marry in 1924 and what happened to her in 1971?

Which players and instruments made up the original Benny Goodman Trio?

… And who joined them, with which instrument, to form the original Benny Goodman Quartet?

Which classically trained French violinist and which Belgian gypsy guitarist founded the Quintet of the Hot Club of France in 1934? And what was remarkable about the guitarist's playing?

Which blues singer from Northern Ireland was first influenced by Jelly Roll Morton's 'Smokehouse Blues', joined the Chris Barber Band, and was likened by some to a 'reincarnation of Bessie Smith'?

Starting as a clarinettist, he brought the soprano saxophone into jazz. Touring Europe with Josephine Baker's *Revue Nègre* in 1925, he was billed as 'The Talking Saxophone'. Hailed as an artist of genius by the Swiss conductor, Ernest Ansermet, he became one of the greats of the world of jazz. Who was he?

Charlie 'Bird' Parker (alto and tenor saxophonist), Dizzy Gillespie (trumpeter) and Thelonious Monk (pianist), are acknowledged as the initiators of which style of jazz, in New York, in the early 1940s?

This brilliant cornet player died at the age of 28. He is the subject of Dorothy Baker's novel of 1938, *Young Man with a Horn*. Can you name him?

WHOSE WORDS?

Not long before he died (in 1833) a French operatic composer said, 'I am going too soon. I am just beginning to understand the stage.' A little earlier, his most successful work, *Zampa*, had been performed. Who was he?

Sir Thomas Beecham once described the last movement of a certain symphony as '… like a lot of yaks jumping about.' Which symphony, by whom?

Who wrote, 'I must show the English what a blessing they have in "God Save the King".'?

Who said (and about which of his works), '… It is not a lament for a little princess who has just died, but what she might have danced at the Spanish court, long ago.'?

Which well-known jazz performer once said, 'Thank you ladies and gentlemen for your magnificent indifference!'?

This story may be apocryphal. It concerns a conductor who became well known at the lighter end of the musical spectrum. He was renowned for his less than academic knowledge of the 'mysteries of the orchestra'.

It seems that, after a stormy rehearsal, this conductor was stamping out of the room when the timpanist gave a quick roll on the side-drum, followed by a stroke on the cymbal. This was the timpanic equivalent of blowing a raspberry.

Red in the face, the conductor turned around. '… And if I ever find out who did that …!' he shouted. The whole orchestra collapsed in mirth; its point was made!

PASTICCIO

Earlier, we mentioned Auber's opera *The Dumb Girl of Portici*. Who starred in the 1916 (silent) film of the opera?

The long-running TV series, *Taggart*, was introduced by which music? Who was the composer and who sang the theme?

A Staffordshire-born composer, he finished his tenth symphony at the age of 78. Before he died at the age of 96, he had completed 22 more. Who was he?

… And why is his first symphony, 'The Gothic', written between 1919 and 1927, rarely performed?

Which operatic overture is nicknamed 'The Egg-timer'? And why?

He was an American composer whose father was Portuguese and whose mother was Bavarian. He wrote several operettas, a very successful novel and nearly a hundred marches, including *Liberty Bell* and *The Washington Post*. Who was he?

What was the one-letter name of the vocalist and multi-instrumentalist who, in 1979, achieved success with 'Pop Muzik' and ten years later came back with a remix? Who was he?

In the late 1940s, the Andrews Sisters had a hit with a piece of ballet music to which words had been attached. The original music was quite 'new', dating from 1943, and was by Aram Khachaturian. In 1968, the group Love Sculpture got into the charts with a guitar instrumental of the same work. What was the original called?

Who was the first composer to use the term 'nocturne' for a piano work?

Who wrote (among many other hits), 'Raindrops Keep Falling on my Head' and 'I'll Never Fall in Love Again'?

A particular harpsichord fugue by Domenico Scarlatti is known as *The Cat's Fugue*. How did it get that name?

She has many compositions to her name, mainly orchestral or choral. Her most enduringly popular orchestral work is a *Fantasia on Welsh Nursery Tunes*, written in 1940. Can you name her?

Which suite by Handel was so appreciated by George I at its first performance that he had it played twice more?

In 1705, a 20-year-old organist at Arnstadt walked more than 300 miles to Lübeck to hear a 68-year-old Danish composer and organist play at the Marienkirche. The elderly organist was Dietrich Buxtehude (1637–1707) and he profoundly influenced the young organist's style of composition. Who was the young organist?

Diderik (Dietrich) Buxtehude was appointed organist at the Lübeck Marienkirche in 1668, at the age of 31. It was the custom there that an organist so appointed should marry his predecessor's daughter – and this he did.

Buxtehude was a remarkable improviser on the organ and he initiated Sunday evening concerts of his own choral and organ works. When he was thinking of retiring, two young musicians travelled from Hamburg to meet Buxtehude and to look at the job prospects. They were the 18-year-old George Frederick Handel and his friend Johann Mattheson (four years older – he was to become a noted composer, harpsichordist and author).

Apparently, their interest waned since neither of them fancied marrying Buxtehude's daughter, Anna Margreta, who was 28 years old.

ONE-LINERS

71 Who wrote *The Harmonious Blacksmith*?
72 In ballet, what is the function of the choreographer?
73 Where would you find *The Polovtsian Dances*?
74 … And, who were these Polovtsi?
75 Who wrote the *James Bond* theme and had a 1962 hit with it?
76 What type of instrument is an angelica?
77 What is a dotted note?
78 What is a barcarolle?
79 Lulu and the Luvvers had a 1964 hit with what?
80 Who wrote the opera *Lulu*?
81 Which character kills Lulu in the opera?
82 What is to be found an Kneller Hall, Twickenham?
83 Contra-bassoon; contrabass. What does 'contra' mean?
84 Which vocalist had a 1975 hit with 'The Last Farewell'?
85 Which company and band had a 1978 hit with 'The Last Farewell'?
86 What, in hymn-singing, is lining-out or deaconing?
87 What is a euphonium?
88 How many ballets were written by Tchaikovsky?
89 Who was referred to as 'The Red Priest'?
90 Who is Dave Brubeck?
91 What is a sextet?
92 Who was the Beatles' original drummer?
93 Many British military band drummers wear leopard skin. Why?
94 The actor Derek Guyler was an expert of which instrument?
95 Who had a 1975 hit with 'The Trail of the Lonesome Pine'?
96 … And where, geographically, was that trail?
97 What is a puzzle canon or riddle canon?
98 Which Rondo is used for the Eurovision fanfare?
99 What is the subtitle of *HMS Pinafore*?
100 … And who wrote the words, and who the music?

1812

Probably the most performed of any piece of orchestral music in this country is Tchaikovsky's *1812 Overture*, which he wrote some 70 years after the event. It is usually accompanied by fireworks as well as the scored cannon and mortar effects and bells.

1993 saw the 100th anniversary of the composer's death and, as part of a commemoration concert at Covent Garden, the work was staged even more dramatically with an added chorus, a ballet, flame effects and falling snow. The whole performance was conducted by Placido Domingo.

As is well known, *In the Year 1812* (which is the more correct translation of Tchaikovsky's title) celebrates Napoleon's defeat and retreat from Moscow. The music depicts the army of French invaders (represented by *La Marseillaise*) being overwhelmed by the Russian patriots, represented by the Tsarist anthem. (We, perhaps, best know this tune, today, as that used for the hymn 'God the All Terrible'.)

In fact, the Tsarist tune was commissioned by Nicholas I in 1833 and written in that year by Alexis Lvov, the Director of Music in the Imperial Court Chapel.

Its appearance as representing the stirring events 21 years earlier is thus an anachronism.

In 1812, Russia's national anthem was sung to the tune we know as *God Save the Queen.*

UNLIKELY ...

A Around 1812, the inventor Johann Nepomuk Maelzel (1772–1838) of Vienna was a very busy chap! He'd invented a mechanical trumpeter – a representation of a human figure that actually played a trumpet, and a chronometer – which was the forerunner of his metronome.

A certain composer living in Vienna was, at the time, in the throes of both increasing deafness and an impossible love affair. He, Ludwig von Beethoven, often called in at Maelzel's workshops and the two became friends. To help his friend with one of his problems, Maelzel invented for him an ear-trumpet.

Interested in the chronometer/metronome, Beethoven wrote its tick-tock beat into the Allegretto scherzando of his Eighth Symphony (completed in October 1812).

Meanwhile, Maelzel was busy extending his mechanical trumpeter by creating a panharmonicon, a mechanical system that produced all the sounds of a complete symphony orchestra.

Beethoven wrote his 'Battle Symphony' for performance on his friend's panharmonicon. Later, he rescored the work for an orchestra proper.

Maelzel successfully completed the development of his metronome. Today, we often see reference to it on scores, with such as MM♩ = 100, indicating the composer's intentions for timing. MM stands for Maelzel Metronome. The 100 in our example calls for 100 crochet beats per minute.

During the later years of his life, Maelzel went to America, still inventing and demonstrating (and trying to sell) his inventions.

He perfected a mechanical chess player, which inspired an essay by Edgar Allan Poe. His musical automata of 42 orchestral robotic figures, which actually played music, actions and all, as a complete orchestra, created immense interest.

Then, on his way to the West Indies on a promotional visit, he died on board the American sailing ship, *Otis*. Maelzel's old friend had died 11 years earlier, in Vienna.

... FRIENDS

By 1824, Beethoven had completed his Ninth Symphony, 'The Choral', and was totally deaf. He worked on what were to be his last works, his famous string quartets.

The last of these quartets was annotated by the composer. The main theme is marked: 'Must it be? It must be!', and the finale is headed: 'The difficult resolution'.

Early in 1827, Beethoven became very ill. On his deathbed, and surrounded by those friends who could be with him, it was reported that Beethoven was suddenly stirred by the sight of a flash of lightning. Painfully, he raised himself and shook his fist at the heavens. It was his last conscious act. He died in March. His funeral was an occasion of national mourning. It is said that more than 20,000 people gathered to pay their last respects.

. . . .

No doubt, Johann Nepomuk Maelzel would have been amazed that musical automata such as his became commonplace in fairgrounds and then virtually passed into history.

He would also have been amazed that, well into the twentieth century, composers were still introducing the metronome into their compositions. Two that come to mind are Villa-Lobos's piece that has three metronomes 'playing' at different speeds, and György Ligeti's work for 100 metronomes.

TWO PUZZLES

Note Names

Read the notes and find something that can be eaten in each bar.

Now read the notes in each of these bars and find: a pop group, a folk music expert, and the surnames of a negro operatic conductor, a tenor, and two composers. The order of these has been mixed.

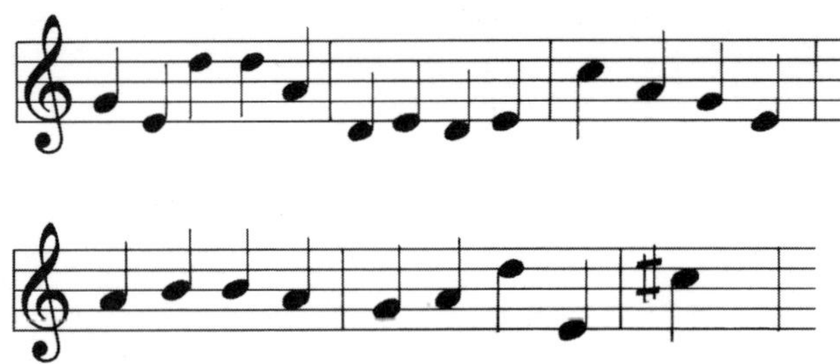

Dates

Below is a list of 15 well-known composers. The chart, opposite, shows their life-spans, but they are identified only by letters. Can you correctly match the composers' names to these letters? If you need help, here are some clues. Only one surname begins with its code letter and only one ends with its code letter; four other surnames, and only four, contain their respective code letters.

BEETHOVEN
BERLIOZ
BRAHMS
CHOPIN
DVORAK
LISZT (Franz)
MOZART (Wolfgang)
RACHMANINOV
SCHUBERT (Franz Peter)
SCHUMANN (Robert)
SIBELIUS
STRAUSS (Richard)
TCHAIKOVSKY
WAGNER (Richard)
VERDI

Dates

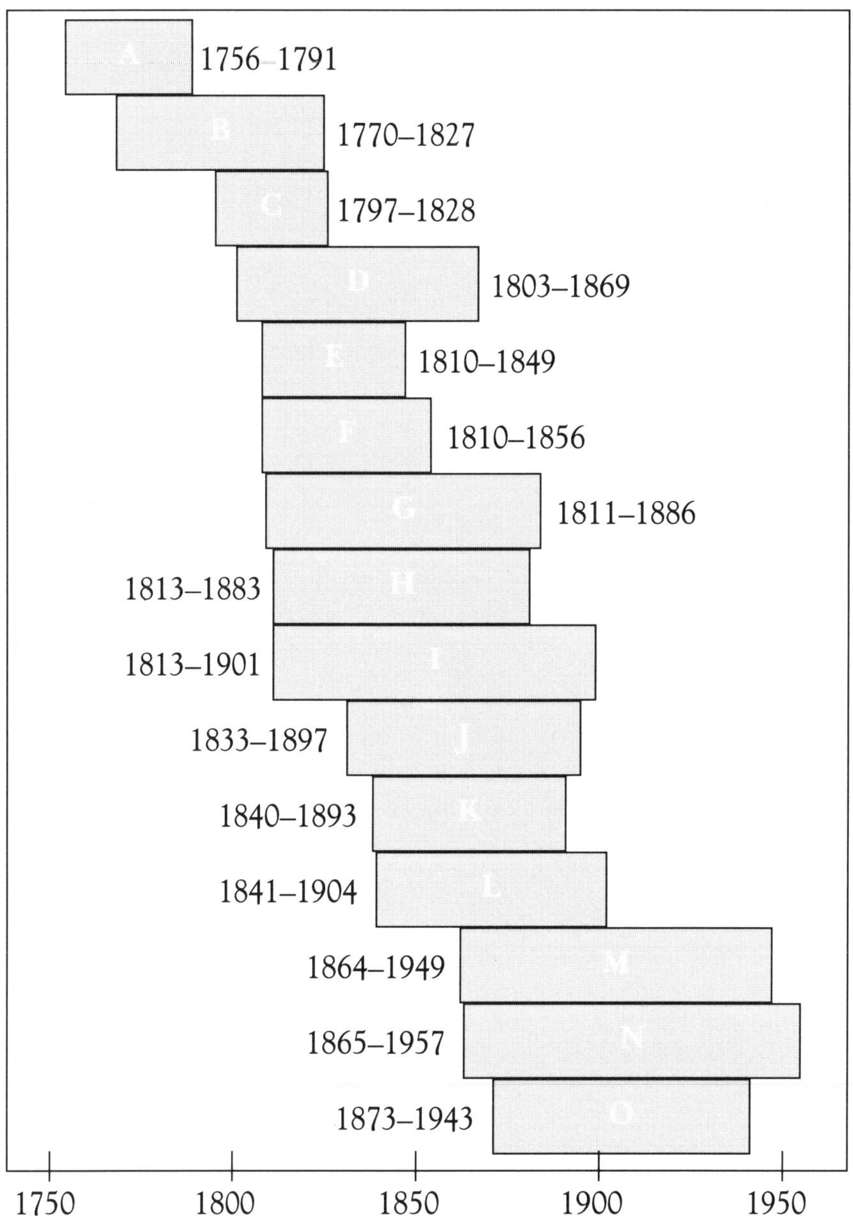
A
1756–1791
B
1770–1827
C
1797–1828
D
1803–1869
E
1810–1849
F
1810–1856
G
1811–1886
H
1813–1883
I
1813–1901
J
1833–1897
K
1840–1893
L
1841–1904
M
1864–1949
N
1865–1957
O
1873–1943
1750
1800
1850
1900
1950

MUSIC AND FILMS

In 1946, Ealing Studios produced a film in Australia. The subject was a 2,000-mile cattle drive of a thousand head, in face of the threat of a Japanese advance. *The Overlanders* made a star of Chips Rafferty. It was backed by some splendid music which was later arranged into a suite. Who was the composer?

Who wrote and performed *The Harry Lime Theme* for the 1949 film, *The Third Man*?

Can you name this French composer? He was a pupil of d'Indy, was one of '*Les Six*', and in about 1945 turned to writing film scores. He achieved hit status when Mantovani took his theme from *Moulin Rouge* to the No 1 spot.

Who wrote the original music for the film *Voyage of Terror (The Achille Lauro Affair)*?

Who wrote, and played, the theme music for the 1953 film *Genevieve*, about rivals on the London to Brighton veteran car race? And, on what instrument did Kay Kendall 'jazz up' *Genevieve*?

The 1957 film *The Bridge on the River Kwai* won a best music Oscar. The theme music incorporates two tunes. Can you name them and say who composed them?

Who wrote the score for the 1994 film *Schindler's List?*

Which piano concerto, by whom, featured strongly in the story and the background music of the 1945 film *Brief Encounter?*

Orchestrated music from the score for the film *The Piano* got into the charts in 1994. Some of this music was then arranged as *The Piano Concerto*, and this also attained chart status. Who was the composer?

In 1957, he had a No 1 hit with his first song – about his puppy-love for the family baby sitter. Six years later, after numerous chart successes, he wrote music for, and acted in, *The Longest Day*. Can you name him?

Who composed the music for the 1965 film *Zorba the Greek?*

Who composed the music for the 1962 film *Lawrence of Arabia*, and for the 1965 and 1966 films *Doctor Zhivago* and *Is Paris Burning?*

A very sad Swedish film of 1967 became very popular, largely because of its beautiful theme music. The film was *Elvira Madigan* and the music became popularly known as *The Elvira Madigan Theme*. From where did the music come?

In 1946, a film was produced to illustrate the instruments of a modern symphony orchestra. The music accompanying it was called *The Young Person's Guide to the Orchestra* and, today, it is regularly given in concert performance. Who wrote the work? And, can you complete its subtitle: *Variations and Fugue on a Theme of ______?*

CONDUCTORS

A pupil of Saint-Saëns, he wrote several light operas and a ballet, *The Two Pigeons*. Debussy dedicated his opera *Pelléas and Mélisande* to him and he conducted the first performance in 1902. Can you name this composer and conductor?

Which German composer and conductor insisted 'You should not perspire whilst conducting' – and never did?

Which composer and conductor is reputed to have said to which other, 'Great chief, we are pledged to exchange tomahawks!' as they exchanged batons?

Which conductor is this? He premièred Hindemith's opera *Cardillac* in Dresden in 1926 and two operas by Richard Strauss, *Intermezzo* and *The Egyptian Helen* in 1924 and 1928. He was Glyndebourne's first conductor and, in 1934, opened the Opera House with a performance of Mozart's *The Marriage of Figaro*.

He was conductor of the Concertgebouw Orchestra, the London Philharmonic and at Covent Garden. In May 1994, exactly 60 years after that first performance at Glyndebourne of *The Marriage of Figaro*, he conducted the opera at the opening of the new Festival Opera House at Glyndebourne – where he had been music director from 1978 to 1988. Can you name this Dutch conductor?

Which violinist and conductor began the Boston Pops concerts in America in 1930 and, because of a completely different interest, was made Honorary Fire Chief by more than a hundred cities around the world?

21

This conductor was involved in the French Resistance Movement during the war and went to Vietnam with the Foreign Legion. He was released from service in Algeria in 1956 to become conductor of the National Orchestra of Monte Carlo. In 1969, he was appointed Principal Conductor and Musical Director of the City of Birmingham Symphony Orchestra. Can you name him?

22

Which American composer, pianist and conductor, conducted the 1989 Brandenburg Gate Concert in Berlin? What notable change did he make to Beethoven's Ninth Symphony for that concert?

23

'For Glorious John, the gracious conductor of a glorious orchestra.' This was how Ralph Vaughan Williams annotated the conductor's programme for the first performance, in 1953, of *Sinfonia Antartica*. Who was Glorious John? And which was his glorious orchestra?

24

He made a name as conductor of the Philadelphia Orchestra. He conducted using his hands only. He appeared as himself in a Deanna Durbin film *A Hundred Men and a Girl*, in 1937, and three years later in Walt Disney's *Fantasia*. Who was he?

Louis Antoine Jullien (1812–60) was a French conductor and composer of dance music. He was given 36 baptismal names – his father's attempt to appease the local Philharmonic Society, all of whom wanted to be godfather.

Jullien came to London and established the first Promenade Concerts. Both his ability and his showmanship drew huge audiences.

He was portly and he dressed extravagantly. He often conducted in the 'French style' – facing the audience, with his back to the orchestra, and collapsed on to a velvet chair between works. When conducting Beethoven he had a jewelled baton and white gloves brought to him on a silver salver.

He was ruined by the extravagance of the production of his own opera *Peter the Great* in 1852. Arrested for debt in Paris a few years later, he lost his reason and died in a lunatic asylum.

THE 'WEAKER' SEX

25

She made her London debut at the age of 17, as the soloist in Beethoven's Fourth Piano Concerto. A year later she made her Promenade Concerts debut, playing Liszt's First Piano Concerto. During the blitz of World War Two, she organised morale-boosting concerts at the National Gallery in London, for which she was awarded the DBE. Who was she?

26

Of what nationality was the great Wagnerian soprano Kirsten Flagstad? And, who was said to have become, with her performance in 1957 as Isolde, in Bayreuth, the unrivalled successor to Kirsten Flagstad?

27

Although a composer, organist and conductor, her real claim to fame is as a teacher of composition at the Paris *Conservatoire*. Amongst her pupils were Aaron Copland, Roy Harris, Walter Piston, Virgil Thomson and the jazz trumpeter Quincy Jones. Her sister, also a composer, was the first woman to win *Le Grand Prix de Rome*. Can you name them?

28

Her maiden name was Gertrude Melissa Nix Pritchett. Under her married name she became famous as a blues singer and was one of the first blues singers to make recordings. She discovered the 12-year-old Bessie Smith and taught her the rudiments of the blues. Who was she?

29

The song 'When You Come to the End of a Perfect Day' sold 5 million sets of sheet music and sobbed its way through many a parlour and drawing room. Who wrote it?

Singer, actress, songwriter, producer and director, she started her working life as a switchboard operator and a theatre usherette. She has made hit records alone and with such as Donna Summer, Neil Diamond and Barry Gibb. Her record of German *Lieder* sold a million. Who is she?

Who was Euterpe?

Both Manuel de Falla and Francis Poulenc wrote concertos for Wanda Landowska (1879–1959). For what was she renowned?

She was an English contralto who made her debut in Sullivan's *The Golden Legend.* Elgar wrote the song cycle *Sea Pictures* for her. In 1922 she became the first musician to be made a Dame. Can you name her?

34

Which New Zealand soprano is this? She was born in 1912, brought up in Australia where she trained as a violinist. She won the first Junior Golf Championship of New South Wales and was runner-up of the Australian Open in 1933 and the NSW State Squash Championship in 1934. She was a volunteer ambulance driver in London during the war. Her London debut as a singer was in the *Messiah* in 1938. Her recorded version of 'O Silver Moon' was responsible for the first British professional production of Dvořák's opera *Rusalka*, staged at Sadler's Wells in 1959. Her recording of Puccini's *Turandot* sold over a million. She was made a dame in 1974 and died in 1996.

Fanny Crosby was born in New York State in 1820. At the age of six weeks she became blind. She was interested in religious work and was closely associated with both Sankey and Moody, the gospel hymn writers. In 1858 she married Alexander Van Alstyne. During her 95 years, she wrote the words for more than 8,000 hymns, 2,000 more than Charles Wesley. Amongst her hymns are 'Safe in the Arms of Jesus', 'Blessed Assurance' and 'Saviour, More Than Life to Me'.

DESCRIPTIONS

35

What, in a vocal sense, is the difference between '*alt*' and '*altissimo*'?

36

Badinerie is often found as the title of an eighteenth-century piece. Some of the most familiar are by Bach. What does the word mean?

37

What is *opera buffa* (or *opéra bouffe*)?

38

Chopin, amongst others, used the term *spianato*. What does it mean?

39

What is programme music?

40

What is the difference between spasm and skiffle?

41

What is a *concerto grosso*?

42

For some of his compositions, John Cage used what he called a 'prepared piano'. What was this?

43

What is ragtime?

44

What is a humoresque?

45

What was known as 'janissary music'?

Counterpoint may be 'strict', 'double', 'triple, 'linear', 'invertible', etc., etc., but what does it mean?

What is 'Boogie-woogie'?

In the mid-1950s, when rock 'n' roll was just taking off, Leo Fender of California launched his **Stratocaster** guitar. This was a specially hand-made range, designed specifically for the new rock 'n' roll music.

When it was taken up by Buddy Holly and used, for example in his version of 'Peggy Sue' in 1957, the Stratocaster became famous in America, almost overnight. Britain was longer in taking to the instrument. Hank Marvin wrote to Leo Fender for a brochure – and ordered a Stratocaster. The Beatles were won over in the mid-1960s and used the instruments for their album *Rubber Soul*.

Then, an unknown guitar player from Seattle, Jimi Hendrix, created a sensation by producing a whole new range of sound on his Stratocaster – such as had never been heard before – playing anything from blues to hard rock. He played the instrument behind his back, with his teeth, banged it about and even set fire to it during a concert – and it stayed in tune! He died in 1970 but, with the success of his album *Experience*, orders for the high class instrument rolled in; rock music had moved up into another gear.

Leo Fender died in 1991 – still hand-crafting his guitars. Two years later, perhaps the greatest exponent of the Fender Stratocaster – Frank Zappa – died. The instrument had taken him to the top, and he had proved its worth.

EXTRACTS …

Between 1874 and 1879, Smetana wrote six orchestral tone poems under the title *Ma Vlast (My Country)*. The country in question was Bohemia. The second of the tone poems, *Vltava* – originally *Moldau* – traces that river from its source. Here is the theme that represents the flowing river. The folk music of which country was its influence? And why?

49

Here is the solo entry in a well-known concerto. Which concerto, and by whom?

50

Beethoven's last works for string quartet were, for many years, regarded as the most difficult works in that form – both to perform and to appreciate. Nowadays that attitude has somewhat changed. Opus 130 is now sometimes referred to, rather facetiously, by the name of a nursery rhyme. Do you know which? Here is an extract from the fourth movement, *Alla danza tedesca (In the manner of a German dance)*.

Note: The extracts, above and opposite, have been simplified.

… AND THEMES

Here is a theme which was used by Brahms in a set of orchestral variations. Who wrote the theme and what is the title of the variations?

52

Between 1800 and 1803, Beethoven used the same theme on four separate occasions. These were: as No 7 in a set of twelve *Contratanze (Country dances)*; in the Finale of the *Prometheus* ballet music; as the basis of the Piano Variations Opus 35; and – what was the fourth occasion? Here is the theme:

53

A particular nineteenth-century Romantic concerto begins with a descending cascade of notes from the soloist, followed by the theme, below, from two oboes. To give an idea of the basic harmony, the support of two flutes is shown. What is the work?

54

Here, reduced to single notes, is the opening of Brahms' Third Symphony. What was the significance of the notes F/A/F?

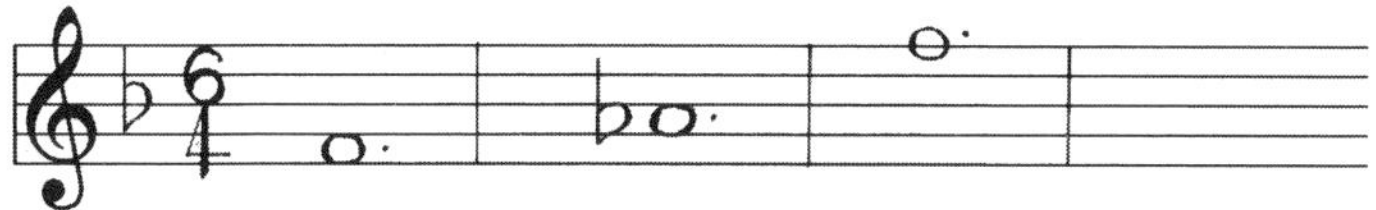

ROCK

55

Which British group took its name from American blues players and made a rock album *The Division Bell* which included a track 'Keep Talking', featuring Stephen Hawking?

56

Which American vocalist won the Best Female Vocal Award at the 1994 Grammy Awards ceremony? It was for her version of the song 'I Will Always Love You', from the film *The Bodyguard.*

57

At this same ceremony, the former lead singer of a British group was awarded Best Engineered Album for his *Ten Summoners' Tales* and Best Music Video for *If I Ever Lose My Faith in You*. Can you give the name by which he is known?

58

Which husband and wife duo had million-sellers in the 1950s with 'Mockin' Bird Hill', 'How High the Moon', 'The World is Waiting for the Sunrise' and 'Vaya con Dios'? She sang; he was a talented guitarist who created a guitar, known by his name.

59

Can you name the members of the Traveling Wilburys? They had hits in 1988 and 1990 with 'Handle with Care' and 'Nobody's Child'.

60

Can you name the members of Eurythmics? They composed the soundtrack for the film *1984*. What was the title of their hit single based on this?

61

Who joined the Eurythmics in 1985 to record 'Sisters Are Doing It for Themselves'? …

62

… and with whom did *she* join, in 1987, for the No 1 hit ' I Knew You Were Waiting (For Me)'?

Which American instrumentalist and composer was especially known for his 'twangy' guitar? He had a No 1 hit with the *Peter Gunn* theme in 1959, acted in the film *Because They're Young* (the theme was a No 2 hit for him in 1960), and wrote the theme for the film *Ring of Fire* (which took him into the charts in 1961).

Most people know that Buddy Holly died in a plane crash, on tour, in 1959. Two other Rock stars died with him. Can you name them? The first had hits with 'Donna' and 'La Bamba'; the second had a hit with 'Chantilly Lace' and wrote Johnny Preston's No 1 hit of 1960, 'Running Bear'. And can you name Don McLean's 1972 hit which mourned their deaths?

She had hits with 'You're No Good' and 'When Will I Be Loved' in 1975. She sang as Mabel in *The Pirates of Penzance*, on Broadway and in the 1982 film (with Kevin Kline). Can you name her? …

… and, with whom did she join to make the 2-million-selling album *Trio*, in 1987?

Rock Around the Clock was the trigger for the **rock 'n' roll revolution** when, in 1955, it featured in the film *Blackboard Jungle*. It was recorded by a 28-year-old American vocalist and guitarist, Bill Haley, and his band, the Comets. It was to sell more than 20 million.

Bill Haley (with his famous kiss-curl) and his 'middle-aged' group made hit rock record after hit rock record – some 70 million sales in all. On concert tours fans became hysterical, as never before. Cinema audiences rioted when their films *Rock Around the Clock* and *Don't Knock the Rock* were shown.

Then, suddenly, the fans found other idols. Reissues still made the charts, but live performances dwindled to nil.

In 1980, the group planned a nostalgic tour. But Bill Haley was not to see a rock 'n' roll revival. He had developed a brain tumour and he died, aged 54, in 1981.

FAMILIES

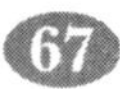

Can you name the father who, in 1740, wrote the music of 'Rule Britannia!', and his natural son who wrote 'The Lass with a Delicate Air'?

Which husband and wife created the *Slaughter on Tenth Avenue* ballet for the Rodgers and Hart musical *On Your Toes* in 1936 and the film in 1939?

Can you name this group? It comprised Irish brothers Finbar, George, Eddie and Paul, and Davey Arthur, a Scottish pupil of their father. They were multi-instrumentalists, composers and singers, their instruments included the bodhran, mandola and uileann pipes. Amongst their international hits were 'When You Were Sweet Sixteen' and 'Yesterday's People'.

Can you name the father who wrote *The Radetzky March* and his three sons who wrote, respectively, *The Blue Danube Waltz*, *Village Swallows*, and *The Bahn Frei* (or *Clear the Tracks*) *Polka*?

Eugène Goossens (1845–1906) was a Belgian conductor. One of the talented **Goossens family**, in England he was principal conductor of the Carl Rosa Company from 1873 and, in 1894, he founded the Goossens Male Voice Choir.

His son, Eugène Goossens (1867–1958), a violinist, took over the Carl Rosa from his father in 1899.

Then there was *his* son, also Eugene but without the accent. He was Sir Eugene Goossens (1893–1962) and was a composer and conductor. He worked under Sir Thomas Beecham before conducting in America and then, very notably, in Australia.

Sir Eugene's brother, Léon Goossens (1897–1988), was one of Britain's leading oboists. His sisters, Marie Goossens (1894–1991) and Sidonie Goossens (b 1899), were talented harpists.

As a 26-year-old, Léon had been admonished by Sir Henry Wood for being a jokester at a Promenade Concert. Two years later he premièred his brother's *Oboe Concerto* at a Prom. Then, in 1958, the Proms saw Marie, Sidonie and Léon performing together the *Concert Piece for Two Harps, Oboe, Cor Anglais and Orchestra*, which Sir Eugene had written for them.

ONE-LINERS

71 The Australian group Bjorn Again gained fame doing what?
72 Which opera, by whom, features *The Dance of the Seven Veils*?
73 What is the difference between an *alborada* and an *aubade*?
74 How many symphonies did Brahms write?
75 Where was the original Tin Pan Alley?
76 Who wrote the song 'Home Sweet Home'?
77 What is absolute pitch (sometimes called 'perfect pitch')?
78 Who wrote the theme march for the 1954 film *The Dam Busters*?
79 … And which rock group's 1982 film featured footage from that film?
80 What is a patter song?
81 Where would you find Utopia Ltd?
82 Whose 1967 hit was 'Simon Smith & His Amazing Dancing Bear'?
83 Who was known as 'The Swedish Nightingale'?
84 Who was called 'The Father of Swedish Music'?
85 Who was called 'The Swedish Glinka'?
86 Who wrote the marches *On the Quarterdeck* and *The Thin Red Line*?
87 Who wrote the song 'I'll Take You Home Again, Kathleen'?
88 'Don't Go Breaking My Heart' was a 1976 chart topper for whom?
89 Who wrote *Mrs Winslow's Soothing Syrup*, a piece for wind quintet?
90 Philip Glass's *Low Symphony* is based on whose music?
91 Who was the leader of Mothers of Invention?
92 Which group had a 1967 chart topper with 'Massachusetts'?
93 … And who wrote it?
94 Who was the first conductor to record, in 1909, a whole symphony?
95 What was the bandleader Henry Hall's signing-off tune?
96 What is a sordino?
97 Which of Mozart's symphonies is known as 'The Haffner'?
98 Who, in 1986, composed what he called a 'zoological fantasy'?
99 What is the difference between a sonata and a cantata?
100 Who wrote the opera *Henry VIII*?

MELODY OUT OF ...

Can you recall the haunting and emotional background music of the films of the mid-1940s: *The Spiral Staircase; Spellbound*; and *The Lost Weekend*? Or, in the 1950s, Bernard Hermann's score for *The Day the Earth Stood Still*; and the plot of *The Delicate Delinquent*?

The eerie themes came from the **theremin**, an early electronic instrument played without physical contact. Relying on an oscillator system, the right hand controls pitch as it nears a vertical rod; the left hand approaches a loop antenna to control volume.

The theremin was developed in the 1920s at his New York studio, by Leon Theremin. Born in St Petersburg in 1896, he was an inventor and musician who was to have an extraordinary life.

Einstein visited his studio and tried out the instrument and then, in 1927, ten theremins performed to an enraptured audience at Carnegie Hall. The concert was reported as drawing 'music out of the air', and a promotional tour was sponsored.

Theremin carried on inventing. He developed a cello that worked on a similar principle to that of the theremin. He invented a burglar alarm and was commissioned to wire Sing Sing Prison with proximity alarms. He planned a system for carrying cars across rivers – but this was a failure. He looked at systems to relate the movements of dance, to sound (and married the prima ballerina of the American Negro Ballet Company).

Then, suddenly, he disappeared. It was assumed that he had died, but Leon Theremin was, in fact, very much alive – in Russia!

As far as can be determined, what had happened was this. In the mid-1930s, Theremin was 'kidnapped' from his studio and taken back to the Soviet Union. He spent seven years in a Siberian labour camp and was then 'allowed' to work for the KGB in Moscow, applying his knowledge to various electronics projects. He designed 'bugs' for official premises and analysed voice recordings as part of his work.

... THE AIR

Eventually, he was permitted to return to music, building theremins at the Moscow Conservatory and setting up a demonstration display at the Gorky Museum. However, an American press report about the display angered the authorities and Theremin was fired and his instruments demolished.

Then, at the time of 'glasnost', he was found again – almost by chance – by a lady named Clara Rockmore, a theremin virtuoso taught by Theremin in the 1920s. Arrangements were made for him to visit America and, in 1991, after close on 60 years, he returned to his studio and played, one last time, in New York. In November 1993, the death of Leon Theremin, in Moscow, was announced. He was 97 years of age.

. . . .

Martinu wrote a Fantasy for theremin. Joseph Schillinger (who concentrated on mathematical music methods) wrote the *First Airphonic Suite* for theremin in his score for the French film *L'Idée* in 1934. This was the first use of electronic music on a film soundtrack.

The rocket propulsion engineer, Dr Samuel Hoffman, wrote *Music out of the Moon* for the theremin, and the Apollo astronauts played a track, *Celestial Nocturne*, on the moon voyage.

The instrument was brought into popular music by the Beach Boys with their huge hit of 1966, 'Good Vibrations'. And, a young American inventor, Robert Moog, not born when Leon Theremin 'disappeared', became fascinated by the instrument. This fascination was to lead him to pioneer a system that we take for granted today – the synthesiser.

'LIGHT' CROSSWORD

Clues Across

1 Composer of such songs as 'I Get a Kick Out of You' and 'You're the Top'. (6)

3 Pop group whose four members included Eric Clapton and whose chart hits included 'I Feel Free', in 1966. (5)

6 What Brenda Lee was doing round the Christmas tree in 1962, and Status Quo all over the world in 1977. (7)

9 These make music and are found on the sleeves of most albums. (5)

10 'Maria _____' was a 1969 chart hit for Gene Pitney. (5)

11 First name of American trombonist and band leader, whose many hit recordings included 'Moonlight Serenade'. (5)

12 First name of the lyricist of *South Pacific*. (5)

'LIGHT' CROSSWORD

Clues Across (cont)

14 Surname of the drummer in 'The Fab Four'. (5)

19 Shirley Bassey urged us to do this to ev'ry mountain, in her No 1 hit of 1961. (5)

20 A Brazilian dance. (5)

21 A lively dance in 2/4 time, of Bohemian origin. (5)

22 Stage name of Paul Goddard, whose most successful record was 'Puss 'n Boots', in 1983. (4, 3)

23 The 'Long and Winding', 'Country', and 'Tobacco' were types of these. (5)

24 Lyricist of music in the films *My Fair Lady*, 1964, and *Camelot*, 1967. (6)

Clues Down

1 American jazz musician, by-name 'Bird', and a leading exponent of bebop. (6)

2 Musical based on the life and times of Eva Peron. (5)

3 A performance of musicians. (7)

4 First of Reginald Dwight's stage names. (5)

5 How the prolific English composer of such songs as 'Dance Little Lady' and 'I'll See You Again' was known in the profession. (6)

7 Musical, on which Tim Rice collaborated with two of the formers members of 17 Down. (5)

8 Musical, for which 24 Across wrote the film score in 1958 and the music for the stage version in 1973. (4)

13 Group whose members included Eric Burdon and Alan Price, and whose best known hit was 'House of the Rising Sun'. (7)

15 A rhythmic Cuban dance. (5)

16 J P Richardson, who had a hit in 1958 and 1959 with 'Chantilly Lace', was better known as 'The Big ____ (6)

17 Group whose many No 1 hits included 'Waterloo', in 1974 and 'Super Trouper', in 1980. (4)

18 Carlene is currently carrying on the tradition of this famous country music family. (6)

19 Singer and TV personality who made a nostalgic 1993 recording of 'Through the Years'. (5)

20 Wolverhampton group who had a 1973 No 1 hit with 'Merry Xmas Everybody'. (5)

BALLET

The ballets *Monotones I* and *Monotones II*, choreography and costumes by Frederick Ashton, were first performed in 1965. Whose music was used?

In 1934, the murder of a communist official was Stalin's excuse for starting 'The Great Purge'. As far as is known, the murdered man had no connection with ballet. However, his name was perpetuated in the world of ballet. How?

In 1860, Marie Taglioni came out of retirement to create *La Papillon*, the only ballet she choreographed. For which dancer, and to whose music?

In which opera by Meyerbeer, staged at the Paris Opera in 1849, did the *corps de ballet* perform on roller skates?

Music from two Meyerbeer operas was arranged by Constant Lambert for a ballet, the scene of which is a frozen pond. It was first performed in 1937, choreographed by Frederick Ashton. Can you name the ballet and the operas?

John Cranko's ballet of 1972, *Initials RBME*, was choreographed by him to the music of Brahms' Piano Concerto No 2 in A major. What is the significance of the 'Initials'?

John Cranko died in 1973. He had been artistic director of the Stuttgart Ballet since 1961. Kenneth MacMillan choreographed *Requiem* in memory of Cranko. It was first performed by the Stuttgart Ballet in 1976. Which music was used? And what connection did the performance have with *Initials RBME*?

In 1957, John Cranko had choreographed *The Prince of the Pagodas*, the first full-length ballet with a score by a British composer. Which composer?

Which one-act ballet, choreographed by Frederick Ashton and first performed in 1968, is set to music by Elgar and features the composer and his wife and *My Friends Pictured Within*?

What relation were the Russian dancers and choreographers Bronislava Nijinksa (1891–1972) and Vaslav Nijinsky (1889–1950)?

What is the relationship between the French choreographer and dancer Roland Petit and the French dancer Zizi Jeanmaire? Both were born in 1924.

What is unusual about *A Wedding Bouquet*, first performed in 1937, with choreography by Frederick Ashton and music and scenery design by Lord Berners?

George Balanchine choreographed *Union Jack* in 1976, to traditional British music orchestrated by Hershy Kay. In the ballet, a Pearly King and Queen dance a *pas de deux*, there is a scene at the Edinburgh Tattoo, and there is a hornpipe saluting the Royal Navy. What is unusual about the Finale?

INSTRUMENTS

What is the difference between a harpsichord and a piano?

In 1709, in Florence, Bartomoleo Cristofori devised a musical instrument (an improvement on an existing instrument) which was to revolutionise music-making. Do you know what it was?

From the sixteenth to the eighteenth centuries, three families made the small, north Italian town of Cremona famous. Can you name the families?

In which section of the orchestra would you find the basset horn?

On a bowed, string instrument, what are stopped strings and what are open strings?

What was Paul Tortelier's instrument?

With which two instruments do you associate Julian Bream?

In Charles Dickens' *David Copperfield*, David is sent to Salem House School. The Master, Mr Mell, played a musical instrument (very badly!). Which instrument?

In the early 1830s, Niccolo Paganini bought a Stradivarius viola. He approached Berlioz to compose a score for him (and the viola). When he saw Berlioz' score, however, he lost interest, thinking there was not enough in it to show off his playing. Nevertheless, the work was published – as a symphony with solo viola. What was the work?

Lionel Tertis and Yuri Bashmet: exponents of which instrument?

Four woodwind instruments are shown, above. Can you name them?

… And which of them is known as a '*fagotto*' in Italian, and a '*Fagott*' in German?

Which is the only wind instrument in an orchestra that is fully chromatic and is capable of producing *glissandi* ('sliding' notes)?

27

Transposition means the writing or performing of music at another pitch, and thus in another key, without changing the intervals between notes. Many woodwind and brass instruments of the orchestra are referred to as 'transposing instruments'. What is meant by this?

TV AND RADIO ...

28

What is the signature tune of BBC's long-running radio series *The Archers*? And who wrote the music?

29

Some years ago, a series of short horror/mystery plays on TV gained great success. Each was introduced by Alfred Hitchcock, and the long-running series bore his name. The signature tune gained an instant popularity. What was it?

30

Who wrote the title/theme music for these TV series: *Mr Bean*; *Blackadder*; and *Red Dwarf*?

31

Who was commissioned by Blake Edwards to write the music for the TV series *Peter Gunn* and *Mr Lucky*, in the late 1950s?

32

In 1972, a piece of ballet music written in 1956 by Khachaturian reached the charts, having been used for the theme of the TV series *The Onedin Line*. The chart version was played by the Vienna Philharmonic Orchestra. Can you name the ballet from which the music came?

33

By a Sleepy Lagoon, associated with *Desert Island Discs*; *Calling All Workers!*, which introduced *Music While You Work*; and *The Knightsbridge March*, the signature tune of *In Town Tonight*. Can you name the composer of those radio themes?

34

For many years, 'With a Song in My Heart', introduced, on radio, the requests programme, *Family Favourites*. Who wrote the words, and who the music, of the song?

... THEMES

Joe Fagin took 'That's Living Alright' into the charts in January 1984. The episodes of which TV series did it introduce?

Who wrote *The Devil's Galop*, the signature tune of the radio series, *Dick Barton*?

The TV series, *Lovejoy*, is associated with a distinctive theme. Do you know who wrote it?

In 1905, Sibelius wrote a suite of incidental music for Maeterlinck's play *Pelléas et Mélisande*. One piece from it, *At the Castle Gate*, gained fame as the theme for the longest-running British TV series. Which series?

Who composed the music used as the theme for the TV serial, *Reilly, Ace of Spies*?

At the age of 15, Scotsman **Hamish MacCunn** was one of the first students at the Royal College of Music, in London, where he was to be a pupil of (Sir) Hubert Parry.

By the time he was 19, he had written three overtures, one of which, *The Land of the Mountain and the Flood*, became very popular. In 1898, it was the opening overture at a Henry Wood Promenade Concert, 'British Composers' Night. In the meantime, he had written some choral works and two operas, and was Professor of Harmony at the Royal Academy of Music.

He died in 1916, aged 48, and became virtually forgotten for the next 60 years.

Then a TV series, *Sutherland's Law*, used *The Land of the Mountain and the Flood* as theme music.

Again it became highly popular and was much asked for in request programmes. The music sounded so fresh and modern that listeners could not believe it had been written 90 years previously.

OPERA

1993 saw the world première of Michael Berkeley's first opera. The opera explores the implications of Kipling's *Jungle Book* stories. What is the opera's title?

Jenufa, subtitled *Her Stepdaughter*, the first performed opera of a Czech composer, is often referred to as his 'Lyrical Masterpiece'. Who was he?

Which modern opera, about the last days of Captain Scott, calls for a chorus of penguins? And do you know the composer?

In Rimsky-Korsakov's opera *Sadko*, one of the characters, Nejato, is described as 'a gusli player from Kiev'. What is a gusli?

In the opera, Sadko asks three merchants to sing about their native lands so he can decide where to visit. The first is a Viking, the third – Sadko's choice – is from Venice. The second is a Hindu merchant. Which well-known song does he sing?

The American composer, Virgil Thomson (1896–1989) wrote an opera called *Four Saints in Three Acts*, which was first staged in 1934. Can you name the librettist – a close friend of the composer? (If you need a clue, this librettist shared an apartment with *the* Alice B Toklas!)

Salieri (1798), Balfe (1838), Nicolai (1849), Adam (1856), Verdi (1893), Vaughan Williams (1929). All these composers wrote operas based on a particular Shakespearean character. Which character?

Both Niccolo Piccini (1728–1800) and Christoph Gluck (1714–87) lived and worked in Paris at the same time (the 1770s). Both were composers of operas and they were friendly towards each other. So, why are their names linked with street violence?

He was born in Hungary in 1830. With the 1848 revolution, he had to give up his studies at the Vienna Conservatorium and take a job in Hungary. Here, he was mistaken for a revolutionary and very nearly executed by firing squad. He wrote six operas, the best known being *Die Königin von Saba (The Queen of Sheba)*, of 1875. His *Rustic Wedding Symphony* (1876) was a favourite of Sir Thomas Beecham. Can you name this composer?

An opera by Verdi, produced in Milan in 1842, identified him publicly with much of his country's hopes for liberty and self-government. One chorus in particular was taken up as a song of protest and hope. This was 'Va, pensiero sull' ale dorate' ('Fly, my thoughts on golden wings'). Can you name the opera? And why did the slogan 'Viva Verdi' begin appearing on Italian walls?

***Giuseppe Verdi* ...** (1813–1901) had requested a modest funeral, without music or singing.

At 6.30 am on a damp, foggy morning in Milan, a huge crowd softly and spontaneously sang 'Va, pensiero' as his single hearse passed on its way to the cemetery.

Verdi had founded, in Milan, the *Casa di Riposa* – a home for aged musicians. It had been his wish that he and his wife Giuseppina (who had died four years previously) should be buried in the Oratory of the Casa, when it was completed.

So it was that later there was a second funeral for Verdi. This time, 20,000 lined the Milan streets as the two coffins were moved. And, at the cemetery gates, Arturo Toscanini conducted a choir of 800, in 'Va, pensiero'.

BACH TUNES

This extract will be familiar to many who have learned to play a keyboard instrument. It is from a piece in one of the *Anna Magdalena Notebooks*. Can you give its title and say who was Anna Magdalena?

In 1965, the Toys had a hit with a song based on this same Bach piece. Can you name the song?

During a pestilence in 1597, a Westphalian pastor, Philip Nicolai, wrote many hymns with fine melodies. One of these melodies has been much used, arranged and developed. It features in Mendelssohn's oratorio *St Paul* and themes are found in Handel's *Messiah.* Bach used it in several Cantatas – notably No 140, which is popularly known by the hymn's opening words. Can you say what these are? In 1967 and 1972, Procol Harum had a hit in which surreal lyrics were set against adaptations of the Chorale tune from Cantata No 140 and the *Air* from Bach's Suite No 3 in D major. Can you name the hit record?

William Walton arranged pieces from Bach Cantatas for a Ballet Suite in the late 1930s. Can you name it? And can you say how its title is related to Bach's Cantata No 140? This extract, from Bach's secular Cantata No 208, is one of the melodies used in the Ballet Suite. How is it popularly known?

Note: The extracts, above and opposite, have been simplified.

This is an extract from Bach's Cantata No 147. In a transcription by Dame Myra Hess, it became a popular piece. Can you name the cantata and the title by which we usually know the transcribed piece?

In 1979, the Beach Boys had a UK hit with a very pretty song which was based on the above theme. Can you name it?

The second movement of Bach's Suite No 3 in D major has been popular since 1871, when the virtuoso violinist, August Wilhelmj, arranged it for violin and piano, transposing it into a lower key. Familiar today, particularly for its use with the TV advertisements for a well-known cigar, it is known as *Air on the G String*. Do you know why?

This is an extract of a theme which was, obviously, a great favourite of Bach's. We, perhaps, know it best as the hymn tune for 'O Sacred Head, Sore Wounded'.

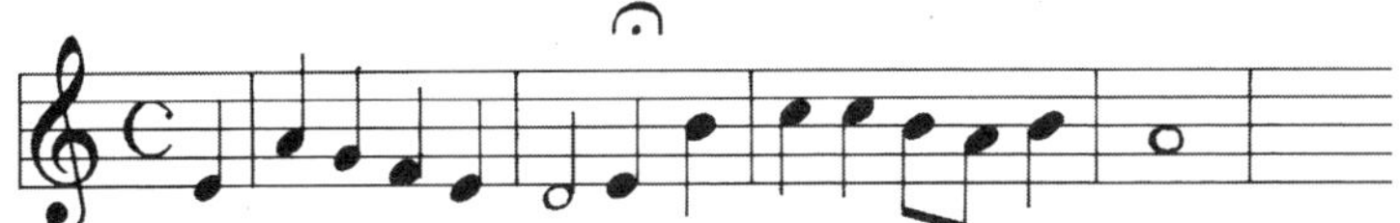

Bach made eleven harmonisations of the tune, five of which are in his *St Matthew Passion*. It also appears in his *Christmas Oratorio*, and in several of his cantatas. It features in the Walton Ballet Suite mentioned opposite. However, the melody was written as a secular song by a German organist and composer who died more than 70 years before Bach was born. Can you name him?

'Ein' Feste Burg' ('A Safe Stronghold') is a well-known hymn. Bach used an arrangement in his Cantata No 80, written for Reformation Sunday. Who wrote the original hymn?

PASTICCIO

He was born in Pennsylvania in 1910 and was a prodigy. He was taught to sing by his aunt, the contralto, Louise Homer, and in 1931 he wrote *Dover Beach*, a setting of the poem by Matthew Arnold, for himself to sing. He died in 1981, having written in almost every form. Yet, generally speaking, he is remembered for only one work, the haunting *Adagio for Strings*, which he wrote in 1936. Can you name him?

Born in 1921, he was probably the greatest horn player of his time. He was a son of a distinguished performer on the same instrument, and had works written for him by Arnold, Britten and Hindemith. In 1957, hurrying home from the north, he 'ran out of road' near Hatfield and was tragically killed. Who was he?

He was born in 1896 and was handicapped by having no fingers on his left hand. Nevertheless, he became a proficient pianist and a successful songwriter. Among his hits were: 'When the Red, Red Robin …'; 'Side by Side'; 'River Stay 'Way from my Door'; and 'Try a Little Tenderness'. Can you name him?

Can you name the Birmingham-based reggae band whose cover version of 'Can't Help Falling in Love' was featured in the Sharon Stone film *Sliver*?

Armas Järnefelt and Jean Sibelius were Finnish-born composers and conductors whose lives spanned virtually the same period. There was another relationship between them. Do you know what it was?

This French operatic composer was born in 1838. His only symphony was written when he was 17 years old. He married the daughter of his composition professor, Jacques Halévy. At his funeral in 1875, two of his own compositions were sung in special arrangements. These were: the *Agnus Dei*, a vocal arrangement of the Intermezzo from his Suite No 2, *L'Arlésienne*; and a *Piè Jesu* from the music of *The Pearl Fishers* duet, *Au fond du Temple Saint*. Both arrangements were by Ernest Guiraud. Can you name the composer?

Can you give the following operatic surnames? (They follow a sort of pattern!)
The Armourer (a tenor) in Bizet's *The Fair Maid of Perth*.
An Impressed Man (a baritone) in Benjamin Britten's *Billy Budd*.
An English Milord (a bass) in Cimarosa's *The Secret Marriage*.
A Young English Officer (a tenor) in Boïeldieu's *The White Lady*.

Boïeldieu's *The White Lady* is based on works by Sir Walter Scott. It seems appropriate, then, that the chorus, in Act III, should sing a version of the old Scottish air, ***Robin Adair***. Except that it's an Irish air called *Eileen Aroon*! It was first brought to Scotland by the blind harpist, Dennis Hempson, in the early 1700s. In the 1730s, a parody of the air was heard in Ireland – this being for a politician named Robin Adair.

Twenty years later, Lady Caroline Keppel wrote the words we know today – but addressed to another Robin Adair. This one was an Irish surgeon. She married him and he became surgeon general to George III.

The White Lady was completed in 1825. By then, the Scotch Snap (see Answer 77) had been introduced into the original air, but it was not present at the time the opera was set – 1759. However, its use in the opera seems very acceptable today.

Incidentally, Dennis Hempson lived to be 112 years old (he lived in three centuries!) Thomas Moore made a lot of money putting words of his own to *Eileen Aroon*. And, Robin Adair's son became a noted and important diplomat; he was named after his father.

ON SCORE

In the extract of music in Question 53 there are curves with the figure '3' under them over groups of notes and there is the instruction *simile*. Do you know what these mean? And, in Question 55, there is a curve with a dot under it above one note. What does this mean?

Suppose you are an orchestral string player. At a certain point in the score you find the word *arco* (or, perhaps, *coll' arco*). What do you do?

One of Bach's last (and uncompleted) works was a fugue based on the four letters of his name. How was that possible?

In June 1778, Mozart's Symphony No 31 in D (known as 'The Paris') was performed in that city by the Concerts Spirituels – the orchestra for whom he had written the work. Parisians were very proud of their orchestra's ability to execute the '*premier coup d'archet*'. What was meant by this?

What is meant by the instruction *accelerando*?

What does the instruction *perdendosi* indicate to the performer?

In many concertos there is, towards the end the last (or sometimes, the first) movement, a passage which allows the soloist to display his or her virtuosity. It also serves to delay the end of the movement (especially the last movement) which might, otherwise, be too sudden. What name is given to this passage?

ONE-LINERS

71 For Mozart's works, what is the significance of the K numbers?
72 What is (or was) a cassation?
73 In which country did the flamenco originate?
74 What is a snare-drum?
75 Who wrote the American National Anthem?
76 Who wrote the libretto for Gustav Holst's opera *The Perfect Fool*?
77 What is a Scotch Snap?
78 What is an accidental?
79 Who, in 1893, wrote *Vexations*? And what is strange about it?
80 In the 1934 film *Blossom Time*, Richard Tauber played whom?
81 In the 1954 film *Deep in My Heart*, José Ferrer played whom?
82 Who, in 1923, wrote *Pacific 231*? And what does it represent?
83 The theme from *Harry's Game* was which Irish group's 1982 hit?
84 ... And which two singers recorded 'In a Lifetime' in 1986?
85 Who wrote the score for the 1983 film *Local Hero*?
86 ... And which group did he found in 1977?
87 Which French Queen was taught singing by the composer, Gluck?
88 Which Haydn symphony is nicknamed after this French queen?
89 And which Haydn symphony is nicknamed after her mother?
90 Which pop group played at a 1970 Promenade Concert?
91 In which 'Land' would you find 'You Are My Heart's Delight'?
92 ... And who wrote the music for that operetta?
93 In 1889, whose opera *Cavalleria Rusticana* was a prize winner?
94 Who wrote the patriotic song 'Heart of Oak'?
95 Who wrote the songs 'Camptown Races' and 'Beautiful Dreamer'?
96 What is a broken chord?
97 What is an ocarina?
98 Whose first big hit, in 1956, was 'Heartbreak Hotel'?
99 Who, in the eighteenth century, was Johann Joachim Quantz?
100 What is a torch song?

THE GADFLY

You may have thought it strange that the theme music for the TV serial *Reilly, Ace of Spies* was part of the music that Shostakovich wrote for a Russian film *The Gadfly* (see Question 39). However ...

The TV serial was based on Robert Bruce Lockhart's account of the incredible life of the master spy, Sidney Reilly. The Russian film was based on a remarkable novel, *The Gadfly*, written by EL Voynich. This is a story of heroism and sacrifice, in Italy, at the time of the *Risorgimento*. So, what can be the connection?

EL Voynich was born Ethel Lilian Boole, in Ireland, in 1864. Her father was George Boole (of Boolean algebra fame); her mother, Mary Everest, was a philosopher, and Mary's brother, an explorer and surveyor, gave his name to Mount Everest. As a young girl, Lily Boole (as she was known) idolised Giuseppe Mazzini, the Italian patriot and *Risorgimento* leader. Later, she married a Polish patriot, named Voynich, who escaped from Russia to the West.

In 1897, *The Gadfly*, by EL Voynich, was published – and became a sensation worldwide. Those who know that Lily was the author, believed it was based on her husband's adventures – but set in Italy.

However, it seems that, early in the 1890s, a young, embittered and amorous adventurer and spy, Sidney Reilly, came into her life. She became his devoted mistress (he was to have many devoted mistresses in his life). Lily cared for him, hearing the appalling stories of his early life and his bizarre activities. For a while they lived happily – in Italy – and then, true to form, Sidney deserted her.

She wrote the novel soon after. Reilly's story was transposed into the *Risorgimento*. He became, in retrospect, 'The Gadfly'. With the inspired choice of music written for *The Gadfly* film to provide the Reilly theme for TV, the wheel, surely, had turned full circle.

. . . .

Sidney Reilly was executed, as a spy, in 1925. EL Voynich died, in New York, in 1960. She was 96 years of age.

VERDI'S *REQUIEM*

In 1873, Alessandro Manzoni, Italy's all-time most noted poet and author, died. He had achieved fame through his novel *I Promessi Sposi (The Betrothed)*. He was a patriot and (as was Verdi) he was elected a senator in the first free Italian parliament. Verdi venerated Manzoni, who, at the age of 82, had given him a photograph inscribed: 'To Giuseppe Verdi, a Glory of Italy, from a Decrepit Lombardy Writer'. He was much too moved to attend the funeral.

During the year that followed, Verdi composed his *Requiem Mass* in memory of Manzoni. He paid for its publication and conducted its first performance at the Church of St Marco, Milan on 22 May 1874 – exactly one year after the author's death.

Verdi later toured Europe with the *Requiem*. It was performed three times at the Albert Hall – with a chorus of 1,200! There were criticisms. The work was considered by many to be much too operatic. Others thought that Verdi, an agnostic, should not have written a Requiem Mass for Manzoni, a devout Catholic.

Perhaps, today, we hear the work as Verdi intended – a beautiful, emotional and dramatic commemoration of a man's life. As Verdi said, 'If men worshipped men, I would have knelt before him'. He 'knelt' in the only way he could – with his music.

Davidsbündlertanze is a one-act ballet, using piano music of the same name, by Schumann. The ballet was choreographed by George Balanchine (1904–83) and first performed in 1980. It suggests certain aspects of Schumann's life.

The title refers to the composer's personal mythology of the 'League of David' (against the Philistines). Most of the 18 piano pieces have the inscription 'E' or 'F', signifying the two aspects of his personality. 'E' is for Eusebius (lyric and dreaming) and 'F' is for the impassioned Florestan.

NUMBER OPERA

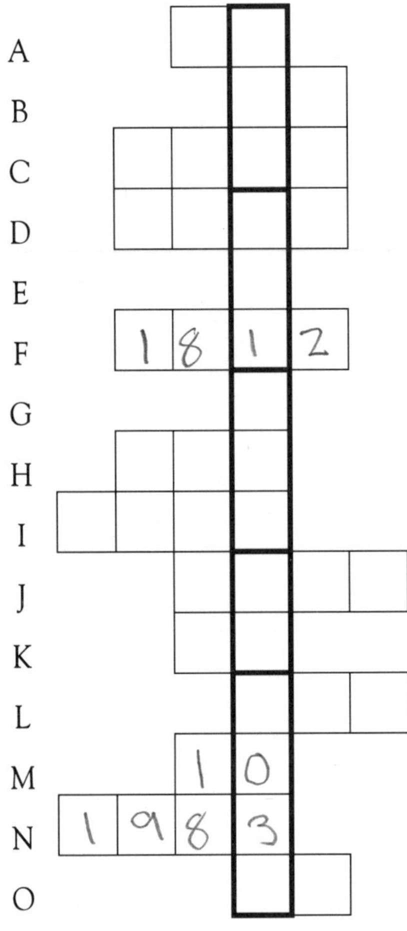

The answers to the clues A to O are all numbers. Fill these in on the grid. Some answers are easy; others you may have to look up – in this book or elsewhere.

Clues

A The number of tons that Tennessee Ernie Ford hauled in 1956, for a No 1 hit.

B The ____ is a common name for Bach's collection of preludes and fugues, which he called *The Well Tempered Clavier.*

C Gustav Nahler's Symphony No 8 in E flat major is known as 'Symphony of a ____'.

D 'In the Year ____' was, in 1969, the one hit of Zager and Evans.

E ____ *Pieces in the Shape of a Pear,* was written in 1903 by Erik Satie.

F Tchaikovsky's overture, his Opus 49, is known as this.

G Francis Poulenc's last opera, *La Voix Humaine (The Human Voice)*, was premièred in 1959. How may singers does it require?

H The number of Haydn's Symphony in G, known as 'The Military'. (It is one of the London Symphonies.)

I *Pacific* ____ was the 1946 Noël Coward musical, that was not the success he had hoped for, even with Mary Martin as its star.

J The year of the Rolling Stones' hit '(I Can't Get No) Satisfaction'.

K *Etchmiadzin* is the name given to Alan Hovhaness's Symphony No ____ Opus 234.

L Beethoven's *Rage over a Lost Penny* was his Opus ____.

M Paul Simon's '____ Ways to Leave Your Lover', of 1976, won two Grammys.

N This was the year of John Lennon's murder.

O The total number of symphonies composed by Havergal Brian.

. . . .

When you have completed the grid, you will see that there are five numbers displayed in the vertical column marked by thicker lines. In order, they have: 3 digits, 3 digits, 3 digits, 2 digits and 4 digits.

These numbers should 'ring a bell' with opera buffs – especially when we tell you that they total 2,065. Are you able to say where, in opera, they appear? And what they refer to? If you need help, here are some more clues:

- It is a Mozart opera.
- They appear in a catalogue sung by the servant of the eponymous 'hero'.
- 'The numbers' are in Italy, Germany, France, Turkey and Spain.

CROSS-OVER ...

Based on an Andante for organ by the British-born composer Edwin Lemare (1865–1934), this song was written by Neil Moret and Ben Black in 1925. It was sung by Betty Grable in the 1940 film *Tin Pan Alley* and was a posthumous Jim Reeves hit in 1973. Can you name the song?

This is an extract from an English folk song which was originally collected by an Australian-born pianist and composer. Can you name him and the folk song?

With a slight change of title, an American vocalist took a version of the song into the charts in 1962. Who was he?

In 1980, Sky – the group that included John Williams and Herbie Flowers – had a big hit with *Toccata*. From which work was this arranged?

In 1960, Jackie Wilson's chart entries 'Night', and 'Alone at Last', were based, respectively, on an operatic aria and a well-known piano work. Can you name the works and the composers?

Note: The extracts above and opposite have been simplified.

... TUNES

Can you recall the comic song that Richard Murdoch used to sing – about his aunt from Burton-on-Trent ... who got her handlebars in a problematic state? If so, can you say where the tune came from, and who wrote it?

The slow movement from Beethoven's Sonata No 8 in C minor, Opus 13, begins something like this:

What nickname did Beethoven give to this piece? There is a passing resemblance, in the opening, to a theme in a well known work by Elgar. Can you say which? On Billy Joel's 1983 album, *An Innocent Man*, one of his songs is based on the melody of the Beethoven slow movement. Can you name it?

Greg Lake had a Christmas hit in 1975 with that is, arguably, one of the best ever songs of peace, 'I Believe in Father Christmas'. The instrumental sections were based on a theme from a suite by Prokofiev. Can you name this?

The following extract approximates to the opening of a popular folk song from Russia, *Stefan* (or *Stenka*) *Razin*. In 1965, Tom Springfield's song, based on this melody, took the Seekers to the top chart spot for 17 weeks. What as it called?

This music has been used as background to a TV ad for wool; to a TV play, *The Silver Collection*; and for the 1980 film *Ordinary People*. Cleo Laine used the melody for 'How, Where, When?' and the Greek group, Aphrodite's Child, took it into the charts in 1968 as 'Rain and Tears'. The seventeenth century German organist and composer of the music would scarcely be known today but for this one piece. Can you name the composer and the work?

'Asia Minor' was a 1961 hit for pianist Kokomo (alias Jimmy Wisner). On which concerto was it based?

WHO WROTE CASANOVA?

In 1932, a recording was issued of the *Nun's Chorus*, from a Strauss operetta, *Casanova*. The soloist was Anni Frind – a fine soprano with a good Mozartian track record. The recording became immensely popular, despite 'purists' calling it 'schmaltzy' and scoffing at the concept of a nun, complete with choir and organ accompaniment, in an operetta about the great womaniser.

In the 1950s the recording company tried to delete the record, but public opinion prevailed, and they had to reissue it, more than once.

In the 1990s a new version – by Kiri Te Kanawa (and the Mormon Tabernacle Choir) became very popular.

However, Johann Strauss II cannot be blamed or praised for the strange concept. He never wrote an operetta called *Casanova*! This was an arrangement of (largely) Strauss's music by the German-born Ralph Benatsky.

Benatsky is best remembered, otherwise, for his own *The White Horse Inn*, of 1930. Even more confusing, this included some music by Robert Stolz.

OPERETTA

What is the connection between Gilbert and Sullivan's *Pirates of Penzance* and the Royal Bijou Theatre, Paignton, Devon? Who was satirised in the famous song of the character, Major-General Stanley, about his being 'the very model of a modern Major-General'?

This Austrian-born tenor sang in most of Léhar's operettas, and is particularly remembered for his role in *Land of Smiles*, which he brought to London in 1931. In 1943, he wrote and starred in his own operetta, *Old Chelsea*, the best known song from this being 'My Heart and I'. Who was he?

Der Vogelhändler (The Bird Seller) was first produced in 1891. Amongst its many delightful songs is *The Nightingale Song*, for which the soprano, Elisabeth Schumann was famed. *Der Obersteiger (The Master Miner)* was by the same Austrian composer and first produced in 1894. From this operetta, 'Sei nicht bös' ('Don't be cross') was popularised by both Elisabeth Schumann and the tenor of Question 12. Can you name the composer?

His many operettas and musical plays are mostly forgotten today, except for their lively overtures, which are much performed by brass bands in particular. These include: *Light Cavalry*, *Poet and Peasant*, *Pique Dame (Queen of Spades)* and *Beautiful Galatea*. Can you name this composer?

Which Hungarian composer's operettas included *Countess Maritza* and *The Gipsy Princess*?

Which composer was born in Prague, studied under Dvořák, wrote film music in Hollywood, and is best known for his operettas: *Rose Marie*, *The Firefly*, and *The Vagabond King*? And, can you say from which of these came: 'The Donkey Serenade', and 'The Indian Love Call?' Who was 'the vagabond king'?

Can you say what these three operettas have in common? *Fra Diavolo*, by Daniel Auber, 1830; *The Bohemian Girl*, by Michael Balfe, 1843; and *Babes in Toyland*, by Victor Herbert, 1903.

The Mountebanks was an operetta in two acts, first produced at the Lyric Theatre, London, in January 1892. The libretto was by WS Gilbert. Who wrote the music?

Which operetta by Johann Strauss II concerns the revenge of a character dressed as a bat, at carnival?

AT THE PROMS

20

Henry Wood conducted the first of his Promenade Concerts, at the Queen's Hall, London, in August 1895. Can you name the very first work to be played?

21

Sir Henry Wood died in 1944. In those first 50 years of the Proms, only five others conducted at the concerts. Can you name any of them?

22

In 1901, Henry Wood's star singing pupil made her Prom debut with *Elisabeth's Prayer*, from Wagner's *Tannhäuser*. Four years later she was the soloist when Mahler's Symphony No 4 in G major was performed at a Prom, and heard for the very first time in England. At the last Prom of the 1909 season, she sang two songs by Sir Charles Stanford at their première. She died two months later. Do you know how she was billed on concert programmes?

23

In 1901, Henry Wood conducted the first performance in England of the suite *King Christian II*. The 36-year-old composer was at the Prom for the performance. Who was he?

24

In 1907, an arrangement was made for orchestra of Chopin's *Funeral March* (from his Piano Sonata No 2) by Henry Wood, for a Prom tribute to Joseph Joachim, the Hungarian violinist and composer, whose death had just been announced. In the event, in that same season, the work was performed again as a tribute to another composer. Can you name him?

25

In 1932, the Austrian pianist, Paul Wittgenstein, gave a Prom performance of a new work by Ravel – not previously heard in England. What was unusual about the work and the pianist?

As a tribute to Sir Henry Wood on his Golden Jubilee as a conductor, Vaughan Williams dedicated a new work, *Serenade to Music*, to him. What was remarkable about the vocalists?

In 1967, after his Last Night speech, conductor (Sir) Colin Davis brought on a special guest to address the Promenaders. This guest commented that he felt like an intruder since he hadn't won a seat in the ballot for tickets. It was a very emotional occasion. Who was the guest?

In a 1974 televised Prom, André Previn was conducting Carl Orff's *Carmina Burana*. Among the Promenaders, and following the performance with his score, was a young man named Patrick McCarthy. The baritone, Thomas Allen, was nearing the end of a solo ... What happened then?

One Prom in 1954 – an eye- (and ear-) witness account ... The rather frail figure perched himself on a narrow bench on the rostrum. He smoothed his hair and tweaked his goatee beard – both snow-white. The packed Royal Albert Hall howled with delight as he went through the anticipated ritual of pretending to have the wrong score. Then, as he frowned and raised his baton, there was utter silence – for Sibelius, as only he could conduct Sibelius.

'Forza!, Forza!' he shouted out above the fortissimos; it seemed the roof would lift. Then, quieter and quieter; more *ps* than seemed possible – but then, even more. The atmosphere was ultra-electric; the audience transfixed – straining to catch every nuance of an incredible performance.

Then, suddenly, one elderly double bass player, concentrating so very hard, slipped on the spike of his instrument and tumbled. The audience tensed as one. 'Damn you, man!' roared the conductor – his eyes livid with anger.

But there was no falter in the beat, no hesitation in the music, no break in the atmosphere. The incident might never have happened.

This was the Diamond Jubilee year of the Proms. After 40 years away, Sir Thomas Beecham, by then 75 years young, had returned for the second, and last, time.

JAZZ

This so-called 'Father of the Blues' collected, structured formally and published, traditional blues of the labourers and travelling players of America. His first success, in 1914, was *St Louis Blues*. He also wrote *Memphis Blues*, *Beale Street Blues*, *Yellow Dog Blues*, *Long Gone* and dozens of other works. Can you name him?

Which vocalist, when 16 years old, won a talent contest in Harlem, New York, the prize being an engagement with Chick Webb's band? She stayed with the band and her big hit with them was 'A-Tisket, A-Tasket'.

In some areas of traditional jazz, a style of trombone-playing is known as 'tailgate'. Do you know how this came about?

He was born blind, in England, yet came to be one of the great jazz pianists, with a very distinctive style. He settled in America in the late 1940s. Amongst his compositions are *Lullaby of Birdland* and *September in the Rain*. Who is he?

Many say that he was the leader of the finest orchestra ever known to jazz. He wrote more than 2,000 pieces, many of them extended works. Among his compositions were *Mood Indigo*, *Sophisticated Lady*, *Reminiscing in Tempo* and the *Black, Brown and Beige Suite*. Who was he?

Can you name the Italian-born exponent of the jazz violin who, along with guitarist Eddie Lang, originated 'chamber-music' jazz in the late 1920s?

In 1952, Gerry Mulligan formed his famous Quartet. Can you name the members and their instruments?

In 1945, a certain composer heard, on the radio, Woody Herman's Band playing one of their hits – *Caldonia*. He asked if he could write a piece for Woody Herman. Who was the composer, and what was the name of the piece he wrote?

George Melly has, in recent years, sung an excellent version of 'Salty Dog'. Some of you may remember Ottilie Patterson's incredible version, also. But, who was the original composer? (He sang it with Freddie Keppard and his Jazz Cardinals, in a 1926 recording.)

He wrote: 'Charleston'; 'I Can't Give You Anything but Love'; 'If I Could Be With You One Hour Tonight'; 'Running' Wild'; and much else. Known as 'The Grandfather of Hot Piano', he was a champion of 'stride'. Can you name him?

'If you have to ask – you ain't got it!' was **Thomas 'Fats' Waller's** answer to 'What is rhythm?' Pianist, organist, composer and vocalist, he was a very funny and entertaining performer. He also loved his food and liked his gin. He performed the songs that people wanted to hear – but he turned them into jazz.

At fifteen, he was already playing professionally and composing (*Squeeze Me*). The great stride piano player, James P Johnson became his tutor and friend, and with his powerful left hand, Fats took to stride with ease. In turn, he coached another pianist of the same age as himself – William 'Count' Basie. Fats toured widely and composed. *Honeysuckle Rose* and *Ain't Misbehavin'* became standards; other tunes he, naively, sold cheaply – and 'lost'.

On tour in Paris, he performed expertly (with Marcel Dupré) on the organ of Notre Dame Cathedral.

At the age of 39, he collapsed and died aboard a train taking him home for Christmas. It was a great loss to the jazz world.

WHO WROTE ...

In 1904, a Swedish composer wrote a work for orchestra in which he incorporated a folk tune that he'd heard whistled by a cowman. He called the work *Midsommarvaka (Midsummer Vigil)*. Nearly 50 years later, a version of this was used as background music for a clever little English film, *The Stranger Left No Card* – which starred Alan Badel. The tune became extremely popular – both Mantovani and Frank Martin took it into the charts in 1953. Can you name the tune and the original composer?

Arthur Sullivan was devoted to his brother, Fred, who was an architect and a singer – he was the first 'Judge' in *Trial by Jury*. Fred died in 1877, aged 39 years, and Arthur composed a sorrowful melody for verses which were to hand. The result was an incredibly popular ballad. Can you name it?

In 1962, a record producer was inspired by a technological development to compose an organ-dominated piece. The Tornadoes, a band he put together, had a 25-week No 1 hit with the piece. Can you name it, and the composer?

In 1916, Ernest Bloch – just before leaving Switzerland for America – visited the home of the cellist, Alexander Barjanski. There he saw a statue of King Solomon. Can you name the rhapsody he was inspired to write?

Which English composer wrote a string quartet, *Dialectic*, in 1929, the operas *Wat Tyler* and *Men of Blackmoor* in the 1950s, and *Lidice* – which he conducted at the site of the massacre in Czechoslovakia?

… WHAT?

This English composer, with fierce single-mindedness, tried to create an English equivalent of Wagner's Bayreuth at Glastonbury – with his Arthurian cycle of operas. One of these was performed at Glastonbury in 1914, with the composer singing a baritone lead. Elgar said it was a work of genius. It was successful in London in the early 1920s, playing for 216 performances. Can you name the composer and the opera?

He was born in Birmingham in 1875. He wrote some of the most successful popular/serious tone pictures ever, including: *In a Monastery Garden* (with bird songs and monks chanting); *Bells Across the Meadow*; *In a Persian Market* (with its famous 'backsheesh' chorus); *The Sanctuary of the Heart*; and *Bank Holiday ('Appy 'Ampstead)*. Can you name this composer?

In the years between the wars, an annual event at the Royal Albert Hall was a semi-dramatised performance of a musical trilogy based on Longfellow's *The Song of Hiawatha*. Can you name the composer? Hiawatha's song to Minnehaha at their wedding feast, became a solo tenor favourite. How was it known?

The Song of Hiawatha, by Longfellow, published in1855, made a huge impact in Europe. **Dvořák** planned to write an opera on the story – but he never did.

In 1892, he was in New York, teaching, and writing his symphony *From the New World*. Needing a holiday, he took his family on a tour. In Minneapolis, they visited the now famous 'Falls of Minnehaha', and he jotted down a tune that he 'heard in the falls'. This was used, not for a Hiawatha opera, but for his Sonatina in G, Opus 100, for violin and piano.

The family also stayed in Spillville, Iowa, a community of Bohemian immigrants. Inspired by the tranquillity and a species of bird – the scarlet tanager – that kept him awake at night, he wrote the American Quartet No 6 in F, Opus 96; the bird features in the third movement.

Back home in Bohemia, he did, in 1901, write an opera, and the music was inspired by the Spillville visit. But it was not Hiawatha. It was *Rusalka*, the story of a water nymph.

PASTICCIO

One of the most remarkable infant prodigies ever, was born in 1755 in Norwich. At the age of four he was giving organ recitals; by seven, he could play the piano and the violin. His first oratorio, *The Captivity of Judah*, was performed when he was 14 years old. Today, only one of his compositions is heard with any regularity. This is an anthem, *Lo Star-led Chiefs*, from his oratorio of 1812, *Palestine*. Can you name him?

In the 1942 film *Casablanca*, Humphrey Bogart says, 'Play it, Sam' (not 'again' – that is a misquotation). So, what was 'it'? A version of 'it' got into the charts in 1977, sung by 'Sam'. Who played the part of Sam? Finally, which unlikely performer sang 'it' on the soundtrack of the 1993 film *Sleepless in Seattle*?

Jeremias Friedrich Witt (1771–1837) was an Austrian composer of masses and orchestral works. In 1957, one of his symphonies gained some temporary fame. Do you know why?

One method of teaching children to sing from music is known as 'Tonic Sol-fa'. Do you know who devised it?

In which musical, by whom, would you hear a song extolling 'Paul Revere', 'Valentine', 'Epitaph' and 'Big Threat'?

Can you name the Polish composer whose Symphony No 3, *The Symphony of Sorrowful Songs*, written in 1976, hit the classical and pop charts in 1993? And, can you say which words, from where, inspired the work?

The anthem 'I was glad' was written in 1902 for the coronation of Edward VII and has been sung for the three subsequent coronations as the Sovereign enters Westminster Abbey. Who wrote it?

Grieg's song, 'Ich Liebe Dich' ('I Love Thee'), Opus 5, No 3, is one of his most popular. Do you know who wrote the words?

Debussy once wrote musical criticism under the pseudonym, 'M Croche'. What is a *croche*?

Who wrote the 1966/67 hits, 'I Love My Dog' and 'Matthew and Son'?

The Three Tenors gained great popularity after their concerts at the end of the 1990, 1994 and 1998 World Cups. Can you name them? Which of them was, in his youth, a member of a prize-winning choir at the Llangollen International Eisteddfod, returning there to perform on stage 40 years later? Which of them was a soloist at Llangollen in 1968? And which of them sang the title role in Verdi's opera, *Stiffélio*, at Covent Garden, in 1993?

Johann Georg Albrechtsberger (1736–1809) was a celebrated organist and teacher. He taught Mozart's son – but who was his most famous pupil? Albrechtsberger became preoccupied with fugues, but he did write some delightful concertos. One of these, in E major, featured in the score for the 1991 film *Doc Hollywood*. It is for Jew's harp and mandora. What are these instruments?

Klopstock's Morgengesang am Schöpfungfeste must surely take the prize for the prettiest music with the most off-putting title. In the 1780s, CPE Bach (the 'Hamburg' Bach) was the city's leading musical light. Friedrich Gottlieb Klopstock was its leading poet. The two combined their talents for this work – which translates as *Klopstock's Morning Song on the Celebration of Creation*.

DESCRIPTIONS

The 'lecture-recital' is a familiar form of musical education/ entertainment. Which musician was the first to present such lectures in Britain?

Berlioz used the expression '*idée fixe*' for something that is more commonly known as a 'motto theme'. What do they mean?

What, in harmony, is false (or cross) relation?

The few bars, below, (much simplified) are from the *Alla Hornpipe* of Handel's *Water Music*. They show an example of syncopation. What is syncopation?

63

Which collection of works is sometimes known as 'The Old Testament of Keyboard Music'? And which as 'The New Testament of Keyboard Music'?

64

The descriptions 'strophic' and 'through-composed' are sometimes given to types of vocal composition. What do they mean?

65

What is the tonic of a musical scale? And what is the supertonic?

66

What is meant by *portamento*? And, what is meant by *glissando*?

THE 'WEAKER' SEX

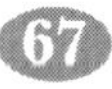

This Greek coloratura soprano was born in New York, made her stage debut in Athens, at the age of 14, as the lead in Mascagni's *Cavalleria Rusticana*, and her professional debut singing in a barrel, in Suppé's *Boccaccio*. Her last operatic stage performance – at Covent Garden – was in 1965, as an incredible 'Tosca', to Tito Gobbi's unsurpassed 'Scarpia'. Can you name her?

Can you name the Scottish composer, whose opera, *Blond Eckbert*, was acclaimed in 1994?

The songs of the soprano, Jetty Treffz, were the inspiration for Johann Strauss II's *Lieder Quadrille*. How? And, do you know how her next-but-one successor inspired a Gershwin song?

The English composer (Dame) Ethel Smyth once conducted a March that she had specially composed, using a toothbrush as a baton. Do you know how this came about?

Ethel Smyth (1858–1944) was the first woman to succeed as a composer of a wide range of major works – and, she had the additional handicap of being British. It was a real battle for her to be accepted – as her several literary works reveal.

She studied music in Leipzig and several of her early works were first performed in Germany. In 1893, her Mass in D (an oratorio setting) was premièred at the Royal Albert Hall. It was not heard again for 30 years.

Her first opera, *Fantasio*, was produced in Weimar in 1898. Other operas followed: *Der Wald (The Wood)* in 1902; *The Wreckers* in 1906; and *The Boatswain's Mate* in 1916.

In her battle for recognition, she had become caught up in Women's Suffrage, composing *March of the Women*, and spending several months in prison, as a militant suffragist. The 1920s were better. Sir Henry Wood premièred several of her short works at the Proms, and she was created a Dame. In 1927, she wrote a concerto for violin and horn.

In the 1930s, her oratorio *The Prison* was first performed, and, in her mid-70s, she conducted her one-act operas, *Fête galante* and *Entente Cordiale* at Christmas Proms. Feminists of today, take heart!

ONE-LINERS

71 Who wrote *The RAF March Past*?

72 What, in the eighteenth century, was 'The War of Buffoons'?

73 Who wrote *The Lambeth Walk* and for which musical?

74 Which note of a musical scale is the subdominant?

75 The dancers of what represent a matador and his cloak?

76 Who wrote Kim Wilde's first hit single 'Kids in America'?

77 Whose creations include *Oxygène* and *Equinoxe*?

78 Which French composers were called, in 1917, '*Les Six*'?

79 Who were 'The Frankfurt Five'? (Four English, one Australian.)

80 And who, in the 1950s, were the Manchester Group?

81 Which rhapsody connects Delius, Grainger and Joseph Taylor?

82 Who wrote and produced *The Ballad of Sally Rose*, in 1985?

83 Who wrote the title music for the TV series *Secret Army*?

84 Who, at the age of ten, played Beethoven at a 1937 Prom?

85 The oratorio *A Child of Our Time* was written, in 1941, by whom?

86 Which of Dvořák's symphonies was known as 'The English'?

87 For which virtuoso did Tchaikovsy write his violin concerto?

88 ... But which violinist premièred it in 1881, and why?

89 Who wrote the theme music for the TV series *Morse*?

90 Which trumpeter wrote, in 1992, *In this House, On this Morning*?

91 Who was Josef Lanner (1801–43)?

92 Who was Karl Ditters von Dittersdorf (1739–99)?

93 Who was Juan Crisóstomo Jacobo Antonio Arriaga (1806–26)?

94 Who was the librettist of Albéniz's opera *Henry Clifford*?

95 Whose affliction was echoed in his first string quartet (1876)?

96 Who wrote Janis Joplin's 1971 hit 'Me and Bobby McGee'?

97 ... And who starred as Janis in the 1979 film *The Rose*?

98 Larry Adler may perform whose *Bolero* without paying a fee?

99 Whose hit single, 27 years after her death, was called 'Crazy'?

100 Who, apart from Elgar, wrote a work called *Enigma Variations*?

TOM BOWLING

On 21 October 1905, the Promenade Concert celebrated the centenary of Nelson's Victory at Trafalgar with appropriate music and songs. A new work was played: Henry Wood's *Fantasia on British Sea Songs*. Who could have guessed that, every year since then, Promenaders would stamp and clap to the *Hornpipe*, weep at 'Home, Sweet Home', and sing their hearts out with 'Rule, Britannia!'? Or that, when the leading cello starts its beautiful and plaintive theme, *Tom Bowling* would still bring a lump to the throat of many. After all, who was Tom Bowling?

In Southampton, in 1745, Charles Dibdin was born, one of a large family, and with a passion for music, the theatre and the sea. His eldest brother, Tom, was a sailor and he paid for young Charles to go to London – where he found work playing the organ and tuning harpsichords. Before long, he was writing ballads and music for the theatres and pleasure gardens. He soon prospered and wrote literally hundreds of songs, dozens of musical plays, and operas and operettas. Today, one of his best remembered songs is 'The Bells of Aberdovey', from his opera *Liberty Hall*. He wrangled with such as Garrick, Sheridan and Grimaldi. His marital and his financial dealings caused eyebrows to be raised.

Brother Tom, in the meantime, had been captured at sea by the French, imprisoned, released, and gone to work in India. Charles wanted to join him, but got only as far as Torquay! Then, tragically, on board ship returning to England, Tom was struck by lightning and paralysed. He died off the Cape of Good Hope.

Charles was devastated. He turned to writing sea songs and performing them in his own theatre. 'Tom Bowling' was written as a portrait of his brother. His patriotic songs were appreciated by the public and by the authorities. He was encouraged to join in naval recruitment drives and even sent to Portsmouth to sing to the Spithead and Nore mutineers. It was said that, during the war with France, Charles Dibdin – through his songs – brought more men into the Navy than did the press gangs.

He died in 1814 and was buried at Camden Town. Lines from 'Tom Bowling' were carved on his tombstone.

MORE SAD ENDS

Williams Lawes (1602–45), whose compositions included 'Gather Ye Rosebuds While Ye May', looked out of a window and was shot by a sniper, at the siege of Chester, during the Civil War.

Henry Purcell (1659–95), described as '... one of the most celebrated Masters of the Science of Musick in the Kingdom and scarce inferior to any in Europe', died from catching cold after being accidentally locked out of his own house at night.

Franz Kotzwara (1750–93), a Czech composer best remembered for his sonata *The Battle of Prague*, was known to have indulged in 'strange sexual practices'. These led to his accidental death by hanging, in a house of ill repute, in Covent Garden, London.

Robert Schumann (1810–56), died in an asylum two years after throwing himself in the Rhine.

Stephen Foster (1826–64), died after fainting and falling across a washbasin, cutting his neck and face.

Josef Strauss (1827–70), was conducting in Warsaw when the orchestra 'got out of hand'. He collapsed, dying shortly after, in Vienna.

Charles Alkan (1813–88), a brilliant French pianist and composer (real name, Morhange), reportedly died when, reaching for his Talmud, he brought down a bookcase on to himself. (Since then, others have said that he died of 'natural causes'.)

Mieczyslaw Karlowicz (1876–1909), a noted Polish composer, died, buried in an avalanche, whilst skiing in the Tatra Mountains.

Gustave Kobbé (1857–1918), the American musicologist known for his *Complete Opera Book*, was sailing off Long Island when a landing seaplane struck his boat. He died instantly.

George Gershwin (1898–1937), suddenly stopped playing when performing his own Piano Concerto at a Los Angeles concert. He had suffered a temporary blackout. A few months later, he died of a brain tumour.

Ivor Gurney (1890–1937), English poet and composer, died in an asylum to which he had been committed in 1922. At that time he had become mentally and physically incapacitated by his very bad experiences in the trenches during World War One.

Bessie Smith (1894–1937), the American blues singer, died in an ambulance after a car crash. It was said that she was refused admittance to a 'whites only' hospital. Now, this is said to be untrue.

Joe 'King' Oliver (1885–1938), the great jazz cornetist, started to lose his teeth and could get little work in the depression of the 1930s. Stranded in Georgia doing menial jobs, he saved dimes for his fare back to New York and for a set of dentures. He never saved enough. He fell ill and, unable to afford medical treatment, he died.

Anton von Webern (1883–1945), the Austrian composer, was denounced by the Nazis as a 'cultural Bolshevik' and his music was banned. With the end of World War Two he was visiting his family near Salzburg. Strolling out of the house to smoke a cigarette, he was shot dead by an American soldier of the army of occupation whom he startled.

Wallingford Riegger (1885–1961), an American cellist, conductor and composer, died from the head injuries he incurred after becoming entangled in the leads of two dogs that were fighting.

Otis Redding (1941–67), American soul singer and composer, drowned when his plane crashed into a lake in Wisconsin.

John Lennon (1940–80), was murdered by a so-called 'fan' in New York.

John Denver (1943–97), American singer-songwriter, died when the plane he was piloting dived into Monterey Bay.

'CLASSICAL' CROSSWORD

1		2			3	■	4		5			6
	■		■	■		■		■		■	■	
7				■		■	8					
	■		■	■		■		■		■	■	
	■		■	9				10	■	11	■	
	■		■		■	■	■		■		■	
■	12					■	13					■
14	■		■		■	■	■		■		■	15
	■		■	16	17		18		■		■	
	■	■	19	■		■		■	■		■	
20						■		■	21			
	■	■		■		■		■	■		■	
22						■	23					

Clues Across

1 Belgian organist, composer and teacher, whose tone poems included *The Djinns* and *The Accursed Hunter (Le Chasseur Maudit)*. He died in 1890 after being struck by a horse-omnibus. (6)

4 He wrote 'Ein' Feste Burg' ('A Safe Stronghold'), the hymn of the Reformation. (6)

7 In the USA, a semibreve is known as a whole ____. (4)

8 Title of Richard Strauss's one-act opera of 1905, after Oscar Wilde's stage poem. (6)

9 B, E, A, D, G, C, F, is the order of these in the key signature. (5)

12 Mendelssohn wrote melodic pieces for the piano, which he called ____ *Without Words*. (5)

Clues Across (cont)

13 The five lines upon which music is written. (5)

16 English composer of the five *Pomp and Circumstance Marches.* (5)

20 Sir Arthur Bliss's symphony of 1922, whose movements are called *Purple, Red, Blue* and *Green.* (6)

21 French composer of the opera *Le Roi d'Ys (The King of Ys)*. His *Symphonie Espagnole* was written for the violin virtuoso, Sarasate. (4)

22 Drum beat, or bugle call. (6)

23 The title of operas by Jacopo Peri (in 1597) and Richard Strauss (in 1938). (6)

Clues Down

1 The last movement of a work. (6)

2 Alternate chanting, or singing, by a choir divided into two parts. (9)

3 Emmy ____ was a Czech soprano who sang as Emmy Destinn. She sang the lead in the first performance (New York, 1910) of Puccini's *The Girl of the Golden West*, opposite Caruso, and with Toscanini conducting. (5)

4 This composer and pianist was the first to use the term 'symphonic poem'. He became Wagner's father-in-law. (5)

5 ____ *Eulenspiegel,* is a symphonic poem composed, in 1895, by Richard Strauss. (4)

6 The title of Wagner's opera of 1842, from Bulwer Lytton's novel, about the last of the Roman tribunes. (6)

9 JS Bach's *The Art of* ____ was unfinished at his death. (5)

10 In 1968, Ravi Shankar wrote a concerto for this instrument. (5)

11 His first big success, in 1858, was *Orpheus in the Underworld.* (9)

14 Sweet and soothing sound; a four-foot organ stop. (6)

15 Play it again! (6)

17 Broad. Slow and stately. (5)

18 The finest of all Stradivari's violins, made in 1715. (5)

19 The bass note of a chord. Or, the name of the composer of the American Civil War marching song, 'We'll Rally Round the Flag!'. (4)

RECAPITULATION ...

Now try these questions to see if you have widened your musical horizons. You will be able to work out the answers to the eight Recapitulation Questions from this book. For the answers to the Coda Questions, you may like to do a little investigation on your own. Give yourself one mark for any answer you are happy with, plus one mark per question for any extra information you can provide. Take as much time as you like!

Which jazz pianist wrote *Ain't Misbehavin'*?

Beethoven's 'Battle Symphony' was originally written for performance by what?

Which Christmas carol was the first real carol to come from America?

Wagner, on hearing a certain tune, is supposed to have said that the first eight notes expressed the true British character. This tune had been written by Thomas Arne for his 1740 masque, *Alfred*. It has been arranged and used (in part or whole) by several composers since then. Can you name it from these eight notes?

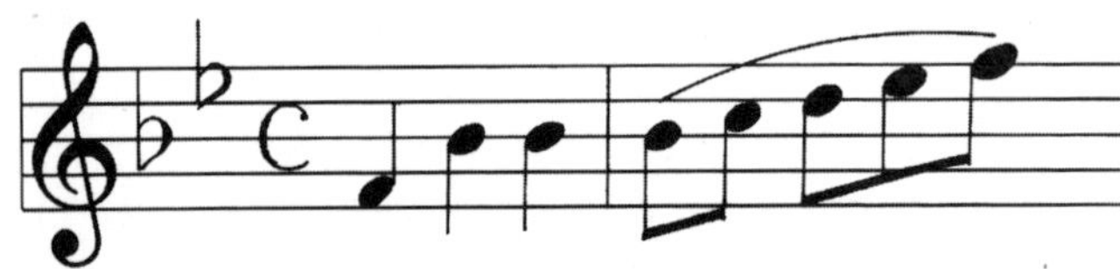

Who wrote the operetta *La Belle Hélène*?

In which section of an orchestra would you find the oboe?

Which member of '*Les Six*' wrote the theme music for the 1952 film *Moulin Rouge*?

Can you name John Denver's hit of 1974 which was No 1 in both the UK and the USA?

... AND CODA

Edward Elgar originally intended to write six *Pomp and Circumstance* marches. How many did he complete?

Which instruments did Jack Teagarden (1905–64) play?

The theme music for the TV series *Van der Valk* put the Simon Park Orchestra into the charts for more than 70 weeks in the early 1970s. What was it called?

Which Puccini opera has its setting in the California Gold Rush? And, do you know who wrote the play on which the opera was based?

Here are the titles of three works by an American composer who lived from 1874 to 1954: *Central Park in the Dark; The Unanswered Question*; and *General Booth Enters into Heaven*. Who was he?

Which group (from Montserrat and Germany) had No 1 hit in 1982 with 'Seven Tears'? (It happens to be a 'favourite' of one of the authors!)

Paul Dukas composed one of the pieces interpreted in the Walt Disney film, *Fantasia*. Which?

What is a fugue? (This will require a somewhat lengthy answer!)

. . . .

Now, if – since opening up this book – you have listened to any piece of music that, previously, would have been outside your range, give yourself an extra eight marks. You will now have a score somewhere between 0 and 40.

0 *Da Capo al Fine*!!
1–10 Well, you've made a good start
11–20 You are to be applauded
21–30 Bravo!
31–40 *Bravissimo*!!

PART TWO

CROSSING OVER

Placido Domingo

Note: *Zarzuela* (pronounced thar-thway-la) is a kind of short operetta with (often improvised) dialogue. The name comes from the royal palace, *La Zarzuela*, near Madrid, where such performances were once popular.

Beverley Sills. She retired from the stage at the age of 50, becoming a director of the New York City Opera.

Benny Goodman (1909–86)

Note: The Bartók work was *Contrasts* for clarinet, violin and piano. The Copland clarinet concerto was later used for a ballet by Jerome Robbins.

Hugo Rignold (1905–76)

Elvis Costello

Ferde Grofé (1892–1972)

Tommy Steele

David Hughes (1929–72)

Robert Russell Bennett

Richard Rodney Bennett

NOTATION

The five parallel lines on which music is written. Either name (staff or stave) may be used. Leger lines are short lines added above or below a stave, where necessary, to indicate notes that lie outside the range of the stave.

The four notes are all 'C' but at different pitches. The Cs are each an octave apart. The C on the leger line between the staves is known as 'Middle C'. (In practice, leger lines will be added, separately, below the upper stave and/or above the lower stave.)

Note: In simple terms, pitch can be thought of as the height or depth of a sound. An octave (meaning 'eight notes') is the interval between two notes that have the same name.

The clefs are signs placed at the beginning of each stave to indicate the pitch of the notes written on the staves.

Note: Clef is from the Latin word for 'a key'. It is the key (in the sense of 'the clue') to the names of the notes on the stave.

The clef on the upper stave is the Treble (or G) Clef. It circles around the second line of the stave and 'fixes' that line as 'G'. The clef on the lower stave is the Bass (or F) Clef. The two dots are either side of the fourth line of the stave and 'fix' the pitch of 'F'.

Note: There are other clefs, but the G Clef and F Clef are those most commonly used. Originally, the signs were a capital letter G and a capital letter F.

Respectively, flat and sharp

It indicates the key in which the music that follows is to be played; that is, which sharps or flats are involved.

These indicate the time signature, that is the rhythm of the music that follows. 2/4 time means there are two quarter note (crochet) beats to a bar (measure). 4/4 time (four crochet beats to a bar) is sometimes called common time and shown by a sign that looks like a 'c'. This is not intended as the first letter of 'common'. In early times, music in 3 time was considered 'perfect' and was represented by a circle (of perfection). Other music was thought 'imperfect' and was represented by an incomplete circle (looking like a 'c').

Note: A semibreve is taken to be a whole note. Two minims make a semibreve, so the minim is a half note. Two crochets make a minim, so the crochet is a quarter note. Two quavers make a crochet, so a quaver is an eighth note, and so on.

TV ADS

Carole Bayer Sager and Marvin Hamlisch

Ron Grainer

Note: Australian-born Ron Grainer has written musicals and incidental music for the stage as well as film and TV scores. The latter include such as *Maigret*, *Dr Who*, *Paul Temple*, *Panorama* and *South Riding*.

Cyndi Lauper

'First Time Ever I Saw Your Face' composed by Ewan MacColl

'He Ain't Heavy He's My Brother'

From the TV commercial song, 'I Want To Buy the World a Coke', with the words modified

Kal Mann and Dave Appell

OPERA

We have counted 232, but that number should not be taken as definitive. Incidentally, 42 is the number of works based on *The Tempest*, alone.

26

'Ombra mai fù'. In orchestral arrangements, this is known as 'Handel's Largo'.

27

She smoked!

28

1600. That year saw the first performance of *Euridice* by Jacopo Peri. This included some music by Giulio Caccini who, later the same year, set the same text for an opera of his own.

Note: 1597 was the year of *Dafni* (or *Daphne*) by Peri, but the score is lost. 1643 was the year in which Monteverdi died.

29

At the dying composer's request, completed by César Cui and Nicholas Rimsky-Korsakov (who orchestrated it).

Note: Cui (1835–1918) and Rimsky-Korsakov (1844–1908) were members of the (Russian) group of 'The Five'.

30

It was commissioned for Covent Garden, London, with words by the English writer, James Robinson Planché.

Note: Poor Weber had problems! Planché sent him the verses, piecemeal and out of sequence. He had to compose the music in Dresden, with Planché in London. Weber died in London, two months after conducting the first performance, in 1826.

31

Weber's cousin, Constanze, became Mrs Mozart in 1782.

32

Giacomo Puccini (1858–1924)

33

The last word of the aria (sung three times) is 'Vinceró!', which means 'I shall win!'.

34

Love

35

Franco Alfano (1876–1954)

36

Arturo Toscanini

Note: Toscanini had visual problems but an incredible memory which enabled him to conduct to perfection without a score.

37

Cecchina

38

La Belle Hélène

Le Châlet, called in English, *The Swiss Cottage*

The opera was written and rehearsed in Terezín, the German 'showplace' concentration camp in the north of Czechoslovakia. The opera was anti-Hitler and anti-war and performance in the camp was forbidden. Within a few weeks the composer, Ullmann (a pupil of Schoenburg), and the librettist, Kien, were sent to Auschwitz, to death.

Note: Among the singers at the rehearsal was the Czech bass, Karel Berman. He sang the part of 'Death', but did survive to have an acclaimed career with the Czech National Opera.

Ullmann's opera was not publicly performed until 1975. It was filmed for British TV in 1979.

There were 15 performances of Verdi's *Requiem* at Terezín in 1943 and 1944. After the first performance, half of the singers were sent to Auschwitz.

BALLET

Charles Louis Beauchamp (1636–1705) is thought to have defined the Five Positions in 1661, when he was director of the Royal Academy of Dance, established by Louis XIV.

Gaetano Vestris (1729–1808)

He helped to get rid of the heavy wigs, the masks and padded costumes that the court dancers wore. He encouraged natural movements and dramatic action.

Note: Early performances of ballet carried on the traditions of the court dancers. Until the late 1600s, female roles were danced by men since women did not dance professionally.

Tchaikovsky's Serenade for Strings in C, Opus 48.

Choreartium used Brahms' Symphony No 4 in E minor. *Rouge et Noir* used Symphony No 1 in E minor by Shostakovich.

Tchaikovsky's ballet, *The Nutcracker*. (At the end of Act 1, the singing accompanies the dancers who are depicting snowflakes.)

Billy the Kid, the 1938 ballet music by the American composer Aaron Copland (1900–90).

Note: Eugene Loring choreographed *Billy the Kid* and danced as Billy in the first production of the ballet.

Frédéric Chopin. *Chopiniana*. Diaghilev changed the title to *Les Sylphides* in 1909, for his Paris production, as a tribute to Marie Taglioni.

Note: It seems that Michel Fokine, shopping in St Petersburg, came across the unpublished score of an orchestral suite, *Chopiniana*, Glazounov's Opus 46. It was based on music by Chopin. In 1907 this suite was arranged as a ballet. The following year, a different selection of Chopin's music was arranged for a ballet which was called *Chopiniana*. This was produced in St Petersburg, starring Pavlova and Nijinsky. All the female dancers wore long white Romantic dresses. It was this version that was performed in Paris as *Les Sylphides*.

FAMILIES

49

Carl Philipp Emanuel (CPE) Bach (1714–1788) was the third son. The ninth son was Johann Christoph Friedrich Bach (1732–93). The eleventh son was Johann Christian (JC) Bach (1735–82). (You may well find that different books of reference number the sons differently. We are not sure why, but it could possibly be because J S Bach was married twice.)

50

Charles Wesley and his son Samuel Wesley

Note: Charles and John Wesley were brothers who founded the Methodist movement. Charles's son, Samuel, turned to Roman Catholicism in his teens. He was a champion of J S Bach in England.

51

Antonin Dvořák (1841–1904) and his son-in-law Joseph Suk (1875–1935)

Note: 'Asrael' is the angel of death. Suk married Dvořák's daughter, Otilia, but she died the year after her father. Suk's symphony, written in the year of her death, mourns their loss.

52

Alessandro Scarlatti and his son Domenico Scarlatti

Note: Both the Queen of Sweden and the Queen of Poland were living in Rome at the time of their patronage.

53

Giuseppina Strepponi and Giuseppe Verdi

PASTICCIO

54

A work composed in the style of another composer. ('Pasticcio' can also be used for, say, variations which are written, one each, by a group of composers.)

55

Bing Crosby

56

Richard Wagner. The work is *Grosser Festmarsch (American Centennial March)*.

Note: The march was commissioned from Philadelphia. Somewhat lengthy for such a march, the work takes nearly a quarter of an hour to play!

Franz Liszt

Iolanthe, or *The Peer and the Peri*, first produced in 1882

THEMES

'The Last Rose of Summer'. It features in the opera *Martha* by Friedrich von Flotow.
Note: Martha is subtitled *Richmond Fair* (The Surrey Richmond). Mendelssohn wrote a Piano Fantasia on the tune and Beethoven made a setting of it.

'The Lass of Richmond Hill'
Note: This was the Yorkshire Richmond. The 'Lass' did become Mrs McNally. Leonard McNally went on to lead a strange and exciting life, far removed from the Arts!

Symphonic Variations for Piano and Orchestra

The Fair Melusine, Opus 32

NICKNAMES

Because of the 'ticking' motif in the slow movement

It was said that the Devil appeared to him in a dream and played to him. That visitation inspired the work.

'The Little Wonder', from which: Stevie Wonder

Duke Ellington, Louis Armstrong, Count Basie and Glenn Miller. Louis Armstrong was nicknamed 'Satchelmouth' (or 'Satchmo').

67

The fourth movement contains a set of variations on the theme of his song, 'Die Forelle' ('The Trout').

68

In the last movement, the players of the orchestra, one by one, blow out their candles and quietly leave, until only two players remain at the end of the work.

Note: The work was a hint to Haydn's employer at Esterhaz that the orchestra were anxious to get away to their homes in Vienna at the end of performances. It is said that the Prince did take the hint.

69

It was considered to be written by Leopold Mozart (the father of Wolfgang Amadeus) as part of a larger work. However, recent researchers say it was the work of Haydn's brother, Michael.

70

Luigi Boccherini (and very unfairly, we think!)

Note: Boccherini (1743–1805) wrote nearly 500 works, mostly chamber music, but also flute and cello concertos. His output has been described as imitative of Haydn. Sadly, except for his famous 'Minuet', his works are rarely performed today.

ONE-LINERS

Thespis or *The Gods Grown Old*, produced at the Gaiety Theatre in 1871. Now believed 'lost'.

72

Dublin (at the Music Room, Fishamble Street) in April 1742.

Note: Handel wrote *Messiah* in 23 days, in 1741.

73

Coppélia. (It is the subtitle of Delibes' ballet.)

Franz Liszt

Note: It was all very complicated! Wagner married Minna Planer in 1836. She died 30 years later. In 1870 he married Cosima, the divorced wife of Hans von Bülow. He, Bülow, had studied piano with Liszt and conducted with Wagner. Liszt had conducted the first performance of Wagner's *Lohengrin* in 1850. Bülow had conducted the first performances of Wagner's *Tristan and Isolde* (1865) and *Die Meistersinger* (1868)...

75

Gloria Gaynor

Note: The song was featured in the 1994 film *Four Weddings and a Funeral.*

76

Arpeggio. This indicates that the notes of a chord should be played successively, not simultaneously. *Adagio* and *allegro* indicate the pace of the music. *Adagio* indicates slow, leisurely; *allegro* indicates lively, reasonably fast.

77

St Cecilia, since the fifteenth century. (No one seems to know why she was chosen.)

78

Giovanni Paisiello (1740–1816)

Note: Paisiello wrote over 100 operas including a *Barber of Seville* which predated Rossini's.

79

Strictly speaking, 'in the church style'. Generally, it indicates a composition or arrangement for unaccompanied voices.

80

In the style of gypsy music

81

Julie Covington, Rula Lenska, Charlotte Cornwell, Sue Jones-Davies

82

'Don't Cry for Me Argentina'

83

Evita. Lyrics by Tim Rice.

84

Joseph Haydn

Note: Haydn is also known as 'The Father of the Symphony'.

The flute

Note: Theobald Boehm (1793–1881) made many improvements to the mechanism of the flute. He developed a system of fingering which was accepted almost universally.

Count Basie. He used it as his signature tune.

Seven. The eighth, long hoped for, never materialised.

A passing note is one which moves, by step, between two chords and temporarily creates a discord. The 'starred' note below is an example.

89

The saxophone

Note: Sax, a few years later, designed a whole family of what were known as 'saxhorns'. There ranged from high treble to deep bass. They were much featured in French military bands.

Carl Nielsen (Danish composer, 1865–1931)

Berry Gordy

The Village People

In the musical, *Hair*

Note: Hair was first produced in 1968. The music is by Gerome Ragni and the lyrics by James Rado.

Mario Cavaradossi was the painter hero (tenor) in Puccini's opera *Tosca.*

Dangerous Moonlight

96

Richard Addinsell (1904–77)

97

Adolphe Charles Adam (1803–56)

98

Gerry and the Pacemakers

Note: The first three releases were: 'How Do You Do It?'; 'I Like It'; and 'You'll Never Walk Alone'.

99

The American expression for what we know as 'Nursery Rhymes'.

100

Jona Lewie (who wrote and performed the song).

Note: The tune has a passing resemblance to a polka, *The Little Hen*, from Smetana's *Bohemian Dances*.

OPERA HOSPITALITY

The Polka Inn: *The Girl of the Golden West*; Puccini; 1910

The Café Momus: *La Bohème*; Puccini; 1896

The Three Cousins: *La Périchole*; Offenbach; 1868

The Tavern of Lillas Pastia: *Carmen*; Bizet; 1875

Luther's Tavern: *The Tales of Hoffmann*; Offenbach; 1881

The Garter Inn: *The Merry Wives of Windsor*; Nicolai; 1849

Inn of the Golden Fleur de Lys: *The Journey to Reims*; Rossini; 1825

The Boar Inn: *Peter Grimes*; Britten; 1945

The Black Eagle: *Elegy for Young Lovers*; Henze; 1961

The Vikárka Inn: *The Adventures of Mr Brouček*; Janáček; 1920

Notes: Arturo Toscanini (1867–1957) conducted the first performances of the two Puccini operas. The third Act of *La Périchole* was not added until a revival in 1874. Written as a gala piece for the actual coronation, *The Journey to Reims* had only four performances in 1825. It was revised and revived for modern-style performance in 1984.

POP

Adam Faith's 'As You Like It'; David Essex's 'A Winter's Tale'; Dire Straits' 'Romeo and Juliet'. (There may be others.)

The jazz pianist, Erroll Garner

Nancy Sinatra

Nancy Sinatra and her father, Frank Sinatra

'Get Back' (in 1969). It featured Billy Preston, the keyboard virtuoso and vocalist.

Note: Billy also participated in all the tracks for *Let It Be*, the Beatles farewell album and appeared in the film of the same name. Guided by George Harrison, he went on to make a string of hit records, firstly alone, and then with Syreeta.

'Ernie', alias Benny Hill. He was top of the charts for 17 weeks.

Phil Spector

Cilla Black

'Ol' Man River'; 'Summertime'; 'What'd I Say'; 'Angels Listened In'; 'Ko Ko Mo'; 'Look at Me'; 'Over and Over'; 'Sick and Tired'; 'Soul City'; 'There is a Woman'.

Note: At this time the Brothers were Bobby Hatfield and Billy Medley.

John Denver, himself

James Galway (flute)

'Save your Kisses for Me'. It was top of the charts for 16 weeks.

In 1967, 'Puppet on a String', sung by Sandie Shaw. In 1969, 'Boom Bang-A-Bang', sung by Lulu. This was, in fact, joint winner. Four entrants tied for the first place.

Right Said Fred

Bernard Cribbens

Note: Bernard Cribben's song was about a pair of furniture removers, Fred being the boss.

Johnny Mathis

Lonnie Donegan

Note: Lonnie Donegan took his name from the blues singer, Lonnie Johnson.

HOME-GROWN

The Music Makers, Opus 69. This is a setting of the poem, *Ode*, by Arthur O'Shaughnessy. The poem begins: 'We are the music makers, and we are the dreamers of dreams' – as does Elgar's work.

(Sir) Edward German

Note: Edward German (1862–1936) was an English composer. His original name was Edward German Jones; he 'dropped' the surname in his youth.

20

Stanley Myers

Note: Stanley Myers (1930–93) was the first musician to win the Cannes Festival award for best artistic contribution, in 1987, with his score for the film *Prick Up Your Ears*.

21

(Sir) William Walton (1902–83)

22

(Sir) John Stainer (1840–1901)

23

The music of Handel

24

Gustav Holst (1874–1934). From his orchestral suite, *The Planets*, specifically, *Jupiter, the Bringer of Jollity*. The tune is also known as the hymn tune, *Thaxted*, for the well-loved hymn, 'I Vow to Thee My Country'.

Note: Holst was living in Thaxted, Essex, when he began writing *The Planets*.

Sir Arthur Sullivan

Note: The music was mostly taken from the Savoy operas and the story was based on a 'Bab Ballad' by Gilbert. 'Bab' was Gilbert's nickname as a child. His 'Bab Ballads' appeared in the magazine *Fun* in the 1860s. They were amusing tales, often concealing a sort of schoolboyish unkindness. The copyright on Sullivan's music expired in 1950.

26

(Sir) Arnold Bax (1883–1953). He called the work, simply, *Tintagel*.

Note: Bax regularly wrote Irish short stories under the name of Dermot O'Byrne. He was appointed Master of the King's Musick in 1942.

27

(Sir) Peter Maxwell Davies wrote the opera called *Taverner*. John Taverner (1495–1545) composed church music, was choirmaster and organist in Oxford, was thrown into a cellar for heresy, and actively supported Thomas Cromwell in his persecution and dissolution of monasteries. Quite a story for the book of an opera!

John Tavener (b 1944). *Ultimos Ritos* was a meditation in music on San Juan de la Cruz (St John of the Cross). San Juan founded, in 1568, with St Teresa of Avila, the Order of Discalced (bare-footed) Carmelites. Tavener's *Song for Athene* was heard at the funeral service for Diana, Princess of Wales.

Note: Taverner and Tavener are separated by 450 years, but it is known for them to be confused! One of the authors, trying to buy a recording of John Tavener's *The Protecting Veil*, was told by the catalogue-searching shop assistant, 'I can't trace it. Isn't he a bit ancient to be making new records?'

The Fringes of the Fleet

NOTATION

A minim (𝅗𝅥) is the value of two crochets (♩), and a crochet is the value of two quavers (♪). Until the introduction of the crochet, the minim was the smallest (i.e. minimum) note.

It is a musical scale which ascends or descends by semitones.

Note: A diatonic scale is made up of the notes that are pertinent to the key involved. A chromatic scale, involving as it does any of the semitones, includes notes that are not part of the key involved.

It is the basic three-note chord in harmony, known as a triad. We have shown the Tonic Triad of C major, since it starts with C and then has E and G in ascending order.

Note: The Tonic is the key-note, the note by which a key is named.

(a) C major; (b) G major; (c) D major; (d) F major; (e) B flat major; (f) E flat major.

(a) None sharpened or flattened; (b) F sharpened; (c) F and C sharpened; (d) B flattened; (e) B and E flattened; (f) B, E and A flattened.

(a) A minor; (b) E minor; (c) B minor; (d) D minor; (e) G minor; (f) C minor.

INSTRUMENTS

A musical instrument in which resonant wooden bars of graduated sizes are struck by hammers. The work was *Danse Macabre*, Opus 40.

Note: The work was one of four symphonic poems composed by Saint-Saëns. The xylophone was used to depict skeletons dancing.

The largest of the now extinct 'key bugle' family. A brass instrument, it had either 11 or 12 keys. Its place has now been taken by the bass tuba.

Note: 'Ophicleide' comes from the Greek for 'keyed serpent'.

It is a crwth. An ancient, bowed, string instrument, it has been known since the sixth century and was still played in Wales about 200 years ago.

Note: In English, it was called a crowd, and the Irish name was crot or cruit.

(b) French horn (or just 'horn'), it is a wind-instrument, found in the brass section of the orchestra. (c) Double bass; the largest member of the string section of the orchestra. (d) Timpano, or kettledrum; found in the percussion section of the orchestra.

Note: One kettledrum is a timpano. Two or more are timpani (*not* tympani).

WHAT HAPPENED NEXT?

A riot, which grew into revolution, resulting in Belgium's independence from the Dutch, which was ratified five months later.

Note: Auber did not witness the riot. He was a very shy man and never attended performances of his own works. The opera later became known as *Masaniello*, after its hero (the Dumb Girl's brother who dies from poisoning).

Strangely, Haydn's Symphony No 96 (written three years earlier) became known as *The Miracle*. Why the wrong symphony was so nicknamed, we do not know.

A member of the audience tried to shoot the composer.

The new work was not much appreciated. However, Franz Clement, apparently, played very well, mostly from memory. To inspire the audience, he gave a very extrovert performance of a piece of his own composition between the first two movements of the concerto.

Note: In 1840 (34 years later, and 13 years after Beethoven's death) the concerto was at last acclaimed. This was following a performance directed by Mendelssohn with, as soloist, the 13-year-old Joseph Joachim.

Clement did well in life. He became conductor of the Vienna Opera.

An incendiary bomb landed on the roof a few hours later. The Queen's Hall was burned down.

Granados and his wife managed to book a passage on the SS *Sussex*, which was crossing to France via England. The ship was torpedoed in the English Channel by a German submarine. Reports said that the composer drowned in an unsuccessful attempt to save his wife. He was 49 years of age.

Jesse toppled backwards and, hanging by one talon, he flapped upside down close to a flaming torch. He was unharmed, but 'retired' from the opera.

Note: It was reported that an angry voice from the audience cried 'Free the bird, you ... (expletive deleted)!'

Duke Ellington so appreciated the extempore vocalese that he invited Adelaide Hall to record the number with him. It was a huge success. In 1974, she sang it, most beautifully and movingly, at a memorial service for Duke Ellington at St Martin-in-the Fields, London.

Note: Still performing and recording in her 90s, Adelaide Hall died in 1993. When close on 70 years of age, she recorded 'Creole Love Call' with Brian Lemon and Humphrey Lyttleton.

48

He produced a baton and thus introduced conducting (as we know it) to this country.

49

The song was 'Who's Sorry Now?'. It went to the top of the charts. Many hits followed. That one last 'take' had opened up a brilliant career for the singer.

Note: Among Connie Francis's big hits were 'Stupid Cupid', 'My Happiness' and, 'Lipstick on your Collar', perhaps best remembered from the Dennis Potter TV play.

NAMES AND NOTIONS

50

Paul Hindemith. (He played the violin in a spa band as a young man.)

51

The American aviator, Charles Lindbergh

52

Lindberghflug (The Lindbergh Flight). The date refers to that of the work's performance. Lindbergh's solo, non-stop transatlantic crossing was in 1927.

Note: Other composers were quick to commemorate the flight, too. Bohuslav Martinu's first big success was *La Bagarre (The Tumult)*, an orchestral work on the theme, written in 1927.

53

He had sought to combine certain aspects of Bach's style with Brazilian folk melody and rhythms.

54

This is an extraordinary evocation of a local locomotive. With startling realism, we hear it getting up steam, starting, chugging happily along, and finally arriving at its destination.

Toccata is, literally, a 'touch' piece. Usually a single movement, originally the term related to a performer demonstrating 'touch' on a keyboard, but – like so many terms – it has become diluted.

55

A tragic motorbike ride

Note: At the time of writing, the trombonist, Christian Lindberg, is recognised as *the* great performer of this work (and an amazingly acrobatic performance it is).

56

Alexander Mossolov (1900–73)

Note: Mossolov came back into favour during World War Two with the composition of patriotic songs and works for large choirs.

57

'Yesterday'

58

Mahler's Symphony No 8 in E flat, because of the very large musical forces required in its performance. It is Mahler's only completely choral symphony.

Note: The symphony was so nicknamed by the impresario, Emil Gutmann, who found the organising of its first performance, in Munich in 1910, a truly formidable task. It was performed and televised on the first night of the 1995 Centenary Proms.

59

The American composer, John Adams (b 1947)

60

John Alden Carpenter (1876–1951)

61

Igor Stravinsky (1882–1971)

62

The English composer, Sir Harrison Birtwhistle (b 1934)

PASTICCIO

Frédéric Chopin (1510–49) and his Opus 2, *Variations on 'Là ci darem la mano'*, for piano and orchestra. The theme is the duet from Mozart's opera *Don Giovanni*.

Note: In the opera, the duet is sung as Don Giovanni is attempting another conquest. It translates (roughly) as 'There we shall hold hands' and is considered by many to be one of the gems of all opera.

Sir Arthur Bliss (1891–1975). The ballet is called *Checkmate*.

Note: It is a symbolic game of chess, played between Love and Death. The ballet was created for the first visit of the Sadler's Wells company to Paris, in 1937.

Carl Orff (1895–1982). *Carmina Burana* means *Songs of Beuron*. The work is a setting of lively (and sometimes bawdy) medieval poems.

Claude Debussy (1862–1918). The piece was *La Cathédrale Engloutie (The Submerged Cathedral)* and was No 10 of his *Preludes, Book 1*.

They are all works by Igor Stravinsky.

Oscar Straus. (Unlike the Waltz family of Strauss, there was only a single 's' at the end of his name.)

Eric Fenby (1906–97). He is almost invariably referred to as 'Delius's amanuensis'.

Note: Eric Fenby was a talented organist and composer in his own right. Amongst his works was a lively overture, *Rossini on Ilkla Moor*, and a symphony.

Sir Edward Elgar

ONE-LINERS

A slow and stately dance, probably of Italian origin but much used by sixteenth-century English composers

The French composer, Charles Gounod. He founded the Gounod Choral Society, which became the Royal Albert Hall Choral Society, and then (by permission of Queen Victoria) it succeeded to its present title in 1888.

Note: Gounod was in England from 1870 to 1875 at the time of the Franco-Prussian War.

A concert version of Gershwin's *Porgy and Bess*

Cuba

Note: The rumba became popular in America and Europe in the early 1930s. The original is said to be a dance of the lower classes, and erotic.

Enrico Caruso

'Vesti la giubba' ('On with the motley') from Leoncavallo's opera *Pagliacci* (*The Clowns*).

Note: The first recording of this was in 1902. There were later recordings and reissues of the original with an orchestra dubbed on.

The two f-shaped holes cut in the belly of instruments of the violin family. They are sometimes known as 'sound holes'.

Note: Not only do they 'let the sound out', but they give more 'spring' to the instrument so it vibrates more freely.

Trombone

William Wordsworth

In the 1680s, Richard Sadler discovered a well in his garden, reportedly with medicinal properties. He set up a garden for taking the waters whilst enjoying musical entertainment. He later built a 'Musick House'.

It moved to Birmingham and became the Birmingham Royal Ballet.

Johann Strauss I (1804–49)

Johann Strauss II (1825–99)

J S Bach

Note: This is one of Bach's secular cantatas (No 211). Rather like a one-act operetta, it makes fun of the (then) new craze for coffee.

Gheorghe Zamfir (known as 'The Virtuoso of the Panpipes')

A sound produced by resonance

Ignacy (Jan) Paderewski (1860–1941). He became the first Prime Minister of Poland, in 1919.

Sir Edward Heath

The opera *William Tell*, in 1829

Cooking and entertaining

Note: William Tell was Rossini's 36th opera in 19 years. After that, he gave the remaining 39 years of his life largely to his hobby – cooking – and to entertaining lavishly.

91

Amahl and the Night Visitors; music and libretto by Gian Carlo Menotti. It was first shown on Christmas Eve 1951, by NBC Television. (BBC TV presented the opera in 1967.)

Note: Amahl, a crippled boy, wants the three kings on their way to Bethlehem to take his crutch to the baby Jesus. (It all ends happily; he is cured!)

It is interesting that Menotti had a crippled leg as a child, which was cured after a visit to a holy shrine.

92

The Electric Prunes (1967). The Mass was made up of the movements: Kyrie Eleison, Gloria, Credo, Sanctus, Agnus Dei and Benedictus.

Note: This was an early example of what became known as 'God Rock'. One critic said the work sounded like tone deaf monks singing Gregorian chants. (Actually, one of us rather liked it!)

93

Ivor Novello wrote the music and supplied the first line. An American lady, Mrs Lena Ford (who was killed in a London air raid in 1918) wrote the verses. The song was a huge hit during World War One.

94

Whistling Jack Smith, in 1967

95

Lonnie Donegan

96

Johann Strauss II. It was first performed in Vienna in 1874.

97

His last: No 41 in C, K 551. It was written in 1788.

Note: Mozart wrote his last three symphonies (Nos 39, 40 and 41) in seven and a half weeks.

98

A small piece of (usually) wood or metal, with which the strings of a mandoline, banjo, zither etc. are plucked.

99

Johnny Cash

100

Sue

MUSICAL ACROSTIC

1 PERCUSSION

2 ADDINSELL (Richard)

3 UKELELE (or UKULELE)
Note: The ukelele originated in Portugal but was patented in Hawaii in 1917.

4 *LOUISE*
Note: This is Gustave Charpentier (1860–1956)

5 HAMMERSTEIN

6 IMPROMPTU
Note: The song was written by Harry Carroll in about 1918.

7 NICKELODEON

8 DONIZETTI

9 EIGHTH

10 MESSIAEN (Olivier)
Note: The symphony has ten movements and calls for a very large orchestra. It was commissioned by Serge Koussevitski and first performed in 1948, conducted by Leonard Bernstein.

11 ISOTONIC
Note: Isotonic notation, (a concept of Dom John Stéphan OSB, of Buckfast Abbey) uses notes that have differently shaped heads to indicate sharps, flats, etc.

12 TCHAIKOVSKY

13 HURDY-GURDY
Note: The original hurdy-gurdy used a rosinated wheel to vibrate the strings, whose pitch was altered by means of a keyboard. The barrel organ (a kind of barrel-and-pin piano – hence 'barrel') could have become spoken of as a hurdy-gurdy because both used a wheel in operation.

Quotation

MUSIC IS A

MEANINGLESS

NOISE UNTIL

IT TOUCHES

A RECEIVING

MIND

Author

Paul Hindemith
(From: *A Composer's World*, 1961)

MUSICALS

Jerome Kern, who died from a heart attack, collapsing in the street

Irving Berlin. He wrote both the lyrics and the music.

Note: Rodgers and Hammerstein were the producers; Herbert and Dorothy Fields were writing the book. They had commissioned Jerome Kern (see above), with whom Dorothy Fields had intended to write the lyrics.

Paint Your Wagon. Alan Jay Lerner wrote the lyrics and Frederick Loewe the music.

Lionel Bart

Laurie Johnson. Launched at Bernard Miles' Mermaid Theatre, in 1959.

Note: One of the authors, with a friend, was fortunate in seeing an early performance in a temporary theatre, before the Mermaid opened at Puddle Dock. We sat on benches, and interaction with the cast was encouraged. During one song, Bernard Miles sat on the edge of the stage, swinging his legs, as if impatient. Then he climbed down, walked over, and asked us the time. Our reply – 'twenty to eight' – made us feel we 'acted with Bernard Miles' – if only for one performance.

Joseph and the Amazing Technicolour Dreamcoat. Music by Andrew Lloyd Webber, lyrics by Tim Rice.

Georges Bizet's music (from his opera *Carmen*) was used for *Carmen Jones*.
Richard Rodgers wrote the music for both *Oklahoma!* and *Carousel.*

Note: It was originally intended to call *Oklahoma!*, *Away We Go!*.

Cole Porter. 'Night and Day' came from *Gay Divorce*; 'Ev'ry Time We Say Goodbye', from *Seven Lively Arts*; 'So in Love,' from *Kiss Me Kate*; and 'I Love Paris' came from *Can Can*.

Richard Rodgers wrote the music and Lorenz Hart the lyrics.

The composer was Burton Lane and the lyricist 'Yip' Harburg.

Note: EY (Yip) Harburg came from a poor family. He became a poet and lyric writer having gained a degree in science. 'Brother Can You Spare a Dime?' and 'April in Paris' featured his lyrics, as did the songs of the film *The Wizard of Oz*.

Chu-Chin-Chow

The Maid of the Mountains

ON SCORE

You should continue playing from the beginning. ('*Da*' is Italian for 'from' and '*Capo*' is Italian for 'head'; so, from the head i.e. from the beginning).

Nothing. '*Fine*' is Italian for 'end'.

Note: Where you see 'D.C. al Fine', this means you should go back to the beginning and finish playing when you come to the word 'Fine' on the score.

p (or *piano*) means 'soft', so the passage should be played softly. *pp* (or *pianissimo*) means 'very softly'. The more *p*s there are, the more softly it should be played. The instruction *ppppp* is rarely marked but it does occur, for example, close to the end of Tchaikovsky's Sixth Symphony.

Note: Although one *p* means *piano* (soft), any other *p*s preceding it signify the Italian word '*più*', which means 'more'. So, for example, *ppp* means 'more, more soft'.

Gradually slow down the music.

Turn the bow around and draw the wooden part (rather than the hair) across the strings. The words are Italian for 'with the wood'.

Note: There are other intentions. For example, at the beginning of Rossini's overture *Il Signor Bruschino*, the strings are required to tap the lamps over their desks.

'Minore' means 'minor'. It is generally used to warn of a sudden change into the minor key. 'Marcato' means 'marked' and is used as an indication of expression. 'Maestoso' indicates that the piece should be played 'majestically'.

You should play it in a lively manner, that is animatedly.

INSTRUMENTS

The smallest is the violin, the next in size is the viola and the largest is the violoncello (usually called the cello). These instruments all belong to the violin family.

Note: The violin's strings are normally tuned to G, D, A and E. The viola's are normally tuned to C, G, D and A, and the cello's also, but an octave lower.

21

The celesta is a member of the percussion family which looks rather like a small upright piano but in which the hammers strike tubes or sheets of metal. It became known as an instrument of the orchestra when used in *The Dance of the Sugar Plum Fairy* for Tchaikovsky's *The Nutcracker*, in 1892. However, Charles Widor had used it 12 years earlier, for his ballet, *La Korrigane*.

Note: The celesta was invented in Paris, in about 1880, by the Mustel firm of instrument makers.

A trumpet

Not a lot! Both refer to a dancing master's fiddle, which was small enough to fit into his pocket.

Note: These 'portable' instruments were much used in the eighteenth and early nineteenth centuries.

The pitch of the note is raised (sharpened).

The oboe, which is found in the woodwind section of the orchestra

FROM RUSSIA

Mikhail Ivanovitch Glinka (1804–57)

Note: Glinka studied piano with John Field and Italian opera with Bellini and Donizetti. Glinka was a pioneer of the introduction of *'Leitmotiv'* (thematically linking subjects or characters, running through a work) in his operas.

The opera was based on an early poem by Alexander Pushkin. The poet was to write a dramatic version for Glinka, but was killed in a duel. It was several librettists and five years to the first performance of the opera.

Sometimes known as 'The Mighty Handful'. The other members were Balakirev, Borodin and Mussorgsky.

Rimsky-Korsakov (1844–1908) had been a naval officer.

Cui (1835–1918) was an army officer, becoming a general, and an expert on fortifications.

Balakirev (1837–1910) was a student of mathematics.

Borodin (1833–87) was a medical man and a professor of chemistry. He founded a women's medical school.

Mussorgsky (1839–81) was an army officer and later a civil servant.

Dmitri Tiomkin (1899–1979)

Note: Tiomkin's teacher, Glazounov, had been a pupil of Rimsky-Korsakov. Glazounov's first symphony, written when he was 16 years old, was conducted at its first performance, by Balakirev.

Mikhail Ippolitov-Ivanov (1859–1935)

Rachmaninov's Concerto No 2 in C minor. It was dedicated to Dr Nikolai Dahl who had treated the composer without charge following severe depression and alcoholism. Dr Dahl was an amateur cellist.

Dmitri Shostakovich (1906–75). The march theme evokes the song 'Da geh'ich zu Maxim' ('Then I'll go to Maxim's') from Franz Lehár's *The Merry Widow*.

Note: The symphony was heard in Russia, the USA and Britain in 1942. In August of that year a very moving performance was given in Leningrad, with the 15 survivors of the Philharmonic Orchestra supplemented with players released from the battle fronts.

The march theme was probably deliberately 'lifted'. Shostakovich's son's name was Maxim.

Piotr Ilyich Tchaikovsky (1840–93). What actually caused his death may never be known.

Pathétique. The Russian version of this means 'emotional' rather than 'pathetic'. The feelings would, hence, be emotional rather than pitiable.

Note: The title *Pathétique* was suggested by Tchaikovsky's elder brother, Modest, and the composer agreed. Later, he changed his mind – and at this point inserted a dedication to his much loved nephew, Vladimir Lvovich (Bob) Davidov.

Dmitri Kabalevsky (1904–87)

HYMNS AND CAROLS

It is the metrical version of the Hundredth Psalm.

Note: The tune was certainly known as long ago as the 1560s.

'O God Our Help in Ages Past'. Croft was also organist at St Anne's, Soho.

'Amazing Grace'

Note: Successful versions have been recorded by Mahalia Jackson, Judy Collins, and the Pipes and Drums and Military Band of the Royal Scots Dragoon Guards, for example.

Sir Arthur Sullivan. The words of 'Onward Christian Soldiers' were written by Sabine Baring-Gould; those of '"Forward!" Be our Watchword' by H Alford.

America. It was written by the Revd Dr J H Hopkins in about 1856. It was the first real Christmas carol from America.

Adolphe Adam. He called it *Cantique Noël.*

Note: This was the Adolphe Adam who wrote the ballet *Giselle.*

Cranbrook. (It is interesting that the first six notes are identical to those used in the hymn tune *New Sabbath*, to which the hymn 'We Thank Thee, Lord', is usually sung.)

Note: Cranbrook was written by Thomas Clark (1775–1859), a cobbler from Canterbury. He wrote many other hymn tunes, including *Crediton* and *Greenland.*

JAZZ

Louis Armstrong. When Louis died in 1971, Lil Hardin took part in a memorial concert in St Louis. She collapsed and died on stage.

Note: Lil Hardin was Louis Armstrong's second wife. They were divorced in 1932.

Benny Goodman (clarinet), Teddy Wilson (piano) and Gene Krupa (drums)

Lionel Hampton (vibraphone)

Note: Lionel Hampton was a drummer and xylophonist, who introduced the vibraphone (vibes) into jazz.

Stephane Grappelli (violin) and Django Reinhardt (acoustic guitar). Reinhardt's left hand was mutilated following a caravan fire when he was young. He had lost the use of two fingers.

Ottilie Patterson

Sidney Bechet

50

Bebop

51

Bix Beiderbecke (1903–31)

Note: Bix Beiderbecke loved serious music as well as jazz. He was particularly fond of the works of Ravel and Debussy. Sadly, he became too fond of alcohol and so died in his prime. He is considered by many to have been the first outstanding white jazz soloist.

WHOSE WORDS?

Ferdinand Hérold

Note: *Zampa* was the first opera to call for a church organ on stage. Before the French Revolution, the Roman Catholic Church would never have countenanced this. The overture to *Zampa* is a familiar bandstand piece, even today.

Beethoven's Symphony No 7 in A

Beethoven, in 1813. He then wrote a set of variations on it together with an arrangement for solo and chorus. It also features in his 'Battle Symphony' of 1813, sometimes called *Wellington's Victory at the Battle of Vittoria.*

Note: It may be of interest to you that the 'Battle Symphony' was Beethoven's Opus 91; the Seventh Symphony (see Question 53, above), his Opus 92.

Maurice Ravel (1875–1937), about his *Pavane pour une Infante Défunte*, which is usually translated as *Pavane for a Dead Infanta.* (Presumably it would be better translated as *Pavane of an Infanta of Earlier Times.*)

Note: It is reported that, on another occasion, Ravel said of his *Pavane*, 'The title is meaningless. I just liked the sound of it.'

Dizzy Gillespie

PASTICCIO

Anna Pavlova

Note: This was not as strange as one might at first think. In the opera, the dumb girl is played by a dancer.

No Mean City, written by Mike Moran and sung by Maggie Bell.

Havergal Brian (1876–1972)

It requires rather large forces, for example a 200-strong orchestra plus four brass bands and an organ, with several hundred singers.

The overture to Mozart's *The Marriage of Figaro*. It is reckoned (jocularly) to take four minutes to play.

John Philip Sousa (1854–1932)

Note: Sousa's novel, *The Fifth String*, sold more than 50,000 copies. He first joined the United States Marine Band at the age of 13. He later returned to the band and was its leader for 12 years.

M. He was Robin Scott.

The *Sabre Dance* from the ballet *Gayaneh*

Note: Aram Khachaturian (1903–78) was an Armenian.

The Irish-born pianist and composer, John Field (1782–1837), while living in Russia

Burt Bacharach

Note: At one time, Burt Bacharach was accompanist to Marlene Dietrich.
In 1970, he won an Academy Award for 'Raindrops Keep Falling on my Head', from the film, *Butch Cassidy and the Sundance Kid*.

Legend has it that the composer's cat walked over the keyboard and gave him the fugue's subject. (A Chopin waltz is known as the *Cat Valse*, for the same reason!)

Grace Williams (1906–77)

The *Water Music*, written about 1717 and first played for a royal picnic on the Thames.

Note: Originally there were 21 movements, so two encores must have been quite exhausting. Later the suite grew to 41 movements. Now, we usually hear a seven-movement version which was arranged by Sir Hamilton Harty.

Johann Sebastian Bach (1685–1750). He was granted a month's leave for the trip but was away for four months.

ONE-LINERS

Handel. Written in 1720, it was an *Air and Variations* from his Harpsichord Suite No 5. In case you are not familiar with the *Air*, it starts rather like this:

Note: The story that Handel heard the *Air* being whistled by a blacksmith working in Edgware is, to say the least, spurious. Handel never used the nickname for the Suite or any part of it.

He or she is the designer of the dances.

Concluding Act II of the opera *Prince Igor* by Alexander Borodin (premièred in St Petersburg in 1890)

74

A Tartar tribe

James Barry

76

An instrument of the lute family with a large number of strings.

Note: The organ stop known as the 'Vox Angelica' (Angelic Voice) is not related to the instrument, the angelica, except that they are both 'angelic'.

A dot *after* a note means that the length of that note is increased by half its length again. For example, a dotted crochet is equal in length to a crochet plus a quaver.

Note: When a note has two dots after it, the second dot adds on half the length of the first dot. So, a crochet with two dots is equal in length to a crochet plus a quaver plus a semi-quaver.

Dots *above* or *below* a note instruct that the note is played 'staccato', meaning 'short' or 'detached'.

A boat song (derived from the songs of the Venetian gondoliers).

'Shout'

Alban Berg (1885–1935)

Jack the Ripper

Note: Berg died with the opera in an unfinished form. Lulu was to be killed in Act III, but this Act was only in a short state. It was not until 1979 (44 years later) that the full opera was staged, completed by Friedrich Cerha.

The Royal Military School of Music, dating from 1857

It describes the 'lowest' form of an instrument, generally an octave below the usual pitch. ('Double' is often used for the same purpose.)

Roger Whittaker

The Ship's Company and Royal Marine Band of HMS *Ark Royal*

Each line of a hymn was read out (sometimes sung out) before it was sung by the congregation. Still in use in some parts of the world, it does rather upset the progression of a hymn tune!

Note: Lining-out was introduced in the mid-1600s with the advent of metrical psalms, for the benefit of those in the congregation unable to read.

A similar system is used in music hall and pantomime etc. when the audience is invited to join in with the singing.

It is the highest-pitched of the tuba group of brass valved instruments. It is much used in brass bands but only rarely in symphonic works.

Note: It is also known as the tenor tuba in B flat.

Three. They were: *Swan Lake* (1876), *The Sleeping Beauty* (1889) and *The Nutcracker* (1892).

Antonio Vivaldi (*c* 1675–1741). He had red hair and he was a priest.

An American jazz pianist, composer and bandleader. Born in 1920, he studied with Milhaud and Schoenburg.

Note: Dave Brubeck became the leader of the so-called 'Cool School' of jazz. *Take Five*, the work in 5/4 time with which he is always associated, was written by Paul Desmond, the alto-saxophonist with the Dave Brubeck Quartet.

A composition (vocal or instrumental) for six voices or players

Note: Sextet is also the name sometimes given to the group of six singers or players. So, for example, a work might be described as a sextet for strings or a piece for a string sextet. It would come to the same thing, either way.

Pete Best

Note: Pete Best's drums were heard again on the Beatles' new anthology album of 1995.

As a relic from the late eighteenth century when it was common for a European military band to have a negro time-beater and other negro drummers who wore exotic dress.

The washboard. He was a great enthusiast and expert on jazz.

Laurel and Hardy with the Avalon Boys

Note: The song was written in 1901 by Harry Carroll with lyrics by Ballard MacDonald. It was sung in the 1937 Laurel and Hardy film *Way Out West.*

In the Blue Ridge Mountains of Virginia

A puzzle or riddle must be solved to establish the rules of the canon before it can by played or sung.

The Rondo from *Te Deum*, composed about 1690 by Marc Antoine Charpentier (1634–1704).

99

The Lass that Loved a Sailor

Note: The operetta, first produced in London in 1878 caused something of a sensation because of its caricature of the publisher WH Smith, who had just been appointed First Lord of the Admiralty.

100

WS Gilbert wrote the words and Arthur Sullivan the music.

Note: Sullivan's father had been an army bandsman, then Professor of Clarinet at the Royal Military School of Music (Kneller Hall).

TWO PUZZLES

Note Names

BEEF and CABBAGE

GEDDA (Nicolai): the half-Russian, half-Swedish, lyrical tenor.

DEDE (Edmund): who became conductor of the opera at Bordeaux.

CAGE (John): America composer.

ABBA: Swedish pop group.

GADE (Niels): nineteenth-century Danish composer.

C Sharp (for Cecil Sharp): he who saved English folk music for posterity.

Note: Cecil Sharp (1859–1924) was a lawyer and musician. He was organist at Adelaide Cathedral in Australia for a time, before becoming principal of the Hampstead Conservatory. He then collected, published, and arranged the performance of English folk songs and dances, founding what is now the English Folk Dance and Song Society.

Dates

A MOZART (Wolfgang)

B BEETHOVEN

C SCHUBERT (Franz Peter)

D BERLIOZ

E CHOPIN

F SCHUMANN (Robert)

G LISZT (Franz)

H WAGNER (Richard)

I VERDI

J BRAHMS

K TCHAIKOVSKY

L DVORAK

M STRAUSS (RICHARD)

N SIBELIUS

O RACHMANINOV

We gave the given names of some of the composers, where there are other well-known musicians of the same surname. And yes, we did realise there is a Boris Tchaikovsky, but he would have fitted well outside our chart.

MUSIC AND FILMS

John Ireland (English composer 1879–1962)
Note: John Ireland taught composition to Benjamin Britten.

The zither player, Anton Karas

Georges Auric (1899–1983)
Note: Auric also wrote scores for *It Always Rains on Sunday*, in 1947, and *Passport to Pimlico*, in 1949. *Moulin Rouge* told the story of the artist Toulouse-Lautrec.

Ennio Morriconi (b 1928)
Note: John Adams' 1991 opera *Death of Klinghoffer*, is about the same event. Leon Klinghoffer was the American Jew murdered by the hijackers in 1985.

The harmonica virtuoso, Larry Adler. Kay Kendall 'played' a trumpet.

Colonel Bogey by Kenneth J Alford (in 1914) and *The River Kwai March* by Malcolm Arnold (in 1957)

John Williams (b 1932)

Rachmaninov's Concerto No 2 in C minor for Piano and Orchestra, of 1901

Michael Nyman (b 1944)

Paul Anka

Note: Paul Anka's first hit was 'Diana'. He wrote Buddy Holly's big hit of 1959, 'It Doesn't Matter Any More', and the English version of *Comme D'Habitude* as 'My Way'.

The Greek composer, Mikis Theodorakis

The French composer, Maurice Jarre (father of Jean-Michel Jarre)

Note: There were references to Shostakovitch's *Leningrad Symphony* in Jarre's music for *Is Paris Burning?*

13

The second movement (Andante) from Mozart's Piano Concerto No 21 in G, K 467. Here is a snippet, much simplified:

14

Benjamin (later Lord) Britten. The subtitle is *Variations and Fugue on a Theme of Purcell*. The theme, from the seventeenth century, starts something like this:

Note: Henry Purcell (1659–95). The theme is from his incidental music to a play called *Abdelazer*.

CONDUCTORS

André Messager (1853–1929)

Richard Strauss (1864–1949)

Berlioz, to Mendelssohn

Fritz Busch (1890–1951). His brothers, Adolph (a violinist), and Hermann (a cellist), founded the Busch Quartet and the Busch Trio.

Note: The Busch family found it expedient to leave Germany in 1933. Adolph's daughter married the pianist, Rudolf Serkin.

Bernard Haitink. (He was created an honorary KBE in 1977.)

Note: The inspiration for building the first Glyndebourne theatre was given to John Christie by his wife, the soprano Audrey Mildmay. She sang in the first performance in 1934 (see Question 18). Also, together with Rudolph Bing, she was the founding brain behind the Edinburgh Festival in 1947.

For the 1994 performance, Roy Henderson (who also sang in 1934) and Evelyn Rothwell (who, in 1934 played oboe under Busch's baton), were in the audience. Evelyn Rothwell married John Barbirolli in 1939.

Arthur Fiedler (1894–1979). His life-long hobby and interest was the prevention and fighting of fire.

Louis Frémaux

Leonard Bernstein (1918–90). In the choral finale, the word '*Freude*' (joy) was changed to '*Freiheit*' (freedom), very appropriately. Actually, it is believed that Schiller's original ode was 'Ode to Freedom', but that it was changed by him to 'Ode to Joy' for political reasons. Beethoven would have been well aware of this.

Sir John Barbirolli (1899–1970); the Hallé Orchestra

Note: Vaughan Williams wrote the score for the 1948 film *Scott of the Antarctic* and developed this into Symphony No 7 (*Antartica*), often known as *Sinfonia Antartica.*

The American conductor who was born and died in England, Leopold Stokowski (1882–1977)

THE 'WEAKER' SEX

Dame Myra Hess (1890–1965)

Note: Dame Myra's transcription *Jesu, Joy of Man's Desiring* from Bach's Cantata No 147, became a popular favourite.

Norwegian. Birgit Nilsson (Swedish).

Nadia Boulanger (1887–1979) and her sister Lili (1893–1918)

Note: Nadia Boulanger was the first woman to conduct a Royal Philharmonic Society concert (in 1937). She went on to conduct other major orchestras. In 1938, she conducted the first performance of Stravinsky's *Dumbarton Oaks* concerto. Lili died looking after the families of musicians fighting in the war.

'Ma' Rainey (1886–1939). She married a man known as 'Pa' Rainey.

The American songwriter Carrie Jacobs Bond (1862–1946)

Barbra Streisand

She was the Muse of Music, one of the nine Greek Muses.

A celebrated Polish-born composer, author, pianist and renowned harpsichordist.

Note: Wanda Landowska set up a school, near Paris, to give special training in the performance of early music. This was looted in World War Two and she had to flee the country, finally settling in America.

Dame Clara Butt (1872–1936)

Dame Joan Hammond

DESCRIPTIONS

'*In alt*' (meaning 'high') refers to the notes within the octave immediately above the treble stave (that is, G to F). So, C *in alt* means the C within the octave immediately above the top line of the treble stave. '*In altissimo*' refers to the next octave up.

Literally, 'teasing'. Usually given to quick movements in 2/4 time.

The Italian and French terms for 'comic opera'. Mozart's *The Marriage of Figaro* and Rossini's *The Barber of Seville* are examples. It is the opposite of '*opera seria*', which means 'serious opera'.

Note: '*Opéra-comique*' is *not* comic opera, but is opera in which some of the dialogue is spoken. As an example, *Carmen*, a tragic story, is an *opéra-comique*.

Strictly speaking it means 'levelled' – in other words, a smoothness in the style of performance.

Music which has a programme – that is, works which purport to tell a story. Examples are *Scheherazade*, *Till Eulenspiegel*, etc.

Not a lot! Both refer to playing with makeshift instruments. Skiffle is a Chicago word. Spasm comes from New Orleans.

A type of work in which a small group of instruments interplays with a larger orchestral force

An ordinary piano, the strings of which were doctored by inserting almost anything, from rubber bands to screws, pieces of wood, and glass, between them

Note: John Cage (1912–92) was exploring unusual tone colours when he prepared his piano. *Second Construction*, *Bacchanale* and *Sonatas and Interludes* were composed for the instrument, as well as a piano concerto.

Composed music (not improvised), usually played on the piano, and heavily syncopated. Scott Joplin was one of the originators.

Note: Scott Joplin's first published work was *Maple Leaf Rag*. *The Entertainer*, another of his compositions, was used some 80 years later in the film, *The Sting*. In 1922, he wrote a ragtime opera, *Treemonisha*.

A type of instrumental composition supposedly of a somewhat good-humoured or capricious style. Dvořák, Schumann and others used the term for compositions.

Music written in imitation of Turkish music. Janissaries formed the Sultan's bodyguard.

It is the simultaneous combining of two or more strands of melody, which singly, and together, make musical sense.

A style of jazz piano playing of the blues, characterised by a rolling bass part against a rhythmic and often syncopated treble part.

Note: In 1928, a few months before he died in a dance-hall fight, Clarence 'Pinetop' Smith made a recording called *Boogie-woogie*. This record gave the name to this style of jazz. It has been suggested that boogie-woogie began when performers in bars and the like had to cover for missing piano notes by fast fingering and improvisation.

EXTRACTS AND THEMES

The folk music of Sweden (*Ack Varmeland du Skona*, which translates, *In Praise of Varmeland*, the Swedish province). Smetana worked as a conductor and teacher in Sweden for much of the years from 1856 to 1861.

Note: Bedřich Smetana (1824–84) took refuge in Sweden, following the political revolutions in Bohemia that began in 1848 which left him a 'marked man'. At that time he was greatly depressed by family misfortunes. His wife had TB and three of his four young daughters had died.

49

Mendelssohn's Violin Concerto in E minor. It was first performed in 1845 with the composer's friend, Ferdinand David, as soloist.

Note: David advised Mendelssohn considerably during the six years of the work's composition.

50

The 'Oranges and Lemons' Quartet. The tune we extracted shows a passing resemblance to that nursery rhyme.

51

The 'official' title is *Variations on a Theme by Haydn (St Anthony Chorale)* Op 56a, by Brahms. However, recent scholarship indicates that the theme was not Haydn's: more likely it was by his pupil, Ignaz Pleyel.

Note: Ignaz Pleyel (1757–1831) became well regarded as an all-round musician and composer. In 1807, he founded, in Paris, the still esteemed piano factory which bears his name.

52

In the Finale of his Symphony No 3 in E flat major, Opus 55, 'The Eroica'

53

Schumann's Piano Concerto in A minor, Opus 54

54

It was a motto that he (and Schumann) used, musically, on several occasions. It represented the concept *'Frei Aber Froh'* (free but happy).

Note: The motto of the great violinist, Joachim, was F/A/E. *'Frei Aber Einsam'*, meaning 'free but lonely'. F/A/F represented a more optimistic echo of this.

ROCK

55

Pink Floyd. Originally the Pink Floyd Sound, it is thought that the name came from the blues men, Pink Anderson and Floyd Council.

Note: Stephen Hawking is the English physicist whose best-selling book, *A Brief History of Time*, is a popular account of cosmology.

56

Whitney Houston. *The Bodyguard* music was named Album of the Year, also. (The song was written in 1973 by Dolly Parton.)

57

Sting. Originally lead singer of the Police.

58

Les Paul and Mary Ford. The famous 'Les Paul' electric guitar appeared about 1952.

59

Bob Dylan, George Harrison, Jeff Lynne, Roy Orbison and Tom Petty.

Note: 'Wilbury' is the name given to a recording studio gremlin. The team of established musicians pretended to be half-brothers whose father was a Charles Truscott Wilbury.

'Nobody's Child' was a charity record made for George Harrison's wife's Romanian Angel Appeal.

60

David A Stewart and Annie Lennox. *Sexcrime (Nineteen Eightyfour)*.

61

Aretha Franklin

62

George Michael

63

Duane Eddy

Note: Peter Gunn was back in the charts in 1986, when Duane Eddy joined up with Trevor Horn's Art of Noise. It was written by Henry Mancini.

64

Ritchie Valens, and the Big Bopper (J P Richardson). 'American Pie'.

65

Linda Ronstadt

66

Emmylou Harris and Dolly Parton

FAMILIES

Thomas Arne (1710–78) and Michael Arne (1740–86)

Note: Thomas Arne's sister, Susannah, was a fine contralto. He wrote an opera, *Rosamond*, for her professional stage debut in 1733. She then married a son of Colley Cibber, the Poet Laureate, and performed as Mrs Cibber.

'Rule Britannia!' first appeared in Arne's masque, *Alfred*, written for a garden party of the Prince of Wales at Cliveden.

Michael Arne composed for the stage, dabbled in alchemy, and was often in debt. He conducted the first performance in Germany of Handel's *Messiah*, in 1772.

George Balanchine and Vera Zorina

The Fureys. They often performed as Davey Arthur and the Fureys. However, their lead singer was Finbar Furey.

Note: The bodhran is an Irish folk drum. Uilleann pipes (sometimes called 'elbow pipes') are a type of Irish bagpipe.

The father was Johann Strauss I (1804–49). The sons were: Johann Strauss II, 'The Waltz King', (1825–99); his brother Josef Strauss (1827–70); and their younger brother Eduard Strauss (1835–1916). Eduard's son, known as Johann Strauss III (1866–1936) toured European centres with an orchestra.

ONE-LINERS

They recreated the songs and performance of the group, Abba.

Richard Strauss's opera *Salome* (1905), based on the tragedy by Oscar Wilde.

Note: The opera asks a lot of a soprano. It is an exacting singing and acting role – and then she must also dance erotically!

Not much, except that *alborada* is Spanish and *aubade* is French. They both mean 'morning song'.

Four (between 1876 and 1885)

In New York. It was 28th Street, where, by the end of the nineteenth century, most of the music publishers were to be found.

Sir Henry Rowley Bishop; it appeared in his opera *Clari, the Maid of Milan* (1823). The lyrics were by John Howard Payne, the American actor and dramatist.

Note: The tune became the subject of litigation, the claim being that Bishop had stolen a Sicilian air. It turned out that Bishop had, in fact, written this Sicilian air. In 1842, Bishop became the first musician to be dubbed Knight by a British monarch (Queen Victoria).

The relatively rare ability to give the name of a note on hearing it or to sing any note asked for.

Note: One possessor of absolute pitch mentioned – at the age of five – that his father blew his nose in G!

Eric Coates (1886–1957)

Pink Floyd. The film was *Pink Floyd: The Wall.*

A song or aria in which the rapid iteration of a string of words is an essential character.

Note: The *Largo al Factotum* from Rossini's *The Barber of Seville* is a good example. Many Gilbert and Sullivan works contain patter songs. Rap is a form of patter singing.

In the Gilbert and Sullivan opera of the same name, first performed in 1893.

The Alan Price Set. (It was written by Randy Newman.)

The soprano, Jenny Lind (1820–87)

Johan Helmich Roman (1694–1758), violinist and composer. He became Director of the Court Music.

Ivar Hallström (1826–1901), composer of operas using Swedish subjects and folk music

Kenneth J Alford (1881–1945)

An American school teacher, Thomas P Westendorf, in 1875

Note: The story goes that Mrs Westendorf was visiting relatives in New York, and back home in Indiana, Mr Westendorf was missing her and wrote the song. Strange, though, her name was Jennie – we can only assume that 'Kathleen' fitted the tune better!

Elton John and Kiki Dee

Edward Elgar. It is the name given to his *Adagio Cantabile* and is one of his many lightweight pieces.

Note: Elgar called such lightweight compositions 'shed music'. He wrote them for himself and his friends to play, for pleasure.

David Bowie and Brian Eno (from their electronic work, *Low*).

Frank Zappa

The Bee Gees

93

Barry and Robin Gibb

94

Artur Nikisch recorded Beethoven's Fifth Symphony, with the Berlin Philharmonic Orchestra.

Note: Artur Nikisch (1855–1922) was a Hungarian-born violinist and conductor. As a young man, he played in the orchestra at the ceremony of laying the foundation stone for Wagner's Festival Opera House in Bayreuth.

95

Here's to the Next Time

96

A mute for a string or wind instrument. So, *con sordino* means 'with the mute'; *senza sordino* means 'without it'.

Note: For the piano, the plural, *sordini*, means 'dampers'. So, *senza sordini* instructs 'without dampers', that is, 'use the right pedal'.

97

No 35 in D, K 385. It was written in a rush in 1782, for the Haffner family. Sigmund Haffner (by then deceased) had been the Burgomaster of Salzburg.

Note: In 1776, Mozart had written a suite in D for the wedding of Sigmund Haffner's daughter. Mozart was 20 years old at the time. The work is now known as the *Haffner Serenade*.

98

Camille Saint-Saëns. It is better known as *The Carnival of the Animals*.

99

A sonata (from the Italian *sonare*, to sound) is basically an instrumental work. A cantata (from the Italian *cantare*, to sing) is a vocal piece, now usually choral.

100

Camille Saint-Saëns. Now rarely heard, the opera was first performed in Paris in 1883.

'LIGHT' CROSSWORD

Clues Across

1 PORTER (Cole)
Note: Both songs came from the 1934 musical *Anything Goes*.

3 CREAM

6 ROCKING (Actually, ROCKIN')

9 NOTES

10 *ELENA*

11 GLENN (Miller)
Note: Glenn Miller (1904–44) is especially remembered for his Army Air Force Band. An aircraft in which he was a passenger was lost without trace over the English Channel.
His version of *Moonlight Serenade* got into the UK charts again in 1954 and 1976.

12 OSCAR (Hammerstein II)

14 STARR (Ringo)

19 CLIMB

20 SAMBA

21 POLKA

22 ADAM ANT

23 ROADS
Note: 'The Long and Winding Road' took Ray Morgan into the charts in 1970. 'Take Me Home Country Road' was a 1973 hit for Olivia Newton-John. 'Tobacco Road' was a 1964 hit for the Nashville Teens.

24 LERNER (Alan Jay)

Clues Down

1 PARKER (Charlie 'Bird')

2 *EVITA*

3 CONCERT

4 ELTON

5 MASTER (Noël Coward)
Note: Sir Noël Coward (1899–1965) was an actor, singer, dramatist and composer. 'Dance Little Lady' is from his 1928 revue *This Year of Grace*. 'I'll See You Again' is from his 1929 operetta *Bitter Sweet*.

7 *CHESS* (Björn Ulvaeus and Benny Andersson)

8 *GIGI*

13 ANIMALS

15 RUMBA

16 BOPPER

17 ABBA

18 CARTER

19 CILLA (Black)
Note: Her first chart entry, in 1963, was 'Love of the Loved'. In 1964 she reached No 1 positions with 'Anyone Who Had a Heart' and 'You're My World'.

20 SLADE

BALLET

The music of Erik Satie. *Monotones I* uses the *Trois Gymnopédies* and *Monotones II* the *Trois Gnossiennes*.

The man's name was (Sergei Mironovich) Kirov. The authorities changed the name of the State Theatre in Leningrad (now St Petersburg), which housed the famous ballet school, from Maryinski to Kirov. At the time of writing, the theatre is once again known as the Maryinski.

For the gifted 18-year-old Emma Livry. The music was by Offenbach.

Note: Tragically, Emma Livry died two years later when, during an opera rehearsal, her costume caught fire. The ballet 'died with her'. It was not revived until 1979 when Ronald Hynd was the choreographer.

La Prophète. They were representing (rather incredibly!) milkmaids skating over a frozen lake to take provisions to Anabaptist soldiers during the 1534 uprising.

From *La Prophète* and also from *L'Etoile du Nord (North Star)*. The ballet was *Les Patineurs (The Skaters)*.

They were the initials of the given names of the principal dancers.

Note: The principals were Richard Cragun, Birgit Keil, Marcia Haydée and Egon Madsen (hence RBME).

Fauré's *Requiem*, which he wrote in 1887 in memory of his father. The same four principals danced for the first performance.

Note: In 1965, the Stuttgart Ballet had staged Kenneth MacMillan's ballet, *Song of the Earth*, which used the music of Mahler (*Das Lied von der Erde*, written in 1908). Marcia Hardée and Egon Madsen were two of the principals. MacMillan was greatly indebted to John Cranko for having confidence in his ability to bring about the ballet. This confidence had not been shown to him by Covent Garden.

Benjamin Britten

Enigma Variations. The setting is Elgar's house and garden in Worcester in the 1890s. *My Friends Pictured Within* was Elgar's subtitle for his *Variations on an Original Theme*, Opus 36, *Enigma*. The ballet features all these friends, as Elgar represented them in his music. (The first performance of the Elgar work was conducted by Hans Richter, in London, in 1899.)

Note: At the end of the ballet, a telegram arrives saying that Hans Richter agrees to conduct the first performance of the Elgar work. Huw David Steuart-Powell (the HDS-P of the Second Variation) takes a group photograph.

They were sister and brother.

Husband and wife

A narrator, seated at a table, declaims words, written for the ballet by Gertrude Stein. The story is a comedy of disasters at a provincial wedding.

The whole company semaphores the words of 'Rule Britannia!' in front of a Union Jack backcloth.

Note: In 1958, Balanchine had choreographed *Stars and Stripes* using Sousa's music. He choreographed many hit shows, including: *On Your Toes*, *Babes in Arms*, *The Boys from Syracuse*, *Cabin in the Sky* and *Song of Norway*, for the New York stage.

INSTRUMENTS

In a harpsichord the strings are plucked (by quills or leather 'tongues'). In a piano the strings are struck by hammers.

Note: The harpsichord family comprises the harpsichord proper, virginals, and the spinet.

What he called a '*gravicembalo col piano e forte*'. In other words, the pianoforte (now usually shortened to piano).

Note: '*Gravicembalo col piano e forte*' translates as 'harpsichord with soft and loud'.

The Amati family, the Guarneri family and the Stradivari family. They were all violin makers for several generations and they made Cremona the violin centre of Europe.

Note: Andrea Guarneri (1626–98) and Antonio Stradivari (1644–1737) were pupils of Nicoló Amati (1596–1684), grandson of Andrea Amati (*c* 1511–79). Andrea Amati was one of the first to make violins. Stradivari made some 1,200 violins, violas and cellos.

The woodwinds; it is a member of the clarinet family.

Note: When he was a music critic, George Bernard Shaw used the pseudonym 'Corno di Bassetto', the Italian name for the basset horn.

'Stopping' a string means placing a finger on it so as to shorten the vibrating length. An 'open' string is one which is not 'stopped'.

The cello

The guitar and the lute. (He was a protégé of Segovia.)

The flute

Harold in Italy, Op 16. It was based on Byron's *Childe Harold* and was first performed in 1834.

Note: When, in 1838, two years before his death, Paganini heard the work, he told Berlioz how wonderful he thought it was. Shortly after, Berlioz received a large sum of money which he believed had come from Paganini. It enabled Berlioz to write his third symphony, *Romeo and Juliet*, Opus 17, which he dedicated to Paganini. Actually, the money had come from a kind friend, Armand Bertin.

The viola

From left to right: piccolo, flute, oboe and bassoon.

The bassoon

The trombone. This capability is because its U-shaped tube is extended, not by valves, but by a telescopic slide.

A transposing instrument is one which, if played in its 'natural' key (without using any valves), sounds at a pitch other than C. To simplify the fingering of such instruments, the notation is transposed so that the correct pitch results. For example, a horn in F will produce a sound a fifth lower than written (the note written as C sounds as F).

Note: It is impossible, here, to list all the transposing instruments of the orchestra. However, as examples: the cor anglais sounds a fifth lower than written; B flat trumpets and clarinets, a tone lower; and the A clarinet, a minor third lower.

TV AND RADIO THEMES

Barwick Green, written by Arthur Wood

Funeral March of a Marionette, by Charles Gounod. (He wrote the opera *Faust* and founded the Royal Choral Society.)

Howard Goodall

Henry Mancini (1924–94)

Note: Henry Mancini wrote music for more than a hundred films. Probably his best known song is 'Moon River', from *Breakfast at Tiffany's* (1961). In 1945 he was pianist and arranger with the Glenn Miller Band.

Spartacus. (It is the love theme.)

Eric Coates (1886–1957)

The words were by Lorenz Hart and the music was by Richard Rodgers.

Note: The song was written in 1929 for the show *Spring is Here*.

Auf Wiedersehn, Pet

Charles Williams

Denis King

Note: He was, originally, one of the King Brothers, who had hits with such as 'A White Sport Coat' in 1957 and 'Standing on the Corner' in 1960.

The Sky at Night

Dmitry Shostakovich. It was the *Romance* from the music he wrote, in 1955, for the Russian film *The Gadfly* (Opus 97a).

OPERA

Baa-Baa Black Sheep

Note: The librettist was David Malouf. The performance was given by Opera North.

Leoš Janáček (1854–1928)

Note: The opera was premièred in Brno in 1904. Because of personal enmities, it was not performed in Prague until 1916.

Das Opfer (The Sacrifice), by Winfried Zillig, a pupil of Schoenburg

A gusli (or guslee or gousli) is a Russian musical instrument of the zither class. In the eighteenth century it had a keyboard.

Note: It should not be confused with a gusla (or gusle, or guzla), which, it seems, is an ancient one-string bowed instrument – but still popular in Bulgaria.

'Chant Hindu', popularly known as 'The Song of India'

Gertrude Stein

Note: Despite its title, the opera has four acts (and two St Teresas!). In 1934, the first performance (in Hartford Connecticut) was staged by Frederick Ashton and was sung by a black cast.

Falstaff

In Paris, Marie-Antoinette (a formal pupil of Gluck), actively promoted his music. Opponents engaged Piccini to write works in opposition. A kind of war broke out between the Gluckists and the Piccinists, and street battles actually did take place.

Carl Goldmark (1830–1915)

Note: He was a friend of Brahms. His nephew, Rubin Goldmark (1872–1936) was a composer in America. He taught Aaron Copland and George Gershwin.

Nabucco. The story of the Hebrew slaves (who sing *Va, pensiero* in the opera) under Nebuchadnezzar was seen as reflecting the plight of the Italians, the majority of whom were under Austrian rule. Verdi's surname was used as an acronym: V(ittorio) E(mmanuel) R(e) D'I(talia); that is, Victor Emmanuel, King of Italy.

Note: In his early days, Verdi was happy to be considered *the* composer of the *Risorgimento* (the movement for a free and united Italy). Later, he was less involved, politically, although he was elected as a senator in the first free Italian parliament, in 1860. The following year, Victor Emmanuel was proclaimed King of Italy. It was not until 1870 that Rome became part of his kingdom.

BACH TUNES

Minuet in G. Anna Magdalena (Wilcken) was Bach's young second wife. Bach wrote a collection of keyboard practice pieces for her as a 'Notebook'. A second volume was prepared for their children. It is thought that some of the pieces in the Notebooks were by Bach's pupils. The Toys' hit was called 'A Lover's Concerto'.

Note: Bach's first wife, Maria, died suddenly in 1720. Of their seven children, four had survived. In 1722, Anna Magdalena, aged 20, became their stepmother. She became an excellent singer and harpsichord player, and copied scores for her husband. They had thirteen children, but seven died in infancy.

'Wachet Auf' ('Sleepers, Awake'). The 'Sleepers' in Bach's Cantata No 140 are the ten virgins of the parable (*Matthew*, 25, 1–14) who were not ready for the arrival of the bridegroom. Procol Harum's hit was 'A Whiter Shade of Pale', written by Gary Brooker and Keith Reid.

52

The Wise Virgins. These were the five who had oil for their lamps! (see Answer 51, above). *Sheep May Safely Graze*.

Note: Cantata 208 is known as 'The Birthday Cantata', *Was Mir Behagt (What Pleases Me)*. It was written in 1716, in celebration of the birthday of Duke Christian of Saxe-Weissenfels. Since a hunting party was held in celebration, it is sometimes known as 'The Hunt Cantata'.

53

Jesu, Joy of Man's Desiring, from the Cantata *Herz und Mund und Tat und Leben (Heart and Mouth and Deed and Life)*. The Beach Boys' hit was 'Lady Lynda'.

The G string is the lowest string on a violin and it gives a very rich tone. The transposition allowed the piece to be played on this string. Mostly, when we hear the piece, today, it is not transposed. Nevertheless, it still keeps this nickname.

Hans Leo Hassler (1564–1612)

Note: Hassler's song title translates to something like 'My Heart is All Mixed Up'. He was very interested in clockwork musical instruments and spent some of his later years in legal wrangles concerning them.

Martin Luther (1483–1546). It is his rendering of the 46th Psalm to his own tune. It was *the* hymn of the Reformation.

PASTICCIO

Samuel Barber

Note: The *Adagio* was, originally a movement from a string quartet. Nowadays, it stands alone, usually in a form for a string, or a full, orchestra.

Dennis Brain. (His father was Aubrey Brain, principal horn with the BBC Symphony Orchestra, 1930–45.)

Harry Woods

UB 40

They were brothers-in-law. (Sibelius married Järnefelt's sister, Aino, in 1891.)

Note: Sibelius (1869–1958). Järnefelt (1865–1957). Järnefelt is best remembered in Britain for a small orchestral work called *Praeludium*. He took Swedish citizenship in 1910.

Georges Bizet

Note: Suite No 1, *L'Arlésienne*, was rescored by Bizet from his incidental music for Alphonse Daudet's play. His friend Guiraud arranged the Suite No 2 after Bizet's death.

Henry SMITH
Arthur JONES
Count ROBINSON
George BROWN

ON SCORE

Each set of three notes (in this instance, quavers) to be played in the time of two. *Simile* means 'in a similar way'; thus, all the sets of three quavers are triplets. The curve with the dot underneath instructs 'pause'.

At that point, you cease plucking the strings with your fingers (*pizzicato*) and return to using your bow.

Note: The terms mean 'bow' and 'with the bow'.

In German, there are two differences in the pitch-names of the notes. The German B is our B flat; H is used instead of our B. Thus, the fugue was based on the German BACH, which is our B flat, A, C, B.

67

That the whole string section played the bow stroke that opened the symphony, forcefully and in unison.

Note: Mozart wrote home, 'What a lot of asses they (the Paris Orchestra) are. Yes, they begin together – but so do orchestras in other places. It's stupid!' (That is an expletives deleted version of his actual words.)

68

A gradual quickening of the speed of the music

That the music should be played more and more softly until it dies away

A Cadenza. (These are sometimes written into the score, and sometimes they are improvised by the soloist.)

ONE-LINERS

They are Köchel numbers. The Austrian scholar, Ludwig von Köchel, was the first to compile a catalogue of Mozart's works. It was published in 1862.

Note: Sometimes KV is used instead of K. This stands for *Köchel Verzeichnis* (Köchel Index). In 1937, Alfred Einstein revised Köchel's catalogue, but retained the 'K'.

A term used in the eighteenth century for an instrumental suite suitable for outdoor performance

Spain. It is a type of Spanish melody which is sung and often danced also.

Another name for the side drum. Stretched gut strings (or wires) are fitted over the lower head of the drum. This gives a rattling effect to the sound of the drum when struck.

The music of 'The Star-Spangled Banner', officially adopted as the National Anthem in 1931, seems to have been composed by John Stafford Smith (1750–1836). He was the son of a Gloucester organist.

Note: The words were written by Francis Scott Key (1779–1843), whilst observing the bombardment of Fort McHenry, Baltimore, by the British, in 1814.

76

The composer. The opera was completed in 1921.

A rhythmic figure in which a short note on the beat is followed by a longer note held until the next beat. This rhythm is found in some Scottish music.

Note: Think of a semi-quaver on the beat, followed by a dotted quaver held until the next beat:

78

A sharp, double sharp, flat, double flat or natural sign, which is not part of the key signature. It affects the note so marked only during the bar in which it occurs.

79

It is a short piano piece, by Erik Satie, with the instruction that it should be played 840 times without variation, the player preparing in advance to do this.

Note: Performance of the work is an act of great self-discipline, and of endurance. It has been publicly performed by pianists in relays and lasts more than 18 hours to complete. There have been solo attempts.

80

Franz Schubert

Sigmund Romberg

Arthur Honegger (1892–1955), a member of *'Les Six'*. The impression of, and the enjoyment gained by, a speeding steam locomotive.

Note: 2–3–1 is the wheel grouping, European notation. (This would be 4–6–2 in Britain, where wheels on both sides of the locomotive are 'counted'.)

Clannad

Note: The *Harry's Game* single won Clannad an Ivor Novello songwriting award.

Maire Ni Bhraonain (of Clannad) and Bono (of U2)

Mark Knopfler

Dire Straits

Marie-Antoinettte (when she was a princess in Vienna and Gluck was Musical Director to the court).

Symphony No 85 in B flat, *La Reine de France*

Note: The symphony was one of the six 'Paris' Symphonies commissioned from Haydn by a Paris society, '*Concerts Spirituels*'. It was completed in about 1785. Apparently, Marie-Antoinette much liked the work when it was played in the Tuileries in her presence. (She was guillotined only eight years later.)

Symphony No 48 in C, *Maria Theresia*

Note: It was written in about 1772. It is said that the work greatly pleased the Empress when she visited Esterhazy in 1773.

She had ten children. Marie-Antoinette was born in 1755.

The Soft Machine. The group featured in a late-night Prom of avant-garde music.

The Land of Smiles (written in 1929)

Note: Despite its title, it's a real 'weepie'.

Franz Lehár. (Lyrics by Ludwig Herzer and Fritz Löhner. The English version was by Harry Graham.)

Pietro Mascagni (1863–1945). The one-act opera won first prize in a competition organised by the publisher, Sonzogno. It was premiered in Rome in 1890. (The title is usually translated as *Rustic Chivalry*.)

The tune was written by the English composer and organist, William Boyce (1711–79), for a pantomime, *Harlequin's Invasion*, by David Garrick.

> *Note:* Garrick's pantomime (a play with extempore dialogue and songs) was written in 1759 – the year of the victories of Minden, Quiberon Bay and Quebec. The patriotic words of the song relate to those victories.

The American composer of popular songs, Stephen Foster (1826–64)

The notes of the chord are played one after the other, not simultaneously.

It is a type of vessel flute with a whistle head and up to eight finger holes which sound different pitches.

> *Note:* Vessel flutes are globe-shaped. Giuseppe Donati invented the ocarina in the late nineteenth century.

Elvis Presley

A German flautist and composer (1697–1773). He taught Frederick the Great (King of Prussia) to play the flute. Quantz wrote more than 300 flute concertos.

> *Note:* Frederick the Great was himself an accomplished composer. He wrote a symphony and over a hundred pieces for the flute.

A sentimental popular ballad, usually sung by a female, dealing with lost or unrequited love. (The name comes from the expression 'carrying a torch' for someone.)

NUMBER OPERA

Note: 'Number Opera' is intended as a pun in the title. A number opera was one that had arias, duets, etc. ('numbers') held together by dialogue.

A 16

B 48
Note: Bach wrote two sets of preludes and fugues, in all the keys. The clavier was a keyboard instrument. 'Well tempered' meant that, in tuning, some intervals, particularly the third and fifth, were varied slightly from their 'precise' values.

C 1000

D 2525

E 3

F 1812

G 1
Note: The only character is a young soprano. She talks on the telephone to her lover who is deserting her.

H 100

I 1860

J 1965

K 21
Note: Hovhaness (b 1911) wrote more than 1,200 pieces, but, self-critically, destroyed most of them. He is of Armenian descent. Etchmiadzin is the centre of the Armenian religion; its church is the oldest established Christian church.

L 129
Note: Otherwise, *Rondo a Capriccio in* G, *for Piano*. Published after Beethoven's death. The significance of the nickname is not known.

M 50

N 1980

O 32

In Mozart's *Don Giovanni*, Leporello (his servant) lists his master's female conquests. These are: 640 in Italy; 231 in Germany, 100 in France, 91 in Turkey, and (up to then) 1,003 in Spain. The formidable total is 2,065. (At the end of the opera, Don Giovanni meets a particularly unpleasant come-uppance!)

CROSS-OVER TUNES

'Moonlight and Roses'

Percy Grainger (1882–1961) collected the tune, which became known as *Country Gardens*. Jimmie Rodgers took in into the charts as 'English Country Garden'.

Note: It is believed that the original folk song was used by Morris Men as an accompaniment for a Handkerchief Dance.

Bach's *Toccata and Fugue* in D minor. (This toccata featured in Walt Disney's film *Fantasia*.)

Note: Somewhat unbelievably, Herbie Flowers (string bass player with Sky) wrote Clive Dunn's No 1 hit of 1970, 'Grandad'!

'Night' was based on an aria from *Samson and Delilah*, by Saint-Saëns. The aria is known as 'My Heart at Thy Sweet Voice' or 'Softly, Awakes My Heart'. 'Alone at Last' was based on the first movement of Tchaikovsky's Piano Concerto No 1 in B flat minor, Opus 23.

Note: Several popular songs have used themes from this Piano Concerto. For example, 'Tonight We Love', from 1939, and 'Concerto for Two', from 1941.

Ballet Egyptienne, Opus 12, by the French composer, violinist and conductor, Alexandre Luigini (1850–1906).

'Pathétique', or *Grande Sonate Pathétique*. There is a resemblance to the theme of the Ninth Variation, *Nimrod*, from Elgar's *Enigma Variations*. Billy Joel's song was 'This Night Can Last for Ever'.

Note: Elgar stated that *Nimrod* was written in memory of a summer evening discussion about the slow movements of Beethoven sonatas, that he had with his friend August Jaegar (a reader for the music publisher, Novello). 'Nimrod' was a hunter; *'Jaegar'* is the German word for hunter. (Incidentally, *sonate* is the French word corresponding to the Italian *sonata*.)

The *Troika* from the suite *Lieutenant Kijé*, Opus 60. The suite is based on music that Prokofiev wrote, in 1933, for a film about an 'invented' army officer.

'The Carnival is Over'. Stenka Razin was a Don Cossack who led many rebellions (and massacres). He was executed, (particularly unpleasantly) in what became Red Square, in 1671. Several composers have based works on Razin's life and death. Glazounov's orchestral tone poem, *Stenka Razin*, features several Russian folk themes, most notably, *The Song of the Volga Boatmen.*

Note: This story is true! Foreign passengers, disembarking at St Petersburg were, as is customary (and now, an economic practicality), being greeted by an excellent performance of national tunes, by a group of local musicians. They struck up *Stenka Razin* with great fervour. 'Gosh', said an English passenger, 'Fancy them knowing that record by the Seekers already!'

Johann Pachelbel (1653–1706). He called it *Canon for Three Parts on a Ground in D major*. It has been recorded with 'more popular' orchestration as *Pachelbel's Canon* and *Pachelbel's Immortal Canon.* In fact, he wrote many such canons – most of which are now 'lost'.

Note: Pachelbel also wrote many chorales, including seven sets of chorale variations in memory of his wife and young son, who died in the plague, in 1683.

The Piano Concerto in A minor, Opus 6, by Edvard Grieg (1843–1907). The work, composed in 1868, was revised many times with help from his friend, Franz Liszt. It was finalised just before Grieg died.

OPERETTA

The first performance took place there, on 30 December 1879, to maintain British copyright. Viscount Garnet Wolseley, who commanded the 1884 Sudan expedition that arrived too late to save General Gordon at Khartoum.

Note: Virtually simultaneously, the first performance in America (to establish American copyright) was given at New York's Fifth Avenue Theater.

Richard Tauber (1892–1948)

Karl Zeller (1842–98)

Franz von Suppé (1819–95)

Note: Suppé was born in Dalmatia, of Belgian descent. He wrote one opera, *Boccaccio*, in 1879.

Emmerich Kálmán (1882–1953)

Rudolf Friml (1879–1972). 'The Donkey Serenade' came from *The Firefly* but, only the film version, of 1937. (Previously, the tune, dating from 1923, was known as *Chansonette*. Otto Harbach provided the lyrics about the donkey.) 'The Indian Love Call' came from *Rose Marie*. The vagabond king was the fifteenth-century French poet (and villain!) François Villon. (The operetta somewhat romanticised his true character.)

Note: Jeanette MacDonald and Allan Jones both starred in the films of *Rose Marie* (1936) and *Firefly* (1937). 'The Donkey Serenade' was a huge hit for Allan Jones. *The Vagabond King* was filmed in 1956, starring Kathryn Grayson and Oreste.

They were all made into feature films starring Laurel and Hardy. *Fra Diavolo* became *The Devil's Brother* in (1933); *The Bohemian Girl* kept that title (in 1936); and so did *Babes in Toyland* (in 1934).

Alfred Cellier (1844–91), the English organist, composer and conductor. He wrote many operettas of his own. *Dorothy* was the most successful.

Note: Gilbert's idea for the subject was that of a lozenge which, when swallowed, made people what they pretended they were. Sullivan didn't like the idea. Cellier became very worried about the production. He died, just after his 47th birthday, a few days prior to the opening (thus, never seeing the work performed).

Die Fledermaus (The Bat). The first performance was in 1874.

Note: The operetta was filmed, in 1956, as *O Rosalinde*. Michael Redgrave and Anneliese Rothenberger starred (singing and acting).

AT THE PROMS

The Overture *Rienzi*, by Wagner

In 1902, Henry Wood was taken ill. Arthur Payne, who was the leader of the Queen's Hall Orchestra, stood in for him for three weeks. In 1908, the French conductor, Edouard Colonne, took over part of the Prom season. In 1915, Thomas Beecham was invited to conduct one concert. In 1941, Sir Henry Wood shared each concert with Basil Cameron. From 1942 to 1944, the seasons were shared amongst Sir Henry Wood, Basil Cameron and Sir Adrian Boult.

Note: In May 1941, the Queen's Hall was burned to the ground during a bombing raid. It was decided to move the Proms to the Royal Albert Hall.

Basil Cameron had played the violin in Henry Wood's Queen's Hall Orchestra in 1908. In 1912, he became the conductor of the Torquay Municipal Orchestra and the following year conducted an unprecedented season of Wagner. At Torquay, he assumed the name Basil Hindenburg, because of 'prejudice against British musicians'. When war broke out, in 1914, he used his own name again.

Mrs Henry J Wood. She was a Russian princess – Princess Olga Ouroussoff. She and Henry Wood married in 1898. (Wood taught singing throughout his life.)

Note: Mrs Henry Wood was a kind and much loved lady. She showed particular kindness to a young viola player and composer in pressing for the performance of his new work, *Four New Shakespeare Songs with Orchestra*, in a 1909 Prom. This young man later became principal violist with the Queen's Hall Orchestra – and a very popular composer. His name was Eric Coates.

Jean Sibelius

Edvard Grieg, who died a few weeks later. (The work was repeated a year later as a tribute to Pablo Sarasate, the Spanish violinist and composer. Its performance in 1927, at a Queen's Hall concert, was in memory of Robert Newman, the founder of the Proms and the man who had appointed Henry Wood as their conductor in 1895.)

The work was Ravel's Piano Concerto in D major, for the Left Hand Only. Paul Wittgenstein had been wounded and taken prisoner during World War One. His right arm was amputated because of injuries. Born in 1887, he was a talented pianist prior to enlisting in the Austrian army. His brother was the great philosopher, Ludwig Wittgenstein.

Note: Paul Wittgenstein commissioned several composers to write works that he could play with one hand. These included Britten, Hindemith and Prokofiev.

The Ravel Piano Concerto was very jazz influenced – the composer having recently met Paul Whiteman and George Gershwin in America.

There were sixteen named vocal soloists, all of whom had been associated with Sir Henry Wood's concerts. These were: Isobel Baillie, Margaret Balfour, Muriel Brunskill, Astra Desmond, Mary Jarred, Stiles-Allen, Elsie Suddaby, Eva Turner, Norman Allin, Robert Easton, Roy Henderson, Parry Jones, Heddle Nash, Frank Titterton, Walter Widdop and Harold Williams.

Note: In 1994, at the 100th season of the Proms, the work was performed in tribute to Sir Henry Wood. The soloists, all 'acclaimed' singers, were: Nancy Argenta, Heather Harper, Yvonny Kenny, Yvonne Minton, Felicity Palmer, Jean Rigby, Joan Rodgers, Catherine Wyn-Rogers, Thomas Allen, Kim Begley, John Mitchison, Anthony Rolfe Johnson, Robert Tear, John Tomlinson, Willard White and David Wilson-Johnson.

Sir Malcolm Sargent. He had, for ten years, been principal conductor of the Proms. (Sir) Colin Davis, Sir Adrian Boult and others took over the 1967 Proms when Sir Malcolm was too ill to conduct. He died of cancer a few weeks after his last visit to the Proms.

Thomas Allen fainted. The performance continued. In time for the next baritone entry, on walked Patrick McCarthy – who sang admirably to the end of the work.

Note: Patrick McCarthy was a professional singer who had sung the part, once, at a Midlands concert. He rushed out and found his way backstage. Having persuaded the organisers that he was 'genuine', he was given a bow tie – and on he went. The story didn't have a fairy-tale ending; Patrick was famous only 'for a day', sadly.

JAZZ

WC Handy (1873–1958). The WC was for William Christopher. He was black and was the first to publish the Negro blues as printed music. His book, *Father of the Blues*, was published in the year of his death.

30

Ella Fitzgerald. She was born, in 1918, in Newport News, Virginia, but the family moved to New York.

Note: After Chick Webb's death in 1939, she ran the band for three years. In the 1940s, she turned to scat vocals, such as 'Lady Be Good' and 'How High the Moon'. In the 1950s she excelled in interpretations of the songs of Gershwin, Berlin, Kern and Porter.

31

In the days when jazz bands trundled around towns on carts (band wagons), the trombonists had to sit at the back – on the tailgate – so they had room to use their slides.

Note: The tailgate position allowed the trombonist to fill in the melodies with *glissando* notes. Kid Ory (1889–1973) was an acknowledged expert at tailgate effects.

32

George Shearing (b 1919). In America, his Quintet was renowned in the 1950s.

33

Duke Ellington (1899–1974), the American pianist and bandleader

Note: In 1937, Duke Ellington wrote *Diminuendo and Crescendo in Blue*. At the Newport Festival in 1956, his orchestra played this extended work and his legendary tenor sax player, Paul Gonsalves, blew an amazing 27 choruses.

34

Joe Venuti (1904–78). Their 1929 number, *Doing Things* is a good example of their chamber-music jazz, being an arrangement of Debussy's prelude (written only 20 years previously) *The Girl with the Flaxen Hair.*

Note: Joe Venuti was born in Italy (*not* on the boat over to America, as many references state). Eddie Lang was also of Italian extraction; he died in 1933, aged only 30.

35

Gerry Mulligan, baritone saxophone; Chet Baker, trumpet; Bob Whitlock, string bass; and Chico Hamilton, drums.

36

Igor Stravinsky. Concerto for Clarinet and Orchestra, known as the 'Ebony Concerto'. Strangely, although the work calls for six saxophones, five trumpets and three trombones, it does not call for a solo clarinet.

Note: Three years earlier, Stravinksy had written *Circus Polka.* This was specifically for a ballet performed by elephants at the Barnum and Bailey Circus.

37

The vocalist and banjo player of the very early days of jazz, Papa Charlie Jackson.

38

James P Johnson (1894–1955)

Note: Stride piano developed from ragtime. It took its name from the striding motion of the left hand (rather like the motion of a metronome), alternating bass note with chord.

WHO WROTE WHAT?

39

The Swedish Rhapsody, by Hugo Alfvén (1872–1960). He wrote three Swedish Rhapsodies. *Midsummer Vigil* was the first of these. He wrote many other works, including five symphonies.

40

'The Lost Chord'. (The verses were by Adelaide Proctor.)

41

Telstar. This was the name of the first telecommunication satellite, launched in 1962. The composer was Joe Meek.

42

The Hebraic rhapsody *Schelomo* for cello and orchestra. (*Schelomo* means Solomon.)

Note: The work was part of Bloch's 'Jewish Cycle' written from 1911 to 1918. He was born in 1880 and died in 1959.

Alan Bush (1900–95). Of Marxist beliefs, the two operas are concerned with social injustice. The libretti of *Wat Tyler* and *Men of Blackmoor* (about Northumbrian miners problems in the last century) were by his wife, Nancy Bush.

Note: Alan Bush founded the Workers' Labour Choral Association in the 1930s.

Rutland Boughton (1878–1960). The opera was *The Immortal Hour*. 'The Fairy Song' from the opera is still quite well known.

Note: *The Immortal Hour* had a libretto based on works by Fiona Macleod. This was the pseudonym of a Scottish writer, William Sharp.

Albert Ketelby (1875–1959). He sometimes wrote as Anton Vodorinski.

Note: Bank Holiday ('Appy 'Ampstead) is a real 'cheerer-up'. Try spotting some of the tunes that are interwoven, for example: 'Tell Me the Old, Old Story'; the overture to the opera *Il Trovatore;* 'There is a Tavern in the Town'; 'Over the Waves'; and many more.

Samuel Coleridge-Taylor (1875–1912). The song is 'Onaway! Awake, Beloved'. Coleridge-Taylor wrote an opera and an oratorio as well as various orchestral and chamber works. However, in the public's eyes he was never able to reach the heights of his *Hiawatha's Wedding Feast*.

Note: Samuel Coleridge-Taylor was the son of an English mother and a West African doctor father. When the father was unsuccessful in London, he returned to Africa, leaving the family with little money. (Sir) Charles Stanford, believing in Samuel's talent, did much to help and encourage him, whilst teaching him composition.

PASTICCIO

William Crotch (1755–1847)

'It' was 'As Time Goes By'. 'Sam' was Dooley Wilson. Jimmy Durante sang the song on the soundtrack of *Sleepless in Seattle*.

Note: 'As Time Goes By' was written in 1931 by Herman Hupfield, for a musical now largely forgotten – *Everybody's Welcome*.

In 1909, a manuscript was found at Jena. On the score was written '*par Louis van Beethoven*', and it became known as Beethoven's 'Jena' Symphony. In 1957, the American musicologist, HC Robbins Landon, established that the work was by Witt.

John Curwen (1816–80), a Congregational minister

Note: He established a publishing group and founded a college in London, to promote and teach the system.

Guys and Dolls, words and music by Frank Loesser (1910–69). The 1953 musical was made into a film in 1955. The names are those of race horses.

Note: The song is performed by the gamblers, as a fugue.

Henryk Górecki (b 1933). He was taken, on a school trip, to Auschwitz. He saw the words of an 18-year-old scratched on the wall of her cell: 'No, mother, do not weep ...'

Note: The work also uses the texts of a Polish prayer and a folk song. The American soprano, Dawn Upshaw, was the soloist in the charts' version.

The English composer, Sir Hubert Parry (1848–1918)

Hans Christian Andersen. In Norwegian the song is 'Jeg Elsker Dig'. *(Two Brown Eyes, Love, The Poet's Last Song* are other poems of Andersen, set to music by Grieg.)

Note: Most of Grieg's songs were written for his wife, who was a singer.

Edvard Grieg's great-grandfather was a Scot, named Alexander Greig. He left Scotland after Culloden and moved to Bergen (where his name had its vowels reversed!) He eventually became British Consul – as did his son and grandson.

It is the French word for what we call a 'quaver'.

Cat Stevens

Note: Cat Stevens was born Steven Georgiou, in London, in 1947. In the late 1970s he retired from the world of music to devote himself to religious studies, having converted to Islam.

Placido Domingo; Luciano Pavarotti; José Carreras.

Pavarotti and his father, Fernando, were members of a local Italian choir, the *Chorale G Rossini di Modena*, which travelled to North Wales in 1955 and took first prize in its class.

Domingo was referred to as 'A Mexican tenor' in the 1968 programme. Carreras sang as Stiffélio.

58

Beethoven. The Jew's harp is a simple instrument comprising a small metal frame, held in the player's teeth, and a vibrating strip, which is twanged by the fingers. It is a harmonic instrument. The mandora (or mandore) is a small plucked instrument of the lute family.

Note: The Jew's harp has nothing to do with Jews. Neither is it a corruption of 'Jaw's harp'. It was once known as a Jew's trump. It has been suggested that Jew's trump is a corruption of the Dutch, *'jeugdtromp'*, which translates as 'child's trumpet'.

DESCRIPTIONS

Sir Willian Sterndale Bennett (1816–75), the English pianist, composer and teacher

Note: He also founded the Bach Society, in 1849.

A theme which recurs throughout a piece of music (sometimes in several music guises), almost in the manner of a quotation

Note: Berlioz used this in his *Symphonie Fantastique*, Opus 14, to evoke – over and over – his musical image of Harriet Smithson, by whom he was besotted.

The conflict when, say, C sharp in one part occurs together with, or in immediate succession to, C in another part

An alteration in stress from that which might normally be expected. In the extract shown, in triple-time, the accent would normally be expected on the first note of the bar, but (after the first bar) it is, clearly, on the second note of each bar.

Note: Syncopation is a characteristic of ragtime music.

'The Old Testament' refers to J S Bach's '48 Preludes and Fugues for the Well Tempered Clavier'.

'The New Testament' is Beethoven's 32 piano sonatas.

Strophic means the music accompanying the words is repeated exactly (or nearly so) for each successive stanza of the poem being set to music.

Through-composed refers to a song composed in a continuous form and not repeating itself in successive stanzas (that is, the opposite of strophic).

The tonic is the first note of a scale. The supertonic is the next note up. (So, in the key of C, the tonic is the note C and the supertonic is the next note up, D.)

Note: It therefore follows that the tonic is the key-note.

Portamento means 'carried'. It is the vocal effect obtained by carrying the sound in a continuous glide from one note to the next. *Glissando* means 'sliding'. It is a similar effect instrumentally.

Note: In piano music, *glissando* effects are achieved by 'sliding' the back of the finger through a sequence of white notes, from one note to the next. (*Glissando* is a hybrid word, not true Italian.)

THE 'WEAKER' SEX

Maria Callas (1923–77)

Judith Weir (b 1954)

Jetty Treffz was Strauss's first wife. In the 1860s, she accompanied him to Russia, where he was giving concerts, and sang some German songs. These he reworked in his *Lieder Quadrille*.

Strauss's third wife, Adele (Deutsch) outlived him by many years. George Gershwin, an admirer of Strauss, visited her in Vienna. The result was the song, 'By Strauss', with words by Ira Gershwin (George's lyricist brother).

Note: Jetty Treffz was a remarkable singer, once considered to rival Jenny Lind. She died in 1877. Strauss's second marriage was not successful.

'By Strauss' featured in the Gershwins' 1936 revue, *The Show is On*. This was a year before George's death. (The song's publishers considered it too long, but the brothers would not cut it.) In 1951, the song was included in the film *An American in Paris* (with other Gershwin songs).

Ethel Smyth, imprisoned in Holloway as a militant suffragist in 1911 (at the age of 53), used a toothbrush to conduct – through her cell window – the strains of her *March of the Women*, composed for the Women's Social and Political Union as their battle-cry.

ONE-LINERS

Sir Henry Walford Davies (1869–1941). He became Director of Music to the RAF in 1918. He was a distinguished composer and broadcaster on music. *The RAF March Past* is undoubtedly his most frequently performed composition.

Note: Walford Davies' *Solemn Melody* is another well-known work. It was written for the Milton tercentenary celebrations and had its first concert performance at a Prom in 1909. On the death of Elgar, in 1934, Sir Walford Davies was appointed Master of the King's Musick.

The clash between the champions of the composers: Jean Philippe Rameau, French (1683–1764); and Giovanni Battista Pergolesi, Italian (1710–36). It started in Paris, in 1752, and everything became very heated and political.

Note: The *Bouffons* (Buffoons or Comedians) were Italians invited to Paris to perform comic operas composed by Pergolesi and other Italians.

Noel Gay, for Lupino Lane's *Me and My Girl*, in 1937

The fourth note. For example, in the key of C, the subdominant is F. (The dominant in this key is G.)

The *pasa doble*, a Spanish dance. The man represents a matador and the woman represents his cloak.

Her brother, Ricky, and her father, Marty Wilde

Note: This took the No 2 spot on the charts in 1981. (Marty Wilde's own first hit record was 'Endless Sleep', in 1958.)

Jean-Michel Jarre, in the mid-1970s. The works were created using a range of synthesisers.

Note: In 1979 Jarre put on a spectacular show using *Oxygène* and *Equinoxe*, in the heart of Paris. It is said that there were one million spectators. His incredible *Concert for Tolerance* was similarly performed on Bastille Day in 1995.

For a while they were a group influenced by the ideas of Erik Satie and Jean Cocteau. They were: George Auric (1899–1982); Louis Durey (1888–1979); Arthur Honegger (1892–1955); Darius Milhaud (1892–1974); Francis Poulenc (1899–1963); and Germaine Tailleferre, the only woman in '*Les Six*', (1892–1983).

Note: The group was artificially labelled '*Les Six*' as an analogy with the famous Russian group 'The Five'.

In the late 1890s, 'The Frankfurt Five' studied in Frankfurt under the German teacher and composer, Iwan Knorr (1853–1916). They were: Henry Balfour Gardiner (1877–1950); Norman O'Neill (1875–1934); Roger Quilter (1877–1953); Cyril Scott (1879–1970); and Australian Percy Grainger (1882–1961).

A group who, in the 1950s studied at the Royal Manchester College of Music and shared a progressive outlook. They were: Harrison Birtwhistle (b 1934); Peter Maxwell Davies (b 1934); Alexander Goehr (b 1932); and John Ogdon (1937–89).

Note: Alexander Goehr's father was the conductor, Walter Goehr (1903–60). John Ogdon was joint winner (with Vladimir Ashkenazy (b 1937)) of the International Tchaikovsky Piano Competition, in Moscow, in 1962.

The *English Rhapsody on a Lincolnshire Folk Song, Brigg Fair*, by Frederick Delius, 1907. Percy Grainger acquired the folk song from the Lincolnshire singer, Joseph Taylor, recording it on a wax cylinder. Delius heard the recording and asked if he might make an orchestral arrangement from it.

Emmylou Harris and Paul Kennerley

Note: Emmylou Harris has been called 'the first lady of contemporary country music'. Paul Kennerley is a British-born songwriter. They were married in 1985 – the year of the album.

The Canadian composer, Robert Farnon (b 1917)

Note: Robert Farnon's best known work is *Portrait of a Flirt*. In 1941 he wrote a symphony in the unusual key for a major work, D flat major. (This key has five flats.)

84

Ida Haendel (b 1928). (Apparently, she let the organisers believe she was 14.) She performed Beethoven's Violin Concerto in D, Opus 61.

Note: After dozens of Prom appearances, Ida Haendel returned to play Britten's Violin Concerto in D minor, Opus 15, for the 100th season. At this concert (all British music) were HM The Queen and HRH The Duke of Edinburgh – their first time at a Prom.

85

Sir Michael Tippett (1905–98) wrote both the text and the music. It concerns the battle between good and evil, using a true story of a Jewish child who kills a Nazi.

86

What we know now as Symphony No 8 in G, Opus 88. Dvořák was having one of his many quarrels with his German publishers Simrock when, in 1889, he was offered an honorary doctorate by Cambridge University. He presented the symphony as his thesis piece and it was published in England by Messrs Novello. It became, then, known as his 'English' symphony.

Note: What Cambridge didn't know was that a present of the same work had been made by the composer, to the Franz Joseph Academy in Prague.

87

The Hungarian-born violinist, Leopold Auer (1845–1930)

88

The Russian-born violinist, Adolf Brodsky (1851–1929). Auer looked at the score and said it was not playable. He refused to perform the work, as did other violinists. Brodsky agreed to première it.

Note: In 1895, Brodsky came to England and became leader of the Hallé Orchestra. He succeeded Sir Charles Hallé as principal of the Royal Manchester College of Music and was leader of the original Brodsky Quartet.

89

Barrington Pheloung

Note: In this theme music, the name of the chief character is heard, in the morse code.

90

Wynton Marsalis (b 1961)

An Austrian composer and violinist, often referred to as 'The Father of the Viennese Waltz'. At the age of 17, he formed a dance group – a string quartet in which Johann Strauss I (an elderly 24!) played the viola. The group expanded and Lanner wrote music for his orchestra. After a while, he and Strauss separated – each with his own orchestra.

He was an Austrian-born composer with more than 40 operas to his credit, plus oratorios, concertos, over 100 symphonies, and much else, including string quartets – rather too much like Haydn's.

Note: Originally, he was Karl Ditters. It is said he bought himself into the nobility (as was quite usual at the time). This provided him with the impressive name! He was a fine violinist and played in a quartet with Haydn. Amongst his operas was a *Marriage of Figaro* which predated that by Mozart.

A formidable name – but a more formidable prodigy. Without any teaching in harmony, he wrote an opera, *Los Esclavos Felices (The Happy Slaves)*, at the age of 13. When he died (from 'decline') six years later, he had completed a symphony, an overture and three string quartets.

Note: Arriaga was also a brilliant violinist. His opera was the very first Spanish opera.

The English banker, Francis Money-Coutts, who paid Albéniz to write the music for his libretto, and then provided him with an income for the rest of his life. Albéniz also set some of the banker's Arthurian verses to music, but not very successfully.

Note: Isaac Albéniz (1860–1909) gave piano recitals in Spain before running away at the age of nine to the West Indies. For four years he toured the west coast of American and parts of South America, quite alone, giving concerts. Returning to Europe, he studied for a while with Liszt, d'Indy and Dukas. He is best remembered today for his piano suite *Iberia*.

Smetana's. The work is subtitled *From My Life*. In 1874 he became deaf (painfully). However, he suffered from the sound of a high E, continually, in his head. This note is echoed in the finale of the string quartet, in E minor. He continued composing, but died (in an asylum) in 1884, without hearing again.

Kris Kristofferson (b 1936)

Note: This is the same Kris Kristofferson as acted in the films *A Star in Born* and *Rollover*, for example. Other songs of his include 'Help Me Make It Through the Night' and 'For the Good Times'.

Bette Midler

Ravel's *Bolero*, written in 1928. Larry Adler, the harmonica virtuoso, has told how he sent a recording of his version of the work to Maurice Ravel, not long before Ravel's death in 1937. Apparently Ravel was not too impressed. Nevertheless, in his will, he wrote that his permission was given for Larry Adler to play the work anywhere and at any time, without paying a performance fee.

Patsy Cline (1932–63), who died in a plane crash returning from a benefit concert. 'Crazy' was in the UK charts in 1990.

Note: In the 1985 film *Sweet Dreams*, Jessica Lange played Patsy Cline.

Philip Cipriani Potter (1792–1871). His full title was *The Enigma-Variation and Fantasia on a Favorite Irish Air for the Piano Forte, in the style of Five Eminent Artists*. It was published in 1825; the Elgar work dates from 1899.

'CLASSICAL' CROSSWORD

Clues Across

1 FRANCK (César)

4 LUTHER (Martin)

7 NOTE

8 *SALOME*
Note: After the first performances, the opera was condemned as obscene and blasphemous. It so shocked New Yorkers that it was withdrawn from the Metropolitan Opera House after one performance there.

9 FLATS

12 *SONGS*

13 STAFF

16 ELGAR (Edward)

20 *COLOUR*
Note: The *Colour Symphony* caused great interest at a time when many were attempting to relate colour to music.

21 LALO (Edouard)

22 TATTOO
Note: 'Tattoo' derives from the Dutch word *taptoe* which means 'shut the taps' (of kegs). When the tattoo was sounded, calling soldiers to quarters, that was when the taps on the ale kegs were closed.

23 *DAPHNE*

Clues Down

1 FINALE

2 ANTIPHONY

3 KITTL
Note: Emmy Destinn (1878–1930) sang as Senta in the first production of *The Flying Dutchman*, at Bayreuth, in 1901. She sang as Salome in the first Berlin production (1906), with Richard Strauss conducting.

4 LISZT (Franz)
Note: Symphonic (or tone) poems illustrate, musically, a particular 'programme'. Such works by Liszt include: *Tasso*; *The Preludes*; *Maseppa*; and *Hamlet*.

5 *TILL*

6 *RIENZI*

9 *FUGUE*

10 SITAR

11 OFFENBACH (Jacques)

14 DULCET

15 ENCORE

17 LARGO

18 ALARD

19 ROOT (George, for the second part of clue)
Note: George Root (1820–95) wrote the words and music of this marching song of the North – during the war. It is also known as 'The Battle Cry of Freedom' – from its refrain.

INDEX